P9-CLD-491

K12 Math⁺

Lesson Guide

All photographs are royalty-free. © Artville

About K12 Inc.

K12 Inc. (NYSE: LRN) drives innovation and advances the quality of education by delivering state-of-the-art digital learning platforms and technology to students and school districts around the world. K12 is a company of educators offering its online and blended curriculum to charter schools, public school districts, private schools, and directly to families. More information can be found at K12.com.

ISBN: 978-1-60153-080-6

Printed by Bradford & Bigelow, Newburyport, MA, USA, July 2020.

Contents

Program Overview ix

Read, Write, Count, and Compare Numbers

Numbers Through 50 3
Write Numerals Through 50 7
Count by 10s and 5s Through 50 11
Count by 2s Through 50 16
Numbers Through 100..20
Write Numerals Through 100.....................................24
Count by 10s and 5s Through 100 28
Count by 2s Through 100 32
Compare Numbers Through 100...................................35
Order Numbers Through 100 39
Unit Review 43
Unit Checkpoint..45

Time and Position

Time to the Nearest Hour.......................................49
Time to the Nearest Half Hour 53
About Time...57
Arrange and Describe Position 61
Use Direction Words..64
Unit Review 69
Unit Checkpoint..71

Introduction to Addition

Model Addition 75
Add in Any Order...79

The Plus Symbol. 85

The Equals Symbol 89

Number Sentences: The Equals Symbol. 93

Unit Review 98

Unit Checkpoint. 101

Addition Facts with Sums Through 12

Facts Through 8 105

Sums Through 8. 108

Facts Through 12 113

Sums Through 12. 116

Unit Review 120

Unit Checkpoint. 122

Addition Facts with Sums Through 20

Facts Through 16 125

Sums Through 16. 128

Facts Through 20 132

Sums Through 20. 137

Unit Review 141

Unit Checkpoint. 143

Addition Strategies

One More, 10 More. 147

Count On to Add 152

Different Ways to Add 158

Grouping to Add 162

Grouping Addends 168

Unit Review 175

Unit Checkpoint. 178

Addition Number Sentences

Different Forms of Numbers 183

Ways to Show Numbers 188

Missing Numbers in Addition 196

Missing Numbers in Addition Sentences 200

Unit Review 206

Unit Checkpoint 208

Introduction to Subtraction

Understand Subtraction 213

The Minus Symbol 219

Equal Expressions 224

More Equal Expressions 228

Put Together, Take Away 230

Order and Zero in Subtraction 234

Subtract to Compare 240

Use Pairs to Subtract 244

Unit Review 249

Unit Checkpoint 252

Subtraction Facts Through 20

Subtraction Facts Through 8 257

Relate Addition and Subtraction 260

Subtraction Facts Through 12 266

Count Back Subtraction Facts 269

Subtraction Facts Through 16 275

Facts Using Subtraction 278

Subtraction Through 20 282

All the Subtraction Facts 285

Unit Review 290

Unit Checkpoint 292

Subtraction Strategies

One Less, 10 Less. **297**

Counting Back and Other Strategies. **301**

Use Strategies to Subtract. **306**

Unit Review **310**

Unit Checkpoint. **312**

Semester Review and Checkpoint

Semester Review **314**

Semester Checkpoint. **318**

Subtraction Number Sentences

Same Number Different Ways **323**

Represent Numbers Different Ways. **327**

Missing Parts in Subtraction Sentences **332**

Subtract with Missing Numbers **337**

Unit Review **340**

Unit Checkpoint. **342**

Money and Measurement

Coins **347**

Identify Coins **350**

Equal Money Amounts **354**

Measure and Compare Length **359**

Weight. **364**

Capacity and Volume. **369**

Unit Review **374**

Unit Checkpoint. **377**

Place Value, Addition, and Subtraction

Tens, Ones, and Estimation 381

Place Value.. 386

Represent Numbers 390

Place Value for Numbers 393

Model Numbers Different Ways 497

Use Objects to Add 400

Use Sketches to Add.. 404

Addition with Sums Through 100...................................... 408

Different Ways to Add 412

Use Objects to Subtract.. 415

Use Sketches to Subtract 419

Subtraction with Regrouping 424

More Subtraction with Regrouping.................................... 427

Different Ways to Subtract 431

Add and Subtract 434

Unit Review 439

Unit Checkpoint... 442

Add or Subtract: Problem Solving

Add and Subtract with Base-10 Models................................ 447

Solve Compare and Change Problems 451

Story Problems: More Exploration..................................... 453

Part-Part-Total Problems.. 454

Problems with Parts and Total.. 458

Combine Problems: More Exploration 461

Change Problems 462

Missing Numbers in Story Problems 465

Change Problems: More Exploration 468

Comparison Story Problems 469

Story Problems That Compare... 472

Compare Problems: More Exploration 475

Unit Review 477

Unit Checkpoint... 480

Add or Subtract: More Problem Solving

Equalize Story Problems 485
Make Them Equal 488
More Story Problems 491
Explore Number Sentences 496
Number Sentences 499
Write and Solve Number Sentences 503
Check Your Answers 507
Explain Solution Strategies 510
Justify Selected Procedures 514
Justify Different Solutions 516
Story Problems That Are Alike 520
Write Story Problems 524
Unit Review 529
Unit Checkpoint 532

Geometric Figures, Data, and Attributes

Plane Figures 537
Put Together and Take Apart Shapes 542
Group Shapes Different Ways 548
Classify Objects and Data 552
Patterns 557
Tally Charts and Bar Graphs 562
Data in Pictures and Graphs 565
Unit Review 570
Unit Checkpoint 573

Semester Review and Checkpoint

Semester Review 575
Semester Checkpoint 580

Program Overview

Lesson Overview

The table at the beginning of each lesson tells you what activities are in the lesson and whether students are on the computer (**ONLINE**) or at a table or desk (**OFFLINE**). The expected time for each activity is given.

Objectives and Prerequisite Skills

Each lesson teaches the Lesson Objectives. The lesson assumes that students know the Prerequisite Skills from their previous math experience. The Get Ready activity is designed to remind students of the prerequisite skills, and to prepare them for the lesson.

Common Errors and Misconceptions

Research shows that students might misunderstand certain concepts, which then leads to misunderstanding of more advanced concepts. When certain research applies to a lesson, the lesson has a Common Errors and Misconceptions section.

Content Background

The Content Background tells you what the students will learn in the lesson, and it explains any complex math concepts, putting the lesson into perspective with wider math knowledge.

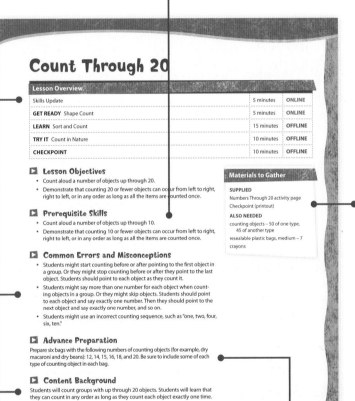

Count Through 20

Lesson Overview

Skills Update	5 minutes	ONLINE
GET READY Shape Count	5 minutes	ONLINE
LEARN Sort and Count	15 minutes	OFFLINE
TRY IT Count in Nature	10 minutes	OFFLINE
CHECKPOINT	10 minutes	OFFLINE

Lesson Objectives
- Count aloud a number of objects up through 20.
- Demonstrate that counting 20 or fewer objects can occur from left to right, right to left, or in any order as long as all the items are counted once.

Prerequisite Skills
- Count aloud a number of objects up through 10.
- Demonstrate that counting 10 or fewer objects can occur from left to right, right to left, or in any order as long as all the items are counted once.

Common Errors and Misconceptions
- Students might start counting before or after pointing to the first object in a group. Or they might stop counting before or after they point to the last object. Students should point to each object as they count it.
- Students might say more than one number for each object when counting objects in a group. Or they might skip objects. Students should point to each object and say exactly one number. Then they should point to the next object and say exactly one number, and so on.
- Students might use an incorrect counting sequence, such as "one, two, four, six, ten."

Advance Preparation
Prepare six bags with the following numbers of counting objects (for example, dry macaroni and dry beans): 12, 14, 15, 16, 18, and 20. Be sure to include some of each type of counting object in each bag.

Content Background
Students will count groups with up through 20 objects. Students will learn that they can count in any order as long as they count each object exactly one time.

Keywords   **count** – to say each number according to a defined sequence, such as consecutively, by 2s, or backward

Materials to Gather

SUPPLIED
Numbers Through 20 activity page
Checkpoint (printout)

ALSO NEEDED
counting objects – 50 of one type, 45 of another type
resealable plastic bags, medium – 7
crayons

COUNT THROUGH 20 **193**

Materials

This box tells you what materials students will need in this lesson. More information about the materials is included on page x.

Keywords

Definitions of keywords are included in the lesson in which the math term is introduced. The Unit Review includes of a list of all keywords for the unit.

Advance Preparation

Some lessons require preparation that extends beyond gathering materials. In these cases, the lesson includes an Advance Preparation section.

Materials

K[12] supplies math materials, including this Lesson Guide and the Activity Book, the student practice book.

The block set includes various counters as well as 2-D and 3-D shapes. Note that the blocks are labeled with letters. The materials lists in each lesson refer to these blocks by their letter (for instance, B blocks or BB blocks or C blocks). The O blocks refer to the cubes. These blocks aren't labeled with the letter O, but the hole in each block resembles this letter. Within the lesson, you might see a more descriptive term, such as "circles" for the B blocks. A set of base-10 blocks contains blocks representing ones, tens, and hundreds.

Printouts, Plastic Sheet Cover, and Dry-Erase Markers

A lesson may ask you to print a document showing a number line, place-value chart, or other math tool. These documents will be reused throughout the course. We recommend that you obtain a plastic sheet cover and dry-erase markers so students can place the sheet over the printout and write answers on the sheet. They can then erase the answers and reuse the printout multiple times.

Number and Symbol Cards

Index cards labeled with numbers or symbols are frequently called for in the lessons. We recommend that you create a set of index cards numbered 0–100, and use them throughout the course. You can also create the symbols that will be used most frequently: $-$ (minus), $+$ (plus), $=$ (equals), $>$ (greater than), $<$ (less than).

Paper and Pencil

Students should always have notebook paper and a pencil handy. These materials are not listed in each lesson.

Also Needed

Other common items are called for in lessons, designated in the materials list as "Also Needed." Common items include, but are not limited to, the following: calendar, containers, craft sticks, crayons, glue, glue stick, index cards, markers (permanent and coloring), paper (construction, drawing, and wide-line handwriting), pencils (coloring), pipe cleaners, play money, scissors (adult and round-end safety), sticky notes, tape (clear, double-stick, and masking), and yarn.

Working Through a Lesson

When you go online with students to do a math lesson, you will see a list of the activities that are included in the lesson. Students will take an assessment on calendar and time. In subsequent units, students will warm up for their math lesson by answering questions in an online Skills Update. Answers will be shown as students work through each question.

The Lesson Guide will give you an overview of the entire lesson.

Instructions for online activities are online, so you should expect to work at the computer with students, reading instructions and activities to them as necessary. The Lesson Guide may, however, include a teaching tip or other information. In some cases, such as when an open-ended Learning Tool is used, there will be instructions to follow in the Lesson Guide. The online screen will guide you to follow the instructions in the Lesson Guide.

Instructions for offline activities are in the Lesson Guide. These activities may use supplied or common materials, and some include pages from the Activity Book.

Types of Activities

Skills Update Short online problem set for warm-up. These problems should take about 5 minutes to complete.

Get Ready Review of previous math knowledge that will be needed for this lesson. The Get Ready can be online or offline.

Learn Presentation of math concepts, or guided practice. The Learn activities can be online or offline.

Try It Students practice what they have just learned, without guidance. The Try It activities are usually found in the Activity Book.

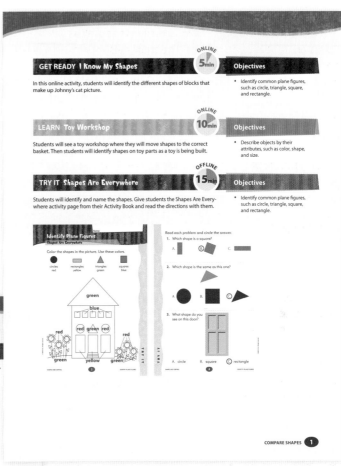

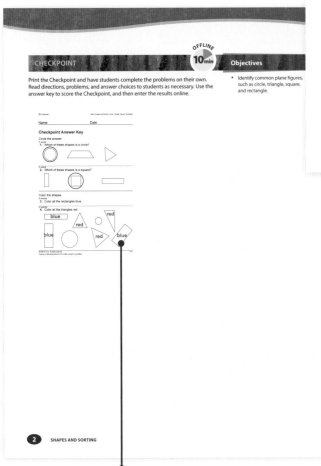

The Lesson Guide includes the answers, shown in magenta, to the Activity Book pages and offline Checkpoints.

Checkpoint Assessments of whether students have learned the objectives taught in the lesson or lessons. Not every lesson has a Checkpoint. In some Checkpoints, students show or explain their answers, and you record their performance.

In addition to the regular Checkpoints, **Unit Reviews** and **Unit Checkpoints** are lessons at the end of each unit. Each semester ends with a Semester Review and Semester Checkpoint.

Online Activities

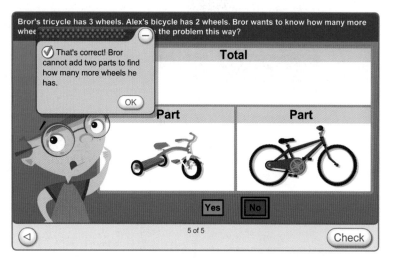

Online activities will show whether students answer correctly.

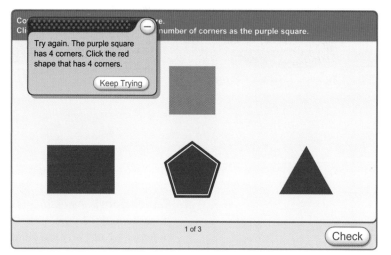

If students answered incorrectly, they will see feedback. They should click Keep Trying to try again. If they answer incorrectly a second time, they can click Show Me to see the correct answer.

Learning Tools are online activities that you set up to give students math exercises that will apply to what they are learning in a specific lesson.

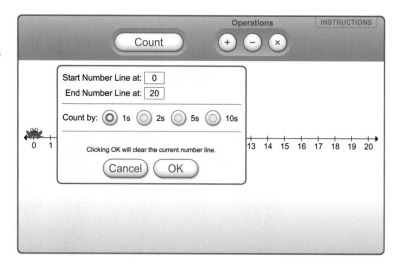

Read, Write, Count, and Compare Numbers

▶ Unit Objectives

- Count aloud whole numbers through 50.
- Read whole numbers through 50.
- Write numerals through 50.
- Count by 10s through 50.
- Count by 5s through 50.
- Count by 2s through 50.
- Count aloud whole numbers through 100.

- Read whole numbers through 100.
- Write numerals through 100.
- Count by 10s through 100.
- Count by 5s through 100.
- Count by 2s through 100.
- Use the symbols for less than, equal to, or greater than ($<$, $=$, $>$) to compare and order whole numbers to 100.

▶ Big Ideas

- Numbers tell us the results of counting.
- The equals symbol shows that two things—one on the left of the equals symbol, and one on the right of the equals symbol—are equivalent

▶ Unit Introduction

Many students can already count aloud. To be successful in math, they also need to be able to read, write, compare, and order numbers. They'll do that in this unit.

Students will first read and write whole numbers. They will skip count by 2s, 5s, and 10s. Doing this will help them compare and order numbers, and will also help them notice repeating number patterns. Counting with whole numbers is a first step toward adding and subtracting, and noticing patterns is a first step toward algebra, still a few years down the road.

While students count, watch for certain typical "speed bumps." In the objects they are counting, they may count one object twice or skip one. In what they are saying aloud, they may forget a number. For instance, when they skip count by 2s, they may say "two, four, six, ten" instead of "two, four, six, eight, ten." Listen to the students and practice counting with them so that they can imitate your proper counting patterns.

Numbers Through 50

GET READY Counting Review	10 minutes	**OFFLINE**
LEARN Count Through 50	15 minutes	**OFFLINE**
LEARN Read Numbers Through 50	15 minutes	**ONLINE**
TRY IT Read Numbers	10 minutes	**OFFLINE**
CHECKPOINT	10 minutes	**OFFLINE**

▶ Lesson Objectives

- Count aloud whole numbers through 50.
- Read whole numbers through 50.

▶ Prerequisite Skills

- Count aloud a number of objects up through 30.
- Write numerals from 1 through 30.

▶ Common Errors and Misconceptions

- Students might say more than one number for each object when counting objects in a group. Or they might skip objects. Students should point to each object and say exactly one number. Then they should point to the next object and say exactly one number, and so on
- Students might skip a number as they count.

▶ Content Background

Students will review counting up to 30 objects in preparation for learning to count and read numbers through 50. They will learn to count through 50 by paying attention to the patterns that occur. Then they will use counting to read numbers through 50.

This lesson assumes that students already know how to count and read whole numbers through 30.

Materials to Gather

SUPPLIED
Read Numbers activity page
Checkpoint (printout)

ALSO NEEDED
counting objects – 30

Keywords

number – a quantity or value
number line – a line consisting of points equally spaced, each of which corresponds to a unique number
pattern – a sequence of objects and/or numbers with attributes that are repeated in a predictable way

Students will practice counting from 1 to 30.
Gather the counting objects (for example, dry macaroni).

1. Make a group of 11 objects. Have students count each object aloud.

   Say: Every time you count a group, the last number you say aloud is the number of objects in the group. It is the answer to the question "How many?"

2. Have students use the name of the object to tell you how many objects are in the group. For example, "There are 26 pennies."

3. Repeat Steps 1 and 2 with groups of 23 and 30 objects.

For counting objects, use small, durable household items (for example, dry macaroni, shells, or twists).

Students will learn how to say the numbers, in order, from 31 to 50. The patterns in the numbers from 1 to 30 can help students count to 50.
There are no materials to gather for this activity.

1. **Say:** You know how to count to 30. Now let's learn how to count to 50.

2. Have students count from 1 to 30. Correct them as necessary.

   Ask: Do you know how to keep counting until you get to 50?

   If students can count correctly through 50 without assistance, proceed to the next Learn activity. Otherwise, continue with Step 3.

3. Tell students to listen as you count on from 30. As you slowly count from 31 to 39, emphasize the numbers from 1 to 9.

   Ask: What word do you hear at the beginning of each number?
   ANSWER: thirty

   Point out that, in 31 to 39, thirty is followed by a number from 1 to 9. Have students count from 31 to 39 with you, emphasizing the 1 to 9 pattern.

4. Tell students that the next number after 39 is 40, and explain that you can use the same pattern they hear in 21 to 29 and 31 to 39 to count from 41 to 49.

   Ask: What comes next after 40?
   ANSWER: 41

   If students answer correctly, have them continue to count through 50. If not, count for them from 41 through 50, emphasizing the word *forty* followed by the 1 to 9 pattern again.

5. Ask students to count from 31 through 50 by themselves. Listen to be sure they count correctly. If they have difficulty, remind them to use the pattern of thirty or forty followed by the 1 through 9 to figure out the number that comes next.

LEARN Read Numbers Through 50

ONLINE
15 min

Objectives

- Read whole numbers through 50.

Students will use counting aloud as a way of beginning to read numbers. They will use an online number line to count and read numbers, and they will use online number tiles to count and read numbers. Then they will read numbers between 31 and 50 when they are out of order.

DIRECTIONS FOR USING THE NUMBER LINE LEARNING TOOL

1. Click Count and choose the following:
   - Start Number Line at: 0
   - End Number Line at: 50
   - Count by: 1s

   Click OK.

2. Have students click each number to count. As they click each number, the frog will hop to the number and it will be said aloud. The number line will slide over automatically when necessary to display more numbers. When they reach 50, students should click Count Again and repeat.

   Go to the next screen to continue with the Learn activity.

TRY IT Read Numbers

OFFLINE
10 min

Objectives

- Count aloud whole numbers through 50.
- Read whole numbers through 50.

Students will count and read numbers from 1 to 50. Give students the Read Numbers activity page from their Activity Book and read the directions with them.

Numbers Through 50

Read Numbers

Name: _____

Read the number on each sport jersey.

4   18   13

22   28   39

47   50   40

36   20   34

READ, WRITE, COUNT, AND COMPARE NUMBERS   1   NUMBERS THROUGH 50

1. Count aloud the numbers in order from 10 to 30.
   Students should say the correct numbers.

2. Count aloud the numbers in order from 15 to 28.
   Students should say the correct numbers.

3. Count aloud the numbers in order from 1 to 50.
   Students should say the correct numbers.

4. Count aloud the number of cats.
   Students should count 15 cats.

5. Which of these numbers is forty-six? Circle the answer.
   A. 64   (B.) 46   C. 406

6. What number is this?
   13 **Students should say thirteen.**

7. What number is this?
   27 **Students should say twenty-seven.**

8. What number is this?
   0 **Students should say zero.**

READ, WRITE, COUNT, AND COMPARE NUMBERS   2   NUMBERS THROUGH 50

Print the Checkpoint. In Part 1, students will take a performance-based assessment. In Part 2, students will complete the problems on their own. Read the directions, problems, and answer choices to students if necessary. Use the answer key to score the Checkpoint, and then enter the results online.

Objectives

- Count aloud whole numbers through 50.
- Read whole numbers through 50.

⚙ Checkpoint   Math | Read, Write, Count, and Compare Numbers | Numbers Through 50

Name _____   Date _____

Checkpoint Answer Key

Part 1

Follow the instructions for each problem. Indicate whether the student performed the task correctly. Enter the results online.

1. Say, "Count aloud in order from 15 to 28."
(1 point)
Did the student correctly count from 15 to 28?
A. Yes   B. No

2. Say, "Count aloud in order from 30 to 49."
(1 point)
Did the student correctly count from 30 to 49?
A. Yes   B. No

3. Say, "Count aloud in order from 10 to 30."
(1 point)
Did the student correctly count from 10 to 30?
A. Yes   B. No

4. Count aloud the numbers in order from 1 to 50.
(1 point)
Did the student correctly count from 1 to 50?
A. Yes   B. No

⚙ Checkpoint   Math | Read, Write, Count, and Compare Numbers | Numbers Through 50

Name _____   Date _____

5. Read this number aloud. 28
(1 point)
Did the student say twenty-eight?
A. Yes   B. No

6. Read this number aloud. 17
(1 point)
Did the student say seventeen?
A. Yes   B. No

Give students Part 2 of the assessment.

⚙ Checkpoint   Math | Read, Write, Count, and Compare Numbers | Numbers Through 50

Name _____   Date _____

Part 2
Circle the answer.
(1 point)
7. Which of these numbers is forty-nine?
Ⓐ 49   B. 409   C. 94

(1 point)
8. Which of these numbers is thirty-six?
Ⓐ 36   B. 63   C. 306

Write Numerals Through 50

Skills Update	5 minutes	ONLINE
GET READY Numbers Through 30	5 minutes	OFFLINE
LEARN Write Numerals on Grid Paper	15 minutes	OFFLINE
LEARN Write What You Hear	15 minutes	OFFLINE
TRY IT Fill In the Numbers	10 minutes	OFFLINE
CHECKPOINT	10 minutes	OFFLINE

▶ Lesson Objectives

Write numerals through 50.

▶ Prerequisite Skills

Write numerals from 1 through 30.

▶ Common Errors and Misconceptions

- Students might start counting before or after pointing to the first object in a group. Or they might stop counting before or after they point to the last object. Students should point to each object as they count it.
- Students might say more than one number for each object when counting objects in a group. Or they might skip objects. Students should point to each object and say exactly one number. Then they should point to the next object and say exactly one number, and so on.
- Students might skip a number as they count.
- Students might say more than one number for each object when counting objects in a group. Or they might skip objects. To avoid such problems, draw a line down the center of a sheet of paper. Have students move objects from one side of the paper to the other as they count.

▶ Advance Preparation

Print the Five-in-a-Row Grid Paper (2 copies) and the Numeral Writing Guide.

▶ Content Background

Students know how to read and write numbers through 30, and have learned how to count and read numbers to 50. In this lesson, students will see how to write numbers through 50 correctly on grid paper and on handwriting paper.

   In mathematics, the term *numeral* means a symbol, and the term number means a quantity. A numeral symbolizes a number. Whether students use the numeral VI (like the ancient Romans) or the numeral 6, both symbolize the same number: six.

   In this course, you will see the word *numeral* used where appropriate. But in everyday life, you most often use the word *number* for both the symbol and the quantity, and it is fine to use just the word *number* with students.

Materials to Gather

SUPPLIED

Five-in-a-Row Grid Paper (printout)
Numeral Writing Guide (printout)
Fill In the Numbers activity page
Checkpoint (printout)

ALSO NEEDED

crayons
paper, wide-line handwriting

GET READY Numbers Through 30

Objectives

- Write numerals from 1 through 30.

Students will practice writing numbers from 1 to 30.
Gather one copy of the Five-in-a-Row Grid Paper, and give it to students.

1. **Say:** In this lesson, you will learn to write numbers through 50. Let's practice writing the numbers through 30 that you already know.

2. Ask students to say and write the numbers from 1 to 30 in the squares. If students have difficulty writing the numbers, show them the correct way to form them. Use the Numeral Writing Guide as a model.

LEARN Write Numerals on Grid Paper

Objectives

- Write numerals through 50.

Tips

If students have difficulty writing the numbers, they should practice writing just the numerals 0 to 9 on wide-line handwriting paper, using the Numeral Writing Guide as a model.

Students will write numbers through 50 on grid paper. Throughout the activity, be sure students write one number in each square.

Gather the crayons, the blank copy of the Five-in-a-Row Grid Paper, and the Five-in-a-Row Grid Paper that students filled out in the Get Ready activity.

1. Ask students to read the numbers from 1 to 30 while pointing to them in the squares on the first sheet of grid paper.

2. Give the students the blank sheet of grid paper and ask them to write 31 through 50 in the squares. If students write the numbers through 50 correctly, proceed to Step 7. Otherwise, continue to Step 3.

3. Explain to students that for all the numbers in the thirties, they should write a 3 for thirty, and then a number from 0 to 9. Demonstrate by writing 31 and 32, and then ask students to continue writing the rest of the thirties.

4. Ask what number comes after 39. Explain that 40 is written "four zero." Ask students to write 40.

5. Explain that for every number that starts with forty, they should write a 4 first and then a number from 0 to 9. Have students write the numbers 41 through 49.

6. Ask students what number comes after 49. After they answer 50, ask what the next ten after 40 is. Have students write 50 in the next grid square.

7. Have students color the numbers on both sheets of grid paper that end in a zero, and then read the numbers aloud to you.

   Ask them to describe patterns they see in these numbers. If they need help, explain that they all end in zero. The first numeral they see within each of these tens number is 1, 2, 3, 4, or 5—in that order.

8. Tell students that they have written 1 to 50, in order, so they can check their work by reading the numbers. If they wrote the numbers correctly, when they read them they should count in order from 1 to 50.

LEARN *Write What You Hear*

Students will hear a number and write the corresponding numeral on handwriting paper.

Gather the wide-line handwriting paper, and give it to students.

Tips

Refer to the Numeral Writing Guide for the correct way to write each numeral.

1. **Say:** Write the number 31.

   If students need help to start writing, say, "31. What number do you write for the 30? What number do you write for the 1?"

2. **Say:** Write the number 48.

3. **Say:** Write the number 13.

4. **Say:** Write the number 40.

5. **Say:** Write the number 29.

6. **Say:** Write the number 50.

TRY IT *Fill In the Numbers*

Students will practice writing numerals through 50. Give students the Fill In the Numbers activity page from their Activity Book and read the directions with them.

Write Numerals Through 50
Fill In the Numbers

Write the missing numbers.

1	2	3	4	5	6	7
8	9	10	11	12	13	14
15	16	17	18	19	20	21
22	23	24	25	26	27	28
29	30	31	32	33	34	35
36	37	38	39	40	41	42
43	44	45	46	47	48	49
50						

1. Write the number eighteen.

18

2. Write the number forty.

40

3. Write the number zero.

0

4. Write the number seventeen.

17

5. Write the missing number.

8, 9, 10, 11, 12, 13

CHECKPOINT

Objectives

- Write numerals through 50.

Print the Checkpoint and have students complete it on their own. Read the directions, problems, and answer choices to students if necessary. Use the answer key to score the Checkpoint, and then enter the results online.

Checkpoint   Math | Read, Write, Count, and Compare Numbers | Write Numerals Through 50

Name _____ Date _____

Checkpoint Answer Key

Read each problem and follow the directions.

(1 point)
1. Write the number forty-two.

                          42

(1 point)
2. Write the number twenty.

                          20

(1 point)
3. Write the number seventeen.

                          17

(1 point)
4. Write the number thirty-nine.

                          39

(1 point)
5. Write the number five.

                          5

Count by 10s and 5s Through 50

Lesson Overview

Skills Update	5 minutes	ONLINE
GET READY Make It Count Through 50	10 minutes	OFFLINE
LEARN Count by 10s	5 minutes	OFFLINE
LEARN Count by 5s	5 minutes	OFFLINE
LEARN Skip Count by 10s and 5s	15 minutes	ONLINE
TRY IT More Skip Counting	10 minutes	OFFLINE
CHECKPOINT	10 minutes	OFFLINE

▶ Lesson Objectives

- Count by 10s through 50.
- Count by 5s through 50.

▶ Prerequisite Skills

Count aloud a number of objects up through 30.

▶ Common Errors and Misconceptions

- Students might say more than one number for each object when counting objects in a group. Or they might skip objects. To avoid such problems, draw a line down the center of a sheet of paper. Have students move objects from one side of the paper to the other as they count.
- Students might skip a number as they count.
- Students might begin by skip counting but then switch to counting by ones.

▶ Advance Preparation

Print the Hundred Chart. Fold the chart in half to show only 1 through 50. Number index cards 21 through 50. Save cards for use in future lessons.

▶ Content Background

Students have practiced counting, reading, and writing numbers through 50. In this lesson, students will learn to count by 5s and 10s through 50. Students will also use a hundred chart to identify skip counting patterns.

Materials to Gather
SUPPLIED
Hundred Chart (printout)
More Skip Counting activity page
Checkpoint (printout)
ALSO NEEDED
crayons
index cards – numbered 21 through 50

Keywords

hundred chart – a 10-by-10 grid displaying the numbers from 1 to 100 in order from left to right

skip count – to count by a number other than 1

GET READY Make It Count Through 50

Objectives

- Count aloud whole numbers up through 50.
- Read whole numbers through 50.

Students will practice counting to 50. Gather the number cards.

1. Lay the 21 number card on the table with the number facing up. Leave a length of blank space (enough to hold about 15 cards) and place the 38 number card at the end of it. There should be enough room between the 21 card and the 38 card to place the numbers 22–37.

2. Ask students to tell you the numbers on the two cards you placed on the table, and then have them count from 21 to 38. As they say each number, place the appropriate number card down next to the previous card.

3. Repeat Steps 1 and 2 using the numbers 30 and 43 as your start and end cards, and then using the numbers 39 and 50 as your start and end cards.

LEARN Count by 10s

Objectives

- Count by 10s through 50.

Students will learn to skip count by 10s using the first half of the Hundred Chart, a 10 by 10 grid that is numbered from 1 through 100. Because of the arrangement of the numbers in rows and columns, it is easy for students to see number patterns. Those patterns will help students learn to skip count.
Gather the crayons and folded Hundred Chart.

1. **Say:** You are going to learn how to skip count by 10s. Point to the number 10 on your chart. Circle the 10 with your red crayon.

2. **Say:** Count on 10 more, and circle that number. What number did you circle?
ANSWER: 20

    Say: Count on 10 more, and circle that number. What number did you circle?
ANSWER: 30

    Say: Count on 10 more, and circle that number. What number did you circle?
ANSWER: 40

    Say: Count on 10 more, and circle that number. What number did you circle?
ANSWER: 50

3. **Say:** When you skip count by 10s, you count by every 10th number. Read the numbers you circled in order to count by 10s through 50.
ANSWER: 10, 20, 30, 40, 50

4. Have students close their eyes and try counting by 10s through 50. Assist them if necessary until they can count on their own.

Tips

Folding the Hundred Chart will keep students from being confused or intimidated by numbers 51–100. If they ask about the half that's hidden, tell them they will learn about those numbers in the future.

LEARN Count by 5s

Objectives

- Count by 10s through 50.

Students will use the first half of the Hundred Chart to learn to skip count by 5s. The numbers 10, 20, 30, 40, and 50 should be circled in red from the previous activity.
Gather the crayons and folded Hundred Chart.

1. **Say:** Skip count by 10s to 50.
ANSWER: 10, 20, 30, 40, 50

If students don't remember how, remind them that they can read the numbers that are circled in red.

Say: Now you are going to learn how to skip count by 5s.

2. **Say:** Point to the number 5 on the chart. Underline the 5 with a blue crayon.

   Ask: Count on 5 more, and underline that number. What number did you underline?
   ANSWER: 10

3. **Ask:** Count on 5 more, and underline that number. What number did you underline?
   ANSWER: 15

4. Continue this way until students have underlined in blue 5, 10, 15, 20, 25, 30, 35, 40, 45, and 50.

   Say: When you skip count by 5s, you count by every 5th number. Read the numbers you underlined to skip count by 5s to 50.

   After students have counted by 5s to 50 one or two more times, have them close their eyes and try counting by 5s to 50.

ONLINE 15min

LEARN Skip Count by 10s and 5s

Students will learn to skip count by 10s and 5s on the number line. Students will then skip count by 10s and 5s to find the missing number in a pattern. They will also skip count to find the total number of objects in a group of objects.

DIRECTIONS FOR USING THE NUMBER LINE LEARNING TOOL

1. Click Count and choose the following:
   - Start Number Line at: 0
   - End Number Line at: 50
   - Count by: 10s

   Click OK.

2. Students should click each number to count by 10s. As they click each number, the frog will hop to the number and it will be said aloud. The number line will slide over automatically when necessary to display more numbers. When they reach 50, students should click Count Again and repeat.

3. Click Count and choose the following:
   - Start Number Line at: 0
   - End Number Line at: 50
   - Count by: 5s

   Click OK.

4. Students should click each number to count by 5s. When they reach 50, have them click Count Again and repeat.

   Go to the next screen to continue with the Learn activity.

Tips

Tell students to skip count by 5s at the same time that you skip count slowly by 10s. Say the 10s at the same time that students say the 10s. Tell them that you are both doing the same thing, but you are just making bigger skips, landing only on the 10s. When they skip count by 5s, they land both on the 5s and on the 10s.

Objectives

- Count by 10s through 50.

Tips

If students need help skip counting on the number line, they may refer to their Hundred Chart during the activity.

TRY IT More Skip Counting

Objectives

Students will practice skip counting to write missing numbers in a pattern, and to count objects arranged in groups of 10s or 5s. Give students the More Skip Counting activity page from their Activity Book and read the directions with them.

- Count by 10s through 50.
- Count by 5s through 50.

Tips

For each problem, have students identify whether they will skip count by 5s or 10s before they begin.

Name: _____

Count by 10s and 5s Through 50
More Skip Counting

Count by 5s or 10s to find the missing number.

1. 10, 15, 20, __25__, 30
2. 10, 20, 30, 40, __50__
3. 20, 25, 30, __35__, 40
4. 25, 30, 35, 40, __45__

Count by 5s or 10s to find the total.

5.
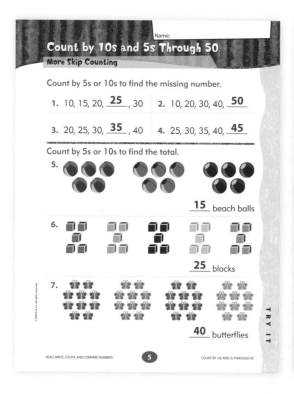

__15__ beach balls

6.

__25__ blocks

7.

__40__ butterflies

TRY IT

Circle the answer.

8. Count by 5s.
   Choose the missing number. 15, _____, 25, 30, 35
   A. 16   (B.) 20   C. 40   D. 26

9. Count by 5s.
   Choose the missing number. 25, 30, 35, 40, _____
   A. 35   B. 20   C. 41   (D.) 45

10. Count by 10s.
    Choose the missing number. 10, _____, 30, 40, 50
    A. 25   B. 11   C. 15   (D.) 20

11. Count by 10s.
    Choose the missing number. 10, 20, 30, _____, 50
    A. 51   (B.) 40   C. 31   D. 45

Say the answer.

12. Skip count aloud by 5s from 25 through 50.
    Students should say 25, 30, 35, 40, 45, 50.

13. Skip count aloud by 10s from 30 through 50.
    Students should say 30, 40, 50.

TRY IT

OFFLINE

10 min

Print the Checkpoint and have students complete it on their own. Read the directions, problems, and answer choices to students if necessary. Use the answer key to score the Checkpoint, and then enter the results online.

- Count by 10s through 50.
- Count by 5s through 50.

☼ Checkpoint   Math | Read, Write, Count, and Compare Numbers | Count by 10s and 5s Through 50

Name _____ Date _____

Checkpoint Answer Key

Read each problem and follow the directions.
(1 point)
1. Skip count aloud by 10s to 50.

   10, 20, 30, 40, 50

(1 point)
2. Count by 10s. Circle the missing number. 10, 20, _____, 40, 50

   (A.) 30   B. 21   C. 15   D. 21

(1 point)
3. Count by 10s. Circle the missing number. 10, 20, 30, 40, _____

   A. 41   (B.) 50   C. 20   D. 30

(1 point)
4. Count by 5s. Circle the missing number. 5, 10, 15, 20, _____

   (A.) 25   B. 30   C. 21   D. 44

(1 point)
5. Count by 5s. Circle the missing number. 30, 35, 40, 45, _____

   A. 25   B. 46   C. 55   (D.) 50

(1 point)
6. Skip count aloud by 5s to 50.

   5, 10, 15, 20, 25, 30, 35, 40, 45, 50

---

1 of 1

Count by 2s Through 50

Lesson Overview

Skills Update	5 minutes	ONLINE
GET READY Skip Count Through 50	10 minutes	OFFLINE
LEARN Count and Color by 2s	10 minutes	OFFLINE
LEARN Skip Count by 2s	15 minutes	ONLINE
TRY IT Count by 2s	10 minutes	OFFLINE
CHECKPOINT	10 minutes	OFFLINE

▶ Lesson Objectives

Count by 2s through 50.

▶ Prerequisite Skills

- Count aloud a number of objects up through 30.
- Count by 10s through 50.
- Count by 5s through 50.

▶ Common Errors and Misconceptions

- Students might say more than one number for each object when counting objects in a group. Or they might skip objects. To avoid such problems, draw a line down the center of a sheet of paper. Have students move objects from one side of the paper to the other as they count.
- Students might skip a number as they count.
- Students might begin by skip counting but then switch to counting by ones.

▶ Advance Preparation

Print the Hundred Chart. Fold the chart in half to show only 1 through 50.

▶ Content Background

Students learned how to count to 50 and skip count by 10s and 5s to 50. In this lesson, they will learn to skip count by 2s to 50. Students will use the patterns that they find in a hundred chart to help them count.

Materials to Gather

SUPPLIED
Hundred Chart (printout)
Count by 2s activity page
Checkpoint (printout)

ALSO NEEDED
counting objects – 40
crayons

GET READY Skip Count Through 50   OFFLINE 10 min

Students will practice skip counting by 5s and 10s to find the number of objects in a group.
   Gather the counting objects (for example, dry macaroni).

Objectives

- Count aloud whole numbers up through 50.
- Read whole numbers through 50.

1. Arrange counting objects in 5 groups with 5 objects in each group.

2. Have students count the objects in the first group. Tell them that there are 5 objects in each group, and that they can count by 5s to find the total number of objects.

3. Ask students to count by 5s to find the total number of objects.

4. Repeat Steps 1–3 with 4 groups of 10 objects. Have students count by 10s to find the total number.

5. Repeat Steps 1–3 again, with 4 groups of 5 objects.

OFFLINE 10 min

LEARN Count and Color by 2s

Objectives

- Count by 2s through 50.

Students will use the first half of the Hundred Chart, a 10 by 10 grid that is numbered from 1 through 100. Because of the arrangement of the numbers in rows and columns, it is easy for students to see number patterns. Those patterns will help students learn to skip count.

Gather the crayons and the folded Hundred Chart.

1. **Say:** You are going to learn how to skip count by 2s. Color the 2 square yellow.

2. **Say:** Count on 2 more, and color that number. What number did you color?
   ANSWER: 4

3. **Say:** Count on 2 more, and color that number. What number did you color?
   ANSWER: 6

4. **Say:** Keep counting by 2s and coloring until you reach 50.

   Students should count and color.

   Say: When you skip count by 2s, you count by every 2nd number. Read the numbers you colored in order to count by 2s through 50.
   ANSWER: 2, 4, 6, 8, 10, 12, 14, 16, 18, 20, 22, 24, 26, 28, 30, 32, 34, 36, 38, 40, 42, 44, 46, 48, 50

5. Have students practice counting by 2s until they can close their eyes and count by 2s through 50.

ONLINE 15 min

LEARN Skip Count by 2s

Objectives

- Count by 2s through 50.

Students will learn to skip count by 2s on the number line. Students will then skip count by 2s to find the missing number in a pattern. They will also skip count to find the total number of objects in a group of objects.

DIRECTIONS FOR USING THE NUMBER LINE LEARNING TOOL

1. Click Count and choose the following:
   - Start Number Line at: 0
   - End Number Line at: 50
   - Count by: 2s

   Click OK.

2. Students should click each number to count by 2s. As they click each number, the frog will hop to the number and it will be said aloud. The number line will slide over automatically when necessary to display more numbers. When they reach 50, students should click Count Again and repeat.

   Go to the next screen to continue with the Learn activity.

TRY IT Count by 2s

Objectives

- Count by 2s through 50.

Students will practice skip counting by 2s to find missing numbers and to find the total number of objects grouped in 2s. Give students the Count by 2s activity page from their Activity Book and read the directions with them.

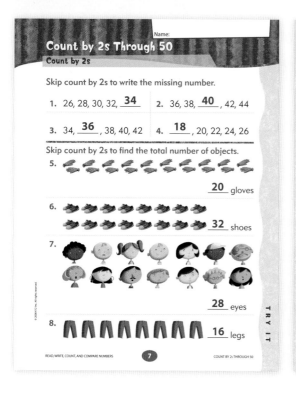

Name:

Count by 2s Through 50

Count by 2s

Skip count by 2s to write the missing number.

1. 26, 28, 30, 32, **34**   2. 36, 38, **40**, 42, 44

3. 34, **36**, 38, 40, 42   4. **18**, 20, 22, 24, 26

Skip count by 2s to find the total number of objects.

5. **20** gloves

6. **32** shoes

7. **28** eyes

8. **16** legs

READ, WRITE, COUNT, AND COMPARE NUMBERS   **7**   COUNT BY 2s THROUGH 50

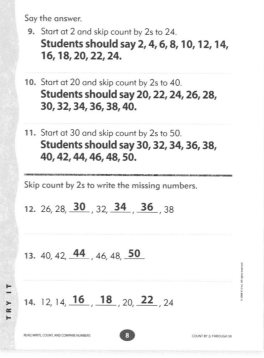

Say the answer.

9. Start at 2 and skip count by 2s to 24.
    Students should say 2, 4, 6, 8, 10, 12, 14, 16, 18, 20, 22, 24.

10. Start at 20 and skip count by 2s to 40.
    Students should say 20, 22, 24, 26, 28, 30, 32, 34, 36, 38, 40.

11. Start at 30 and skip count by 2s to 50.
    Students should say 30, 32, 34, 36, 38, 40, 42, 44, 46, 48, 50.

Skip count by 2s to write the missing numbers.

12. 26, 28, **30**, 32, **34**, **36**, 38

13. 40, 42, **44**, 46, 48, **50**

14. 12, 14, **16**, **18**, 20, **22**, 24

READ, WRITE, COUNT, AND COMPARE NUMBERS   **8**   COUNT BY 2s THROUGH 50

T R Y   I T

CHECKPOINT

Print the Checkpoint and have students complete it on their own. Read the directions, problems, and answer choices to students if necessary. Use the answer key to score the Checkpoint, and then enter the results online.

Gather the crayons. Students will need a crayon to complete Problem 4.

Objectives

• Count by 2s through 50.

Tips

If necessary, allow students to use their Hundred Chart numbered 1–50 already colored with a crayon to help them count by 2s.

☼ Checkpoint   Math | Read, Write, Count, and Compare Numbers | Count by 2s Through 50

Name _____   Date _____

Checkpoint Answer Key

Read each problem and follow the directions.

(1 point)
1. Count by 2s. Choose the missing number. 2, 4, 6, 8, _____

A. 7   (B.) 10   C. 12   D. 14

(1 point)
2. Count by 2s. Choose the missing number. 32, 34, 36, 38, _____

A. 37   B. 39   (C.) 40   D. 45

(1 point)
3. Skip count aloud by 2s to 50. **2, 4, 6, 8, 10, 12, 14, 16, 18, 20, 22, 24, 26, 28, 30, 32, 34, 36, 38, 40, 42, 44, 46, 48, 50**

(5 points)
4. Color the numbers on the chart to show counting by 2s.

1	(2)	3	(4)	5	(6)	7	(8)	9	(10)
11	(12)	13	(14)	15	(16)	17	(18)	19	(20)
21	(22)	23	(24)	25	(26)	27	(28)	29	(30)
31	(32)	33	(34)	35	(36)	37	(38)	39	(40)
41	(42)	43	(44)	45	(46)	47	(48)	49	(50)

1 of 1

Numbers Through 100

Lesson Overview

Skills Update	5 minutes	ONLINE
GET READY Numbers Through 50	5 minutes	OFFLINE
LEARN Count Through 100	10 minutes	OFFLINE
LEARN Count with Number Cards	10 minutes	OFFLINE
LEARN Read Numbers Through 100	10 minutes	ONLINE
TRY IT Count & Read Numbers Through 100	10 minutes	OFFLINE
CHECKPOINT	10 minutes	OFFLINE

▶ Lesson Objectives

- Count aloud whole numbers through 100.
- Read whole numbers through 100.

▶ Prerequisite Skills

- Count aloud whole numbers through 50.
- Read whole numbers through 50.

▶ Common Errors and Misconceptions

Students might skip a number as they count.

▶ Advance Preparation

Number index cards 50 through 100. Save cards for use in future lessons. Separate the number cards into two groups: 50–65 and 66–100.

▶ Content Background

Students will learn to count and read whole numbers through 100.

Materials to Gather

SUPPLIED

Count & Read Numbers Through 100 activity page

Checkpoint (printout)

ALSO NEEDED

index cards – numbered 50–100

GET READY Numbers Through 50

OFFLINE 5min

Objectives

- Count aloud whole numbers through 50.

Students will practice counting from 1 to 50. There are no materials to gather for this activity.

1. Have students count aloud from 1 to 50.
2. Listen and correct as necessary.

   If students needed several corrections, have them count from 1 to 50 again.

LEARN Count Through 100

Objectives

• Count aloud whole numbers through 100.

Students will learn how to count to 100. The patterns in the numbers from 1 to 50 can help students count to 100. There are no materials to gather for this activity.

1. Have students count to 50.

   Ask: What are the tens you say when you count to 50?
   ANSWER: 10, 20, 30, 40, 50

2. **Ask:** What is the pattern that you use when you are counting to 50? What do you do over and over?
   ANSWER: After each ten, you count from 1 through 9 again.

3. Explain that this pattern continues after 50 all the way through 100. Count aloud from 51 to 59, emphasizing the 1 to 9 pattern. Have students count aloud from 50 to 59.

4. Tell students that the next ten is 60.

   Ask: What number do you think comes after 60?
   ANSWER: 61.

   Have students count with you from 61 to 69.

5. Continue counting with students through 100, stopping to tell them each new ten if necessary.

6. Have students count from 51 to 100 by themselves. If they have difficulty, remind them to use the patterns and tell them the next ten when necessary.

LEARN Count with Number Cards

Objectives

• Count aloud whole numbers through 100.

Students will practice counting from 50 to 100 by counting from the number on one number card to the number on another number card.

Gather the number cards that you have separated into two groups. Shuffle each group of cards. Place the two groups face down so that the numerals do not show.

1. Have students turn over one card from each group and count aloud from the lower number to the higher. For example, if they choose 56 and 73, they would start at 56 and say aloud every number through 73.

2. Return the two cards to their groups, and repeat the activity at least three times.

Tips

If students have difficulty counting, review the 1 to 9 pattern between each ten by counting from 51 to 60 aloud and emphasizing the pattern with your voice. Also, review the tens from 50 to 100 by telling students that the next ten after 59 is 60, the next ten after 69 is 70, and so on.

LEARN Read Numbers Through 100

Objectives

• Read whole numbers through 100.

Students will learn to count from 50 to 100 on the number line. Then they will read the numbers in order using online number tiles, and identify numbers on tiles that are not in order.

DIRECTIONS FOR USING THE NUMBER LINE LEARNING TOOL

1. Click Count and choose the following:
   - Start Number Line at: 50
   - End Number Line at: 100
   - Count by: 1s

   Click OK.

2. Students should click each number to count from 51 through 100. As they click each number, the frog will hop to the number and it will be said aloud. The number line will slide over automatically when necessary to display more numbers.

   Go to the next screen to continue with the Learn activity.

OFFLINE 10 min

TRY IT Count & Read Numbers Through 100

Students will practice counting and reading numbers through 100. Give students the Count & Read Numbers Through 100 activity page from their Activity Book and read the directions with them.

Objectives

- Count aloud whole numbers through 100.
- Read whole numbers through 100.

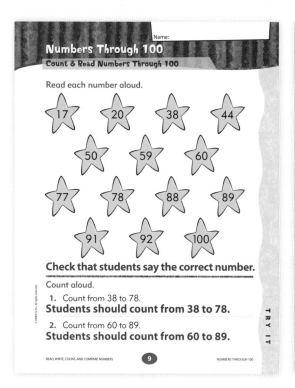

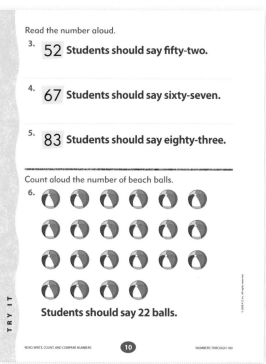

OFFLINE

10 min

Objectives

Print the Checkpoint. In Part 1, students will take a performance-based assessment. In Part 2, students will complete the problems on their own. Read the directions, problems, and answer choices to students if necessary. Use the answer key to score the Checkpoint, and then enter the results online.

- Count aloud whole numbers through 100.
- Read whole numbers through 100.

Math | Read, Write, Count, and Compare Numbers | Numbers Through 100

Name _____ Date _____

Checkpoint Answer Key

Part 1

Follow the instructions for each problem. Indicate whether the student performed the task correctly. Enter the results online.

1. Say, "Say the numbers in order from 85 to 100."
(1 point)
Did the student count correctly from 85 to 100?
A. Yes   B. No

2. Say, "Say the numbers in order from 62 to 79."
(1 point)
Did the student count correctly from 62 to 79?
A. Yes   B. No

3. Say, "Say the numbers in order from 50 to 70."
(1 point)
Did the student count correctly from 50 to 70?
A. Yes   B. No

4. Say, "Say the numbers in order from 1 to 100."
(1 point)
Did the student count correctly from 1 to 100?
A. Yes   B. No

Give students Part 2 of the assessment.

Math | Read, Write, Count, and Compare Numbers | Numbers Through 100

Name _____ Date _____

Part 2

Follow the instructions for each problem. Enter the results online.
(1 point)
5. Which of these numbers is ninety-nine?
A. 19   (B.) 99   C. 90

(1 point)
6. Which of these numbers is seventy-seven?
A. 17   (B.) 77   C. 707

(1 point)
7. Which of these numbers is fifty-two?
A. 25   (B.) 52   C. 502

(1 point)
8. Which of these numbers is eighty-six?
A. 68   B. 806   (C.) 86

Write Numerals Through 100

Lesson Overview

Skills Update	5 minutes	ONLINE
GET READY Numbers Through 50	10 minutes	OFFLINE
LEARN Numbers Through 100	10 minutes	OFFLINE
LEARN Write with Number Cards	15 minutes	OFFLINE
TRY IT Fill In the Hundred Chart	10 minutes	OFFLINE
CHECKPOINT	10 minutes	OFFLINE

▶ Lesson Objectives

Write numerals through 100.

▶ Prerequisite Skills

Write numerals through 50.

▶ Advance Preparation

Number index cards 50 through 100, or gather the number cards you created previously. On the back of each card, write the word for the number.
  Print the Numeral Writing Guide and Hundred Grid.

▶ Content Background

Students will use what they know about saying and reading numbers to help them write numbers through 100. In this lesson, students will write numbers on handwriting paper and complete a hundred chart.

  In mathematics, the term *numeral* means a symbol, and the term *number* means a quantity. A numeral symbolizes a number. Whether we use the numeral VI (like the ancient Romans) or the numeral 6, they both symbolize the same number: six.

  In this course, you will see the word *numeral* used where appropriate. But in everyday life, we most often use the word *number* for both the symbol and the quantity, and it is fine to use just the word *number* with your students.

Materials to Gather

SUPPLIED

Numeral Writing Guide (printout)

Hundred Grid (printout)

Fill In the Hundred Chart activity page

Checkpoint (printout)

ALSO NEEDED

index cards – numbered 50–100 and labeled with number words

paper, wide-line handwriting

Keywords	**digit** – any one of the numerals 0, 1, 2, 3, 4, 5, 6, 7, 8, 9

GET READY **Numbers Through 50**

- Write numerals through 50.

Students will practice writing numerals from 10 through 50. Gather the Numeral Writing Guide and Hundred Grid.

1. Have students write the numerals from 10 through 20 on the Hundred Grid. Be sure students use correct form when writing their numerals. Use the Numeral Writing Guide to check.

2. When the numerals from 10 to 20 are correct, have students continue writing the numerals up through 50. Students should say the numbers aloud as they write.

LEARN **Numbers Through 100**

Objectives

- Write numerals through 100.

Students will learn to write numerals from 51 through 100. Gather the Hundred Grid from the Get Ready activity.

1. Have students write the numerals from 51 to 60 on the second half of the Hundred Grid. Remind them to follow the pattern of writing the number for the new ten first, followed by a number from 0 to 9. Use the Numeral Writing Guide to check that students are forming their numerals correctly.

2. When the numerals from 51 to 60 are correct, have students continue writing the numerals up through 100 following the same pattern. Students should say the numbers aloud as they write.

Tips

If students need help forming the digits, have them use the Numeral Writing Guide to practice writing the numerals 0 to 9.

LEARN **Write with Number Cards**

Objectives

- Write numerals through 100.

Students will use number cards to practice writing numbers from 50 through 100. Point to the number word on the card as you say the number. Students are not expected to be able to read or write the number words themselves, but this activity will expose them to the number words.

Gather the cards and wide-line handwriting paper.

Tips

If students have difficulty writing the numerals from 51 to 100, have them look at the Numeral Writing Guide.

1. Lay number cards 50–60 on the table in order, in a row, with 50, 60, and two other intermediate cards of your choice facing numeral side up, and the rest facing numeral side down. Have students point to the first number card, which is 50.

2. Go through the numbers one by one, having students tell you what number is on the card. When you reach a card with the numeral side facing down, have students write the number on their handwriting paper, and then flip the card over to check their work.

3. Follow Steps 1 and 2 using the number cards 60–70, 70–80, 80–90, and 90–100. Each time place the tens cards and three other cards face up, and the rest face down. Have the students write the numerals for the cards that are facing down and then flip the cards to check their work.

OFFLINE
10min

TRY IT Fill In the Hundred Chart

Objectives

- Write numerals through 100.

Students will practice filling in the missing numbers on a hundred chart, writing a number that you say, and writing the missing number in a sequence. Give students the Fill In the Hundred Chart activity page from their Activity Book and read the directions with them.

For Problems 1–4, read the number words to students.

Write Numerals Through 100
Fill In the Hundred Chart

Complete the hundred chart.

1	2	3	4	5	6	7	8	9	10
11	12	13	14	15	16	17	18	19	20
21	22	23	24	25	26	27	28	29	30
31	32	33	34	35	36	37	38	39	40
41	42	43	44	45	46	47	48	49	50
51	52	53	54	55	56	57	58	59	60
61	62	63	64	65	66	67	68	69	70
71	72	73	74	75	76	77	78	79	80
81	82	83	84	85	86	87	88	89	90
91	92	93	94	95	96	97	98	99	100

TRY IT

READ, WRITE, COUNT, AND COMPARE NUMBERS **11** WRITE NUMERALS THROUGH 100

Write the number.
1. ninety-eight **98**
2. sixty-eight **68**
3. seventy-three **73**
4. ninety-nine **99**

Write the missing number.
5. 96, 97, 98, 99, **100**
6. 50, 51, **52**, 53, 54, 55
7. 68, 69, **70**, 71, 72
8. 74, 75, **76**, 77, 78

TRY IT

READ, WRITE, COUNT, AND COMPARE NUMBERS **12** WRITE NUMERALS THROUGH 100

26 READ, WRITE, COUNT, AND COMPARE NUMBERS

CHECKPOINT

- Write numerals through 100.

Print the Checkpoint and have students complete it on their own. Read the directions, problems, and answer choices to students if necessary. Use the answer key to score the Checkpoint, and then enter the results online.

⚙ Checkpoint   Math | Read, Write, Count, and Compare Numbers | Write Numerals Through 100

Name _____   Date _____

Checkpoint Answer Key

Read the directions and write the numbers.

(1 point)
1. Write the number ninety-nine. __99__

(1 point)
2. Write the number ninety-eight. __98__

(1 point)
3. Write the missing number. 50, 51, __52__, 53, 54, 55

(1 point)
4. Write the numbers sixty through seventy.

__60__ __61__ __62__ __63__ __64__ __65__ __66__

__67__ __68__ __69__ __70__

(1 point)
5. Write the numbers eighty-six through ninety-six.

__86__ __87__ __88__ __89__ __90__ __91__ __92__

__93__ __94__ __95__ __96__

Count by 10s and 5s Through 100

Lesson Overview

Skills Update	5 minutes	ONLINE
GET READY Practice Skip Counting	5 minutes	ONLINE
LEARN Skip Count on a Hundred Chart	20 minutes	ONLINE
LEARN Find the Missing Number	10 minutes	ONLINE
TRY IT Skip Count by 5s and 10s	10 minutes	OFFLINE
CHECKPOINT	10 minutes	OFFLINE

▶ Lesson Objectives

- Count by 10s through 100.
- Count by 5s through 100.

▶ Prerequisite Skills

- Count by 10s through 50.
- Count by 5s through 50.

▶ Common Errors and Misconceptions

- Students might say more than one number for each object when counting objects in a group. Or they might skip objects. To avoid such problems, draw a line down the center of a sheet of paper. Have students move objects from one side of the paper to the other as they count.
- Students might skip a number as they count.
- Students might begin by skip counting but then switch to counting by ones.

▶ Content Background

Students have learned to skip count by 5s and 10s through 50. In this lesson, students will learn to skip count by 5s and 10s through 100. They will use a hundred chart and number line to help them skip count. Skip counting can help students count to greater numbers more quickly than if they counted by ones.

Materials to Gather

SUPPLIED

Skip Count by 5s and 10s activity page

Checkpoint (printout)

ALSO NEEDED

crayons

GET READY Practice Skip Counting

Students will skip count by 10s and 5s to 50.

Objectives

- Count by 10s through 50.
- Count by 5s through 50.

LEARN **Skip Count on a Hundred Chart**

Students know how to count by 5s and 10s through 50, and will continue skip counting by 5s and 10s through 100. They will use a hundred chart to see patterns, and will practice skip counting on the number line.

- Count by 10s through 100.
- Count by 5s through 100.

DIRECTIONS FOR USING THE HUNDRED CHART LEARNING TOOL

1. Have students click the blue circle tool and count by 10s on the chart by clicking every 10th number as they coun t aloud. When they click, the number will be circled and will be said aloud. If an incorrect number is clicked, simply have them click it again to remove the circle. When they have counted by 10s through 100, have them click the speaker icon to hear the numbers counted aloud.

It may be helpful for students to start at 5 or 10 and skip count through the number pattern to find the missing number.

2. Have students click the red underline tool and count by 5s on the chart. The 10s will be circled and underlined. The 5s will be underlined only. They can click the speaker button to hear the numbers again.

3. Have students look for patterns on the chart. Examples: The 10s all end in 0. The 5s all end in 5 or 0. All the 10s are circled and underlined.

4. Click Print to print a copy of students' hundred chart.

DIRECTIONS FOR USING THE NUMBER LINE LEARNING TOOL

5. Click Count and choose the following:
   - Start Number Line at: 0
   - End Number Line at: 100
   - Count by: 10s

   Click OK.

6. Students should click each number to count by 10s through 100. As they click each number, the frog will hop to the number and it will be said aloud. The number line will slide over automatically when necessary to display more numbers. When they reach 100, students should click Count Again and repeat.

7. Click Count and choose the following:
   - Start Number Line at: 0
   - End Number Line at: 100
   - Count by: 5s

   Click OK.

8. Students should click each number to count by 5s through 100. As they click each number, the frog will hop to the number and it will be said aloud. The number line will slide over automatically when necessary to display more numbers. When they reach 100, students should click Count Again and repeat.

LEARN **Find the Missing Number**

Students will skip count by 5s and 10s to find the missing number in different patterns. If necessary, allow students to review skip counting by 10s and 5s using the hundred chart they created in the previous activity.

- Count by 10s through 100.
- Count by 5s through 100.

TRY IT Skip Count by 5s and 10s

OFFLINE
10 min

Objectives

- Count by 10s through 100.
- Count by 5s through 100.

Students will practice skip counting by 5s and 10s through 100. Give students the crayons and Skip Count by 5s and 10s activity page from their Activity Book. Read the directions with them.

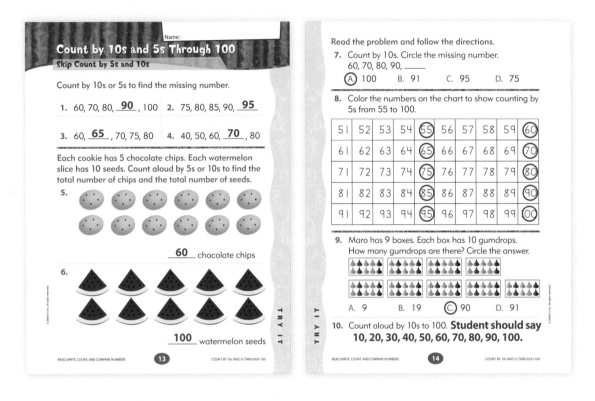

Count by 10s and 5s Through 100

Name: _____

Skip Count by 5s and 10s

Count by 10s or 5s to find the missing number.

1. 60, 70, 80, __90__, 100
2. 75, 80, 85, 90, __95__

3. 60, __65__, 70, 75, 80
4. 40, 50, 60, __70__, 80

Each cookie has 5 chocolate chips. Each watermelon slice has 10 seeds. Count aloud by 5s or 10s to find the total number of chips and the total number of seeds.

5.

_____60_____ chocolate chips

6.

_____100_____ watermelon seeds

READ, WRITE, COUNT, AND COMPARE NUMBERS   13   COUNT BY 10s AND 5s THROUGH 100

Read the problem and follow the directions.

7. Count by 10s. Circle the missing number.
   60, 70, 80, 90, _____
   (A) 100   B. 91   C. 95   D. 75

8. Color the numbers on the chart to show counting by 5s from 55 to 100.

51	52	53	54	(55)	56	57	58	59	(60)
61	62	63	64	(65)	66	67	68	69	(70)
71	72	73	74	(75)	76	77	78	79	(80)
81	82	83	84	(85)	86	87	88	89	(90)
91	92	93	94	(95)	96	97	98	99	(100)

9. Maro has 9 boxes. Each box has 10 gumdrops. How many gumdrops are there? Circle the answer.

   A. 9   B. 19   (C) 90   D. 91

10. Count aloud by 10s to 100. **Student should say 10, 20, 30, 40, 50, 60, 70, 80, 90, 100.**

READ, WRITE, COUNT, AND COMPARE NUMBERS   14   COUNT BY 10s AND 5s THROUGH 100

30 READ, WRITE, COUNT, AND COMPARE NUMBERS

CHECKPOINT

Objectives

- Count by 10s through 100.
- Count by 5s through 100.

Print the Checkpoint. In Part 1, students will take a performance-based assessment. In Part 2, students will complete the problems on their own. Read the directions, problems, and answer choices to students if necessary. Use the answer key to score the Checkpoint, and then enter the results online.

○ Checkpoint   Math | Read, Write, Count, and Compare Numbers | Count by 10s and 5s Through 100

Name _____ Date _____

Checkpoint Answer Key

Part 1

Follow the instructions for each problem. Indicate whether the student performed the task correctly. Enter the results online.

1. Say, "Skip count aloud by 10s to 100."
(1 point)
Did the student skip count correctly by 10s to 100?

A. Yes   B. No

2. Say, "Skip count aloud by 5s to 100."
(1 point)
Did the student skip count correctly by 5s to 100?

A. Yes   B. No

Give students Part 2 of the assessment.

○ Checkpoint   Math | Read, Write, Count, and Compare Numbers | Count by 10s and 5s Through 100

Name _____ Date _____

Part 2

Circle the answer.
(1 point)
3. Count by 10s. Choose the missing number. 60, 70, _____, 90, 100

A. 75   B. 50   (C.) 80   D. 71

(1 point)
4. Count by 10s. Choose the missing number. 60, 70, 80, 90, _____

(A.) 100   B. 91   C. 95   D. 75

(1 point)
5. Count by 5s. Choose the missing number. 45, 50, 55, 60, _____

A. 40   B. 75   (C.) 65   D. 61

(1 point)
6. Count by 5s. Choose the missing number. 60, 65, 70, 75, _____

A. 55   B. 76   C. 95   (D.) 80

Count by 2s Through 100

Lesson Overview

Skills Update	5 minutes	ONLINE
GET READY Skip Count by 2s Through 50	5 minutes	ONLINE
LEARN Skip Count on a Hundred Chart	15 minutes	ONLINE
LEARN Find the Missing Number	15 minutes	ONLINE
TRY IT Skip Count by 2s	10 minutes	OFFLINE
CHECKPOINT	10 minutes	OFFLINE

▶ Lesson Objectives

Count by 2s through 100.

▶ Prerequisite Skills

Count by 2s through 50.

▶ Common Errors and Misconceptions

- Students might say more than one number for each object when counting objects in a group. Or they might skip objects. To avoid such problems, draw a line down the center of a sheet of paper. Have students move objects from one side of the paper to the other as they count.

- Students might use an incorrect counting sequence, such as "one, two, four, six, ten."

▶ Content Background

Students have learned to skip count by 2s through 50. In this lesson, students will learn to skip count by 2s through 100. Students will use a hundred chart and number line to help them skip count.

Materials to Gather

SUPPLIED

Skip Count by 2s activity page

Checkpoint (printout)

ALSO NEEDED

crayons

GET READY Skip Count by 2s Through 50

ONLINE 5 min

Students practice skip counting by 2s on the number line.

Objectives

- Count by 2s through 50.

DIRECTIONS FOR USING THE NUMBER LINE LEARNING TOOL

1. Click Count and choose the following:
   - Start Number Line at: 0
   - End Number Line at: 50
   - Count by: 2s

   Click OK.

2. Students should click each number to count by 2s. As they click each number, the frog will hop to the number and it will be said aloud. The number line will slide over automatically when necessary to display more numbers. When they reach 50, students should click Count Again and repeat.

LEARN Skip Count on a Hundred Chart

ONLINE 15 min

Objectives

• Count by 2s through 100.

Students know how to count by 2s through 50, and will continue skip counting by 2s through 100. They will use a hundred chart to see patterns, and will practice skip counting on the number line.

DIRECTIONS FOR USING THE HUNDRED CHART LEARNING TOOL

3. Have students click the blue circle tool and count by 2s on the chart by clicking every second number as they count aloud. When they click, the number will be circled and will be said aloud. If an incorrect number is clicked, simply have them click it again to remove the circle. When students have counted by 2s through 100, have them click the speaker icon to hear the numbers counted aloud.

4. Have students look for patterns on the chart. For example, the numbers appear in columns on the chart; the numbers end in 0, 2, 4, 6, or 8.

5. Click Print to print a copy of students' hundred chart.

DIRECTIONS FOR USING THE NUMBER LINE LEARNING TOOL

6. Click Count and choose the following:
   • Start Number Line at: 50
   • End Number Line at: 100
   • Count by: 2s
   Click OK.

7. Students should click each number to count by 2s from 50 through 100. As they click each number, the frog will hop to the number and it will be said aloud. The number line will slide over automatically when necessary to display more numbers. When they reach 100, students should click Count Again and repeat.

LEARN Find the Missing Number

ONLINE 15 min

Objectives

• Count by 2s through 100.

Students will skip count by 2s to find the missing number in different patterns.

TRY IT Skip Count by 2s

OFFLINE 10 min

Objectives

• Count by 2s through 100.

Students will practice skip counting by 2s through 100. Give students the crayons and Skip Count by 2s activity page from their Activity Book. Read the directions with them.

If necessary, allow students to use a number line to help them count by 2s.

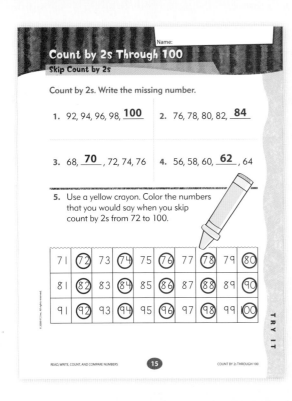

Count by 2s Through 100
Skip Count by 2s

Count by 2s. Write the missing number.

1. 92, 94, 96, 98, **100**
2. 76, 78, 80, 82, **84**

3. 68, **70**, 72, 74, 76
4. 56, 58, 60, **62**, 64

5. Use a yellow crayon. Color the numbers that you would say when you skip count by 2s from 72 to 100.

71	(72)	73	(74)	75	(76)	77	(78)	79	(80)
81	(82)	83	(84)	85	(86)	87	(88)	89	(90)
91	(92)	93	(94)	95	(96)	97	(98)	99	100

TRY IT

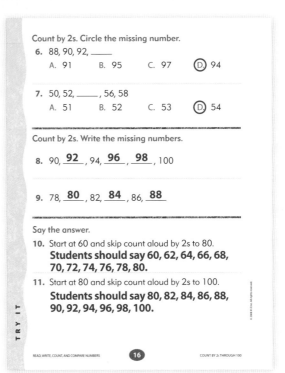

Count by 2s. Circle the missing number.

6. 88, 90, 92, _____
   A. 91   B. 95   C. 97   (D.) 94

7. 50, 52, _____, 56, 58
   A. 51   B. 52   C. 53   (D.) 54

Count by 2s. Write the missing numbers.

8. 90, **92**, 94, **96**, **98**, 100

9. 78, **80**, 82, **84**, 86, **88**

Say the answer.

10. Start at 60 and skip count aloud by 2s to 80.
    Students should say 60, 62, 64, 66, 68, 70, 72, 74, 76, 78, 80.

11. Start at 80 and skip count aloud by 2s to 100.
    Students should say 80, 82, 84, 86, 88, 90, 92, 94, 96, 98, 100.

TRY IT

OFFLINE
10 min

CHECKPOINT

Objectives

- Count by 2s through 100.

Print the Checkpoint. In Part 1, students will take a performance-based assessment. In Part 2, students will complete the problems on their own. Read the directions, problems, and answer choices to students if necessary. Use the answer key to score the Checkpoint, and then enter the results online.

Gather the crayons. Students will need a crayon to complete Problem 5.

○ Checkpoint   Math | Read, Write, Count, and Compare Numbers | Count by 2s Through 100

Name _____   Date _____

Checkpoint Answer Key

Part 1
Follow the instructions for each problem. Indicate whether the student performed the task correctly. Enter the results online.

1. Say, "Skip count aloud by 2s to 100."
(1 point)
   Did the student skip count correctly by 2s to 100?
   A. Yes   B. No

Give students Part 2 of the assessment.

○ Checkpoint   Math | Read, Write, Count, and Compare Numbers | Count by 2s Through 100

Name _____   Date _____

Part 2
Follow the instructions for each problem.
(1 point)
2. Count by 2s. Choose the missing number. 52, 54, 56, 58, _____
   (A.) 60   B. 59   C. 62   D. 50

(1 point)
3. Count by 2s. Choose the missing number. 86, 88, 90, _____
   A. 91   (B.) 92   C. 84   D. 94

(1 point)
4. Count by 2s. Choose the missing number. 62, 64, 66, _____
   A. 61   B. 65   C. 67   (D.) 68

(1 point)
5. Color the numbers on the chart to show skip counting by 2s.

51	(52)	53	(54)	55	(56)	57	(58)	59	(60)
61	(62)	63	(64)	65	(66)	67	(68)	69	(70)
71	(72)	73	(74)	75	(76)	77	(78)	79	(80)
81	(82)	83	(84)	85	(86)	87	(88)	89	(90)
91	(92)	93	(94)	95	(96)	97	(98)	99	(100)

Compare Numbers Through 100

Skills Update	5 minutes	ONLINE
GET READY Compare Bookshelves	5 minutes	ONLINE
LEARN Use Symbols to Compare Numbers	20 minutes	OFFLINE
LEARN Whose Number Is Greater?	20 minutes	OFFLINE
TRY IT Show How Numbers Compare	10 minutes	OFFLINE

▶ Lesson Objectives

Use the symbols for less than, equal to, or greater than ($<, =, >$) to compare and order whole numbers through 100.

▶ Prerequisite Skills

- Given two or more sets of 30 or fewer objects, identify which set has more or fewer objects than another set, or which sets have an equal number of objects.
- Read whole numbers through 100.
- Write numerals through 100.

▶ Common Errors and Misconceptions

- Students might skip a number as they count.
- Students might say more than one number for each object when counting objects in a group. Or they might skip objects. To avoid such problems, draw a line down the center of a sheet of paper. Have students move objects from one side of the paper to the other as they count.
- Students might use an incorrect counting sequence, such as "one, two, four, six, ten."

▶ Advance Preparation

Use rubber bands to make 10 bundles of 10 straws.

Number index cards 1 through 100. Label two other index cards 37 and 56 so that you have two index cards with these numbers. Label three other index cards with the following symbols: $<, >, =$. Save index cards for use in future lessons.

▶ Content Background

Students will learn how to compare numbers up through 100. They will use the symbols for greater than ($>$), less than ($<$), and equal to ($=$) to compare numbers.

Materials to Gather

SUPPLIED

Show How Numbers Compare activity page

ALSO NEEDED

drinking straws – 120

rubber bands – 10

index cards – labeled with $<, >, =$ symbols

index cards – numbered 1 through 100

index cards – numbered 37 and 56

equals symbol (=) – a symbol that shows the relationship between two equal values

fewer – a lesser number than another

greater – larger in number or amount than another

greater-than symbol (>) – a symbol indicating that an amount or number is greater than another amount or number

lesser – smaller in number or amount than another

less-than symbol (<) – a symbol indicating that an amount or number is less than another amount or number

more – a greater number or amount than another

symbol – a figure that is used to represent something else, such as + represents *plus* or *addition*, or = represents *equals*

ONLINE
5min

GET READY Compare Bookshelves

Objectives

Students will practice comparing groups of objects. They will compare shelves of books using the words *more*, *fewer*, and *equal* to describe the number of books.

- Given two or more sets of 30 or fewer objects, identify which set has more or fewer objects than another set, or which sets have an equal number of objects.

OFFLINE
20min

LEARN Use Symbols to Compare Numbers

Objectives

Students will learn how to compare two numbers up to 100 to see which is greater and which is lesser. They will also learn how to use the <, >, and = symbols to compare two numbers.

  Gather the bundles of straws, loose straws, and number and symbol cards.

- Use the symbols for less than, equal to, or greater than (<, =, >) to compare and order whole numbers through 100.

COMPARE BUNDLES OF STRAWS

1. Place 4 bundles of straws (10 to a bundle) and 5 single straws in front of students. Tell students that there are 10 straws in each bundle. Count together by 10s, and then count on by ones to see how many straws there are. (45)

2. Have students find the index card with the number 45 and place the card under the straws.

3. To the right of your first set of straws, repeat this procedure with 6 bundles of 10 straws and 2 single straws. Place the index card with the number 62 below these straws. Leave a few inches of space between the two sets of straws.

4. **Say:** You can use the straws to compare the numbers 45 and 62, and decide which number is greater and which number is lesser. 45 has 4 tens.

   Point to the 4 bundles and then to the 4 in 45.

   Ask: How many tens does 62 have?
   ANSWER: 6

   If necessary, point out the 6 on the index card or the 6 bundles of straws.

5. **Ask:** Which number has more tens?
   ANSWER: 62

   Ask: Which number has fewer tens?
   ANSWER: 45

6. Place the $<$ symbol card between the two numbers. Point to each as you say, "45 is less than 62. This symbol means *less than*. The smaller side points to the lesser number, and the larger side points to the greater number."

7. Repeat Steps 1–6 with the numbers 48 and 43. Since both numbers have 4 tens, point out that students must look at the ones to decide which is greater and which is lesser. Place the $>$ symbol between the two numbers.

8. Repeat Steps 1–6 with the number 37 on both sides. Point out that each groups of straws has the same number of tens and the same number of ones, so the two numbers are the same, or equal. Place the $=$ symbol between the two numbers.

9. Review the three number sentences you have created with the index cards, pointing to the numbers and symbols as you read them together.

COMPARE NUMBERS

10. Place the 21 card and the 15 card on the table, with space between to place a symbol card.

11. Have students compare the tens place to determine which number is greater, and place the correct symbol card between the two numbers. Then read the number sentence together, pointing to each number and symbol as you read.

12. Repeat this procedure with 19 and 30, placing the 19 on the left and the 30 on the right.

13. Repeat with the two 56 cards. If necessary, point out that since both numbers have the same number of tens and the same number of ones, they are equal.

14. Repeat Steps 10–12 with 69 and 63, and again with 44 and 50.

OFFLINE
20min

LEARN Whose Number Is Greater?

Objectives

- Use the symbols for less than, equal to, or greater than ($<, =, >$) to compare and order whole numbers through 100.

Students will learn how to use the $<$, $>$, and $=$ symbols to compare any two numbers up through 100.

Gather the number and symbol cards (without the extra 37 and 56).

1. Shuffle the number cards, and deal them out, giving one half to students and one half to yourself.

2. Turn over one of your own cards, and have students turn over one card from their pile at the same time. Have students choose the correct symbol card to create a number sentence between the two numbers, and then read the sentence aloud. Whoever has the card with the greater number gets to keep the cards.

3. Go through the entire deck. Whoever ends with the most cards wins!

TRY IT **Show How Numbers Compare**

OFFLINE
10 min

Students will compare groups of objects and numbers to determine which is greater, and will use the symbols correctly to identify greater, lesser, or equal numbers. Give students the Show How Numbers Compare activity page from their Activity Book and read the directions with them.

Objectives

- Use the symbols for less than, equal to, or greater than (<, =, >) to compare and order whole numbers through 100.

Tips

If students have difficulty comparing numbers without visual representations, allow them to use the straws again to bundle tens and ones, or to use another set of objects, like coins, to bundle, stack, or group tens and ones.

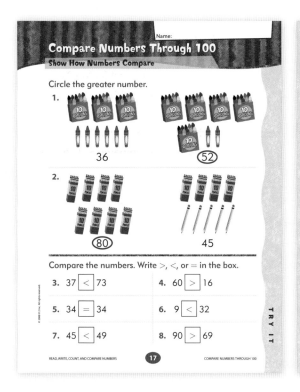

Compare Numbers Through 100

Show How Numbers Compare

Name:

Circle the greater number.

1. 36   (52)

2. (80)   45

Compare the numbers. Write >, <, or = in the box.

3. 37 $<$ 73   4. 60 $>$ 16

5. 34 $=$ 34   6. 9 $<$ 32

7. 45 $<$ 49   8. 90 $>$ 69

Circle the number sentence that is true.

9. 25 > 26   14 < 12
    (38 > 37)   49 < 45

10. (14 = 14)   44 < 35
    23 = 32   23 > 50

Compare the numbers. Write >, <, or = in the box.

11. 23 $<$ 34   12. 43 $>$ 33

13. 63 $>$ 61   14. 83 $<$ 93

Circle the correct symbol to compare the numbers.

15. 33 [ ] 73   16. 66 [ ] 16
    (<)   =   >   <   =   (>)

17. 51 [ ] 51   18. 12 [ ] 21
    <   (=)   >   (<)   =   >

TRY IT

TRY IT

Order Numbers Through 100

Lesson Overview

Skills Update	5 minutes	ONLINE
GET READY Compare Numbers	5 minutes	ONLINE
LEARN Use Symbols to Order Numbers	30 minutes	OFFLINE
TRY IT Order with Symbols	10 minutes	OFFLINE
CHECKPOINT	10 minutes	OFFLINE

▶ Lesson Objectives

Use the symbols for less than, equal to, or greater than ($<, =, >$) to compare and order whole numbers through 100.

▶ Prerequisite Skills

- Given two or more sets of 30 or fewer objects, identify which set has more or fewer objects than another set, or which sets have an equal number of objects.
- Read whole numbers through 100.
- Write numerals through 100.

▶ Common Errors and Misconceptions

- Students might skip a number as they count.
- Students might say more than one number for each object when counting objects in a group. Or they might skip objects. To avoid such problems, draw a line down the center of a sheet of paper. Have students move objects from one side of the paper to the other as they count.
- Students might use an incorrect counting sequence, such as "one, two, four, six, ten."

▶ Advance Preparation

Number index cards 1 through 100, or gather the number cards you created previously. Label two other index cards with the number 32 so that you have three index cards with this number. Label two index cards with the $<$ symbol, two index cards with the $>$ symbol, and two index cards with the $=$ symbol. Save cards for use in future lessons.
   Print the Hundred Chart.

▶ Content Background

Students will learn how to order three numbers from greatest to least and from least to greatest. They will learn how to use the symbols for greater than ($>$), less than ($<$), and equal to ($=$) to show the ordering.

Materials to Gather

SUPPLIED

Hundred Chart (printout)

blocks – B (all colors)

Order with Symbols activity page

Checkpoint (printout)

ALSO NEEDED

index cards – numbered 1 through 100

index cards – numbered 32 (2 of this number)

index cards – labeled with $=, <, >$ symbols (2 of each symbol)

GET READY **Compare Numbers**

ONLINE
5min

Objectives

- Given two or more sets of 30 or fewer objects, identify which set has more or fewer objects than another set, or which sets have an equal number of objects.
- Read whole numbers through 100.
- Write numerals through 100.

Students will compare two groups of objects and choose the correct comparison symbol to place between the groups.

DIRECTIONS FOR USING THE GREATER OR LESSER LEARNING TOOL

1. Click Problem Mode.
   - Choose two objects.
   - Click Yes to use ten-frames.
   - Click Start.
2. Students should count the objects on the left and compare to the number of objects on the right. They should mouse over the question mark and choose the correct symbol: $>$, $=$, or $<$. Remind students that the smaller side of the symbol should point to the lesser amount. When they have chosen a symbol, they should click Check. Then click Try Another to continue.

   Continue as time allows.

LEARN **Use Symbols to Order Numbers**

OFFLINE
30min

Objectives

- Use the symbols for less than, equal to, or greater than ($<$, $=$, $>$) to compare and order whole numbers through 100.

Students will learn how to order three numbers from least to greatest and greatest to least. Explain to students that, when they order numbers, they will start on the left of the work area, and move toward the right.
   Gather the circle blocks, number and symbol cards, and Hundred Chart.

ORDER FROM LEAST TO GREATEST

1. Have students make three piles of circles in this order from left to right: 17, 8, 15. Have them select the number card that matches the quantity of each pile and place it on the pile. Tell them to point to the smallest pile—the pile of 8—and move it to the far left with its number card. Have them say the number aloud.
2. Now have students look at the remaining two piles and choose which is smaller. (pile of 15) Ask them to show how they know it's the smaller pile of the two by counting its circles. Then have them move the smaller pile of 15 to between the pile of 8 on the far left and the pile of 17 on the far right.

   Ask: What do you know about the pile with 17 circles?
   ANSWER: It has the most, or the greatest number, of circles.

   Ask: What is the order of the numbers from least to greatest?
   ANSWER: 8, 15, 17

Tips

If students have difficulty ordering numbers without visual representations, allow them to use straws bundled to show tens and ones. Remind students that the symbol always "points" to the lesser number and "opens" to the greater number.

3. Give students the Hundred Chart. Explain that in the chart, the numbers from 1 to 100 are ordered from least to greatest.
    - In each row, the numbers on the left are less than the numbers on the right.
    - In the columns, the numbers above are less than the numbers below.

    Have students locate the numbers 8, 15, and 17 and explain how they know which is the least and which is the greatest on the chart.

ORDER FROM GREATEST TO LEAST

4. Have students put these three number cards in this order from left to right: 37, 50, 48.
5. Tell students to order the numbers from greatest to least.
    - Tell them that when they order from greatest to least, they should find the greatest number first.
    - Also remind them to use their hundred chart to help them think about counting backward from 100.
6. Check that the order is now 50, 48, 37. If students have made a mistake, help them figure out what went wrong using the hundred chart.

    Ask: Why is 48 between 50 and 37?
    ANSWER: 48 is less than 50 and greater than 37.

USE $>$, $<$, AND $=$ TO SHOW ORDER

7. Have students put these three number cards in this order from left to right: 16, 55, 40. Put the two less-than symbol cards on the table next to each other with space between them.
8. Tell students they will be ordering the number cards from least to greatest. Have them to choose the least number and put it to the left of the $<$ card.
9. Point to the two remaining cards.

    Ask: Which number is lesser, 55 or 40?
    ANSWER: 40

    Have students put the 40 card between the two $<$ cards. Ask students where the 55 card should go and why they know to put it there. The cards should look like this: $16 < 40 < 55$.
10. Read the statement "16 is less than 40 is less than 55" to students, and then have students read the number sentence aloud.
11. Repeat Steps 7–10 with the numbers 61, 26, and 80, having students order the numbers from least to greatest.
12. Repeat Steps 7–10 with the numbers 68, 60, and 99, having students order the numbers from greatest to least.
13. Repeat Steps 7–10 with the numbers 32, 32, and 32. Ask students to order from greatest to least and from least to greatest: the order doesn't change. Students should place the $=$ cards between the numbers.

OFFLINE
10min

TRY IT Order with Symbols

Students will order three numbers from greatest to least and from least to greatest. They will choose the correct symbol to place between numbers that are ordered. Give students the Order with Symbols activity page from their Activity Book and read the directions with them.

Objectives

- Use the symbols for less than, equal to, or greater than ($<$, $=$, $>$) to compare and order whole numbers through 100.

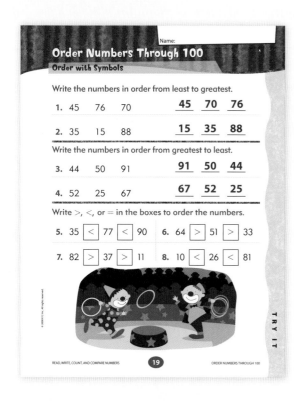

Order Numbers Through 100
Order with Symbols

Write the numbers in order from least to greatest.

1. 45   76   70   **45   70   76**

2. 35   15   88   **15   35   88**

Write the numbers in order from greatest to least.

3. 44   50   91   **91   50   44**

4. 52   25   67   **67   52   25**

Write >, <, or = in the boxes to order the numbers.

5. 35 [<] 77 [<] 90   6. 64 [>] 51 [>] 33

7. 82 [>] 37 [>] 11   8. 10 [<] 26 [<] 81

TRY IT

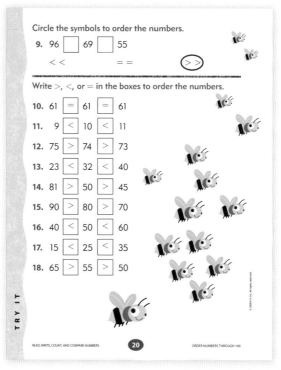

Circle the symbols to order the numbers.

9. 96 [ ] 69 [ ] 55

   < <   = =   (> >)

Write >, <, or = in the boxes to order the numbers.

10. 61 [=] 61 [=] 61

11. 9 [<] 10 [<] 11

12. 75 [>] 74 [>] 73

13. 23 [<] 32 [<] 40

14. 81 [>] 50 [>] 45

15. 90 [>] 80 [>] 70

16. 40 [<] 50 [<] 60

17. 15 [<] 25 [<] 35

18. 65 [>] 55 [>] 50

TRY IT

CHECKPOINT

OFFLINE
10 min

Objectives

Print the Checkpoint and have students complete it on their own. Read the directions, problems, and answer choices to students if necessary. Use the answer key to score the Checkpoint, and then enter the results online.

- Use the symbols for less than, equal to, or greater than (<, =, >) to compare and order whole numbers through 100.

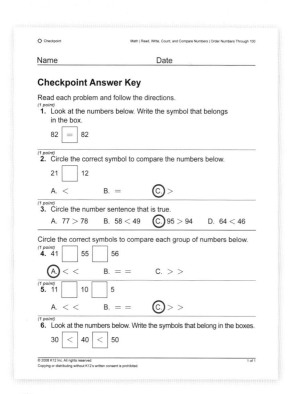

Name _____   Date _____

Checkpoint Answer Key

Read each problem and follow the directions.
(1 point)
1. Look at the numbers below. Write the symbol that belongs in the box.

   82 [=] 82

(1 point)
2. Circle the correct symbol to compare the numbers below.

   21 [ ] 12

   A. <   B. =   (C.) >

(1 point)
3. Circle the number sentence that is true.

   A. 77 > 78   B. 58 < 49   (C.) 95 > 94   D. 64 < 46

Circle the correct symbols to compare each group of numbers below.
(1 point)
4. 41 [ ] 55 [ ] 56

   (A.) < <   B. = =   C. > >

(1 point)
5. 11 [ ] 10 [ ] 5

   A. < <   B. = =   (C.) > >

(1 point)
6. Look at the numbers below. Write the symbols that belong in the boxes.

   30 [<] 40 [<] 50

Unit Review

UNIT REVIEW Look Back	20 minutes	**ONLINE**
UNIT REVIEW Checkpoint Practice	20 minutes	**OFFLINE**
⊞ **UNIT REVIEW** Prepare for the Checkpoint		

▶ Unit Objectives

This lesson reviews the following objectives:

- Count aloud whole numbers through 50.
- Read whole numbers through 50.
- Write numerals through 50.
- Count by 10s through 50.
- Count by 5s through 50.
- Count by 2s through 50.
- Count aloud whole numbers through 100.
- Read whole numbers through 100.
- Write numerals through 100.
- Count by 10s through 100.
- Count by 5s through 100.
- Count by 2s through 100.
- Use the symbols for less than, equal to, or greater than ($<, =, >$) to compare and order whole numbers through 100.

▶ Advance Preparation

In this lesson, students will have an opportunity to review previous activities in the Read, Write, Count, and Compare Numbers unit. Look at the suggested activities in Unit Review: Prepare for the Checkpoint online and gather any needed materials.

Materials to Gather

SUPPLIED

Checkpoint Practice activity page

Keywords

digit	**less-than symbol ($<$)**
equals symbol ($=$)	**more**
fewer	**number**
fewest	**number line**
greater	**numeral**
greater-than symbol ($>$)	**pattern**
greatest	**skip count**
hundred chart	**symbol**
least	
lesser	

Objectives

- Review unit objectives.

In this unit, students have read and written about whole numbers. They have skip counted by 2s, 5s, and 10s. After learning to skip count, they compared and ordered numbers, and looked for repeating number patterns. Students will review these concepts to prepare for the Unit Checkpoint.

Objectives

- Review unit objectives.

Students will complete a Checkpoint Practice activity page to prepare for the Unit Checkpoint. If necessary, read the directions, problems, and answer choices to students. Have students answer the problems on their own. Carefully review the answers with students.

Unit Review
Checkpoint Practice

Name: _____

1. Count aloud from 58 to 62. Then write the numbers on the lines.

Seats 58 to 62

58 59 60 61 62

2. Count aloud from 96 to 100. Then write the numbers on the lines.

Seats 96 to 100

96 97 98 99 100

Skip count to write the missing number.

3. 32, 34, 36, 38, **40**

4. 20, 30, 40, 50, **60**

5. 65, 70, 75, 80, **85**

6. 40, 50, **60**, 70, 80

7. 86, 88, 90, **92**, 94

8. 40, 45, **50**, 55, 60

Compare the numbers. Write >, <, or = in the box.

9. 61 [>] 26

10. 39 [=] 39

11. 46 [<] 52

12. 73 [<] 93

READ, WRITE, COUNT, AND COMPARE NUMBERS   21   UNIT REVIEW

13. What number is this? Say it.

83 Students should say eighty-three.

14. Count aloud from 65 to 80. **Students should count aloud in order from 65 to 80.**

15. Write the number sixty-eight. **68**

16. Write the missing numbers.

40, **50**, 60, **70**, **80**, 90

17. Count by 5s. Circle the missing number.

55, 60, 65, 70, _____

A. 50   B. 75
C. 80   D. 71

18. Count by 2s. Circle the missing number.

42, 44, 46, 48, _____

A. 50   B. 49
C. 52   D. 58

19. Look at the numbers below. Which symbols belong in the boxes? Write the correct symbols.

61 [=] 61 [=] 61

20. Write the missing symbol in the box to compare the numbers.

36 [<] 63

READ, WRITE, COUNT, AND COMPARE NUMBERS   22   UNIT REVIEW

→ UNIT REVIEW Prepare for the Checkpoint

What you do next depends on how students performed in the previous activity, Unit Review: Checkpoint Practice. If students had difficulty with any of the problems, complete the appropriate review activity listed in the table online.

Unit Checkpoint

UNIT CHECKPOINT Online | 60 minutes | **ONLINE**

▶ Unit Objectives

This lesson assesses the following objectives:

- Count aloud whole numbers through 50.
- Read whole numbers through 50.
- Write numerals through 50.
- Count by 10s through 50.
- Count by 5s through 50.
- Count by 2s through 50.
- Count aloud whole numbers through 100.
- Read whole numbers through 100.
- Write numerals through 100.
- Count by 10s through 100.
- Count by 5s through 100.
- Count by 2s through 100.
- Use the symbols for less than, equal to, or greater than ($<$, $=$, $>$) to compare and order whole numbers through 100.

UNIT CHECKPOINT Online

ONLINE 60 min

Objectives

- Review unit objectives.

Students will complete the Unit Checkpoint online. In Part 1, students will take a performance-based assessment. In Part 2, students will complete the problems on their own. Read the directions, problems, and answer choices to students if necessary. Use the answer key to score the Unit Checkpoint, and then enter the results online.

Name _____ Date _____

Unit Checkpoint Answer Key

Part 1

Follow the instructions for each problem. Indicate whether the student performed the task correctly. Enter the results online.

(1 point)
1. Say, "Count aloud in order from 88 to 99."

   Did the student count correctly from 88 to 99?

   A. Yes   B. No

(1 point)
2. Say, "Count aloud in order from 36 to 54."

   Did the student count correctly from 36 to 54?

   A. Yes   B. No

(1 point)
3. Write the number 99 on paper and show it to the student. Say, "What number is this?" Did the student say ninety-nine?

   A. Yes   B. No

(1 point)
4. Write the number 13 on paper and show it to the student. Say, "What number is this?" Did the student say thirteen?

   A. Yes   B. No

(1 point)
5. Say, "Write this number: seventy." Did the student write 70?

   A. Yes   B. No

(1 point)
6. Say, "Write this number: thirty-seven." Did the student write 37?

   A. Yes   B. No

Give students Part 2 of the assessment.

Name _____ Date _____

Part 2

(1 point)
7. Write the missing number. 50, 60, 70, **80**, 90

(1 point)
8. Write the missing number. 60, 70, 80, 90, **100**

(1 point)
9. Count by 5s. Circle the missing number. 45, _____, 55, 60, 65

   (A.) 50   B. 46   C. 51

(1 point)
10. Count by 5s. Circle the missing number. 60, 65, _____, 75, 80

    A. 66   (B.) 70   C. 71

(1 point)
11. Count by 2s. Circle the missing number. 62, 64, 66, 68, _____

    (A.) 70   B. 69   C. 72

(1 point)
12. Count by 2s. Circle the missing number. 76, 78, 80, _____

    A. 81   (B.) 82   C. 84

(1 point)
13. Compare the numbers. Write the missing symbol in the box.

    36 $\boxed{<}$ 63

(1 point)
14. Compare the numbers. Write the missing symbol in the box.

    76 $\boxed{>}$ 66

(1 point)
15. Compare the numbers. Write the missing symbol in the box.

    98 $\boxed{>}$ 53

Time and Position

▶ Unit Objectives

- Tell time to the nearest hour.
- Tell time to the nearest half hour.
- Relate time to events (for example, before/after, shorter/longer).
- Arrange objects in space by proximity, such as near, far, below, or above.

- Describe objects in space by proximity, such as near, far, below, or above.
- Arrange objects in space by direction, such as behind, in front of, next to, left of, or right of.
- Describe objects in space by direction, such as behind, in front of, next to, left of, or right of.

▶ Unit Introduction

Students will learn about time and position. Students will learn to tell time on an analog clock—a clock with a face and hands. They will learn about the hour and minute hands, and they will read these hands to tell time to the nearest hour and half hour. They will learn how to tell whether it is exactly, just before, or just after the hour or half hour.

After learning how to read time on the clock, students will relate times to events in the day (for example, "I wake up just before 7 o'clock in the morning.") Students will order their daily activities by time using the words *before, after, first,* and *last*. Students will also compare the amount of time it takes to complete different activities.

Students will also learn about position. They will compare, arrange, and describe the position of objects using the words *up, down, behind, in front of, next to, to the left of,* and *to the right of*.

Time to the Nearest Hour

Lesson Overview

Skills Update	5 minutes	ONLINE
GET READY Activity Times	5 minutes	ONLINE
LEARN Hour Hand	20 minutes	ONLINE
LEARN Tell Time to the Nearest Hour	10 minutes	ONLINE
TRY IT What Time Is It?	10 minutes	OFFLINE
CHECKPOINT	10 minutes	OFFLINE

▶ Lesson Objectives

Tell time to the nearest hour.

▶ Prerequisite Skills

Identify the time to the nearest hour of everyday events (for example, lunchtime is 12 o'clock; bedtime is 8 o'clock at night).

▶ Common Errors and Misconceptions

Students might confuse the hour hand and minute hand.

▶ Content Background

Students will learn how to tell time on an analog clock to the nearest hour.

Materials to Gather

SUPPLIED

What Time Is It? activity page

Checkpoint (printout)

Keywords

analog clock – a clock that displays the time with the continual movement of an hour and a minute hand

face of a clock – the part of a clock that shows the numbers and hands

hand of a clock – a part of a clock that points to the numbers to show the time in hours, minutes, and seconds

hour – a time period of 60 minutes; the time that the hour hand indicates on an analog clock; in 7:15, 7 is the hour

hour hand – a clock's short hand that points to the hour

minute – a time period of 60 seconds; the time that the minute hand indicates on an analog clock; in 7:15, 15 indicates the minutes

minute hand – a clock's long hand that points to the minute

time – the measurement from past to present to future, as indicated by a clock or calendar

GET READY Activity Times

ONLINE 5 min

Objectives

- Identify the time to the nearest hour of everyday events (for example, lunchtime is 12 o'clock; bedtime is 8 o'clock at night).

Students will relate times of day to times on the clock. They will match pictures of Rosa doing different activities to clocks that show the times Rosa does these activities.

If students have difficulty, make a chart listing students' daily activities and the time of each. Be sure to include waking up, getting dressed, eating breakfast, eating lunch, eating dinner, and going to bed. Divide the chart into three sections, labeled **morning**, **afternoon**, and **evening**. Students can refer to this chart when deciding what time Rosa does each of her daily activities.

LEARN Hour Hand

ONLINE 20 min

Objectives

- Tell time to the nearest hour.

Students will learn how to identify times on the hour by reading the hour hand on a clock.

DIRECTIONS FOR USING THE CLOCK LEARNING TOOL

1. Click Begin and choose the following:
   - Click the clock display button.
   - Uncheck the AM/PM box.
   - Uncheck the digital clock box.
2. Have students drag the minute hand around the clock until the hour hand points to the 7 and the minute hand points to the 12.
3. Tell students to click the minute and hour buttons at the bottom right of the screen. The minute and hour hands will highlight individually.

   Ask: What number is the hour hand pointing to?
   ANSWER: 7

   Ask: What number is the minute hand pointing to?
   ANSWER: 12
4. Explain that when the minute hand points to 12, the time is exactly on the hour, such as 7 o'clock. Have students click the speaker icon to hear the time. Have students repeat the time, guiding them to say the hour followed by *o'clock*.
5. Repeat Steps 2–4 with the times 1:00, 5:00, 12:00, and 3:00.

LEARN Tell Time to the Nearest Hour

ONLINE 10 min

Objectives

- Tell time to the nearest hour.

Students will learn how to identify times to the nearest hour by reading the hour and minute hands on a clock. For example, they will learn that 7:55 is *almost* or *just before* 8:00.

DIRECTIONS FOR USING THE CLOCK LEARNING TOOL

1. Click Begin and choose the following:
   - Click the clock display button.
   - Uncheck the AM/PM box.
   - Uncheck the digital clock box.

2. **Say:** We often do activities on the hour. We might eat lunch at 12:00. Or we might go to a friend's house at 3:00. So it's helpful to tell time to the nearest hour. If a clock shows a time just before or just after 8 o'clock, we can say, "To the nearest hour, it is 8 o'clock," or, "It is about 8 o'clock."

3. Drag the minute hand around the clock to show the following times. For each time, have students say the time to the nearest hour, and then click the speaker icon to check their answer.

   - 3:52
   - 10:02
   - 7:49

Go to the next screen to continue with the Learn activity.

TRY IT What Time Is It?

OFFLINE
10 min

Students will practice telling time to the nearest hour. Give students the What Time Is It? activity page from their Activity Book and read the directions with them.

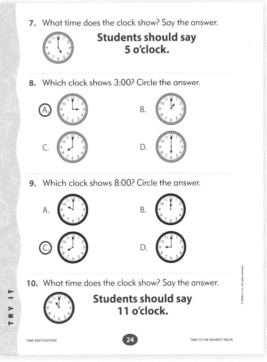

CHECKPOINT

Objectives

- Tell time to the nearest hour.

Print the Checkpoint and have students complete it on their own. Read the directions, problems, and answer choices to students if necessary. Use the answer key to score the Checkpoint, and then enter the results online.

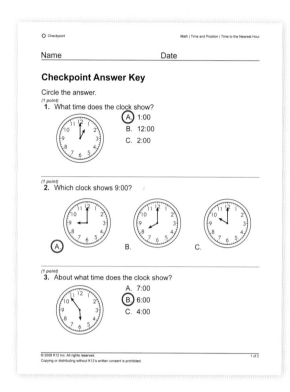

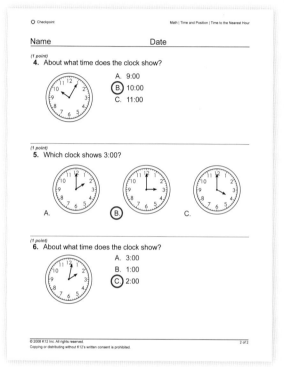

Time to the Nearest Half Hour

Lesson Overview

Skills Update	5 minutes	ONLINE
GET READY What Hour Is It?	10 minutes	ONLINE
LEARN Tell Time	15 minutes	ONLINE
LEARN Use Clocks	20 minutes	OFFLINE
TRY IT Tell Time to the Nearest Half Hour	10 minutes	OFFLINE

▶ Lesson Objectives

Tell time to the nearest half hour.

▶ Prerequisite Skills

Tell time to the nearest hour.

▶ Common Errors and Misconceptions

Students might confuse the hour hand and minute hand.

▶ Advance Preparation

Prepare the Paper Clock Model by cutting out the hands and attaching them using the metal brad.

▶ Content Background

Students have learned how to tell time to the nearest hour. In this lesson, they will learn how to tell time on an analog clock to the nearest half hour

Materials to Gather

SUPPLIED

Paper Clock Model (printout)

Tell Time to the Nearest Half Hour activity page

ALSO NEEDED

metal brad

scissors, adult

ONLINE

10 min

GET READY What Hour Is It?

Students will practice telling time to the nearest hour on analog clocks.

Objectives

- Tell time to the nearest hour.

LEARN Tell Time

Students will learn how to identify times to the nearest half hour by reading the hour and minute hands on a clock.

Objectives

- Tell time to the nearest half hour.

DIRECTIONS FOR USING THE CLOCK LEARNING TOOL

1. Click Begin and choose the following:
   - Click the clock display button.
   - Uncheck the AM/PM box.
   - Uncheck the digital clock box.

2. Drag the minute hand around the clock until the hour hand points to the 1 and the minute hand points to the 12.

3. Remind students that when the time is exactly on the hour (such as 1 o'clock), the minute hand will always point to the 12. Have students click the speaker icon to hear the time.

4. Help students drag the minute hand around the clock until it points to the 6. Explain that they moved the minute hand *halfway* around the clockface. Show students that the hour hand moved also, so the hour hand is now *halfway between* two numbers.

5. Tell students to click the minute and hour buttons at the bottom right of the screen. The minute and hour hands will highlight individually.

   Ask: The hour hand is halfway between two numbers. Which two numbers?
   ANSWER: 1 and 2

   Ask: What number is the minute hand pointing to?
   ANSWER: 6

6. Explain that when the minute hand points to 6, the time is halfway to the next hour, so we say it is *half past 1*, *1:30*, or *one-thirty*. Have students click the speaker icon to hear the time. Have students repeat the time, guiding them to say the hour and then the word *thirty*.

7. Repeat Steps 4–6 for the time 10:30.

8. Have students move the minute hand to the 5 and keep the hour hand between 10 and 11. Say, "The minute hand is close to the 6, and the hour hand is between the 10 and 11. So we can say it is *about* 10:30."

9. Have students move the minute hand to the 7. Say, "The minute hand is still close to the 6, and the hour hand is between the 10 and 11. So we can say it is *about* 10:30. "

10. Repeat Steps 8 and 9 for the time 3:30.

Tips

You may wish to show students that each number on the clock represents 5 minutes. Using the Clock Learning Tool, move the minute hand to each number on the clock (1, 2, 3, 4, 5, 6), and say, "5, 10, 15, 20, 25, 30." Repeat, having students count with you by 5s to 30 minutes.

Tips

To help students remember which hand is which, tell them that the minute hand is longer than the hour hand, just as the word *minute* is longer than the word *hour*. Write the words *minute* and *hour* so students can recognize the difference between the number of letters in the words.

LEARN Use Clocks

Students will use a clock to show time to the nearest half hour. They will also learn to write the time.

Gather the assembled Paper Clock Model, and give it to students.

Tips

When students model a time, have them place the minute hand first and then the hour hand.

1. Have students point to the minute hand and the hour hand and explain how they know which is which. Have them tell you what each hand tells about the time. (The minute hand is longer than the hour hand. The minute hand tells the minutes; the hour hand tells the hour.)

2. Ask students to move the hands to show 3:00.

   Ask: What number is the hour hand pointing to?
   ANSWER: 3

   Ask: What number is the minute hand pointing to?
   ANSWER: 12

3. Have students move the minute hand so it points to 6. Have them move the hour hand so it is between 3 and 4.

   Say: The clock now shows a time halfway between 3:00 and 4:00. We can say the time is half past 3, or 3:30.

4. Show students how to write the time by putting a colon between the hours and minutes. Have students write 3:30 on a sheet of paper.

   Ask: What number does the minute hand point to when a clock shows a time to the half hour?
   ANSWER: 6

   Ask: Where does the hour hand point when the clock shows a time to the half hour?
   ANSWER: between two numbers

5. Ask students to use the clock to show 12:00. Then ask students to move the hands to show 12:30. (Students should move the minute hand to 6 and the hour hand between 12 and 1.)

   Have them explain how they know how to show the time. (12:30 is between 12:00 and 1:00, so the hour hand points between 12 and 1, and the minute hand points to 6.)

   Have students write the time with a colon. (12:30)

6. Now write 9:30 on a sheet of paper. Have students say the time and then model it on the clock. Have them explain how they knew how to move the hands.

7. Repeat Step 6 with 4:30, 10:30, and 5:30.

Students will practice telling time to the nearest half hour by reading clocks as well as drawings clock hands to show times. Give students the Tell Time to the Nearest Half Hour activity page from their Activity Book and read the directions with them.

When students draw the hour hand and minute hand on each clock, make sure they make the minute hand longer than the hour hand. Make sure they draw the hour hand halfway between the number for the current hour and the number for the next hour.

Tips

Encourage students to use the Paper Clock Model to help them work through the activity page.

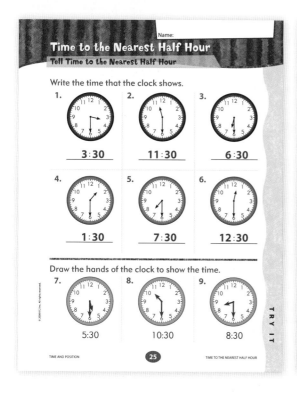

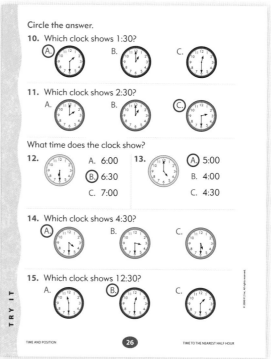

About Time

Lesson Overview

Skills Update	5 minutes	ONLINE
GET READY What Time Is It?	5 minutes	ONLINE
LEARN Nearest Half Hour	10 minutes	ONLINE
LEARN Longer Time, Shorter Time	10 minutes	OFFLINE
LEARN Relate Events	10 minutes	OFFLINE
TRY IT Tell Time and Relate Events	10 minutes	OFFLINE
CHECKPOINT	10 minutes	OFFLINE

▶ Lesson Objectives

- Tell time to the nearest half hour.
- Relate time to events (for example, before/after, shorter/longer).

▶ Prerequisite Skills

- Tell time to the nearest hour.
- Identify the time to the nearest hour of everyday events (for example, lunchtime is 12 o'clock; bedtime is 8 o'clock at night).

▶ Common Errors and Misconceptions

- Students might have difficulty using digital clocks to tell approximate times. For example, to understand that 7:58 is almost 8:00 on a digital clock, students must know that there are 60 minutes in an hour, that 58 is near 60, and that 2 minutes is a short amount of time. On an analog clock, students can more easily see that 7:58 is almost 8:00.
- Students might confuse the hour hand and minute hand.

▶ Content Background

Students have learned to tell time to the nearest hour. In this lesson, they will learn how to tell time to the nearest half hour. They will also decide if an event takes a shorter or longer amount of time than another event, and if an event comes before or after another event.

Keywords	
	longer – having a greater time or distance than another
	shorter – having a lesser time or distance than another

Materials to Gather

SUPPLIED

blocks – O (10 of any color)

Tell Time and Relate Events activity page

Checkpoint (printout)

ALSO NEEDED

index cards – 10

GET READY What Time Is It?

ONLINE 5 min

Students will practice telling time to the nearest hour. They will identify clocks that show times exactly on the hour and times just before or just after the hour.

Objectives

- Tell time to the nearest hour

Tips

Students may use the Paper Clock Model to show the on-screen times.

LEARN Nearest Half Hour

ONLINE 10 min

Students will learn to read time to the nearest half hour.

Objectives

- Tell time to the nearest half hour.

LEARN Longer Time, Shorter Time

OFFLINE 10 min

Students will relate time to events and compare events by their length of time. Gather the cubes.

Objectives

- Relate time to events (for example, before/after, shorter/longer).

1. **Say:** Write your first name on a sheet of paper. Then write the numbers from 1 through 20.

2. **Ask:** Which took more time, writing your name or writing the numbers? **ANSWER:** writing the numbers

   Say: It takes longer to write the numbers through 20 than to write your name. Tell something else that takes more time than writing your name.

3. **Say:** Make a train of 3 cubes. Then make a train of 7 cubes.

4. **Say:** Which train took less time to make? **ANSWER:** the train of 3 cubes

   Say: Tell something that takes less time than making a train of 3 cubes.

LEARN Relate Events

OFFLINE 10 min

Objectives

- Relate time to events (for example, before/after, shorter/longer).

Students will relate and order the events of their day by time. They will record their daily activities on index cards and describe them using the words *first*, *last*, *before*, and *after*. Then students will compare the amount of time it takes to complete the activities.

Gather the index cards.

1. **Say:** In a day, you do many different things, such as brushing your teeth, eating breakfast, and reading books. You can tell the order you do these activities by using the words *before*, *after*, *first*, and *last*.

2. Have students name their daily activities and write each activity on a separate index card. Possible activities include eating meals, reading a book, getting out of bed, brushing teeth, getting dressed, bathing, and completing lessons. Make sure students include activities that take different amounts of time.

3. **Say:** Put the cards in the order that you usually do the activities.

4. Compare two cards using one of the following words: *before*, *after*, *first*, and *last*. For example, "I brush my teeth *after* I get out of bed." Point to the card for each activity as you mention it in your sentence.

5. Have students create their own sentences about the cards using *before*, *after*, *first*, and *last*.

6. **Say:** Now let's use *longer time* and *shorter time* to talk about the activities of your day. For example, you could say, "I spend a *longer time* eating dinner than tying my shoes."

7. Have students create their own sentences using *longer time* and *shorter time*.

OFFLINE

10 min

TRY IT Tell Time and Relate Events

Objectives

Students will practice telling time to the nearest half hour and comparing events by their length of time. Give students the Tell Time and Relate Events activity page from their Activity Book and read the directions with them.

For Problems 11–14, first have students describe what is happening in each picture. Then have them say a sentence comparing the pictures. For example, for Problem 11, students should say, "Playing a soccer game takes a longer time than brushing your teeth."

- Tell time to the nearest half hour.
- Relate time to events (for example, before/after, shorter/longer).

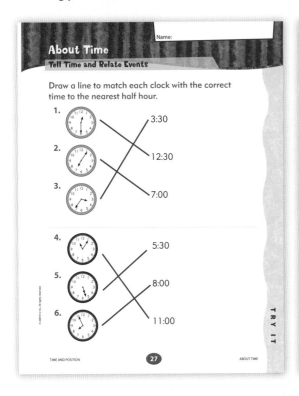

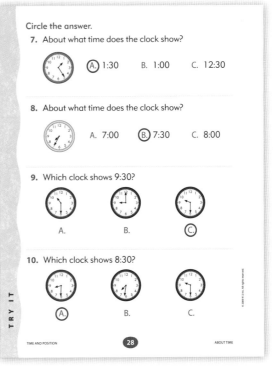

Circle the activity that takes longer.

11.

Brushing your teeth   Playing a soccer game

12.

Watching a movie   Tying your shoes

Circle the activity that comes first.

13.

14.

T R Y I T

15. Which activity would take the shortest amount of time?
- A. writing the word CHAIR
- Ⓑ writing the letter C
- C. writing the words CHAIR DESK LAMP

16. Which activity happens after the other two?
- Ⓐ going to sleep at night
- B. eating dinner
- C. brushing teeth before bed

17. Which activity do you do before getting out of bed?
- A. You brush your teeth.
- Ⓑ You wake up.
- C. You open the door.

18. Which do you do first when you want to read a book?
- Ⓐ You get the book.
- B. You start reading.
- C. You open the book.

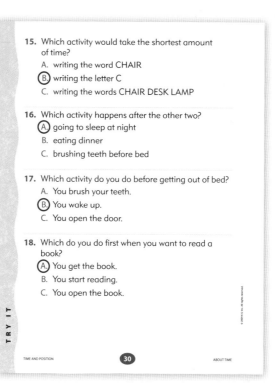

T R Y I T

CHECKPOINT

OFFLINE **10 min**

Print the Checkpoint and have students complete it on their own. Read the directions, problems, and answer choices to students if necessary. Use the answer key to score the Checkpoint, and then enter the results online.

Objectives

- Tell time to the nearest half hour.
- Relate time to events (for example, before/after, shorter/longer).

☼ Checkpoint   Math | Time and Position | About Time

Name _____ Date _____

Checkpoint Answer Key

Circle the answer.
(1 point)
1. What time does the clock show?

Ⓐ 6:30   B. 7:00   C. 6:00

About what time does the clock show?
(1 point)
2.
- A. 5:30
- Ⓑ 6:30
- C. 7:30

(1 point)
3.
- A. 6:30
- Ⓑ 9:30
- C. 10:30

(1 point)
4.
- Ⓐ 10:00
- B. 11:00
- C. 1:00

(1 point)
5.
- A. 10:00
- B. 11:00
- Ⓒ 12:00

1 of 2

☼ Checkpoint   Math | Time and Position | About Time

Name _____ Date _____

(1 point)
6. Which activity usually takes the longest amount of time?
- A. putting on your shoes
- B. blinking your eyes
- Ⓒ eating your breakfast

(1 point)
7. Which activity usually takes the shortest amount of time?
- Ⓐ brushing your teeth
- B. eating your dinner
- C. watching a movie

(1 point)
8. Do you put on your socks *before* or *after* you put on your shoes?
- Ⓐ before
- B. after

(1 point)
9. Which of these happens before you get out of bed in the morning?
- A. You brush your teeth.
- Ⓑ You wake up.
- C. You open the door.

(1 point)
10. Which activity usually takes the longest amount of time?
- A. eating a piece of cake
- B. putting candles on a cake
- Ⓒ baking a cake

2 of 2

Arrange and Describe Position

Lesson Overview

Skills Update	5 minutes	ONLINE
LEARN Position of Objects	20 minutes	ONLINE
LEARN Where Is It?	15 minutes	OFFLINE
LEARN Up or Down?	10 minutes	OFFLINE
TRY IT Arrange and Describe	10 minutes	OFFLINE

▶ Lesson Objectives
- Arrange objects in space by proximity, such as near, far, below, or above.
- Describe objects in space by proximity, such as near, far, below, or above.

▶ Safety
If you complete some of the Up or Down? activity outside, be sure students do not look into the sun when they look up.

▶ Content Background
In this lesson, students will learn to arrange and describe the position of objects by using position words, such as *near*, *far*, *above*, and *below*.

Keywords	**position** – the place or location of an object in relation to another object

Materials to Gather

SUPPLIED
blocks – AA (blue)
blocks – CC (red)
Arrange and Describe activity page

ALSO NEEDED
crayons

LEARN Position of Objects

ONLINE
20min

Students will learn the position words *near*, *far*, *above*, and *below*. They will use these words to describe the position of objects in a bedroom and arrange objects in another room. Then students will learn ordinal numbers, such as *first*, *second*, and *third*, and use them to describe children's positions in a line.

Explain to students that *above* and *below* describe opposite positions. Explain that *near* and *far* describe opposite positions.

Objectives
- Arrange objects in space by proximity, such as near, far, below, or above.
- Describe objects in space by proximity, such as near, far, below, or above.

LEARN Where Is It?

Students will use position words to describe the position of objects and to arrange objects.

Gather the blocks.

1. Explain to students that position words tell where an object is. Position words include *near*, *far*, *above*, and *below*.

2. Place the rectangle in front of students. Hold the circle in the air above the rectangle.

   Say: The circle is above the rectangle. Now use the word *below* to tell about the rectangle and circle.
   ANSWER: The rectangle is below the circle.

   Say: The words *under* and *over* mean the same as *below* and *above*. So you could say, "The rectangle is under the circle," or "The circle is over the rectangle."

3. Now place the rectangle in front of students as close to them as possible. Place the circle in the work area, but as far from students as possible.

   Ask: Which is closer to you, the circle or the rectangle?
   ANSWER: the rectangle

   Say: Use the words *near* and *far* to tell about the circle and rectangle.
   ANSWER: The rectangle is near me. The circle is far from me.

   Have students move the objects so the rectangle is far from them and the circle is near them. Then have them describe the objects again.

4. Have students move the objects as described. Check that they are moving the objects correctly.

   Say: Place the rectangle above the circle.

   Say: Place the circle near me.

   Give students at least four more directions that use the words *above*, *below*, *near*, and *far*.

5. Ask students to use the words *above*, *below*, *near*, and *far* to give you directions for how to arrange the blocks. Arrange the blocks incorrectly for some of the examples, and ask students to explain how to arrange the blocks correctly.

Objectives

- Arrange objects in space by proximity, such as near, far, below, or above.
- Describe objects in space by proximity, such as near, far, below, or above.

Tips

For more practice, create a picture with students and label objects in the picture with position words.

LEARN Up or Down?

OFFLINE 10 min

Students will learn the position words *up* and *down*. They will use these words to describe the position of objects around them.

There are no materials to gather for this activity.

Ask: Sometimes people use the words *up* and *down* to talk about where objects are. I am looking up. Now you look up. What do you see?
ANSWER: a light, the ceiling

Ask: I am looking down. Now you look down. What do you see?
ANSWER: my feet, the floor, the carpet

Ask: If we went outdoors and looked up, what do you think you would see?
ANSWER: the sky, a bird, the top of a building, an airplane, clouds, the stars

Ask: If you looked down when we were outdoors, what do you think you would see?
ANSWER: grass, rocks, flowers, the sidewalk

If possible, allow students to go outdoors and describe what they see when they look up and down.

Objectives

- Arrange objects in space by proximity, such as near, far, below, or above.
- Describe objects in space by proximity, such as near, far, below, or above.

TRY IT Arrange and Describe

OFFLINE 10 min

Students will practice describing objects' positions. Give students the crayons and the Arrange and Describe activity page from their Activity Book.

Read Problems 1–4 aloud. Have students complete the task for each problem before you read the next problem aloud. Then read aloud the directions above Problem 5, and have students complete the remaining problems on their own.

Objectives

- Arrange objects in space by proximity, such as near, far, below, or above.
- Describe objects in space by proximity, such as near, far, below, or above.

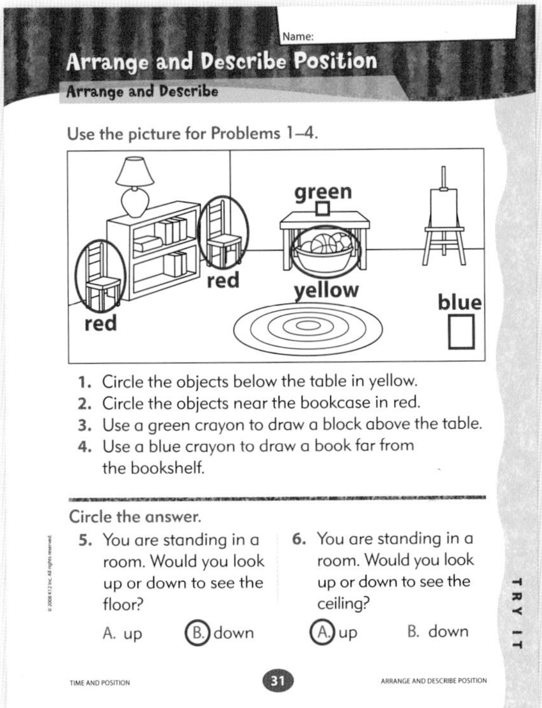
Name:

Arrange and Describe Position

Arrange and Describe

Use the picture for Problems 1–4.

1. Circle the objects below the table in yellow.
2. Circle the objects near the bookcase in red.
3. Use a green crayon to draw a block above the table.
4. Use a blue crayon to draw a book far from the bookshelf.

Circle the answer.

5. You are standing in a room. Would you look up or down to see the floor?
   A. up (B.) down
6. You are standing in a room. Would you look up or down to see the ceiling?
   (A.) up B. down

TRY IT

TIME AND POSITION 31 ARRANGE AND DESCRIBE POSITION

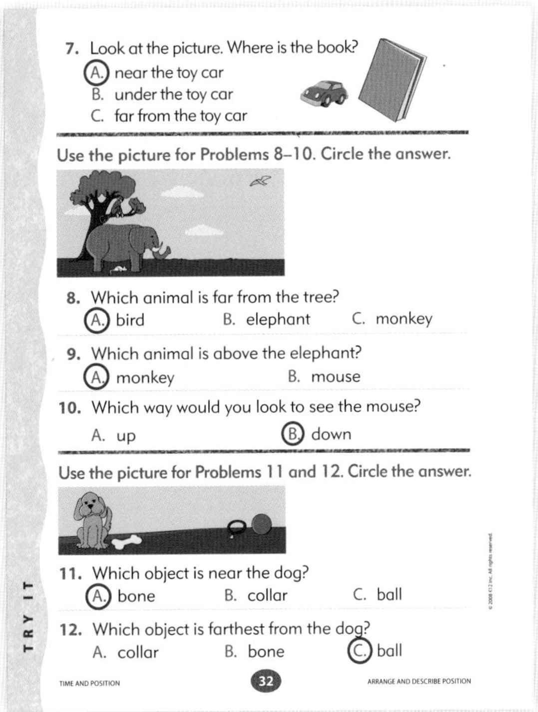
7. Look at the picture. Where is the book?
   (A.) near the toy car
   B. under the toy car
   C. far from the toy car

Use the picture for Problems 8–10. Circle the answer.

8. Which animal is far from the tree?
   (A.) bird B. elephant C. monkey
9. Which animal is above the elephant?
   (A.) monkey B. mouse
10. Which way would you look to see the mouse?
   A. up (B.) down

Use the picture for Problems 11 and 12. Circle the answer.

11. Which object is near the dog?
   (A.) bone B. collar C. ball
12. Which object is farthest from the dog?
   A. collar B. bone (C.) ball

TRY IT

TIME AND POSITION 32 ARRANGE AND DESCRIBE POSITION

Use Direction Words

Lesson Overview

Skills Update	5 minutes	ONLINE
GET READY Serena's Messy Room	5 minutes	ONLINE
LEARN Direction Words	15 minutes	OFFLINE
LEARN Where Am I?	15 minutes	OFFLINE
TRY IT Arrange and Describe Objects	10 minutes	OFFLINE
CHECKPOINT	10 minutes	OFFLINE

▶ Lesson Objectives

- Arrange objects in space by direction, such as behind, in front of, next to, left of, or right of.
- Describe objects in space by direction, such as behind, in front of, next to, left of, or right of.

▶ Prerequisite Skills

- Arrange objects in space by proximity, such as near, far, up, down, below, or above.
- Describe objects in space by proximity, such as near, far, up, down, below, or above.

▶ Safety

Supervise students to make sure they use their scissors safely and stay seated.

▶ Content Background

Students will learn the direction words *behind*, *in front of*, *next to*, *to the left of*, and *to the right of*. They will learn how to follow written and oral directions that use these words.

Materials to Gather

SUPPLIED

Direction Words activity page

Arrange and Describe Objects activity page

Checkpoint (printout)

ALSO NEEDED

glue

scissors, round-end safety

crayons

GET READY Serena's Messy Room

ONLINE 5 min

Students will use position words, such as *near*, *far*, *above*, and *below*, to arrange objects in Serena's room.

Objectives

- Arrange objects in space by proximity, such as near, far, up, down, below, or above.
- Describe objects in space by proximity, such as near, far, up, down, below, or above.

LEARN Direction Words

Students will learn the direction words *behind*, *in front of*, *next to*, *to the left of*, and *to the right of*. Then students will create a picture by following directions that include the direction words they learned.

Gather the Direction Words activity page, glue, and scissors.

1. **Say:** Show me your right hand. Show me your left hand.

   If students do not show the correct hands, tell them which hand they use for specific activities.

   Say: You color with your [left/right] hand; you hold a fork with your [right/left] hand. Your hands can help you remember left and right.

2. In the work area in front of students, place the scissors next to and to the right of the activity page. Ask students to look at the page and the scissors.

3. Place your right hand on students' right hand.

   Say: The scissors are to the right of the activity page because they are on the same side of the page as your right hand. The scissors are also next to the activity page because they are close to the side of the page.

4. Have students move the scissors so they are to the left of the activity page.

   Ask: Are the scissors still next to the activity page? Explain.
   ANSWER: Yes. They are close to the side of the activity page.

5. Give students the activity page.

   Say: Words like *behind*, *in front of*, *next to*, *to the left of*, and *to the right of* are direction words. These words tell where to find objects.

6. Have students cut out the four pictures at the bottom of the page. Read the directions one at a time. After each directive, have students glue the picture in the correct position, assisting students as needed.

7. Have students describe the complete picture using the words *behind*, *in front of*, *next to*, *to the left of*, and *to the right of*.

Objectives

- Arrange objects in space by direction, such as behind, in front of, next to, left of, or right of.
- Describe objects in space by direction, such as behind, in front of, next to, left of, or right of.

Tips

Show students that the pointer finger and thumb of their left hand create the letter L for LEFT.

Sit on the same side of the work area as students sit so their left and right will also be your own left and right.

Use Direction Words
Direction Words

Cut out each picture on the dotted lines. Glue the trees **to the left of** the pond. Glue the flowers **to the right of** the pond. Glue the bench **behind** the pond. Glue the duck **in front of** the pond.

TIME AND POSITION · 33 · USE DIRECTION WORDS

OFFLINE
15min

- Arrange objects in space by direction, such as behind, in front of, next to, left of, or right of.
- Describe objects in space by direction, such as behind, in front of, next to, left of, or right of.

By moving around the room according to your directions, students will practice following directions that include the words *behind*, *in front of*, *next to*, *to the left of*, and *to the right of*.

There are no materials to gather for this activity.

1. **Say:** Listen carefully. I will ask you to move around the room. I will use direction words such as *behind*, *in front of*, *next to*, *to the left of*, and *to the right of*.

2. Stand up, and have students stand.

   Say: Move to the right of me.

   Say: Now use the words *to the left of* to describe how we're standing.
   ANSWER: You are standing to the left of me.

3. **Say:** Move in front of the work area.

   Say: Now move behind the work area.

   Say: Use *in front of* and *behind* to describe where you are compared with the work area.
   ANSWER: The work area is in front of me. I am behind the work area.

4. **Say:** Move next to a chair.

   Ask: Are you to the right of or to the left of the chair?

5. **Say:** Now you tell me where to move. Use the words *behind*, *in front of*, *next to*, *to the left of*, or *to the right of*. Correct me if I move to the wrong place.

6. Have students tell you where to move at least three times. Be sure to move incorrectly at least once so that students can use direction words to explain where you should move.

Tips

Always refer to students' left and right when giving students directions. For simplicity, face the same direction as students as you move around the room.

If time permits, repeat the activity using the words *above*, *below*, *near*, and *far*. If you have access to stairs, students may enjoy moving above you and below you on the stairs.

TRY IT Arrange and Describe Objects

Objectives

- Arrange objects in space by direction, such as behind, in front of, next to, left of, or right of.
- Describe objects in space by direction, such as behind, in front of, next to, left of, or right of.

Students will follow directions to color pictures, make sketches, and answer questions. Give students the crayons and Arrange and Describe Objects activity page. Read the directions with them.

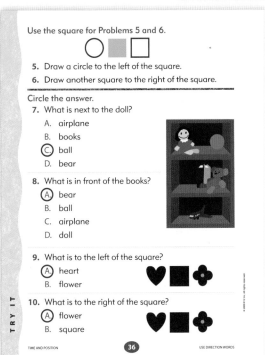

CHECKPOINT

Objectives

- Arrange objects in space by direction, such as behind, in front of, next to, left of, or right of.
- Describe objects in space by direction, such as behind, in front of, next to, left of, or right of.

Print the Checkpoint. In Part 1, students will take a performance-based assessment. In Part 2, students will complete the problems on their own. Read the directions, problems, and answer choices to students if necessary. Use the answer key to score the Checkpoint, and then enter the results online.

Gather the crayons. Students will use a crayon for Problems 1 and 2.

Name   Date

Checkpoint Answer Key

Part 1

Follow the instructions for each item. Choose the response that describes how the student performs on the task. When you have finished, enter the results online.

1. Give the student a pencil and a crayon.
   Say, "Hold these objects, one in each hand, so the pencil is above your head and the crayon is below your head."
   (1 point)
   Did the student hold the pencil above his head and the crayon below his head?

   A. Yes   B. No

2. Give the student a pencil and a crayon.
   Say, "Hold these objects, one in each hand, so the pencil is in front of your head and the crayon is behind your head."
   (1 point)
   Did the student hold the pencil in front of her head and the crayon behind her head?

   A. Yes   B. No

Give students Part 2 of the Checkpoint.

Name   Date

Part 2
Circle the answer.

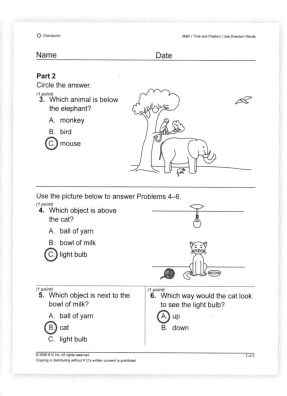

(1 point)
3. Which animal is below the elephant?

   A. monkey

   B. bird

   C. mouse

Use the picture below to answer Problems 4–6.

(1 point)
4. Which object is above the cat?

   A. ball of yarn

   B. bowl of milk

   C. light bulb

(1 point)
5. Which object is next to the bowl of milk?

   A. ball of yarn

   B. cat

   C. light bulb

(1 point)
6. Which way would the cat look to see the light bulb?

   A. up

   B. down

Name   Date

Use the picture to answer Problems 7 and 8.

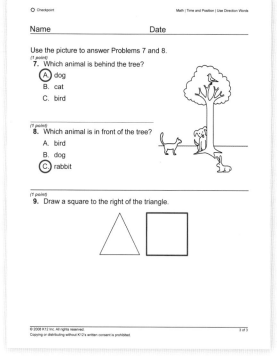

(1 point)
7. Which animal is behind the tree?

   A. dog

   B. cat

   C. bird

(1 point)
8. Which animal is in front of the tree?

   A. bird

   B. dog

   C. rabbit

(1 point)
9. Draw a square to the right of the triangle.

Unit Review

UNIT REVIEW Look Back	20 minutes	**ONLINE**
UNIT REVIEW Checkpoint Practice	20 minutes	**OFFLINE**
➡ **UNIT REVIEW** Prepare for the Checkpoint		

▶ Unit Objectives

This lesson reviews the following objectives:

- Tell time to the nearest hour.
- Tell time to the nearest half hour.
- Relate time to events (for example, before/after, shorter/longer).
- Arrange objects in space by proximity, such as near, far, below, or above.
- Describe objects in space by proximity, such as near, far, below, or above.
- Arrange objects in space by direction, such as behind, in front of, next to, left of, or right of.
- Describe objects in space by direction, such as behind, in front of, next to, left of, or right of.

▶ Advance Preparation

In this lesson, students will have an opportunity to review previous activities in the Time and Position unit. Look at the suggested activities in Unit Review: Prepare for the Checkpoint online and gather any needed materaials.

Materials to Gather

SUPPLIED

Checkpoint Practice activity page

Keywords		
analog clock	hour hand	position
face of a clock	longer	shorter
hand of a clock	minute	time
hour	minute hand	

UNIT REVIEW Look Back

ONLINE 20 min

In this unit, students have learned to tell time to the nearest hour and half hour, relate times to events in the day, and compare the amount of time it takes to complete different activities. They have also learned about position and direction. Students will review these concepts to prepare for the Unit Checkpoint.

Objectives

- Review unit objectives.

UNIT REVIEW Checkpoint Practice

OFFLINE 20 min

Students will complete a Checkpoint Practice activity page to prepare for the Unit Checkpoint. If necessary, read the directions, problems, and answer choices to students. Have students answer the problems on their own. Carefully review the answers with students.

Objectives

- Review unit objectives.

Name:

Unit Review
Checkpoint Practice

Write the time shown on the clock.

1. **2:30**

2. **4:00**

3. **9:30**

Circle the answer.

4. Which activity takes longer?

(A.)   B.

5. Which activity does the boy do after putting on his shoes?

A.   (B.)

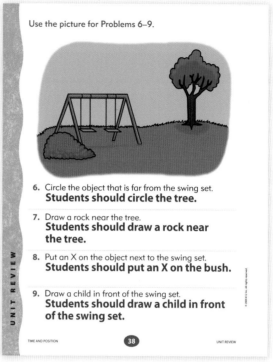

Use the picture for Problems 6–9.

6. Circle the object that is far from the swing set.
   Students should circle the tree.

7. Draw a rock near the tree.
   Students should draw a rock near the tree.

8. Put an X on the object next to the swing set.
   Students should put an X on the bush.

9. Draw a child in front of the swing set.
   Students should draw a child in front of the swing set.

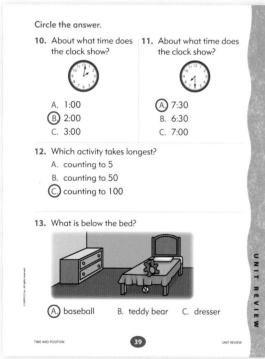

Circle the answer.

10. About what time does the clock show?

    A. 1:00
    (B.) 2:00
    C. 3:00

11. About what time does the clock show?

    (A.) 7:30
    B. 6:30
    C. 7:00

12. Which activity takes longest?

    A. counting to 5
    B. counting to 50
    (C.) counting to 100

13. What is below the bed?

    (A.) baseball   B. teddy bear   C. dresser

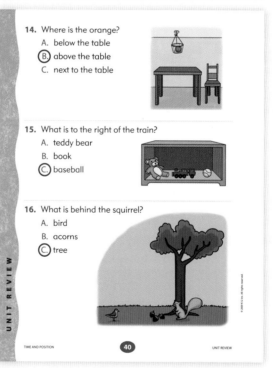

14. Where is the orange?

    A. below the table
    (B.) above the table
    C. next to the table

15. What is to the right of the train?

    A. teddy bear
    B. book
    (C.) baseball

16. What is behind the squirrel?

    A. bird
    B. acorns
    (C.) tree

➜ UNIT REVIEW Prepare for the Checkpoint

What you do next depends on how students performed in the previous activity, Unit Review: Checkpoint Practice. If students had difficulty with any of the problems, complete the appropriate review activity listed in the table online.

Unit Checkpoint

UNIT CHECKPOINT Online	25 minutes	**ONLINE**
UNIT CHECKPOINT Offline	35 minutes	**OFFLINE**

▶ Unit Objectives

This lesson assesses the following objectives:

- Tell time to the nearest hour.
- Tell time to the nearest half hour.
- Relate time to events (for example, before/after, shorter/longer).
- Arrange objects in space by proximity, such as near, far, below, or above.
- Describe objects in space by proximity, such as near, far, below, or above.
- Arrange objects in space by direction, such as behind, in front of, next to, left of, or right of.
- Describe objects in space by direction, such as behind, in front of, next to, left of, or right of.

Materials to Gather

SUPPLIED
Unit Checkpoint (printout)
blocks – O (1 red, 1 green, 1 blue)

ALSO NEEDED
craft stick
ruler
crayon
eraser

ONLINE 20min

UNIT CHECKPOINT Online

Students will complete this part of the Unit Checkpoint online. Read the directions, problems, and answer choices to students. If necessary, help students with keyboard or mouse operations.

Objectives

- Assess unit objectives.

OFFLINE 35min

UNIT CHECKPOINT Offline

Students will complete this part of the Unit Checkpoint offline. Print the Unit Checkpoint. Read the directions and problems to students. Use the answer key to score the Checkpoint, and then enter the results online.

Gather the blocks and other materials.

Objectives

- Assess unit objectives.

Name _____ Date _____

Unit Checkpoint Answer Key

Follow the instructions for each item. Choose the response that best
describes how the student performs on the task. When you have
finished, enter the results online.

1. Give students the red cube and the blue cube.
Say, "Hold these objects, one in each hand, so the red cube is
above your head and the blue cube is below your head."
(1 point)
Did the student hold the red cube above his head?

   A. Yes   B. No

(1 point)
Did the student hold the blue cube below her head?

   A. Yes   B. No

2. Give students the three cubes.
Say, "Place these objects so the red cube is near the green cube
and the blue cube is far from the green cube."
(1 point)
Did the student place the red cube near the green cube?

   A. Yes   B. No

(1 point)
Did the student place the blue cube far from the green cube?

   A. Yes   B. No

Name _____ Date _____

3. Place the ruler near the craft stick.
Ask, "Is the ruler far from the craft stick or near the craft stick?"
(1 point)
Did the student say, "near the craft stick"?

   A. Yes   B. No

4. Give students a pencil, crayon, and sheet of paper.
Say, "Place the paper on the table. Place the pencil to the left of
the paper. Now place the crayon to the right of the paper."
(1 point)
Did the student correctly place the objects?

   A. Yes   B. No

5. Give students a crayon, eraser, and pencil.
Say, "Place the crayon next to the eraser. Hold the pencil in front of
the crayon and eraser."
(1 point)
Did the student place the crayon and eraser next to each other?

   A. Yes   B. No

(1 point)
Did the student hold the pencil in front of the crayon and eraser?

   A. Yes   B. No

Introduction to Addition

5 + 3 = 8

Addition

Sum

5 apples plus 3 apples equals 8 apples

Adding

▶ Unit Objectives

- Use concrete objects or sketches to model and solve addition or subtraction computation problems with sums and minuends up through 30.
- Demonstrate and explain the meaning of addition as putting together or combining sets.
- Demonstrate understanding that the order in which numbers are added does not affect the sum.

- Recognize that the + symbol refers to addition.
- Correctly use the + symbol.
- Use models and math symbols to represent addition.
- Recognize that the equals symbol shows an equality between two expressions.
- Use the equals symbol in number sentences to express equality.

▶ Big Ideas

- Models and mathematical symbols can represent addition and subtraction.
- Addition represents the combining of two sets.
- The equals sign denotes an equivalent relationship.

▶ Unit Introduction

The concept of combining parts to make a whole is the basis for addition and subtraction. Students will explore this relationship using objects as they learn that addition means putting together groups. Using objects, students will learn that the order in which they add groups does not affect the sum.

Students will then begin to represent addition more abstractly by using numbers and symbols. They will learn both the plus symbol (+) and the equals symbol (=), and they will learn how to write number sentences using these symbols.

Model Addition

Lesson Overview

Skills Update	5 minutes	ONLINE
GET READY How Many in All?	5 minutes	ONLINE
LEARN Use Ten-Frames to Add	10 minutes	ONLINE
LEARN Sums Through 30	15 minutes	OFFLINE
LEARN Draw to Add	10 minutes	OFFLINE
TRY IT What's the Sum?	10 minutes	OFFLINE
CHECKPOINT	5 minutes	OFFLINE

▶ Lesson Objectives

Use concrete objects or sketches to model and solve addition and subtraction computation problems with sums and minuends up through 30.

▶ Prerequisite Skills

Use concrete objects or sketches to model and solve addition or subtraction computation problems involving sums or minuends up through 20.

▶ Advance Preparation

Number two sets of index cards from 1 through 15. Keep sets as two separate decks. Save cards for use in future lessons.
   Print the Part-Part-Total Sheet.

▶ Content Background

Students will find sums through 30 by using objects and drawings. Students will use ten-frames for some problems. Ten-frames are charts that show groups of 10 objects.

Materials to Gather

SUPPLIED

blocks – O (yellow, blue)
Part-Part-Total Sheet (printout)
What's the Sum? activity page
Checkpoint (printout)

ALSO NEEDED

index cards – numbered 1 through 15
   (two sets)

Keywords

add – to combine, or put together, groups of objects or numbers
addition – the process of combining, or putting together, groups of objects or numbers; a mathematical operation
model (verb) – to use physical objects, diagrams, or pictures to represent an amount, an expression, an equation, or a problem situation
part-part-total – two groups (parts) that combine to create the whole (total)
sum – the solution to an addition problem
ten-frame – a grid that consists of ten squares, arranged in a two-by-five array; students use ten-frames to organize objects or sketches into groups of ten
total – all of the objects in a set

GET READY How Many in All?

Students will solve addition story problems that involve finding sums through 20. They can solve the problems by counting the objects shown online.

Objectives

- Use concrete objects or sketches to model and solve addition or subtraction computation problems involving sums or minuends up through 20.

LEARN Use Ten-Frames to Add

ONLINE 10min

Students will model addition problems with sums through 30. They will use ten-frames to show the numbers being added.

DIRECTIONS FOR USING THE ADDITION LEARNING TOOL

1. Click Practice Mode.
   - Have students choose an object.
   - Click Yes to use ten-frames.
   - Click Start.
2. Have students drag 4 objects into the ten-frame at the left and 8 objects into the ten-frame at the right.
3. **Ask:** There are 4 objects in one group and 8 objects in the other group. How many objects are there altogether?
   ANSWER: 12
4. Click Menu, and choose Restart. Click Problem Mode II. Choose to use ten-frames, and then click Start.
5. Guide students to find each sum, type it in the box, and click Check. Continue as time permits.

Objectives

- Use concrete objects or sketches to model and solve addition or subtraction computation problems involving sums or minuends up through 30.

LEARN Sums Through 30

OFFLINE 15min

By modeling addition problems with cubes, students will learn that combining groups of objects is the same as adding. Using two different colors of cubes helps show the part-part-total relationship in addition: each part will have one color, and the total, or sum, will have both colors.

Gather the cubes, two decks of number cards, and Part-Part-Total Sheet.

1. Display the Part-Part-Total Sheet, a 6 card, and a 9 card.
   Say: Add a group of 6 and a group of 9. Make a group of 6 yellow cubes and a group of 9 blue cubes.

   Have students place 6 yellow cubes in one Part section of the printout and 9 blue cubes in the other Part section.

Objectives

- Use concrete objects or sketches to model and solve addition or subtraction computation problems involving sums or minuends up through 30.

Tips

Review with students the parts of an addition number sentence. Write "4 and 5 is 9." Point to the 4 and 5 and tell students that the numbers you add are called *addends*. Point to the 9. Say that the number you get when you add, the total, is called the *sum*.

2. **Say:** When we combine two groups of objects, we are adding them. To find the sum of 6 and 9, move the yellow and blue cubes to the Total section. Count the cubes in the Total section.
   ANSWER: 15

   Say: There are 15 cubes in the Total section, so 6 cubes plus 9 cubes is the same as 15 cubes.

3. Shuffle each deck of number cards, and place the decks face down. Have students flip over the top card of each deck and add the two numbers using the cubes and the Part-Part-Total Sheet. Continue as time permits.

LEARN Draw to Add

OFFLINE 10 min

Objectives

- Use concrete objects or sketches to model and solve addition or subtraction computation problems involving sums or minuends up through 30.

Students will use sketches to solve addition problems.
  There are no materials to gather for this activity.

1. **Say:** You can use sketches to add. Let's add a group of 8 and a group of 5. Draw a group of 8 sketches and a group of 5 sketches. Use a different sketch for each addend. For example, draw 8 circles for the group of 8, and 5 X's for the group of 5.

2. Have students count the sketches to find the total.
   Ask: What is 5 plus 8?
   ANSWER: 13

3. Have students make sketches to solve the following problems. For each problem, have them explain how they found the sum.
   - 4 plus 12 (16)
   - 11 plus 10 (21)
   - 4 plus 9 (13)

Tips

Tell students to draw simple shapes for their sketches. Students who enjoy drawing may want to draw pictures that are too detailed. Other students may become discouraged if they feel they must draw lifelike pictures.

TRY IT What's the Sum?

OFFLINE 10 min

Objectives

- Use concrete objects or sketches to model and solve addition or subtraction computation problems involving sums or minuends up through 30.

Students will practice modeling and solving addition problems with sums through 30. Give students the cubes and the What's the Sum? activity page from their Activity Book. Read the directions with them.

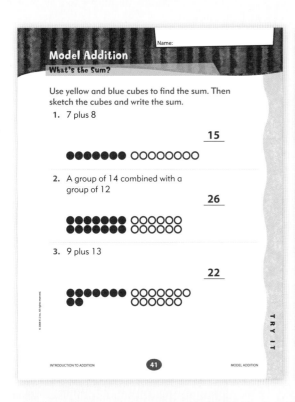

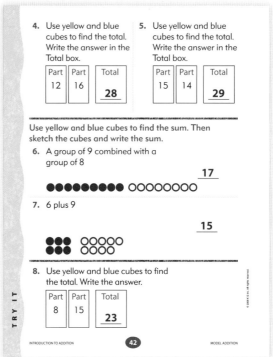

Model Addition

What's the Sum?

Use yellow and blue cubes to find the sum. Then sketch the cubes and write the sum.

1. 7 plus 8

    15

    ●●●●●●● ○○○○○○○○

2. A group of 14 combined with a group of 12

    26

    ●●●●●●● ○○○○○○
    ●●●●●●● ○○○○○○

3. 9 plus 13

    22

    ●●●●●●● ○○○○○○○
    ●● ○○○○○○

TRY IT

4. Use yellow and blue cubes to find the total. Write the answer in the Total box.

Part	Part	Total
12	16	**28**

5. Use yellow and blue cubes to find the total. Write the answer in the Total box.

Part	Part	Total
15	14	**29**

Use yellow and blue cubes to find the sum. Then sketch the cubes and write the sum.

6. A group of 9 combined with a group of 8

    17

    ●●●●●●●●● ○○○○○○○○

7. 6 plus 9

    15

    ●●● ○○○○○
    ●●● ○○○○

8. Use yellow and blue cubes to find the total. Write the answer.

Part	Part	Total
8	15	**23**

CHECKPOINT

OFFLINE
5min

Print the Checkpoint. Students will take a performance-based assessment. Read the directions and problems to students. Use the answer key to score the Checkpoint, and then enter the results online.

Gather the cubes. Students will use the cubes for Problems 2–5.

Objectives

- Use concrete objects or sketches to model and solve addition or subtraction computation problems with sums and minuends up through 30.

Name   Date

Checkpoint Answer Key

1. Give the student a sheet of paper.
    Say, "Ed has 14 baseball cards. His father gives him 10 more baseball cards. Make a sketch that shows how to find how many baseball cards Ed has in all."
    (1 point)
    Did the student draw a group of 14 baseball cards and a group of 10 baseball cards?

    A. Yes   B. No

2. Place 15 yellow cubes and 15 blue cubes in front of the student.
    Say, "Use cubes to show how to add 5 and 10. How many cubes are there in all?"
    (1 point)
    Did the student show a group of 5 cubes and a group of 10 cubes and count 15 cubes in all?

    A. Yes   B. No

3. Place 15 yellow and 15 blue cubes in front of the student.
    Say, "Use cubes to show how to add 11 and 11. How many cubes are there in all?"
    (1 point)
    Did the student show a group of 11 cubes and a group of 11 cubes and count 22 cubes in all?

    A. Yes   B. No

Name   Date

4. Place 15 blue cubes and 15 yellow cubes in front of the student.
    Say, "Use the cubes to show how to add 7 and 9. How many cubes are there in all?"
    (1 point)
    Did the student show a group of 7 cubes and a group of 9 cubes and count 16 cubes in all?

    A. Yes   B. No

5. Place 15 yellow cubes and 15 blue cubes in front of the student.
    Say, "Use cubes to show how to add 13 and 6. How many cubes are there in all?"
    (1 point)
    Did the student show a group of 13 cubes and a group of 6 cubes and count 19 cubes in all?

    A. Yes   B. No

Add in Any Order

Skills Update	5 minutes	ONLINE
GET READY Combine Groups	5 minutes	ONLINE
LEARN Animal Addition	5 minutes	ONLINE
LEARN Add in Different Orders	10 minutes	OFFLINE
LEARN Meaning of Addition	10 minutes	OFFLINE
LEARN Step It Off	10 minutes	OFFLINE
TRY IT Show Addition	10 minutes	OFFLINE
CHECKPOINT	5 minutes	OFFLINE

▶ Lesson Objectives

- Demonstrate and explain the meaning of addition as putting together or combining sets.
- Demonstrate understanding that the order in which numbers are added does not affect the sum.

▶ Prerequisite Skills

- Demonstrate the meaning of addition as the combining of two sets (for sums up through 20).
- Demonstrate with concrete objects representing numbers up to 10 that changing the order in which numbers are added does not affect the sum.

▶ Advance Preparation

Number index cards 0 through 20, or gather the number cards you created previously. Place the index cards in order on the floor, evenly spaced, to make a number line.

▶ Safety

Remind students to step carefully on the index cards so that they don't slip. You may wish to have them step next to the cards instead of on them.

▶ Content Background

The commutative property of addition states that you can add numbers in any order and the sum does not change. For example, $5 + 3 = 8$ and $3 + 5 = 8$. So $5 + 3 = 3 + 5$. This means that addition is commutative. Without using the term *commutative property*, students will add numbers in different orders to learn that the sum is the same.

Materials to Gather

SUPPLIED

blocks – B (red, blue)
Meaning of Addition activity page
Show Addition activity page
Checkpoint (printout)

ALSO NEEDED

index cards – 4
index cards – numbered 0 through 20
paper, construction – 3 sheets
paper, drawing – 1 sheet

<table>
</table>

Keywords   **commutative property of addition** – a rule stating that changing the order of two addends does not change their sum
number line – a line consisting of points equally spaced, each of which corresponds to a unique number

GET READY Combine Groups

Students will add groups of blocks by combining the groups and counting the total.

Objectives

- Demonstrate the meaning of addition as the combining of two sets (for sums up through 20).

LEARN Animal Addition

Students will learn that the order in which they add numbers doesn't affect the sum. They will visit a pond and see groups of frogs that can't seem to stay still. Students will watch the frogs being added in different orders, learning that the total number of frogs does not change when the frogs move.

Objectives

- Demonstrate and explain the meaning of addition as putting together or combining sets.
- Demonstrate understanding that the order in which numbers are added does not affect the sum.

LEARN Add in Different Orders

Students will add blocks in different orders to learn that the order in which they add doesn't affect the sum.

Gather the red circle blocks, construction paper, and blank index cards.

1. Place 3 sheets of construction paper in a row. Place an index card under the first sheet and have students write the number 8 on the card. Place an index card under the second sheet (to the right of the first sheet) and have students write 6 on it. Leave the third index card blank. Place it under the third sheet.
2. Have students place 8 circles on the first sheet of paper and 6 circles on the second.
3. Explain that adding is the same as putting groups together. Have students combine the 8 circles and 6 circles on the third sheet of paper. Ask them how many circles there are in all. (14)
4. **Say:** 8 circles combined with 6 circles makes 14 circles. So the sum is 14.
   Have students write the number 14 on the last index card.
5. Repeat the activity, but this time place 6 circles on the first sheet of paper and 8 circles on the second.

Objectives

- Demonstrate and explain the meaning of addition as putting together or combining sets.
- Demonstrate understanding that the order in which numbers are added does not affect the sum.

80 INTRODUCTION TO ADDITION

6. **Ask:** How was this problem different from the first problem?
    ANSWER: I added 6 and 8 in a different order.

    Point to the third sheet of paper, which should have 14 circles on it.

    Ask: Why is the total the same for both problems?
    ANSWER: I added the same numbers, 6 and 8.

OFFLINE
10min

LEARN Meaning of Addition

Students will use objects and drawings to model addition problems. For Problem 4, they will add the same numbers in different orders to show that adding in a different order doesn't affect the sum. Give students the red and blue circle blocks and the Meaning of Addition activity page. Read the directions with them.

Objectives

- Demonstrate and explain the meaning of addition as putting together or combining sets.
- Demonstrate understanding that the order in which numbers are added does not affect the sum.

Tips

Remind students to use simple shapes for sketches. They may use color to distinguish the groups being added.

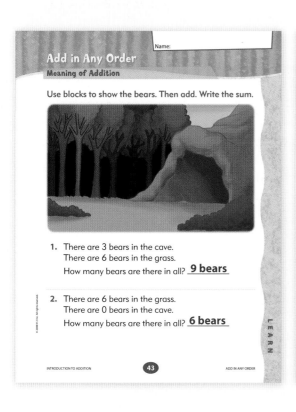

Name: _____

Add in Any Order
Meaning of Addition

Use blocks to show the bears. Then add. Write the sum.

1. There are 3 bears in the cave.
    There are 6 bears in the grass.
    How many bears are there in all? __9 bears__

2. There are 6 bears in the grass.
    There are 0 bears in the cave.
    How many bears are there in all? __6 bears__

Use sketches to show the bears. Then add. Write the sum.

3. There are 7 black bears.
    There are 5 brown bears.
    How many bears are there in all? __12 bears__
    Students should sketch a group of 7 and a group of 5.

Use blocks to show that the statement is true. Explain your answer.

4. Adding 9 and 6 is the same as adding 6 and 9.
    Students should show a group of 9 blocks and a group of 6 blocks, and they should combine the groups to add. Then they should add the groups in the other order. They should explain there are 15 blocks in the combined group whether they add 9 and 6 or 6 and 9.

LEARN Step It Off

OFFLINE 10 min

Objectives

- Demonstrate and explain the meaning of addition as putting together or combining sets.
- Demonstrate understanding that the order in which numbers are added does not affect the sum.

Students will use a number line to learn that the order in which they add doesn't affect the sum.

Gather 1 red circle block and 1 blue circle block. Move to the number line you created earlier.

1. Explain that students will use the number line to add.

2. Have students stand on the 0 card. Tell them to move forward 8 steps, 1 step per card.

   Say: The first number we're adding is 8. Let's add 8 and 5.

   Have them move forward 5 steps to show adding 5.

   Ask: What number are you standing on?
   ANSWER: 13

3. Place the red circle on 13.

   Say: 8 and 5 is 13.

4. Tell students to stand on 0 again. Explain that now they'll add 5 and 8. Have them take 5 steps to show the number 5, and then have them take 8 steps to show adding 8.

   Ask: What number are you standing on?
   ANSWER: 13

5. Place the blue cube on 13.

   Say: 5 and 8 is 13.

6. **Say:** Walking 8 steps then 5 steps is the same as walking 5 steps then 8 steps. Either way, you finish at 13. The order that you add the numbers does not change the sum.

7. Repeat Steps 2–6 with the numbers 9 and 7.

TRY IT Show Addition

OFFLINE 10 min

Objectives

- Demonstrate and explain the meaning of addition as putting together or combining sets.
- Demonstrate understanding that the order in which numbers are added does not affect the sum.

Students will practice finding sums through 30. Give students the red and blue circle blocks and the Show Addition activity page from their Activity Book. Read the directions with them.

As students work through the problems, emphasize the following:

- They combine groups to add.
- They can add numbers in any order without affecting the sum.

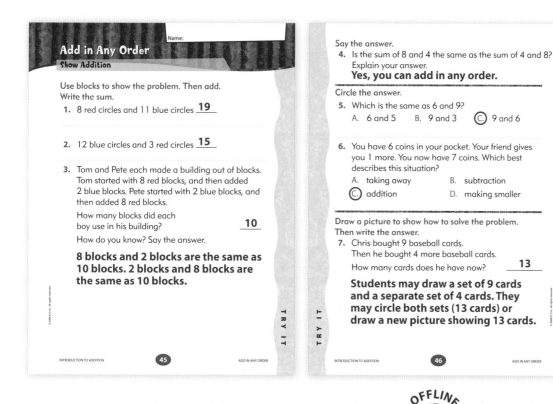

Add in Any Order

Show Addition

Name:

Use blocks to show the problem. Then add.
Write the sum.

1. 8 red circles and 11 blue circles **19**

2. 12 blue circles and 3 red circles **15**

3. Tom and Pete each made a building out of blocks.
   Tom started with 8 red blocks, and then added
   2 blue blocks. Pete started with 2 blue blocks, and
   then added 8 red blocks.

   How many blocks did each
   boy use in his building? **10**

   How do you know? Say the answer.

   **8 blocks and 2 blocks are the same as
   10 blocks. 2 blocks and 8 blocks are
   the same as 10 blocks.**

T R Y I T

INTRODUCTION TO ADDITION   45   ADD IN ANY ORDER

Say the answer.

4. Is the sum of 8 and 4 the same as the sum of 4 and 8?
   Explain your answer.
   Yes, you can add in any order.

Circle the answer.

5. Which is the same as 6 and 9?
   A. 6 and 5   B. 9 and 3   (C.) 9 and 6

6. You have 6 coins in your pocket. Your friend gives
   you 1 more. You now have 7 coins. Which best
   describes this situation?
   A. taking away   B. subtraction
   (C.) addition   D. making smaller

Draw a picture to show how to solve the problem.
Then write the answer.

7. Chris bought 9 baseball cards.
   Then he bought 4 more baseball cards.
   How many cards does he have now? **13**

   **Students may draw a set of 9 cards
   and a separate set of 4 cards. They
   may circle both sets (13 cards) or
   draw a new picture showing 13 cards.**

T R Y I T

INTRODUCTION TO ADDITION   46   ADD IN ANY ORDER

OFFLINE
5min

CHECKPOINT

Print the Checkpoint. In Part 1, students will take a performance-based
assessment. In Part 2, students will complete the problems on their own. Read
the directions, problems, and answer choices to students if necessary. Use the
answer key to score the Checkpoint, and then enter the results online.

Gather the drawing paper and the red and blue circle blocks.

Objectives

- Demonstrate and explain the
  meaning of addition as putting
  together or combining sets.

- Demonstrate understanding that
  the order in which numbers are
  added does not affect the sum.

Name _____ Date _____

Checkpoint Answer Key

Part 1

Follow the instructions for each item. Choose the response that best describes how the student performs on the task. When you have finished, enter the results online.

1. Say, "Erin and Anna each made a bead bracelet. Erin started with 10 red beads and then added 5 blue beads. Anna started with 5 blue beads and then added 10 red beads. How many beads did each girl have on her bracelet? How do you know?"
    (1 point)
    Answers will vary. Example: Each girl had 15 beads. That's correct because 10 and 5 is 15, and 5 and 10 is 15. When the same numbers are added, it doesn't matter what order they are in. The answer is the same.

    Did the student have an answer similar to the example?

    A. Yes   B. No

2. Say, "Is the sum of 5 and 2 the same as the sum of 2 and 5? Explain your answer."

    Answers will vary. Example: Yes, 5 and 2 is the same as 2 and 5. When the same numbers are added, it doesn't matter what order they are in. The answer is the same.

    Did the student have an answer similar to the example?
    (1 point)
    A. Yes   B. No

Name _____ Date _____

3. Say, "Diane buys 4 oranges. Then she buys 5 more oranges. How many oranges does she have now? Draw a picture that shows how to solve this problem."

    Examples: Students may draw a picture showing a set of 4 oranges and a set of 5 more oranges, and then either draw a new picture showing 9 oranges, or encircle both sets to show a total of 9 oranges. Alternatively, students may draw 4 (or 5) oranges, and then continue adding oranges to the same set until they reach 9 oranges.

    Did the student draw a picture similar to one of the examples?
    (1 point)
    A. Yes   B. No

4. Give the student the blocks.
    Write the following on a sheet of paper:
    3 and 7 is _____
    Say, "Use the blocks to show me that 7 and 3 is the same as 10."

    Examples: Students may count out 3 blocks, and then count out a second pile of 7 blocks and merge them together to show 10. Or students may make one group of either 3 or 7 blocks, and then continue adding to that group until they reach 10.

    Did the student use the blocks in a way similar to the examples?
    (1 point)
    A. Yes   B. No

Give students Part 2 of the assessment.

Name _____ Date _____

Part 2

Circle the answer.

5. Which is the same as 6 and 3?
    (1 point)
    A. 5 and 2
    (B.) 3 and 6
    C. 7 and 4

6. Which best describes addition?
    (1 point)
    (A.) putting together
    B. taking away
    C. making smaller
    D. separating sets

7. You have 2 toys. Your friend gives you 2 more. Now you have 4 toys. Which best describes this situation?
    (1 point)
    A. taking away
    B. subtraction
    (C.) addition
    D. making smaller

The Plus Symbol

Skills Update	5 minutes	ONLINE
GET READY Add the Berries	5 minutes	ONLINE
LEARN Addition Lab	15 minutes	ONLINE
LEARN Use the Plus Symbol	15 minutes	OFFLINE
TRY IT Write the Addition	10 minutes	OFFLINE
CHECKPOINT	10 minutes	OFFLINE

▶ Lesson Objectives

- Recognize that the $+$ symbol refers to addition.
- Correctly use the $+$ symbol.
- Use models and math symbols to represent addition.

▶ Prerequisite Skills

Demonstrate the meaning of addition as the combining of two sets (for sums up through 20).

▶ Advance Preparation

Number two sets of index cards 0 through 9, or gather the number cards you created previously.

▶ Safety

Be sure students handle the craft sticks carefully. Be aware of the possibility of splinters from the sticks.

▶ Content Background

Students know how to combine two numbers to find the sum. In this lesson, they will learn that the plus symbol $(+)$ means "and." They will learn how to solve and write addition problems that use the plus symbol.

Although the phrase *plus sign* is used in everyday language, *plus symbol* is more accurate as a mathematical term. In math, *sign* refers specifically to positive signs and negative signs.

The term *expression* is defined as a combination of number(s) and symbol(s) that represents a given value. An expression does not include an equals symbol $(=)$ or other relational symbol, such as a not-equal-to symbol $(\neq)$, a less-than symbol $(<)$, or a greater-than symbol $(>)$. Here are some expressions: 5; $3 + 8$; $2 - 1$.

The term *number sentence* is defined as two expressions that are related to one another by an equals symbol $(=)$ or other relational symbol, such as a not-equal-to symbol $(\neq)$, a less-than symbol $(<)$, or a greater-than symbol $(>)$. Here are some number sentences: $6 + 3 = 9$; $2 - 1 < 5$; $7 + 2 > 3$.

Materials to Gather

SUPPLIED

blocks – B (10 red, 10 blue)

Write the Addition activity page

Checkpoint (printout)

ALSO NEEDED

craft sticks – 17

index cards – numbered 0 through 9 (two sets)

tape, clear

ONLINE
5 min

GET READY Add the Berries

Students will practice adding. They will use pictures of strawberries as models.

Objectives

- Demonstrate the meaning of addition as the combining of two sets (for sums up through 20).

ONLINE
15 min

LEARN Addition Lab

Students will learn that the plus symbol (+) signals that they should add two numbers. They will solve addition problems that use the plus symbol.

Objectives

- Recognize that the + symbol refers to addition.
- Correctly use the + symbol.
- Use models and math symbols to represent addition.

OFFLINE
15 min

LEARN Use the Plus Symbol

Students will use blocks to model addition problems. Then they will use numbers cards and a craft-stick plus symbol to write expressions for the problems they modeled.

Gather the circle blocks, number cards, 2 craft sticks, and tape.

1. Point to the plus symbol on the computer keyboard. Tell students it is a math symbol and is used to show addition.

2. Help students create a model of the plus symbol (+) by taping together 2 craft sticks so that they cross in the middle.

3. **Say:** When you see a plus symbol between two numbers, it means to add, or combine, the numbers to find the sum.

   Set the plus symbols aside.

4. **Say:** Show a group of 6 red circles and a group of 4 blue circles. Find the total number of circles.
   ANSWER: Students should combine the two groups to make one group. The total is 10.

Objectives

- Recognize that the + symbol refers to addition.
- Correctly use the + symbol.
- Use models and math symbols to represent addition.

5. **Say:** Now show 3 red circles and 2 blue circles.

   After students show the groups, explain that you will use numbers and symbols to show the addition problem.

   Have students place the 3 card under the 3 red circles and the 2 card under the 2 blue circles. Have them place the plus symbol between the cards.

6. **Say:** You read this "three plus two." The plus symbol tells to add 3 and 2. When you see a plus symbol, say, "plus."

7. **Ask:** The numbers you add are called *addends*. In this problem, 3 and 2 are addends. The total is called the *sum*. What is the sum of 3 plus 2?
   ANSWER: 5

8. Repeat Steps 5–7 with the following expressions: $0 + 7$, $5 + 3$, and $2 + 6$.

9. Explain that a statement in math that uses numbers and symbols is called an *expression*. They have been working with expressions, such as $0 + 7$ and $5 + 3$, in this activity.

10. Using only the cards and the plus symbol, have students show the following expressions: $6 + 2$, $7 + 1$, and $4 + 0$. For each expression, have them tell the addends and the sum.

TRY IT Write the Addition

OFFLINE 10 min

Objectives

Students will practice solving problems that use the plus symbol. They will also use the plus symbol to write expressions for addition models. Give students 15 craft sticks and the Write the Addition activity page from their Activity Book. Read the directions with them. Students will use the craft sticks in Problem 16. Remind students that they can add numbers in any order and get the same sum.

- Recognize that the $+$ symbol refers to addition.
- Correctly use the $+$ symbol.
- Use models and math symbols to represent addition.

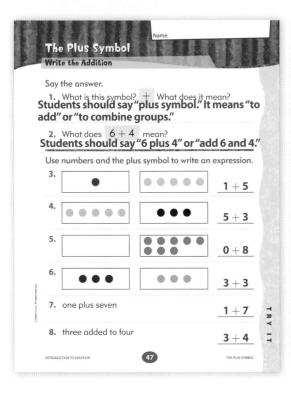

Name: _____

The Plus Symbol

Write the Addition

Say the answer.

1. What is this symbol? $+$ What does it mean?
   Students should say "plus symbol." It means "to add" or "to combine groups."

2. What does $6 + 4$ mean?
   Students should say "6 plus 4" or "add 6 and 4."

Use numbers and the plus symbol to write an expression.

3. $1 + 5$

4. $5 + 3$

5. $0 + 8$

6. $3 + 3$

7. one plus seven $\quad 1 + 7$

8. three added to four $\quad 3 + 4$

INTRODUCTION TO ADDITION 47 THE PLUS SYMBOL

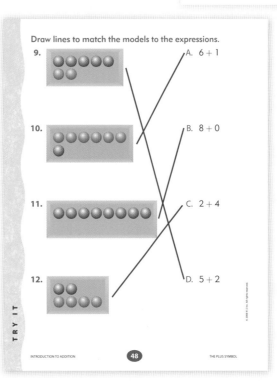

Draw lines to match the models to the expressions.

9.   A. $6 + 1$

10.   B. $8 + 0$

11.   C. $2 + 4$

12.   D. $5 + 2$

INTRODUCTION TO ADDITION 48 THE PLUS SYMBOL

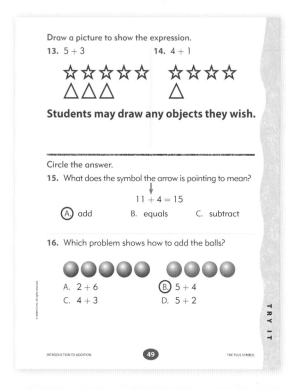

Draw a picture to show the expression.

13. 5 + 3   **14.** 4 + 1

☆☆☆☆☆   ☆☆☆☆
△△△   △

Students may draw any objects they wish.

Circle the answer.

15. What does the symbol the arrow is pointing to mean?

11 + 4 = 15

(A.) add   B. equals   C. subtract

16. Which problem shows how to add the balls?

A. 2 + 6   (B.) 5 + 4
C. 4 + 3   D. 5 + 2

TRY IT

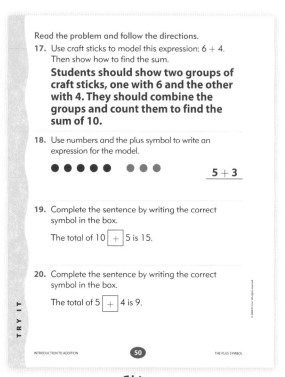

Read the problem and follow the directions.

17. Use craft sticks to model this expression: 6 + 4. Then show how to find the sum.

Students should show two groups of craft sticks, one with 6 and the other with 4. They should combine the groups and count them to find the sum of 10.

18. Use numbers and the plus symbol to write an expression for the model.

●●●●● ●●●   **5 + 3**

19. Complete the sentence by writing the correct symbol in the box.

The total of 10 ┃+┃ 5 is 15.

20. Complete the sentence by writing the correct symbol in the box.

The total of 5 ┃+┃ 4 is 9.

TRY IT

OFFLINE

10 min

CHECKPOINT

Objectives

Print the Checkpoint. In Part 1, students will take a performance-based assessment. In Part 2, students will complete the problems on their own. Read the directions, problems, and answer choices to students if necessary. Use the answer key to score the Checkpoint, and then enter the results online.

Gather the circle blocks. Students will use them in Problem 4.

- Recognize that the + symbol refers to addition.
- Correctly use the + symbol.
- Use models and math symbols to represent addition.

◇ Checkpoint   Math | Introduction to Addition | The Plus Symbol

Name _____   Date _____

Checkpoint Answer Key

Part 1
Follow the instructions for each problem. Choose the response that best describes how the student performs on the task. When you have finished, enter the results online.

1. Give students a sheet of paper.
Say, "Write an expression that shows seven added to five."
(1 point)
Did the student write 7 + 5?

A. Yes   B. No

2. Write the following problem on a sheet of paper: 5 ☐ 3.
Say, "In the box, write the symbol that says to add 5 and 3."
(1 point)
Did the student write + in the box?

A. Yes   B. No

3. Write the following problem on a sheet of paper: 10 ☐ 3.
Say, "In the box, write the symbol that says to add 10 and 3."
(1 point)
Did the student write + in the box?

A. Yes   B. No

4. Give students the blocks. Ask them to model 4 + 6.
(1 point)
Did the student show 4 blocks of one color in one group and 6 blocks of a different color in another group?

A. Yes   B. No

Give students Part 2 of the assessment.

◇ Checkpoint   Math | Introduction to Addition | The Plus Symbol

Name _____   Date _____

Part 2
Circle the answer.
(1 point)
5. Which symbol is the plus symbol?

A. −   (B.) +   C. =

(1 point)
6. Which picture shows that when you add 3 to 4, you get 7?

A. ●●●●●●● + ● is ●●●●●●●●

B. ●●●● + ●●●●●●●● is ●●●●●●●●

(C.) ●●● + ●●●● is ●●●●●●●

(1 point)
7. Complete the number sentence by choosing the correct symbol.

11 ☐ 1 is 12.

A. −   B. =   (C.) +

(1 point)
8. What would the number sentence be for this picture?

●●● + ●●●●●● is ●●●●●●●●●

(A.) 3 + 6 is 9.   B. 3 + 3 is 6.   C. 6 + 9 is 3.

The Equals Symbol

Skills Update	5 minutes	ONLINE
TRY IT The Plus Symbol	10 minutes	ONLINE
LEARN Balance the Sides	10 minutes	ONLINE
LEARN Equal or Not Equal?	15 minutes	OFFLINE
TRY IT Find What Is Equal	10 minutes	ONLINE
TRY IT What Is the Equals Symbol?	10 minutes	OFFLINE

▶ Lesson Objectives

Recognize that the equals symbol shows an equality between two expressions.

▶ Prerequisite Skills

Recognize that the + symbol refers to addition.

▶ Common Errors and Misconceptions

Students might misinterpret the equals symbol ($=$) as a signal they should "do" something. For example, in the number sentence $5 + 3 =$ ___, students might think the equals symbol means "adds up to" or "produces." So they might view $8 = 5 + 3$ or $8 = 8$ as unacceptable or wrong because they believe the equals symbol must be followed by the answer to a problem.

▶ Advance Preparation

Number index cards 0 through 15, or gather the number cards you created previously. Label three other index cards with the following symbols: $+, =, \neq$. Save cards for use in future lessons.

▶ Content Background

Students know how to combine two numbers to find a sum. They know that the plus symbol ($+$) represents addition. In this lesson, they will learn that the equals symbol ($=$) means "the same as." They will also learn that the equals symbol shows that two groups of numbers have the same value.

Although the phrase *equals sign* is often used in everyday language, *equals symbol* is more accurate as a mathematical term. In math, *sign* refers specifically to positive signs and negative signs.

Materials to Gather

SUPPLIED

blocks – O (10 each of 3 colors)

What Is the Equals Symbol? activity page

ALSO NEEDED

index cards – numbered 0 through 15

index cards – labeled with $+, =, \neq$ symbols

Keywords

equal – the relationship of expressions, numbers, or amounts that have the same value
equals symbol (=) – a symbol that shows the relationship between two equal values
equivalent – having the same value
not-equal-to symbol (≠) – a symbol indicating that two quantities or values do not have the same value
number sentence – two expressions related by an equals symbol (=), a not-equal-to symbol (≠), or an inequality symbol; for example, $7 - 2 = 4 + 1$; $5 \neq 4 + 4$; $6 + 2 > 1 + 4$

ONLINE 10min

TRY IT The Plus Symbol

Students will answer questions online to demonstrate what they remember about the plus symbol.

Objectives

- Recognize that the + symbol refers to addition.

Tips

Point to the plus symbol on the computer keyboard to show students what it looks like.

ONLINE 10min

LEARN Balance the Sides

A number sentence is like level a balance—just as the objects on each side of a balance have the same weight, the numbers on each side of the equals symbol have the same value. By putting equal numbers of cubes on the two sides of a balance, students will picture the meaning of the equals symbol.

Objectives

- Recognize that the equals symbol shows an equality between two expressions.

LEARN Equal or Not Equal?

Students will continue to explore the meaning of the equals symbol. They will decide whether to place an equals symbol or a not-equal-to symbol in number sentences.

Gather the cubes and the number and symbol cards.

1. Make the expression 2 + 5 ___ 7 using the number and symbol cards. Place the equals symbol card face down in place of the blank.

   Have students model 2 + 5 using cubes of two different colors, and 7 using cubes of a third color (for example, 2 reds, 5 yellows, and 7 blues). Place the cube models below the appropriate number cards.

2. Ask students to make a train with the red cubes and the yellow cubes.

   Say: Add the 2 red cubes and the 5 yellow cubes. How many cubes do you have now?

   ANSWER: 7

3. **Ask:** Is the red and yellow train equal to the blue train?
   ANSWER: Yes

   If students are unsure, have them count the cubes in each train.

4. Turn over the card that is face down. Point to each card as you say, "Two plus five equals seven."

5. Clear the work area. Repeat Steps 1 and 2 using the expression 7 + 2 ___ 7. Place the not-equal-to symbol card face down in place of the blank.

6. **Ask:** Does 7 + 2 equal 7?
   ANSWER: No

   If students are unsure, have them count the cubes in each train.

7. Turn over the card that is face down.

   Say: Then we cannot put an equals symbol between 7 + 2, and 7. This symbol means "not equal to." It is an equals symbol that is crossed out.

   Point to each card as you say, "Seven plus two does not equal seven."

8. Replace the not-equal-to symbol with the equals symbol. Point to the 7 card that is to the right of the equals symbol.

   Say: What number card should we put here that equals 7 + 2? Find the number card.

   Students should replace the 7 card with the 9 card.

9. Clear the work area. Have students model each of the number sentences below using the number and symbol cards. Students should use the face-down equals symbol for the blanks. For each sentence, ask students if they should use the equals symbol or the not-equal-to symbol. Ask students to explain their decisions.

   Then have them turn over the equals symbol card and find the number card that makes the sentence true.

   - 6 ___ 4 + 4 $(\neq)$
   - 1 + 9 ___ 11 $(\neq)$
   - 10 ___ 6 + 3 $(\neq)$
   - 11 ___ 7 + 4 $(=)$
   - 8 + 2 ___ 10 $(=)$

Objectives

- Recognize that the equals symbol shows an equality between two expressions.

Tips

The addition expression is not always to the left of the equals symbol. Remind students that the addition expression can be on either side of the equals symbol.

TRY IT Find What Is Equal

ONLINE
10 min

Students will answer questions online to demonstrate what they've learned about the equals symbol.

Objectives

• Recognize that the equals symbol shows an equality between two expressions.

Tips

Show students the equals symbol on the computer keyboard.

TRY IT What Is the Equals Symbol?

OFFLINE
10 min

Students will practice identifying and using the equals symbol. Give students the What Is the Equals Symbol? activity page from their Activity Book and read the directions with them.

Objectives

• Recognize that the equals symbol shows an equality between two expressions.

Tips

Students may use counting objects to help them find each sum and determine if the two sides of each number sentence are equal or not equal.

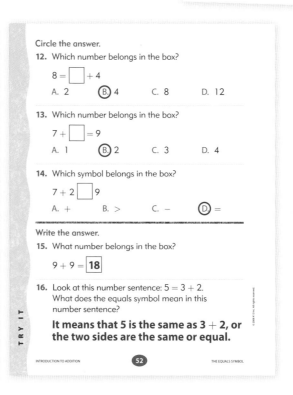

Name:

The Equals Symbol
What Is the Equals Symbol?

Say the answer.
1. What is this symbol? **the equals symbol**
$=$

2. What does $=$ mean? **The amounts on each side of the symbol are the same.**

3. What does $2 + 6 = 8$ mean? **2 plus 6 is equal to 8; 2 plus 6 equals 8; or 2 plus 6 is the same as 8.**

Write an equals symbol if the two sides are equal. Write a not-equal-to symbol if the two sides are not equal.

4. $9 \neq 3 + 5$

5. $9 + 8 = 17$

6. $9 + 1 = 10$

7. $15 = 10 + 5$

8. $14 = 7 + 7$

9. $4 + 9 \neq 15$

10. $20 \neq 13 + 6$

11. $7 + 12 = 19$

INTRODUCTION TO ADDITION   51   THE EQUALS SYMBOL

TRY IT

TRY IT

Circle the answer.
12. Which number belongs in the box?

$8 = \boxed{} + 4$

A. 2   (B.) 4   C. 8   D. 12

13. Which number belongs in the box?

$7 + \boxed{} = 9$

A. 1   (B.) 2   C. 3   D. 4

14. Which symbol belongs in the box?

$7 + 2 \boxed{} 9$

A. +   B. >   C. −   (D.) =

Write the answer.
15. What number belongs in the box?

$9 + 9 = \boxed{18}$

16. Look at this number sentence: $5 = 3 + 2$. What does the equals symbol mean in this number sentence?

It means that 5 is the same as 3 + 2, or the two sides are the same or equal.

INTRODUCTION TO ADDITION   52   THE EQUALS SYMBOL

Number Sentences: The Equals Symbol

Lesson Overview

Skills Update	5 minutes	ONLINE
GET READY Equal or Not?	5 minutes	ONLINE
LEARN Write Number Sentences	15 minutes	OFFLINE
LEARN Explore Number Sentences	15 minutes	ONLINE
TRY IT Equality and Number Sentences	5 minutes	ONLINE
TRY IT Make Number Sentences	10 minutes	OFFLINE
CHECKPOINT	5 minutes	OFFLINE

▶ Lesson Objectives

Use the equals symbol in number sentences to express equality.

▶ Prerequisite Skills

Recognize that the equals symbol shows an equality between two expressions.

▶ Common Errors and Misconceptions

Students might misinterpret the equals symbol ($=$) as a signal they should "do" something. For example, in the number sentence $5 + 3 =$ ___, students might think the equals symbol means "adds up to" or "produces." So they might view $8 = 5 + 3$ or $8 = 8$ as unacceptable or wrong because they believe the equals symbol must be followed by the answer to a problem.

▶ Advance Preparation

Number index cards 0 through 10. Label three other index cards with the following symbols: $+$, $=$, $\neq$. Or gather the number and symbol cards you created previously.

▶ Content Background

Students will use the plus symbol, the equals symbol, and numbers to write addition number sentences. They will learn that the groups of numbers on either side of the equals symbol have the same value.

Although the phrase *equals sign* is often used in everyday language, *equals symbol* is more accurate as a mathematical term. In math, *sign* refers specifically to positive signs and negative signs.

Materials to Gather

SUPPLIED

Make Number Sentences activity page

Checkpoint (printout)

ALSO NEEDED

index cards numbered 0 through 12: 2 sets

index cards: 1 card labeled $=$
1 card labeled $\neq$
2 cards labeled $+$

ONLINE
5 min

GET READY Equal or Not?

Students will practice using the equals symbol and not-equal-to symbol. They will decide which symbol to put in number sentences.

Objectives

- Recognize that the equals symbol shows an equality between two expressions.

Tips

Students can use household objects to model the number sentences if they wish.

OFFLINE
15 min

LEARN Write Number Sentences

Students will use number and symbol cards to practice reading and writing number sentences.

Gather the number and symbol cards.

1. Use the number and symbol cards to make $6 + 1$.

   Say: This expression tells us to add 6 and 1.

   Point to the numbers and symbols as you say, "6 plus 1" and "1 added to 6."

2. Ask students to tell you the sum of $6 + 1$. (7)

3. Place the equals symbol card and the 7 card to the right of $6 + 1$ to make $6 + 1 = 7$.

   Say: I put down an equals symbol and the sum, 7. This is a number sentence.

   Point to each side of the number sentence as you say, "This side is equal to this side."

4. Point to the numbers and symbols as you say, "6 plus 1 equals 7" and "1 added to 6 is the same as 7."

5. Switch the 7 and the $6 + 1$ cards. Ask students what number sentence they see now. (7 equals 6 plus 1)

6. Now remove the 7 card. Replace it with a 3, the plus symbol, and a 4 to make $6 + 1 = 3 + 4$. Point to the numbers and symbols as you say, "6 plus 1 equals 3 plus 4."

   Say: I now have an addition expression on both sides of the equals symbol. What is the sum of $6 + 1$?
   ANSWER: 7

   Ask: What is the sum of $3 + 4$?
   ANSWER: 7

   Say: The amounts are equal, so this number sentence is also true.

Objectives

- Use the equals symbol in number sentences to express equality.

Tips

Tell students they should read number sentences from left to right, just as they read their names.

7. Use the number and symbol cards to make the following incomplete number sentences. Have students place each missing number card. Then ask them to read each number sentence.

- $5 + 3 = \underline{}$ (8)
- $9 = \underline{} + 2$ (7)
- $7 + \underline{} = 1 + 9$ (3)
- $8 + 3 = 6 + \underline{}$ (5)

8. Explain that you will say some incomplete number sentences. Students should use the number and symbol cards to make and complete each number sentence.

Ask: 6 plus 2 equals what?
ANSWER: $6 + 2 = 8$

Ask: 3 added to 9 is the same as what?
ANSWER: $3 + 9 = 12$

Ask: 4 plus 4 equals 1 plus what?
ANSWER: $4 + 4 = 1 + 7$

Ask: 4 added to 6 is the same as 5 added to what?
ANSWER: $4 + 6 = 5 + 5$

Ask: 7 equals 0 plus what?
ANSWER: $7 = 0 + 7$

ONLINE
15min

LEARN Explore Number Sentences

A number sentence is like a level balance—just as the objects on each side of a balance have the same weight, the expressions on each side of the equals symbol have the same value. By putting number bars on the two sides of a balance, students will learn about equality in addition number sentences.

Objectives

- Use the equals symbol in number sentences to express equality.

ONLINE
5min

TRY IT Equality and Number Sentences

Students will answer questions online to demonstrate what they have learned about the equals symbol and addition sentences.

Objectives

- Use the equals symbol in number sentences to express equality.

TRY IT Make Number Sentences

Objectives

Students will practice using the equals and not-equal-to symbols to make true number sentences. Give students the Make Number Sentences activity page from their Activity Book and read the directions with them.

- Use the equals symbol in number sentences to express equality.

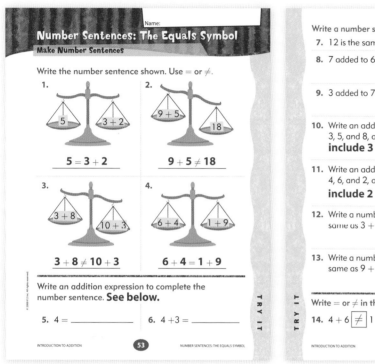

Number Sentences: The Equals Symbol

Make Number Sentences

Write the number sentence shown. Use = or ≠.

1. $5 = 3 + 2$

2. $9 + 5 \neq 18$

3. $3 + 8 \neq 10 + 3$

4. $6 + 4 = 1 + 9$

Write an addition expression to complete the number sentence. **See below.**

5. $4 = $ _____

6. $4 + 3 = $ _____

INTRODUCTION TO ADDITION   53   NUMBER SENTENCES: THE EQUALS SYMBOL

Write a number sentence for the problem.

7. 12 is the same as 4 plus 8. $\underline{12 = 4 + 8}$

8. 7 added to 6 is the same as 5 added to 8.
    $7 + 6 = 5 + 8$

9. 3 added to 7 is the same as 1 added to 9.
    $3 + 7 = 1 + 9$

10. Write an addition sentence that uses the numbers 3, 5, and 8, and the equals symbol. **Examples include 3 + 5 = 8 and 8 = 5 + 3.**

11. Write an addition sentence that uses the numbers 4, 6, and 2, and the equals symbol. **Examples include 2 + 4 = 6 and 4 + 2 = 6.**

12. Write a number sentence that shows that 7 is the same as 3 + 4.
    $7 = 3 + 4 \text{ or } 3 + 4 = 7$

13. Write a number sentence that shows that 13 is the same as 9 + 4.
    $13 = 9 + 4 \text{ or } 9 + 4 = 13$

Write = or ≠ in the box.

14. $4 + 6 \boxed{\neq} 11$ 15. $8 \boxed{=} 7 + 1$

INTRODUCTION TO ADDITION   54   NUMBER SENTENCES: THE EQUALS SYMBOL

TRY IT

Additional Answers

5. Students should write an addition expression equal to 4.
    Examples: $2 + 2, 4 + 0$

6. Students should write an addition expression equal to 7.
    Examples: $2 + 5, 6 + 1$

CHECKPOINT

Objectives

Print the Checkpoint and have students complete it on their own. Read the directions, problems, and answer choices to students if necessary. Use the answer key to score the Checkpoint, and then enter the results online.

- Use the equals symbol in number sentences to express equality.

Checkpoint   Math | Introduction to Addition | Number Sentences: The Equals Symbol

Name _____ Date _____

Checkpoint Answer Key

Read the problems and follow the instructions.

(1 point)
1. Write a number sentence that shows that 2 added to 3 is the same as 5.

$$2 + 3 = 5$$

(1 point)
2. Write a number sentence that shows that 2 + 6 is the same as 8.

$$2 + 6 = 8$$

(1 point)
3. Write a number sentence that shows that 4 + 4 is the same as 8.

$$4 + 4 = 8$$

(1 point)
4. Write a number sentence that shows that 3 is the same as 3 + 0.

$$3 = 3 + 0$$

(1 point)
5. Write = or ≠ in the box.

$$15 \boxed{=} 8 + 7$$

(1 point)
6. Write = or ≠ in the box.

$$2 + 3 \boxed{\neq} 5 + 1$$

1 of 1

Unit Review

UNIT REVIEW Look Back	20 minutes	**ONLINE**
UNIT REVIEW Checkpoint Practice	20 minutes	**OFFLINE**
⏩ **UNIT REVIEW** Prepare for the Checkpoint		

▶ Unit Objectives

This lesson reviews the following objectives:

- Use concrete objects or sketches to model and solve addition or subtraction computation problems with sums and minuends up through 30.
- Demonstrate and explain the meaning of addition as putting together or combining sets.
- Demonstrate understanding that the order in which numbers are added does not affect the sum.
- Recognize that the + symbol refers to addition.
- Correctly use the + symbol.
- Use models and math symbols to represent addition.
- Recognize that the equals symbol shows an equality between two expressions.
- Use the equals symbol in number sentences to express equality.

▶ Advance Preparation

In this lesson, students will have an opportunity to review previous activities in the Introduction to Addition unit. Look at the suggested activities in Unit Review: Prepare for the Checkpoint online and gather any needed materials.

Materials to Gather

SUPPLIED
Checkpoint Practice activity page
blocks – B (red and yellow)

Keywords

add	model (verb)
addend	not-equal-to symbol ($\neq$)
addition	number line
addition sentence	number sentence
commutative property of addition	part-part-total
equal	plus symbol ($+$)
equals symbol ($=$)	sum
equality	symbol
equivalent	ten-frame
expression	total

UNIT REVIEW Look Back

• Review unit objectives.

In this unit, students have used objects to explore the meaning of addition. Using objects, they learned that the order in which they add groups does not affect the sum. Students then represented addition more abstractly by using numbers and symbols. They learned both the plus symbol (+) and the equals symbol (=), and they wrote number sentences using these symbols. Students will review these concepts to prepare for the Unit Checkpoint.

UNIT REVIEW Checkpoint Practice

• Review unit objectives.

Students will complete a Checkpoint Practice activity page to prepare for the Unit Checkpoint. If necessary, read the directions, problems, and answer choices to students. Have students answer the problems on their own. Carefully review the answers with students.

Gather the blocks. Students will use the blocks for Problems 1–3 and 21.

Unit Review
Checkpoint Practice

Name:

Read the problem and follow the directions.
1. Model the problem with yellow and red circles. Sketch your circles. Then write the sum.

   There are 4 puppies in a basket.
   There are 6 puppies on the rug.

   How many puppies are there in all? **10**

2. Use 11 yellow circles and 3 red circles to explain addition. **See below.**

3. Use circles to show that 4 plus 9 is the same as 9 plus 4. **See below.**

4. Use the number line to show that 8 plus 4 is the same as 4 plus 8.

   4   8
   0 1 2 3 4 5 6 7 8 9 10 11 12 13 14 15 16 17 18 19 20
   8   4

INTRODUCTION TO ADDITION   55   UNIT REVIEW

5. Explain what the expression 4 + 7 means. Be sure to explain what the symbol means.
   See below.

Write an equals symbol in the box if the two sides are equal. Write a not-equal-to symbol if they are not equal.

6. $10 \boxed{=} 5 + 5$ 7. $8 + 4 \boxed{=} 12$

8. $7 + 4 \boxed{\neq} 10$ 9. $3 + 9 \boxed{\neq} 11$

Complete the number sentence. Write a number or symbol.

10. $4 = \underline{\textbf{4}}$ 11. $\underline{\textbf{11}} = 8 + 3$

12. $4 + 3 = \underline{\textbf{7}}$ 13. $3 + 4 \underline{\textbf{=}} 2 + 5$

Write a number sentence.

14. 7 added to 8 is the same as 10 added to 5. $\textbf{7 + 8 = 10 + 5}$

15. 16 is the same as 5 plus 11. $\textbf{16 = 5 + 11}$

16. 9 added to 3 is the same as 12. $\textbf{9 + 3 = 12}$

INTRODUCTION TO ADDITION   56   UNIT REVIEW

Additional Answers

2. Students should put together a group of 11 circles and a group of 3 circles and explain that the total (14) is the sum.

3. Students should add a group of 9 circles to a group of 4 circles and count a total of 13. Then they should add a group of 4 circles to a group of 9 circles and count that the total is also 13.

5. Students should say that 4 plus 7 means you put together, or add, a group of 4 and a group of 7.

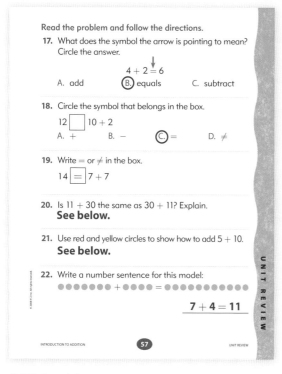

Read the problem and follow the directions.

17. What does the symbol the arrow is pointing to mean? Circle the answer.

$$4 + 2 \overset{\downarrow}{=} 6$$

A. add   B. equals   C. subtract

18. Circle the symbol that belongs in the box.

12 ☐ 10 + 2

A. +   B. −   C. =   D. ≠

19. Write = or ≠ in the box.

14 = 7 + 7

20. Is 11 + 30 the same as 30 + 11? Explain.
See below.

21. Use red and yellow circles to show how to add 5 + 10.
See below.

22. Write a number sentence for this model:

●●●●●●●● + ●●●● = ●●●●●●●●●●●●

7 + 4 = 11

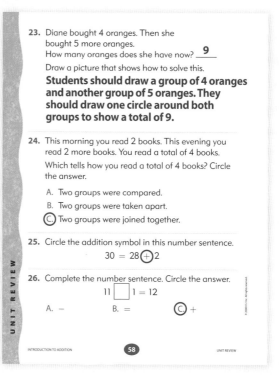

23. Diane bought 4 oranges. Then she bought 5 more oranges. How many oranges does she have now? __9__

Draw a picture that shows how to solve this.

Students should draw a group of 4 oranges and another group of 5 oranges. They should draw one circle around both groups to show a total of 9.

24. This morning you read 2 books. This evening you read 2 more books. You read a total of 4 books.

Which tells how you read a total of 4 books? Circle the answer.

A. Two groups were compared.
B. Two groups were taken apart.
C. Two groups were joined together.

25. Circle the addition symbol in this number sentence.

30 = 28 + 2

26. Complete the number sentence. Circle the answer.

11 ☐ 1 = 12

A. −   B. =   C. +

Additional Answers

20. Yes. When you add two numbers, the order in which you add does not matter.

21. Students should make a group of 5 circles and a group of 10 circles, and then combine and count them to find the total (15).

➔ UNIT REVIEW Prepare for the Checkpoint

What you do next depends on how students performed in the previous activity, Unit Review: Checkpoint Practice. If students had difficulty with any of the problems, complete the appropriate review activity listed in the table online.

Unit Checkpoint

Lesson Overview

UNIT CHECKPOINT Online	25 minutes	**ONLINE**
UNIT CHECKPOINT Offline	35 minutes	**OFFLINE**

Unit Objectives

This lesson assesses the following objectives:

- Use concrete objects or sketches to model and solve addition or subtraction computation problems with sums and minuends up through 30.
- Demonstrate and explain the meaning of addition as putting together or combining sets.
- Demonstrate understanding that the order in which numbers are added does not affect the sum.
- Recognize that the + symbol refers to addition.
- Correctly use the + symbol.
- Use models and math symbols to represent addition.
- Recognize that the equals symbol shows an equality between two expressions.
- Use the equals symbol in number sentences to express equality.

Materials to Gather

SUPPLIED

Unit Checkpoint (printout)

blocks – B (green and yellow)

blocks – O (blue and red)

UNIT CHECKPOINT Online

ONLINE 25 min

Students will complete this part of the Unit Checkpoint online. Read the directions, problems, and answer choices to students. If necessary, help students with keyboard or mouse operations.

Objectives

- Assess unit objectives.

UNIT CHECKPOINT Offline

OFFLINE 35 min

Students will complete this part of the Unit Checkpoint offline. In Part 1, students will take a performance-based assessment. In Part 2, students will complete the problems on their own. Print the Unit Checkpoint. Read the directions, problems, and answer choices to students if necessary. Use the answer key to score the Checkpoint, and then enter the results online.

Gather the blocks. Students will use the circles for Problem 3 and the cubes for Problem 4.

Objectives

- Assess unit objectives.

Name _____ Date _____

Unit Checkpoint Answer Key

Part 1

Follow the instructions for each item. Choose the response that best describes how the student performs on the task. When you have finished, enter the results online.

1. Write $7 = 5 + 2$ on paper and show it to students.
    Say, "What does the equals symbol mean in this number sentence?"
    (1 point)
    Did the student say the equals symbol means that 7 is the same as $5 + 2$, or the two sides are the same or equal?

    A. Yes   B. No

2. Give students the cubes.
    Say, "Use the cubes to show how to add $3 + 19$."
    (1 point)
    Did the student show how to add $3 + 19$ by combining 3 cubes of one color with 19 cubes of another color?

    A. Yes   B. No

3. Say, "Does it matter what order you use to put 9 and 13 together to get 22? Why or why not?"
    (1 point)
    Did the student say, "No. I can add two numbers in any order, and the sum will stay the same"?

    A. Yes   B. No

Give students Part 2 of the assessment.

Name _____ Date _____

Part 2

Write the symbol in the box to complete the number sentence.

(1 point)
4. $5 \boxed{+} 3 = 8$

(1 point)
5. $7 = 3 \boxed{+} 4$

(1 point)
6. Write a number sentence for this model:

    ⦿⦿⦿ + ⦿⦿⦿ = ⦿⦿⦿ $3 + 6 = 9$
             ⦿⦿⦿   ⦿⦿⦿
                      ⦿⦿⦿

(1 point)
7. Write a number sentence that shows that 5 added to 6 is the same as 11.

    $5 + 6 = 11$

(1 point)
8. Write a number sentence that shows that 15 is the same as $15 + 0$.

    $15 = 15 + 0$

Addition Facts with Sums Through 12

▶ Unit Objectives

- Demonstrate automatic recall of addition facts with sums through 8.
- Demonstrate understanding of the rule for adding zero.
- Demonstrate automatic recall of addition facts with sums through 12.

▶ Big Ideas

Adding any number to zero, the additive identity, results in a sum that is the given number.

▶ Unit Introduction

Students will begin by learning different ways to add numbers to make 8, and what happens when adding 0. Students will then learn the addition facts for sums through 8, and then sums through 12.

Students will use online and offline flash cards and other activities to help them develop automatic recall, and they will complete a chart to document their progress.

Facts Through 8

Lesson Overview

Skills Update	5 minutes	ONLINE
GET READY Use Symbols to Add	5 minutes	ONLINE
LEARN Ways to Make Numbers	20 minutes	OFFLINE
LEARN Practice Facts	20 minutes	OFFLINE
TRY IT Addition Facts	10 minutes	OFFLINE

▶ Lesson Objectives

- Demonstrate automatic recall of addition facts with sums through 8.
- Demonstrate understanding of the rule for adding zero.

▶ Prerequisite Skills

- Recognize that the $+$ symbol refers to addition.
- Recognize that the equals symbol shows an equality between two expressions.
- Use models and math symbols to represent addition.

▶ Content Background

Students will recall addition facts with sums through 8 including facts using 0. They will learn different ways to make numbers. For example, 3 is the same as $3 + 0$, $2 + 1$, $0 + 3$, and $1 + 2$. Learning the different ways to make numbers will make it easier for students to recall addition facts.

Keywords	
	addend – one of the two or more numbers that are added to determine a sum
	addition facts – simple addition problems that usually have addends less than or equal to 10 and sums through 20
	expression – a number or a combination of numbers and symbols that represents a given value, such as $2 + 3$ or $10 - 4 + 1$
	sum – the solution to an addition problem

Materials to Gather

SUPPLIED
blocks – B (red and green)
Addition Facts activity page

ALSO NEEDED
index cards – 25

GET READY Use Symbols to Add

ONLINE
5 min

Students will use red and yellow circles to make addition sentences.

Objectives

- Recognize that the $+$ symbol refers to addition.
- Recognize that the equals symbol shows an equality between two expressions.
- Use models and math symbols to represent addition.

LEARN Ways to Make Numbers

Students will add different numbers to make the same sum. They will also explore the results of adding zero to a number.

Gather the red and green circles and index cards.

- Demonstrate automatic recall of addition facts with sums through 8.
- Demonstrate understanding of the rule for adding zero.

1. Place 8 red circles in front of students. Write the number 8 on an index card.

   Ask: How many red circles are there?
   ANSWER: 8

   Ask: How many green circles are there?
   ANSWER: 0

2. **Say:** I am going to write number sentences to show these circles.

3. Write $8 + 0$ and $0 + 8$ on the other side of the index card.

4. Replace one of the red circles with a green circle. Ask students how many circles there are. (8) Write 8 on the back of another index card.

   Ask: What number sentence can we write for this model?
   ANSWER: $1 + 7 = 8$ or $7 + 1 = 8$

   Write $7 + 1$ on the other side of the index card. Write $1 + 7$ below it.

5. Continue trading one red circle for one green circle, stopping each time to have students make another card with the appropriate expressions. You should end up with 5 cards that can be used as flash cards. Each will have the number 8 on one side and expressions on the other side.

   - $8 + 0$ and $0 + 8$
   - $1 + 7$ and $7 + 1$
   - $2 + 6$ and $6 + 2$
   - $3 + 5$ and $5 + 3$
   - $4 + 4$

6. Repeat Steps 1–5 with the numbers 7, 6, 5, 4, 3, 2, 1, and 0. You will end up with a set of addition flash cards with the following cards:

   - sum of 8: 5 cards as listed above
   - sum of 7: $7 + 0$ and $0 + 7$; $1 + 6$ and $6 + 1$; $2 + 5$ and $5 + 2$; $3 + 4$ and $4 + 3$
   - sum of 6: $6 + 0$ and $0 + 6$; $1 + 5$ and $5 + 1$; $2 + 4$ and $4 + 2$; $3 + 3$
   - sum of 5: $0 + 5$ and $5 + 0$; $1 + 4$ and $4 + 1$; $2 + 3$ and $3 + 2$
   - sum of 4: $0 + 4$ and $4 + 0$; $1 + 3$ and $3 + 1$; $2 + 2$
   - sum of 3: $0 + 3$ and $3 + 0$; $1 + 2$ and $2 + 1$
   - sum of 2: $0 + 2$ and $2 + 0$; $1 + 1$
   - sum of 1: $0 + 1$ and $1 + 0$
   - sum of 0: $0 + 0$

   Save these cards to practice these addition facts.

LEARN Practice Facts

Objectives

- Demonstrate automatic recall of addition facts with sums through 8

Students will practice finding sums through 8 while playing a game with flash cards.

Gather the index cards with addition expressions on one side and sums on the other.

1. Remove the $0 + 0$ card. Shuffle and hand out the rest of the cards, expression side up, to the students and yourself. You should each have 12 cards.

2. Keeping the expression side up, each of you should place your top card in the space between you. Students should name the two sums and flip the cards to check. Whoever has the card with the higher sum should keep the cards and add them to the bottom of his or her pile.

3. Continue playing until one of you runs out of cards.

4. Gather the cards and shuffle them. Have students sort the cards into piles by sum, looking at the expression side of the card.

Tips

You may have students use counting objects to model what is on-screen.

TRY IT Addition Facts

Objectives

- Demonstrate automatic recall of addition facts with sums through 8.
- Demonstrate understanding of the rule for adding zero.

Students will practice solving facts through 8. Give students the Addition Facts activity page from their Activity Book and read the directions with them.

Name:

Facts Through 8
Addition Facts

Write the sum.

1. $6 + 2 =$ __8__
2. $0 + 3 =$ __3__
3. __5__ $= 4 + 1$
4. $3 + 3 =$ __6__

5. $\begin{array}{r} 1 \\ + 2 \\ \hline 3 \end{array}$
6. $\begin{array}{r} 4 \\ + 4 \\ \hline 8 \end{array}$
7. $\begin{array}{r} 6 \\ + 0 \\ \hline 6 \end{array}$
8. $\begin{array}{r} 5 \\ + 2 \\ \hline 7 \end{array}$

Write numbers in the boxes to make the number sentence true.

9. ☐ + ☐ = 7 **two numbers that add to 7**

10. ☐ + ☐ = 5 **two numbers that add to 5**

11. $\begin{array}{r} ☐ \\ + ☐ \\ \hline 6 \end{array}$ **two numbers that add to 6**

12. $\begin{array}{r} ☐ \\ + ☐ \\ \hline 4 \end{array}$ **two numbers that add to 4**

TRY IT

Say the answer.

13. What is the sum when you add zero to any number?
    Example: The sum of zero and any number is always that number.

Circle the answer.

14. $0 + 7 = ?$
    A. 70   B. 8
    Ⓒ 7   D. 17

15. $\begin{array}{r} 0 \\ + 5 \\ \hline \end{array}$
    A. 15   Ⓑ 5
    C. 6   D. 50

16. $\begin{array}{r} 2 \\ + 3 \\ \hline \end{array}$
    A. 1   B. 4
    Ⓒ 5   D. 6

17. $\begin{array}{r} 3 \\ + 4 \\ \hline \end{array}$
    Ⓐ 7   B. 6
    C. 5   D. 1

18. $\begin{array}{r} 3 \\ + 3 \\ \hline \end{array}$
    A. 0   B. 3
    C. 5   Ⓓ 6

19. $2 + 2 = ?$
    A. 0   B. 2
    C. 3   Ⓓ 4

20. $3 + 1 = ?$
    Ⓐ 4   B. 3
    C. 2   D. 1

21. $1 + 4 = ?$
    A. 3   B. 4
    Ⓒ 5   D. 6

TRY IT

Sums Through 8

Lesson Overview

Skills Update	5 minutes	ONLINE
GET READY Show Addition	5 minutes	ONLINE
LEARN Make the Number	10 minutes	ONLINE
LEARN Match the Sum	10 minutes	OFFLINE
LEARN Post the Facts	10 minutes	OFFLINE
TRY IT Number Facts	10 minutes	OFFLINE
CHECKPOINT	10 minutes	OFFLINE

▶ Lesson Objectives

- Demonstrate automatic recall of addition facts with sums through 8.
- Demonstrate understanding of the rule for adding zero.

▶ Prerequisite Skills

- Recognize that the + symbol refers to addition.
- Recognize that the equals symbol shows an equality between two expressions.
- Use models and math symbols to represent addition.

▶ Advance Preparation

Gather or prepare the index cards with sums through 8. One side should have the sums, and the other side should have expressions.

Print the Addition Facts Chart. Follow the instructions on the printout to set up the chart. Students will use the chart to keep track of the addition facts they have mastered. Find a place to display the chart so students can see their progress.

▶ Content Background

Students will work with addition facts with sums through 8. They will also demonstrate an understanding of the rule for adding zero.

Students encounter the identity property of addition while learning addition facts, although the term itself is not introduced to the students. The identity property of addition states that when you add zero to any number, the result is that same number, so $x + 0 = x$. The identity of x stays the same. This property is fundamental to the study of all mathematics.

Students will make a chart of addition facts. Although the chart is not an actual coordinate graph, having the students first move the answer horizontally and then vertically lays the foundation for locating points on the coordinate grid. Students need to be able to quickly recall the facts with sums through 8.

Materials to Gather

SUPPLIED

Addition Facts Chart (printout)

Number Facts activity page

Checkpoint (printout)

ALSO NEEDED

index cards – sums through 8

poster board – 2 sheets, standard size (22 in. by 28 in.)

sticky notes, small rectangular – (2 in. by 1.5 in.) – 22 yellow, 45 orange

tape, clear

meterstick or yardstick

Addition Facts Chart

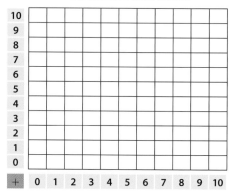

identity property of addition – a rule stating that when zero is added to a number the result is that same number
number sentence – two expressions related by an equals symbol (=), a not-equal-to symbol (≠), or an inequality symbol; for example, $7 - 2 = 4 + 1$; $5 \neq 4 + 4$; $6 + 2 > 1 + 4$

GET READY Show Addition

ONLINE 5 min

Students will practice addition facts through 12 by playing a game.

DIRECTIONS FOR USING THE BUILDING EXPRESSIONS LEARNING TOOL

1. Click Begin and choose the following:
   - Problem Type: Addition (+)
   - Problem Format: $2 + 2 = ?$

2. Click Next and choose the following:
   - Use Numbers: 0–8
   - Equals Symbol Placement: Both Ways
   - Timer Speed: Medium

3. Click Begin.

4. Have students complete the addition facts given. Continue as time allows.

Objectives

- Recognize that the + symbol refers to addition.
- Recognize that the equals symbol shows an equality between two expressions.
- Use models and math symbols to represent addition.

LEARN Make the Number

ONLINE 10 min

Students will practice finding different addition expressions that make the same sum.

DIRECTIONS FOR USING THE BUILDING EXPRESSIONS LEARNING TOOL

1. Click Begin and choose the following:
   - Problem Type: Addition (+)
   - Problem Format: $? + ? = 4$

2. Click Next and choose the following:
   - Use Numbers: 0–8
   - Equals Symbol Placement: Both Ways
   - Timer Speed: Slow

3. Click Begin.

4. Tells students that they will be making sums by choosing what numbers to add together. Encourage students to add in different orders. If they enter $4 + 1$ for a sum of 5, have them also enter $1 + 4$. Continue as time allows.

Objectives

- Demonstrate automatic recall of addition facts with sums through 8.
- Demonstrate understanding of the rule for adding zero.

LEARN Match the Sum

Objectives

- Demonstrate automatic recall of addition facts with sums through 8.
- Demonstrate understanding of the rule for adding zero.

Students will use flash card games to practice addition facts.
Gather the index cards with sums through 8.

1. Hold the cards spread in your hand, with the expressions facing the students.

2. Have students give you the sum for the expression they choose, and tell you another expression that has the same sum. For example, if they choose the card 3 + 5 and 5 + 3, they should tell you that the sum is 8, and give another expression with a sum of 8, such as 6 + 2.

3. Repeat this 5 times.

4. Next lay out an array of cards number sentence side up. Use cards with sums of 2 and above. Make sure there are at least 2 of each sum and an even number of cards with each sum. Then choose a card.

5. **Say:** Find a card with the same sum.

6. Check that students select a correct card. For example, if you choose 5 + 2, students could choose 1 + 6.

7. If students pick an incorrect card,

   Say: 5 plus 2 equals 7 (or whatever sum is on the card you picked). What is the total on your card?

8. **Say:** Now you select the first card, and I will find a fact with the same sum. Check my card, and correct me if the sums are not the same.

9. As time permits, continue choosing cards, taking turns going first. Occasionally choose an incorrect card so that students have to correct you.

LEARN Post the Facts

Objectives

- Demonstrate automatic recall of addition facts with sums through 8.
- Demonstrate understanding of the rule for adding zero.

Show students the Addition Facts Chart that you made earlier. Students will work on facts through 8.
Gather the remaining orange sticky notes.

1. **Say:** The Addition Facts Chart will help you keep track of the addition facts you know and the ones you still need to learn.

2. Explain that the sum of 2 + 3 is 5. As you say 2, move along the bottom to the 2 column, and as you say 3, move up the 2 column to the 3 row. Tell students that when they have shown you that they know 2 + 3 by saying it quickly and often, they will be able to write 5 on a sticky note and place it in the square where the row meets the column.

3. **Ask:** What is 1 + 0?

4. If students are able to quickly recall the sum, have them write the sum (1) on a sticky note and place it in the square that is 1 over and 0 up. If not, tell them that they will need to practice 1 + 0 some more, and then they can put the sum on the chart.

5. Repeat for 0 + 1.

   Say: Remember, if you know 1 + 0, you also know 0 + 1. You can add numbers in any order.

6. Have students repeat these steps for all the facts with sums through 8. Give students the facts in random order.

Addition Facts Chart

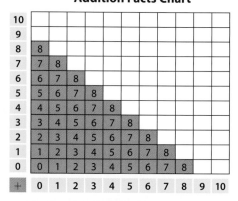

+	0	1	2	3	4	5	6	7	8	9	10
10											
9											
8	8										
7	7	8									
6	6	7	8								
5	5	6	7	8							
4	4	5	6	7	8						
3	3	4	5	6	7	8					
2	2	3	4	5	6	7	8				
1	1	2	3	4	5	6	7	8			
0	0	1	2	3	4	5	6	7	8		

Note: Save the chart. You will use it again in other lessons.

2 + 1 = 3	1 + 2 = 3	3 + 1 = 4	1 + 3 = 4
2 + 2 = 4	2 + 2 = 4	3 + 2 = 5	2 + 3 = 5
2 + 3 = 5	3 + 2 = 5	3 + 3 = 6	3 + 3 = 6
2 + 4 = 6	4 + 2 = 6	3 + 4 = 7	4 + 3 = 7
2 + 5 = 7	5 + 2 = 7	3 + 5 = 8	5 + 3 = 8
2 + 6 = 8	6 + 2 = 8		

3 + 1 = 4	1 + 3 = 4	4 + 1 = 5	1 + 4 = 5
3 + 2 = 5	2 + 3 = 5	4 + 2 = 6	2 + 4 = 6
3 + 3 = 6	3 + 3 = 6	4 + 3 = 7	3 + 4 = 7
3 + 4 = 7	4 + 3 = 7	4 + 4 = 8	4 + 4 = 8
3 + 5 = 8	5 + 3 = 8		

5 + 1 = 6	1 + 5 = 6	6 + 1 = 7	1 + 6 = 7
5 + 2 = 7	2 + 5 = 7	6 + 2 = 8	2 + 6 = 8
5 + 3 = 8	3 + 5 = 8		

7 + 1 = 8	1 + 7 = 8		

TRY IT Number Facts

OFFLINE 10min

Objectives

Students will practice finding sums through 8. They also will practice finding all the different number sentences that have the sum of 5.

Give students the Number Facts activity page from their Activity Book and read the directions with them.

- Demonstrate automatic recall of addition facts with sums through 8.
- Demonstrate understanding of the rule for adding zero.

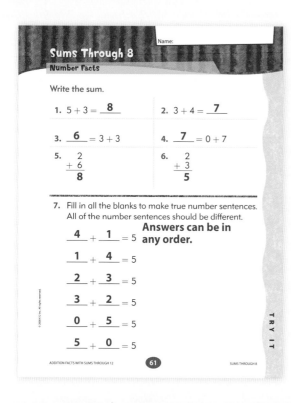

Name:

Sums Through 8
Number Facts

Write the sum.

1. $5 + 3 = \underline{\textbf{8}}$ 2. $3 + 4 = \underline{\textbf{7}}$

3. $\underline{\textbf{6}} = 3 + 3$ 4. $\underline{\textbf{7}} = 0 + 7$

5. $\begin{array}{r} 2 \\ + 6 \\ \hline \textbf{8} \end{array}$ 6. $\begin{array}{r} 2 \\ + 3 \\ \hline \textbf{5} \end{array}$

7. Fill in all the blanks to make true number sentences.
   All of the number sentences should be different.

   Answers can be in any order.

   $\underline{\textbf{4}} + \underline{\textbf{1}} = 5$

   $\underline{\textbf{1}} + \underline{\textbf{4}} = 5$

   $\underline{\textbf{2}} + \underline{\textbf{3}} = 5$

   $\underline{\textbf{3}} + \underline{\textbf{2}} = 5$

   $\underline{\textbf{0}} + \underline{\textbf{5}} = 5$

   $\underline{\textbf{5}} + \underline{\textbf{0}} = 5$

ADDITION FACTS WITH SUMS THROUGH 12   **61**   SUMS THROUGH 8

TRY IT

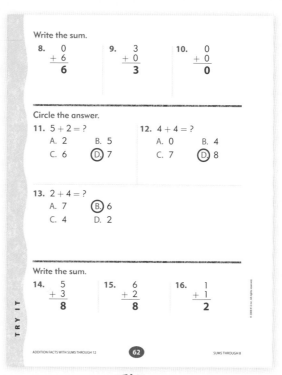

Write the sum.

8. $\begin{array}{r} 0 \\ + 6 \\ \hline \textbf{6} \end{array}$ 9. $\begin{array}{r} 3 \\ + 0 \\ \hline \textbf{3} \end{array}$ 10. $\begin{array}{r} 0 \\ + 0 \\ \hline \textbf{0} \end{array}$

Circle the answer.

11. $5 + 2 = ?$
   A. 2   B. 5
   C. 6   (D.) 7

12. $4 + 4 = ?$
   A. 0   B. 4
   C. 7   (D.) 8

13. $2 + 4 = ?$
   A. 7   (B.) 6
   C. 4   D. 2

Write the sum.

14. $\begin{array}{r} 5 \\ + 3 \\ \hline \textbf{8} \end{array}$ 15. $\begin{array}{r} 6 \\ + 2 \\ \hline \textbf{8} \end{array}$ 16. $\begin{array}{r} 1 \\ + 1 \\ \hline \textbf{2} \end{array}$

ADDITION FACTS WITH SUMS THROUGH 12   **62**   SUMS THROUGH 8

TRY IT

CHECKPOINT

OFFLINE **10** min

Objectives

Print the Checkpoint and have students complete it on their own. Read the directions, problems, and answer choices to students, if necessary. Use the answer key to score the Checkpoint, and then enter the results online.

- Demonstrate automatic recall of addition facts with sums through 8.
- Demonstrate understanding of the rule for adding zero.

✿ Checkpoint   Math | Addition Facts with Sums Through 12 | Sums Through 8

Name _____   Date _____

Checkpoint Answer Key

Write the sum.

(1 point)
1. $0 + 6 = \underline{\textbf{6}}$

(1 point)
2. $1 + 0 = \underline{\textbf{1}}$

(1 point)
3. $0 + 8 = \underline{\textbf{8}}$

(1 point)
4. $1 + 5 = \underline{\textbf{6}}$

(1 point)
5. $\begin{array}{r} 2 \\ + 4 \\ \hline \textbf{6} \end{array}$

(1 point)
6. $\begin{array}{r} 1 \\ + 3 \\ \hline \textbf{4} \end{array}$

(1 point)
7. $2 + 2 = \underline{\textbf{4}}$

(1 point)
8. $4 + 4 = \underline{\textbf{8}}$

(1 point)
9. $3 + 3 = \underline{\textbf{6}}$

Circle the answer.

(1 point)
10. $\begin{array}{r} 5 \\ + 3 \\ \hline \end{array}$
   A. 9
   (B.) 8
   C. 7
   D. 5

(1 point)
11. $\begin{array}{r} 0 \\ + 3 \\ \hline \end{array}$
   A. 0
   B. 2
   (C.) 3
   D. 4

✿ Checkpoint   Math | Addition Facts with Sums Through 12 | Sums Through 8

Name _____   Date _____

(1 point)
12. $\begin{array}{r} 1 \\ + 1 \\ \hline \end{array}$
   A. 3
   (B.) 2
   C. 1
   D. 0

(1 point)
13. $\begin{array}{r} 2 \\ + 1 \\ \hline \end{array}$
   A. 1
   B. 2
   (C.) 3
   D. 4

(1 point)
14. $\begin{array}{r} 0 \\ + 6 \\ \hline \end{array}$
   (A.) 6
   B. 4
   C. 2
   D. 0

(1 point)
15. $\begin{array}{r} 1 \\ + 6 \\ \hline \end{array}$
   A. 5
   B. 6
   (C.) 7
   D. 8

Facts Through 12

Lesson Overview

Skills Update	5 minutes	**ONLINE**
GET READY Garden Addition	5 minutes	**ONLINE**
LEARN Make Flash Cards Through 12	20 minutes	**OFFLINE**
LEARN Play with Sums	20 minutes	**OFFLINE**
TRY IT Practice Number Facts	10 minutes	**OFFLINE**

▶ Lesson Objectives

Demonstrate automatic recall of addition facts with sums through 12.

▶ Prerequisite Skills

Use models and math symbols to represent addition.

▶ Advance Preparation

Gather the completed index cards with sums through 8 from the Facts Through 8 lesson. If you do not have the index cards, refer to the Facts Through 8 lesson in the Lesson Guide for instructions on how to create them.

▶ Content Background

Students will work with addition facts for sums through 12.

Materials to Gather

SUPPLIED

blocks – O (red and green)

Practice Number Facts activity page

ALSO NEEDED

index cards – 24

index cards – sums through 8

GET READY Garden Addition

ONLINE 5 min

Students will match addition facts to models.

Objectives

- Use models and math symbols to represent addition.

Tips

Students can use cubes to model the objects online. Have them count all the cubes to find the sum.

LEARN Make Flash Cards Through 12

Objectives

- Demonstrate automatic recall of addition facts with sums through 12.

Students will show how to add different numbers to make the same sum. They will also explore the results of adding zero to a number.

Gather the cubes and blank index cards.

1. Place a train of 9 red cubes in front of students. Write the number 9 on an index card.

   Ask: How many red cubes are there?
   ANSWER: 9

   Ask: How many green cubes are there?
   ANSWER: 0

2. **Say:** I am going to write two number sentences that this model shows.

3. Write $9 + 0$ and $0 + 9$ on the other side of the index card.

4. Replace one of the red cubes with a green cube. Ask students how many cubes there are. (9) Write 9 on the back of another index card.

   Ask: What number sentence can we can write for this model?
   ANSWER: $1 + 8 = 9$ or $8 + 1 = 9$

   Write $8 + 1$ on the other side of the index card. Write $1 + 8$ below it.

5. Continue trading one red cube for one green cube, stopping each time to have students make another card with the appropriate expressions. You should end up with 5 cards that can be used as flash cards. Each will have the number 9 on one side and the expressions on the other side.

   - $9 + 0$ and $0 + 9$
   - $1 + 8$ and $8 + 1$
   - $2 + 7$ and $7 + 2$
   - $3 + 6$ and $6 + 3$
   - $4 + 5$ and $5 + 4$

6. Repeat Steps 1–5 with the numbers 10, 11, and 12. You will end up with a set of addition flash cards with the following cards:

   - sum of 9: 5 cards as listed above
   - sum of 10: $10 + 0$ and $0 + 10$; $9 + 1$ and $1 + 9$; $8 + 2$ and $2 + 8$; $7 + 3$ and $3 + 7$; $6 + 4$ and $4 + 6$; and $5 + 5$
   - sum of 11: $11 + 0$ and $0 + 11$; $10 + 1$ and $1 + 10$; $9 + 2$ and $2 + 9$; $8 + 3$ and $3 + 8$; $7 + 4$ and $4 + 7$; $6 + 5$ and $5 + 6$
   - sum of 12: $12 + 0$ and $0 + 12$; $11 + 1$ and $1 + 11$; $10 + 2$ and $2 + 10$; $9 + 3$ and $3 + 9$; $8 + 4$ and $4 + 8$; $7 + 5$ and $5 + 7$; $6 + 6$

   Save these cards to practice these addition facts.

LEARN Play with Sums

OFFLINE 20 min

Students will practice finding sums through 12 while playing a game with flash cards.

Gather the index cards with sums through 8 and sums through 12. Combine the sums through 8 cards with the sums through 12 cards.

1. Remove the 0 + 0 card. Shuffle and deal out the rest of the cards, expression side up, to the students and to yourself. You should each have 24 cards.

2. Keeping the expression side up, each of you should place your top card in the space between you. Students should name the two sums and flip the cards to check. Whoever has the card with the higher sum should keep the cards and add them to the bottom of his or her pile.

3. Continue playing until one of you runs out of cards.

4. Gather the cards and shuffle them. Have students sort the cards into piles by sum, looking at the expression side of the card.

Objectives

- Demonstrate automatic recall of addition facts with sums through 12.

TRY IT Practice Number Facts

OFFLINE 10 min

Students will practice addition facts through 12. Give students the Practice Number Facts activity page from their Activity Book and read the directions with them.

Objectives

- Demonstrate automatic recall of addition facts with sums through 12.

Facts Through 12
Practice Number Facts

Name: _____

Write the sum.

1. 9 + 1 = **10**
2. **6** = 2 + 4
3. **11** = 0 + 11
4. 5 + 2 = **7**

5. $\begin{array}{r} 2 \\ + 7 \\ \hline \mathbf{9} \end{array}$
6. $\begin{array}{r} 6 \\ + 5 \\ \hline \mathbf{11} \end{array}$
7. $\begin{array}{r} 4 \\ + 8 \\ \hline \mathbf{12} \end{array}$
8. $\begin{array}{r} 3 \\ + 6 \\ \hline \mathbf{9} \end{array}$

9. Fill in the blank to make the number sentence true.

0 + **10** = 10   6 + **4** = 10

1 + **9** = 10   7 + **3** = 10

2 + **8** = 10   8 + **2** = 10

3 + **7** = 10   9 + **1** = 10

4 + **6** = 10   10 + **0** = 10

5 + **5** = 10

ADDITION FACTS WITH SUMS THROUGH 12   **63**   FACTS THROUGH 12

TRY IT

Write the sum.

10. 5 + 6 = **11**
11. 9 + 1 = **10**

12. **12** = 7 + 5
13. 3 + 9 = **12**

Circle the answer.

14. $\begin{array}{r} 10 \\ + 0 \\ \hline \end{array}$
   A. 11   (B.) 10
   C. 9   D. 0

15. $\begin{array}{r} 6 \\ + 3 \\ \hline \end{array}$
   A. 3   B. 6
   C. 8   (D.) 9

16. $\begin{array}{r} 7 \\ + 4 \\ \hline \end{array}$
   A. 3   B. 7
   (C.) 11   D. 12

17. $\begin{array}{r} 3 \\ + 8 \\ \hline \end{array}$
   A. 12   (B.) 11
   C. 10   D. 5

18. $\begin{array}{r} 10 \\ + 2 \\ \hline \end{array}$
   A. 8   B. 10
   (C.) 12   D. 13

TRY IT

ADDITION FACTS WITH SUMS THROUGH 12   **64**   FACTS THROUGH 12

Sums Through 12

Lesson Overview

Skills Update	5 minutes	ONLINE
GET READY Bee Addition	5 minutes	ONLINE
LEARN Sort Facts	10 minutes	ONLINE
LEARN Build a Fact	15 minutes	ONLINE
LEARN Post the Facts	5 minutes	OFFLINE
TRY IT Only the Facts	10 minutes	OFFLINE
CHECKPOINT	10 minutes	OFFLINE

▶ Lesson Objectives

Demonstrate automatic recall of addition facts with sums through 12.

▶ Prerequisite Skills

Demonstrate automatic recall of addition facts with sums through 8.

▶ Advance Preparation

- Gather the Addition Facts Chart you created in the Sums Through 8 lesson. If you do not have this chart, follow the instructions in the Addition Facts Chart printout.
- Gather the completed index cards with sums through 12 from the Facts Through 12 lesson. If you do not have the index cards, refer to the Facts Through 12 lesson in the Lesson Guide for instructions on how to create them. Choose 20 cards to use for Problem 11 of the Try It: Only the Facts activity. The cards must meet the following criteria:
    1. The sums are numbers through 12.
    2. There are no more than 2 cards with 0 as an addend.
    3. There are no more than 2 cards with 1 as an addend.
    4. The other facts are randomly chosen.

▶ Content Background

Students will practice addition facts with sums through 12.

Materials to Gather

SUPPLIED
Only the Facts activity page
Checkpoint (printout)

ALSO NEEDED
index cards – sums through 12.
completed Addition Facts Chart from Sums Through 8 lesson
sticky notes, small rectangular– (2 in. by 1.5 in.) – 40 orange

---

| GET READY **Bee Addition** | ONLINE 5min | Objectives |

Students will drag sums to their corresponding addition facts. If students have trouble finding a sum, encourage them to model the fact with blocks.

- Demonstrate automatic recall of addition facts with sums through 8.

LEARN Sort Facts

Students will sort addition facts with sums from through 12 by playing a game. Because they are still learning these facts, this game will not be timed.

Objectives

- Demonstrate automatic recall of addition facts with sums through 12.

Tips

If students need help as they play the game, have them model the facts using color circles or cubes. When they see the models, they can visualize the sum. This should help them recall the facts.

LEARN Build a Fact

Students will practice addition facts with sums through 12.

DIRECTIONS FOR USING THE BUILDING EXPRESSIONS LEARNING TOOL

1. Click Begin and choose the following:
   - Problem Type: Addition (+)
   - Problem Format: $2 + 2 = ?$
2. Click Next and choose the following:
   - Use Numbers: 0–12
   - Equals Symbol Placement: Both Ways
   - Timer Speed: Slow
3. Click Begin.
4. Have students complete the addition facts given. Continue as time allows.

Objectives

- Demonstrate automatic recall of addition facts with sums through 12.

Tips

If you play the timed part of the game, be sure to give students only 2 minutes to play. Timed challenges help students increase the ability to quickly recall addition facts.

LEARN Post the Facts

Objectives

- Demonstrate automatic recall of addition facts with sums through 12.

Students will add facts through 12 to the Addition Facts Chart. Gather the sticky notes and Addition Facts Chart from the Sums Through 8 lesson. Make sure they have completed all the facts through 8. Then continue to work on all the facts through 12.

Remember to ask students the facts in a random order. If they are able to quickly recall the fact, have them write the sum on a sticky note and place it on the chart. If not, students will need more practice with finding that sum.

When students have finished placing the addition facts with sums through 12, the chart will look like the one shown.

Tips

Use tape to secure the sticky notes to the Addition Facts Chart, if necessary.

Addition Facts Chart

	0	1	2	3	4	5	6	7	8	9	10
10	10	11	12								
9	9	10	11	12							
8	8	9	10	11	12						
7	7	8	9	10	11	12					
6	6	7	8	9	10	11	12				
5	5	6	7	8	9	10	11	12			
4	4	5	6	7	8	9	10	11	12		
3	3	4	5	6	7	8	9	10	11	12	
2	2	3	4	5	6	7	8	9	10	11	12
1	1	2	3	4	5	6	7	8	9	10	11
0	0	1	2	3	4	5	6	7	8	9	10
+	0	1	2	3	4	5	6	7	8	9	10

TRY IT Only the Facts

Objectives

- Demonstrate automatic recall of addition facts with sums through 12.

Students will practice addition facts with sums through 12. Give students the Only the Facts activity page from their Activity Book and read the directions with them.

For Problem 11, use the flash cards you have set aside to give students practice with 20 addition facts. Time the students. They have 1 minute to tell you the sums to all 20 facts. Repeat as necessary until students are able to recall the sums quickly.

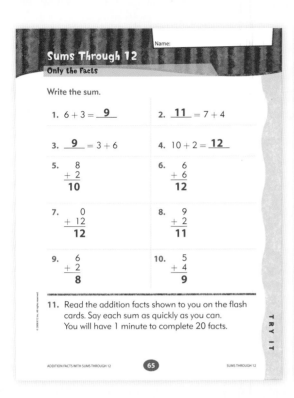

Sums Through 12
Only the Facts

Write the sum.

1. $6 + 3 =$ __9__

2. __11__ $= 7 + 4$

3. __9__ $= 3 + 6$

4. $10 + 2 =$ __12__

5.
$$\begin{array}{r} 8 \\ + 2 \\ \hline 10 \end{array}$$

6.
$$\begin{array}{r} 6 \\ + 6 \\ \hline 12 \end{array}$$

7.
$$\begin{array}{r} 0 \\ + 12 \\ \hline 12 \end{array}$$

8.
$$\begin{array}{r} 9 \\ + 2 \\ \hline 11 \end{array}$$

9.
$$\begin{array}{r} 6 \\ + 2 \\ \hline 8 \end{array}$$

10.
$$\begin{array}{r} 5 \\ + 4 \\ \hline 9 \end{array}$$

11. Read the addition facts shown to you on the flash cards. Say each sum as quickly as you can. You will have 1 minute to complete 20 facts.

TRY IT

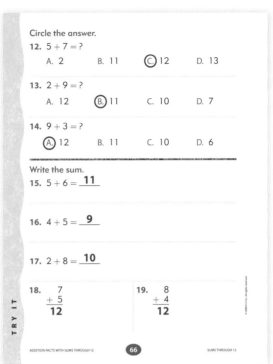

Circle the answer.

12. $5 + 7 = ?$
 A. 2   B. 11   (C.) 12   D. 13

13. $2 + 9 = ?$
 A. 12   (B.) 11   C. 10   D. 7

14. $9 + 3 = ?$
 (A.) 12   B. 11   C. 10   D. 6

Write the sum.

15. $5 + 6 =$ __11__

16. $4 + 5 =$ __9__

17. $2 + 8 =$ __10__

18.
$$\begin{array}{r} 7 \\ + 5 \\ \hline 12 \end{array}$$

19.
$$\begin{array}{r} 8 \\ + 4 \\ \hline 12 \end{array}$$

TRY IT

CHECKPOINT

OFFLINE
10 min

Objectives

Print the Checkpoint and have students complete it on their own. Read the directions, problems, and answer choices to students, if necessary. Use the answer key to score the Checkpoint, and then enter the results online.

- Demonstrate automatic recall of addition facts with sums through 12.

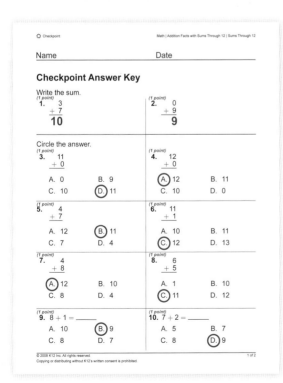

⟲ Checkpoint   Math | Addition Facts with Sums Through 12 | Sums Through 12

Name _____   Date _____

Checkpoint Answer Key

Write the sum.

(1 point)
1.
$$\begin{array}{r} 3 \\ + 7 \\ \hline 10 \end{array}$$

(1 point)
2.
$$\begin{array}{r} 0 \\ + 9 \\ \hline 9 \end{array}$$

Circle the answer.

(1 point)
3.
$$\begin{array}{r} 11 \\ + 0 \end{array}$$
 A. 0   B. 9
 C. 10   (D.) 11

(1 point)
4.
$$\begin{array}{r} 12 \\ + 0 \end{array}$$
 (A.) 12   B. 11
 C. 10   D. 0

(1 point)
5.
$$\begin{array}{r} 4 \\ + 7 \end{array}$$
 A. 12   (B.) 11
 C. 7   D. 4

(1 point)
6.
$$\begin{array}{r} 11 \\ + 1 \end{array}$$
 A. 10   B. 11
 (C.) 12   D. 13

(1 point)
7.
$$\begin{array}{r} 4 \\ + 8 \end{array}$$
 (A.) 12   B. 10
 C. 8   D. 4

(1 point)
8.
$$\begin{array}{r} 6 \\ + 5 \end{array}$$
 A. 1   B. 10
 (C.) 11   D. 12

(1 point)
9. $8 + 1 =$ _____
 A. 10   (B.) 9
 C. 8   D. 7

(1 point)
10. $7 + 2 =$ _____
 A. 5   B. 7
 C. 8   (D.) 9

1 of 2

⟲ Checkpoint   Math | Addition Facts with Sums Through 12 | Sums Through 12

Name _____   Date _____

Write the sum.

(1 point)
11. $6 + 6 =$ __12__

(1 point)
12. $5 + 5 =$ __10__

(1 point)
13. $3 + 6 =$ __9__

(1 point)
14. $4 + 6 =$ __10__

(1 point)
15. $8 + 3 =$ __11__

(1 point)
16.
$$\begin{array}{r} 9 \\ + 2 \\ \hline 11 \end{array}$$

(1 point)
17.
$$\begin{array}{r} 7 \\ + 3 \\ \hline 10 \end{array}$$

(1 point)
18.
$$\begin{array}{r} 5 \\ + 7 \\ \hline 12 \end{array}$$

(1 point)
19.
$$\begin{array}{r} 2 \\ + 7 \\ \hline 9 \end{array}$$

(1 point)
20.
$$\begin{array}{r} 8 \\ + 0 \\ \hline 8 \end{array}$$

2 of 2

Unit Review

UNIT REVIEW Look Back	20 minutes	**ONLINE**
UNIT REVIEW Checkpoint Practice	20 minutes	**OFFLINE**
⏩ **UNIT REVIEW** Prepare for the Checkpoint		

▶ Unit Objectives

This lesson reviews the following objectives:

- Demonstrate automatic recall of addition facts with sums through 8.
- Demonstrate understanding of the rule for adding zero.
- Demonstrate automatic recall of addition facts with sums through 12.

Materials to Gather

SUPPLIED

Checkpoint Practice activity page

▶ Advance Preparation

In this lesson, students will have an opportunity to review previous activities in the Addition Facts for Sums Through 12 unit. Look at the suggested activities in Unit Review: Prepare for the Checkpoint online and gather any needed materials.

Keywords

addend
addition facts
expression
identity property of addition
number sentence
sum

ONLINE
20min

UNIT REVIEW Look Back

In this unit, students have learned there are different addition facts for each sum. They have also learned that when you add zero and a number, the sum is that number. By working with addition facts with sums to 12, they have learned to recall these facts quickly without the use of models. Students will review these concepts in preparation for the Unit Checkpoint.

Objectives

- Review unit objectives.

UNIT REVIEW Checkpoint Practice

Students will complete a Checkpoint Practice activity page to prepare for the Unit Checkpoint. If necessary, read the directions, problems, and answer choices to students. Have students answer the problems on their own. Carefully review the answers with students.

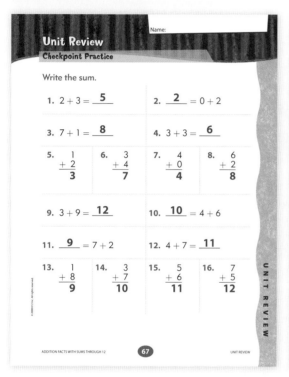

Unit Review
Checkpoint Practice

Name:

Write the sum.

1. $2 + 3 =$ __5__

2. __2__ $= 0 + 2$

3. $7 + 1 =$ __8__

4. $3 + 3 =$ __6__

5. $\begin{array}{r} 1 \\ + 2 \\ \hline 3 \end{array}$

6. $\begin{array}{r} 3 \\ + 4 \\ \hline 7 \end{array}$

7. $\begin{array}{r} 4 \\ + 0 \\ \hline 4 \end{array}$

8. $\begin{array}{r} 6 \\ + 2 \\ \hline 8 \end{array}$

9. $3 + 9 =$ __12__

10. __10__ $= 4 + 6$

11. __9__ $= 7 + 2$

12. $4 + 7 =$ __11__

13. $\begin{array}{r} 1 \\ + 8 \\ \hline 9 \end{array}$

14. $\begin{array}{r} 3 \\ + 7 \\ \hline 10 \end{array}$

15. $\begin{array}{r} 5 \\ + 6 \\ \hline 11 \end{array}$

16. $\begin{array}{r} 7 \\ + 5 \\ \hline 12 \end{array}$

Circle the answer.

17. $0 + 12 = ?$
A. 012   B. 120
C. 12   D. 13

18. $11 + 0 = ?$
A. 110   **B. 11**
C. 011   D. 12

Write the sum.

19. $3 + 5 =$ __8__

20. $5 + 7 =$ __12__

21. $4 + 3 =$ __7__

22. $6 + 3 =$ __9__

23. $\begin{array}{r} 9 \\ + 1 \\ \hline 10 \end{array}$

24. $\begin{array}{r} 3 \\ + 9 \\ \hline 12 \end{array}$

Circle the answer.

25. $\begin{array}{r} 6 \\ + 5 \end{array}$
A. 9   B. 10
C. 11   D. 12

26. $\begin{array}{r} 4 \\ + 7 \end{array}$
A. 12   **B. 11**
C. 7   D. 4

→ **UNIT REVIEW** Prepare for the Checkpoint

What you do next depends on how students performed in the previous activity, Unit Review: Checkpoint Practice. If students had difficulty with any of the problems, complete the appropriate review activity listed in the table online.

Unit Checkpoint

Lesson Overview

UNIT CHECKPOINT Offline   60 minutes   **OFFLINE**

▶ Unit Objectives

This lesson assesses the following objectives:

- Demonstrate automatic recall of addition facts with sums through 8.
- Demonstrate understanding of the rule for adding zero.
- Demonstrate automatic recall of addition facts with sums through 12.

UNIT CHECKPOINT Offline

OFFLINE
60min

Objectives

- Assess unit objectives.

Print the Checkpoint. Read the directions, questions, and answer choices to students if necessary. After students have completed both Parts 1 and 2, use the answer key to score the Checkpoint and then go to the next screen to enter the results.

Students may take a break between completing Part 1 and Part 2 (it's not necessary that they complete these parts back-to-back). Be sure to wait until students have completed Part 2 before entering the results online.

Checkpoint   Math | Addition Facts with Sums Through 12 | Unit Checkpoint

Name _____ Date _____

Unit Checkpoint Answer Key

Part 1   Each answer is worth 1 point.
Solve.

1. $\begin{array}{r} 3 \\ +3 \\ \hline 6 \end{array}$	**2.** $\begin{array}{r} 5 \\ +2 \\ \hline 7 \end{array}$	**3.** $\begin{array}{r} 4 \\ +4 \\ \hline 8 \end{array}$	**4.** $\begin{array}{r} 5 \\ +3 \\ \hline 8 \end{array}$
5. $\begin{array}{r} 4 \\ +2 \\ \hline 6 \end{array}$	**6.** $\begin{array}{r} 1 \\ +5 \\ \hline 6 \end{array}$	**7.** $\begin{array}{r} 8 \\ +0 \\ \hline 8 \end{array}$	**8.** $\begin{array}{r} 2 \\ +6 \\ \hline 8 \end{array}$
9. $\begin{array}{r} 2 \\ +2 \\ \hline 4 \end{array}$	**10.** $\begin{array}{r} 3 \\ +2 \\ \hline 5 \end{array}$	**11.** $3 + 5 = 8$ **12.** $3 + 4 = 7$	

13. $1 + 3 = 4$

14. $6 + 1 = 7$

15. $6 + 2 = 8$

16. $2 + 3 = 5$

17. $4 + 1 = 5$

18. $1 + 6 = 7$

19. $5 + 0 = 5$

20. $2 + 5 = 7$

Checkpoint   Math | Addition Facts with Sums Through 12 | Unit Checkpoint

Name _____ Date _____

Part 2   Each answer is worth 1 point.
Solve.

1. $\begin{array}{r} 8 \\ +2 \\ \hline 10 \end{array}$	**2.** $\begin{array}{r} 6 \\ +6 \\ \hline 12 \end{array}$	**3.** $\begin{array}{r} 9 \\ +2 \\ \hline 11 \end{array}$	**4.** $\begin{array}{r} 6 \\ +3 \\ \hline 9 \end{array}$
5. $\begin{array}{r} 4 \\ +8 \\ \hline 12 \end{array}$	**6.** $\begin{array}{r} 2 \\ +10 \\ \hline 12 \end{array}$	**7.** $\begin{array}{r} 1 \\ +10 \\ \hline 11 \end{array}$	**8.** $\begin{array}{r} 5 \\ +6 \\ \hline 11 \end{array}$
9. $\begin{array}{r} 7 \\ +5 \\ \hline 12 \end{array}$	**10.** $\begin{array}{r} 5 \\ +4 \\ \hline 9 \end{array}$	**11.** $5 + 5 = 10$ **12.** $3 + 8 = 11$	

13. $7 + 2 = 9$

14. $4 + 7 = 11$

15. $0 + 9 = 9$

16. $3 + 7 = 10$

17. $9 + 3 = 12$

18. $4 + 6 = 10$

19. $1 + 11 = 12$

20. $8 + 1 = 9$

Addition Facts with Sums Through 20

▶ Unit Objectives

- Demonstrate automatic recall of addition facts with sums through 16.

- Demonstrate automatic recall of addition facts with sums through 20.

▶ Big Ideas

Adding any number to zero, the additive identity, results in a sum that is the given number.

▶ Unit Introduction

Students will review addition facts with sums through 12 and learn the remaining facts through 16. Then they will continue to learn addition facts through 20. Students will use online and offline flash cards and other materials and tools to help them develop automatic recall. They will complete a chart to document their progress.

Facts Through 16

Lesson Overview

Skills Update	5 minutes	ONLINE
GET READY Hidden Picture Facts	5 minutes	ONLINE
LEARN Jar Facts	20 minutes	ONLINE
LEARN Pizza Facts	20 minutes	OFFLINE
TRY IT Know the Facts	10 minutes	OFFLINE

▶ Lesson Objectives

Demonstrate automatic recall of addition facts with sums through 16.

▶ Prerequisite Skills

Demonstrate automatic recall of addition facts with sums through 12.

▶ Content Background

Students will recall addition facts with sums through 16.

Keywords

addend – one of the two or more numbers that are added to determine a sum
addition facts – simple addition problems that usually have addends less than or equal to 10 and sums through 20

Materials to Gather

SUPPLIED
Know the Facts activity page

ALSO NEEDED
paper plates – 7
crayons
marker, permanent – black

GET READY Hidden Picture Facts

ONLINE 5 min

Students will practice addition facts with sums through 12.

Objectives

- Demonstrate automatic recall of addition facts with sums through 12.

LEARN Jar Facts

ONLINE 20 min

Students will recall addition facts with sums through 16. They will add the objects in Alexander's jar without counting them.

Objectives

- Demonstrate automatic recall of addition facts with sums through 16.

LEARN Pizza Facts

Students will make fact pizzas. They will write addition facts with a given sum on paper plates and then color the correct facts with red circles to make the plate look like a pepperoni pizza. Each pizza will have a different sum.

 Gather the paper plates, crayons, and marker.

1. Give students 4 paper plates.

2. **Say:** In the middle of one plate, use the marker to write 13. Then circle the 13. That is the pizza's sum. Every addition fact you put on this pizza must have a sum of 13.

3. Repeat with sums of 14, 15, and 16.

4. **Say:** Now write 6 facts for each sum on each pizza.

5. Check each fact and have students circle the correct facts with the red crayon. They may color the circles red to make them look like pepperoni.

6. Have students double-check any incorrect facts. Allow them to use a model such as cubes or circles if necessary. Have students revise any facts that are incorrect.

7. Now give students 3 more plates.

8. **Say:** Follow these steps to make 3 more pizzas. You can use any sums through 16.

9. Write some other facts on the completed pizzas. Make some correct and some incorrect. Have students check your facts, coloring red circles around correct facts.

Objectives

• Demonstrate automatic recall of addition facts with sums through 16.

Tips

Allow students to color the facts to represent their favorite pizza topping. For example, they may color the facts gray to represent mushrooms.

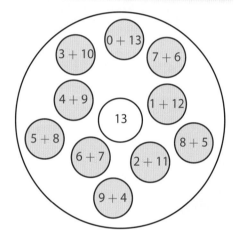

TRY IT Know the Facts

Objectives

Students will practice addition facts with sums through 16. Give students the Know the Facts activity page from their Activity Book and read the directions with them.

- Demonstrate automatic recall of addition facts with sums through 16.

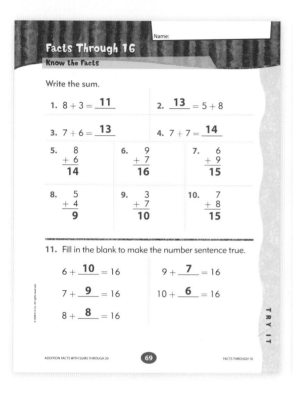

Facts Through 16

Know the Facts

Name: _____

Write the sum.

1. $8 + 3 = \underline{11}$ 2. $\underline{13} = 5 + 8$

3. $7 + 6 = \underline{13}$ 4. $7 + 7 = \underline{14}$

5. $\begin{array}{r} 8 \\ + 6 \\ \hline 14 \end{array}$ 6. $\begin{array}{r} 9 \\ + 7 \\ \hline 16 \end{array}$ 7. $\begin{array}{r} 6 \\ + 9 \\ \hline 15 \end{array}$

8. $\begin{array}{r} 5 \\ + 4 \\ \hline 9 \end{array}$ 9. $\begin{array}{r} 3 \\ + 7 \\ \hline 10 \end{array}$ 10. $\begin{array}{r} 7 \\ + 8 \\ \hline 15 \end{array}$

11. Fill in the blank to make the number sentence true.

$6 + \underline{10} = 16$ $9 + \underline{7} = 16$

$7 + \underline{9} = 16$ $10 + \underline{6} = 16$

$8 + \underline{8} = 16$

ADDITION FACTS WITH SUMS THROUGH 20   **69**   FACTS THROUGH 16

TRY IT

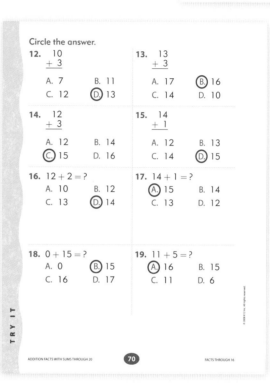

TRY IT

Circle the answer.

12. $\begin{array}{r} 10 \\ + 3 \\ \hline \end{array}$

   A. 7   B. 11
   C. 12   (D.) 13

13. $\begin{array}{r} 13 \\ + 3 \\ \hline \end{array}$

   A. 17   (B.) 16
   C. 14   D. 10

14. $\begin{array}{r} 12 \\ + 3 \\ \hline \end{array}$

   A. 12   B. 14
   (C.) 15   D. 16

15. $\begin{array}{r} 14 \\ + 1 \\ \hline \end{array}$

   A. 12   B. 13
   C. 14   (D.) 15

16. $12 + 2 = ?$
   A. 10   B. 12
   C. 13   (D.) 14

17. $14 + 1 = ?$
   (A.) 15   B. 14
   C. 13   D. 12

18. $0 + 15 = ?$
   A. 0   (B.) 15
   C. 16   D. 17

19. $11 + 5 = ?$
   (A.) 16   B. 15
   C. 11   D. 6

ADDITION FACTS WITH SUMS THROUGH 20   **70**   FACTS THROUGH 16

Sums Through 16

Lesson Overview

Skills Update	5 minutes	ONLINE
GET READY Make Facts	5 minutes	ONLINE
LEARN Fun with Facts	15 minutes	ONLINE
LEARN Target Sums	15 minutes	OFFLINE
LEARN Post the Facts	5 minutes	OFFLINE
TRY IT Fact Sums	10 minutes	OFFLINE
CHECKPOINT	5 minutes	OFFLINE

▶ Lesson Objectives
Demonstrate automatic recall of addition facts with sums through 16.

▶ Prerequisite Skills
Demonstrate automatic recall of addition facts with sums through 12.

▶ Advance Preparation
Gather the completed index cards with sums through 12 from the Facts Through 12 lesson. If you do not have the index cards, refer to the Facts Through 12 lesson in the Lesson Guide for instructions on how to create them.

Gather the Addition Facts Chart you created in the Sums Through 12 lesson. If you do not have this chart, follow the instructions in the Addition Facts Chart printout.

▶ Content Background
Students will continue working with addition facts with sums through 16.

Materials to Gather

SUPPLIED
Fact Sums activity page
Checkpoint (printout)

ALSO NEEDED
completed Addition Facts Chart from Sums Through 12 lesson
sticky notes, small rectangular– (1.5 in. by 2 in.) – 26 orange
index cards – 32
index cards – sums through 12

GET READY Make Facts

ONLINE
5 min

Students will build number sentences for given sums through 12.

DIRECTIONS FOR USING THE BUILDING EXPRESSIONS LEARNING TOOL

1. Click Begin and choose the following:
   - Problem Type: Addition ($+$)
   - Problem Format: $? + ? = 4$
2. Click Next and choose the following:
   - Use Numbers: 0–12
   - Equals Symbol Placement: Both Ways
   - Timer Speed: Slow

Objectives
- Demonstrate automatic recall of addition facts with sums through 12.

3. Click Begin.

4. Have students complete the addition facts given. Continue as time allows.

LEARN Fun with Facts

Students will match addition facts with sums through 16.

In the first activity, have students first try the game in Practice mode. Then have them click Play to compete against a timer.

Objectives

- Demonstrate automatic recall of addition facts with sums through 16.

LEARN Target Sums

Students will find the missing addend when given a target sum and one addend.

Gather the blank index cards and flash cards with addition facts with sums through 12.

1. **Say:** We are going to play a game in which you try to reach a certain sum. The first sum we want to reach is 13. I am going to give you a number. You need to tell me what number we can add to mine to make 13.

2. **Say:** My number is 8. What number can we add to 8 to make 13?
ANSWER: 5

3. Continue with the same sum, 13. Give students 2, 4, 9, and 5, and ask them to name the other number in the fact. (11, 9, 4, and 8)

4. Repeat the activity with 14 as the sum. Choose numbers from 5 through 9 to be the given number.

5. Repeat the activity with 15 as the sum. Choose numbers from 6 through 9 to be the given number.

6. Repeat the activity with 16 as the sum. Choose numbers from 7 through 9 to be the given number.

7. Use the index cards to make flash cards for addition facts with sums 13–16. One side of the card should have the sum. The other side should have pairs of addends, such as 10 + 3 and 3 + 10. You should have the following cards:

   - sum of 13: 0 + 13 and 13 + 0; 1 + 12 and 12 + 1; 2 + 11 and 11 + 2; 3 + 10 and 10 + 3; 4 + 9 and 9 + 4; 5 + 8 and 8 + 5; 6 + 7 and 7 + 6

   - sum of 14: 0 + 14 and 14 + 0; 1 + 13 and 13 + 1; 2 + 12 and 12 + 2; 3 + 11 and 11 + 3; 4 + 10 and 10 + 4; 5 + 9 and 9 + 5; 6 + 8 and 8 + 6; 7 + 7

   - sum of 15: 0 + 15 and 15 + 0; 1 + 14 and 14 + 1; 2 + 13 and 13 + 2; 3 + 12 and 12 + 3; 4 + 11 and 11 + 4; 5 + 10 and 10 + 5; 6 + 9 and 9 + 6; 7 + 8 and 8 + 7

   - sum of 16: 0 + 16 and 16 + 0; 1 + 15 and 15 + 1; 2 + 14 and 14 + 2; 3 + 13 and 13 + 3; 4 + 12 and 12 + 4; 5 + 11 and 11 + 5; 6 + 10 and 10 + 6; 7 + 9 and 9 + 7; 8 + 8

8. Use the flash cards to help students review these sums. Then combine them with the flash cards with sums through 12, and practice all sums through 16.

Objectives

- Demonstrate automatic recall of addition facts with sums through 16.

Tips

If students have difficulty finding the missing number, have them use snap cubes. For example, if the target sum is 13 and your number is 8, make a train of 8 cubes. Then have students add cubes of a different color to the 8-train until there are 13 cubes in all. Then have students count the number of cubes they added. That number is the answer.

LEARN Post the Facts

Students will add facts through 16 to the Addition Facts Chart. Gather the sticky notes and Addition Facts Chart from the Sums Through 12 lesson. Make sure they have completed all the facts through 12. Then continue to work on all the facts through 16.

Remember to ask students the facts in a random order. If they are able to quickly recall the fact, have them write the sum on a sticky note and place it on the chart. If not, students will need more practice with finding that sum.

When students are finished placing the addition facts with sums through 16, the chart will look like the one shown.

Objectives

- Demonstrate automatic recall of addition facts with sums through 16.

Tips

You can use tape to secure the sticky notes to the Addition Facts Chart, if necessary.

Addition Facts Chart

10	10	11	12	13	14	15	16				
9	9	10	11	12	13	14	15	16			
8	8	9	10	11	12	13	14	15	16		
7	7	8	9	10	11	12	13	14	15	16	
6	6	7	8	9	10	11	12	13	14	15	16
5	5	6	7	8	9	10	11	12	13	14	15
4	4	5	6	7	8	9	10	11	12	13	14
3	3	4	5	6	7	8	9	10	11	12	13
2	2	3	4	5	6	7	8	9	10	11	12
1	1	2	3	4	5	6	7	8	9	10	11
0	0	1	2	3	4	5	6	7	8	9	10
+	0	1	2	3	4	5	6	7	8	9	10

TRY IT Fact Sums

Students will practice addition facts with sums through 16. Give students the Fact Sums page from their Activity Book and read the directions with them.

Objectives

Demonstrate automatic recall of addition facts with sums through 16.

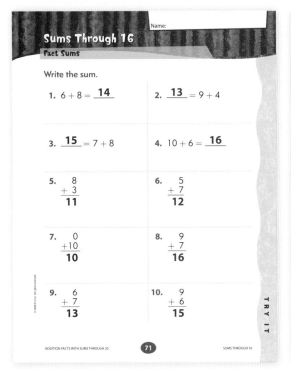

Sums Through 16

Fact Sums

Write the sum.

1. $6 + 8 =$ **14**

2. **13** $= 9 + 4$

3. **15** $= 7 + 8$

4. $10 + 6 =$ **16**

5.
```
   8
 + 3
 ---
  11
```

6.
```
   5
 + 7
 ---
  12
```

7.
```
   0
 +10
 ---
  10
```

8.
```
   9
 + 7
 ---
  16
```

9.
```
   6
 + 7
 ---
  13
```

10.
```
   9
 + 6
 ---
  15
```

Circle the answer.

11.
```
  14
 + 2
```
Ⓐ 16   B. 15
C. 14   D. 12

12.
```
  13
 + 0
```
A. 14   Ⓑ 13
C. 12   D. 11

13. $13 + 1 = ?$
A. 12   B. 13
Ⓒ 14   D. 15

14. $4 + 11 = ?$
A. 7   B. 13
C. 14   Ⓓ 15

15. $1 + 15 = ?$
A. 1   B. 15
Ⓒ 16   D. 17

Write the sum.

16.
```
   7
 + 7
 ---
  14
```

17.
```
   8
 + 8
 ---
  16
```

18. $8 + 6 =$ **14**

CHECKPOINT

Objectives

Print the Checkpoint and have students complete it on their own. Read the directions, problems, and answer choices to student if necessary. Use the answer key to score the Checkpoint, and then enter the results online.

- Demonstrate automatic recall of addition facts with sums through 16.

Name _____ Date _____

Checkpoint Answer Key

Part 1: Solve.

(1 point)
1. $9 + 4 = $ __13__

(1 point)
2. $6 + 5 = $ __11__

(1 point)
3. $\begin{array}{r} 7 \\ + 9 \\ \hline 16 \end{array}$

(1 point)
4. $\begin{array}{r} 8 \\ + 8 \\ \hline 16 \end{array}$

(1 point)
5. $\begin{array}{r} 7 \\ + 6 \\ \hline 13 \end{array}$

(1 point)
6. $\begin{array}{r} 8 \\ + 7 \\ \hline 15 \end{array}$

(1 point)
7. $\begin{array}{r} 9 \\ + 6 \\ \hline 15 \end{array}$

(1 point)
8. $\begin{array}{r} 5 \\ + 8 \\ \hline 13 \end{array}$

(1 point)
9. $\begin{array}{r} 9 \\ + 5 \\ \hline 14 \end{array}$

(1 point)
10. $\begin{array}{r} 12 \\ + 4 \\ \hline 16 \end{array}$

(1 point)
11. $12 + 1 = $ __13__

(1 point)
12. $14 + 0 = $ __14__

Name _____ Date _____

(1 point)
13. $12 + 3 = $ __15__

(1 point)
14. $10 + 4 = $ __14__

(1 point)
15. $13 + 3 = $ __16__

(1 point)
16. $10 + 5 = $ __15__

(1 point)
17. $5 + 9 = $ __14__

(1 point)
18. $0 + 16 = $ __16__

Choose the answer.

(1 point)
19. $\begin{array}{r} 11 \\ + 3 \\ \hline \end{array}$

  (A) 14
  B. 13
  C. 9
  D. 8

(1 point)
20. $\begin{array}{r} 11 \\ + 2 \\ \hline \end{array}$

  A. 9
  B. 11
  (C) 13
  D. 14

Name _____ Date _____

Part 2: Solve.

(1 point)
1. $\begin{array}{r} 9 \\ + 3 \\ \hline 12 \end{array}$

(1 point)
2. $\begin{array}{r} 2 \\ + 8 \\ \hline 10 \end{array}$

(1 point)
3. $\begin{array}{r} 6 \\ + 5 \\ \hline 11 \end{array}$

(1 point)
4. $\begin{array}{r} 11 \\ + 4 \\ \hline 15 \end{array}$

(1 point)
5. $13 + 1 = $ __14__

(1 point)
6. $15 + 0 = $ __15__

(1 point)
7. $9 + 6 = $ __15__

(1 point)
8. $8 + 8 = $ __16__

Facts Through 20

Lesson Overview

Skills Update	5 minutes	ONLINE
GET READY Practice Sums Through 16	10 minutes	ONLINE
LEARN Patterns and Facts	10 minutes	OFFLINE
LEARN Flower Facts	25 minutes	OFFLINE
TRY IT Sum It Up	10 minutes	OFFLINE

▶ Lesson Objectives

Demonstrate automatic recall of addition facts with sums through 20.

▶ Prerequisite Skills

Demonstrate automatic recall of addition facts with sums through 16.

▶ Advance Preparation

WRITE THE FOLLOWING ADDITION EXPRESSIONS ON ONE SHEET OF PAPER

- $8 + 8 =$
- $8 + 7 =$
- $7 + 7 =$
- $8 + 10 =$
- $7 + 6 =$
- $6 + 9 =$
- $4 + 9 =$
- $9 + 9 =$
- $3 + 9 =$
- $8 + 6 =$

WRITE THE FOLLOWING ADDITION EXPRESSIONS ON A SECOND SHEET OF PAPER

- $7 + 8 =$
- $8 + 6 =$
- $7 + 8 =$
- $10 + 9 =$
- $7 + 5 =$
- $4 + 9 =$
- $9 + 9 =$
- $6 + 7 =$
- $5 + 8 =$
- $7 + 10 =$

▶ Safety

Supervise students to make sure they use their scissors safely and stay seated.

▶ Content Background

Students have learned addition facts for sums through 16. In this lesson, they will build on that knowledge to learn addition facts with sums through 20. These addition facts are basic facts that use addends through 10.

Materials to Gather

SUPPLIED

blocks – B (10 red, 10 blue)

Flower Facts activity page

Sum It Up activity page

ALSO NEEDED

timer

scissors, round-end safety

glue

GET READY Practice Sums Through 16

Students will practice addition facts with sums through 16.

DIRECTIONS FOR USING THE BUILDING EXPRESSIONS LEARNING TOOL

1. Click Begin and choose the following:
   - Problem Type: Addition $(+)$
   - Problem Format: $2 + 2 = ?$
2. Click Next and choose the following:
   - Use Numbers: 0–16
   - Equals Symbol Placement: Both Ways
   - Timer Speed: Slow
3. Click Begin.
4. Have students complete the addition facts given. Continue as time allows.

Objectives

- Demonstrate automatic recall of addition facts with sums through 16.

Tips

Students can use counting objects to model the addition facts if they need help.

LEARN Patterns and Facts

Students will use patterns to solve addition facts with sums through 20. Gather the circle blocks, timer, and the addition expressions you wrote earlier.

1. **Say:** Write these addition expressions on a blank sheet of of paper: $10 + 1 =, 10 + 2 =, 10 + 3 =, 10 + 4 =.$
2. **Say:** Write each sum. If you do not know the sum, use the circles to add the numbers.
   ANSWER: 11, 12, 13, 14
3. **Ask:** What pattern do you see when you add a number to 10?
   ANSWER: The sum is 1 ten and the number I added to 10.
4. **Say:** Use this pattern to write the rest of the addition facts through $10 + 10$. Don't forget that if you know the sums of these facts, you know the sums of the facts with the addends switched. For example, if you know that $10 + 5 = 15$, you also know that $5 + 10 = 15$.
5. **Say:** You can use these 10 facts to find the sums for other problems. For example, write $9 + 9$ on your paper. You know that $10 + 9$ is 19, and 9 is one less than 10, so the sum of $9 + 9$ is one less than 19. What is the sum of $9 + 9$?
   ANSWER: 18
6. Repeat Step 5 with $8 + 9$. (17)
7. **Say:** Now let's see how fast you can write these addition sums.

Objectives

- Demonstrate automatic recall of addition facts with sums through 20.

8. Time students as they complete the addition facts that you wrote on the first sheet of paper. Have them use 10 facts, facts they know, or other strategies to find each sum.

- $8 + 8 =$ (16)
- $6 + 9 =$ (15)
- $8 + 7 =$ (15)
- $4 + 9 =$ (13)
- $7 + 7 =$ (14)

- $9 + 9 =$ (18)
- $8 + 10 =$ (18)
- $3 + 9 =$ (12)
- $7 + 6 =$ (13)
- $8 + 6 =$ (14)

9. Now time students as they complete the addition facts that you wrote on the second sheet of paper. Challenge them to try to improve their time from the previous addition facts set.

- $7 + 8 =$ (15)
- $4 + 9 =$ (13)
- $8 + 6 =$ (14)
- $9 + 9 =$ (18)
- $7 + 8 =$ (15)

- $6 + 7 =$ (13)
- $10 + 9 =$ (19)
- $5 + 8 =$ (13)
- $7 + 5 =$ (12)
- $7 + 10 =$ (17)

OFFLINE
25 min

LEARN Flower Facts

Students will make fact flowers for addition facts with sums through 20. Gather the timer, scissors, glue, and Flower Facts activity page.

1. Show students the activity page. Explain that each flower has a target sum on it. Each leaf and petal has an addition expression with one of these sums.

2. Have students cut out the petals and leaves, and put them together in a stack.

   Say: I am going to give you 1 minute to sort the expressions into piles with the same sum.

3. Start the timer, and give students 1 minute to sort. If students are unable to complete the task in a minute, discuss different strategies that they can use to find each sum. For example, they could use facts they know.

4. **Say:** Now group the leaves and petals with the same sum.

   Have students glue the leaves and petals to the flowers to make fact flowers.

5. **Say:** Now I am going to set the timer again. I am going to give you 1 minute for each flower. Think of as many other addition expressions with that same sum as you can. Write the addition expressions on your flower.

Objectives

- Demonstrate automatic recall of addition facts with sums through 20.

Tips

Be sure students group the correct leaves and petals for the sum on the flower. Remind them that all the expressions listed on the leaves and petals are a way to express the sum on the flower.

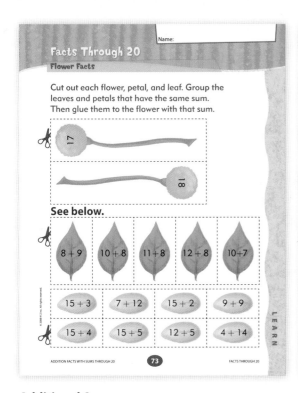

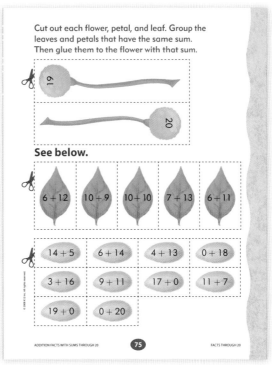

Additional Answers

17 flower: leaves: $8 + 9, 10 + 7, 6 + 11$; petals: $15 + 2, 12 + 5, 4 + 13, 17 + 0$

18 flower: leaves: $10 + 8, 6 + 12$; petals: $15 + 3, 9 + 9, 4 + 14, 0 + 18, 11 + 7$

19 flower: leaves: $11 + 8, 10 + 9$; petals: $7 + 12, 15 + 4, 14 + 5, 3 + 16, 19 + 0$

20 flower: leaves: $12 + 8, 10 + 10, 7 + 13$; petals: $15 + 5, 6 + 14, 9 + 11, 0 + 20$

OFFLINE

10min

Students will practice addition facts with sums through 20. Give students the Sum It Up activity page from their Activity Book and read the directions with them.

- Demonstrate automatic recall of addition facts with sums through 20.

Name:

Facts Through 20

Sum It Up

Write the sum.

1. $10 + 8 = \underline{18}$

2. $\underline{13} = 5 + 8$

3. $\underline{8} = 7 + 1$

4. $10 + 10 = \underline{20}$

5. $10 + 9 = \underline{19}$

6. $7 + 10 = \underline{17}$

7. $\begin{array}{r} 6 \\ + 7 \\ \hline 13 \end{array}$

8. $\begin{array}{r} 9 \\ + 8 \\ \hline 17 \end{array}$

9. $\begin{array}{r} 8 \\ + 0 \\ \hline 8 \end{array}$

10. $\begin{array}{r} 9 \\ + 9 \\ \hline 18 \end{array}$

TRY IT

---

11. $\begin{array}{r} 4 \\ + 4 \\ \hline 8 \end{array}$

12. $\begin{array}{r} 7 \\ + 6 \\ \hline 13 \end{array}$

13. $\begin{array}{r} 10 \\ + 7 \\ \hline 17 \end{array}$

14. $\begin{array}{r} 8 \\ + 9 \\ \hline 17 \end{array}$

15. $9 + 8 = \underline{17}$

16. $10 + 6 = \underline{16}$

17. $3 + 6 = \underline{9}$

18. $10 + 8 = \underline{18}$

19. $4 + 9 = \underline{13}$

20. $8 + 8 = \underline{16}$

TRY IT

Sums Through 20

Skills Update	5 minutes	ONLINE
GET READY Create Facts	5 minutes	ONLINE
LEARN Number Line Facts	10 minutes	ONLINE
LEARN Flash Card Facts	10 minutes	OFFLINE
LEARN Post the Facts	10 minutes	OFFLINE
TRY IT All Sums	10 minutes	OFFLINE
CHECKPOINT	10 minutes	OFFLINE

▶ Lesson Objectives
Demonstrate automatic recall of addition facts with sums through 20.

▶ Prerequisite Skills
Demonstrate automatic recall of addition facts with sums through 16.

▶ Advance Preparation
Gather the completed index cards with sums through 16 from the Sums Through 16 lesson. If you do not have the index cards, refer to the Sums Through 16 lesson in the Lesson Guide for instructions on how to create them.

Use the blank index cards to make flash cards for addition facts with sums 17–20. One side of the card should have the sum. The other side should have pairs of addends, such as $16 + 1$ and $1 + 16$. You should have the following cards:

- sum of 17: $17 + 0$ and $0 + 17$; $16 + 1$ and $1 + 16$; $15 + 2$ and $2 + 15$; $14 + 3$ and $3 + 14$; $13 + 4$ and $4 + 13$; $12 + 5$ and $5 + 12$; $11 + 6$ and $6 + 11$; $10 + 7$ and $7 + 10$; $9 + 8$ and $8 + 9$
- sum of 18: $18 + 0$ and $0 + 18$; $17 + 1$ and $1 + 17$; $16 + 2$ and $2 + 16$; $15 + 3$ and $3 + 15$; $14 + 4$ and $4 + 14$; $13 + 5$ and $5 + 13$; $12 + 6$ and $6 + 12$; $11 + 7$ and $7 + 11$; $10 + 8$ and $8 + 10$; $9 + 9$
- sum of 19: $19 + 0$ and $0 + 19$; $18 + 1$ and $1 + 18$; $17 + 2$ and $2 + 17$; $16 + 3$ and $3 + 16$; $15 + 4$ and $4 + 15$; $14 + 5$ and $5 + 14$; $13 + 6$ and $6 + 13$; $12 + 7$ and $7 + 12$; $11 + 8$ and $8 + 11$; $10 + 9$ and $9 + 10$
- sum of 20: $20 + 0$ and $0 + 20$; $19 + 1$ and $1 + 19$; $18 + 2$ and $2 + 18$; $17 + 3$ and $3 + 17$; $16 + 4$ and $4 + 16$; $15 + 5$ and $5 + 15$; $14 + 6$ and $6 + 14$; $13 + 7$ and $7 + 13$; $12 + 8$ and $8 + 12$; $11 + 9$ and $9 + 11$; $10 + 10$

Gather the Addition Facts Chart you created in the Sums Through 16 lesson. If you do not have this chart, follow the instructions in the Addition Facts Chart printout.

▶ Content Background
Students will continue to practice addition facts with sums through 20.

Materials to Gather

SUPPLIED
All Sums activity page
Checkpoint (printout)

ALSO NEEDED
index cards – sums through 16
index cards – 40
completed Addition Facts Chart from Sums Through 16 lesson
sticky notes, small rectangular – (1.5 in. by 2 in.) – 10 orange

GET READY Create Facts

ONLINE 5 min

Objectives

- Use models to represent numbers (to 1,000).
- Use expanded forms.

Students will drag number magnets to create sums of 12.

LEARN Number Line Facts

ONLINE 10 min

Objectives

- Demonstrate automatic recall of addition facts with sums through 20.

Students will use a online number line to practice addition facts with sums through 20.

DIRECTIONS FOR USING THE NUMBER LINE LEARNING TOOL

1. Click Count and choose the following:
   - Start Number Line at: 0
   - End Number Line at: 20
   - Count by: 1s

   Click OK.

2. Click + and choose the following:
   - Sums Through: 20

   Click OK.

   An addition number sentence will be shown, such as $1 + 3 = ?$.

3. Have students click the first addend (1) on the number line. Then have them add the second addend (3) and click the answer (4) on the number line.

4. Click New Problem to continue. Continue as time allows.

Tips

Discuss with students any patterns they see in addition facts. Patterns will help students remember the facts more easily.

LEARN Flash Card Facts

OFFLINE 10 min

Objectives

- Demonstrate automatic recall of addition facts with sums through 20.

Students will use flash cards to practice addition facts with sums through 20. Gather the flash cards with sums through 20.

1. **Say:** You are going to practice addition facts with sums through 20. Say the sum as quickly as you can as I show you a card. Try to complete as many cards as you can in 3 minutes.

2. Keep track of the facts that students know and those they do not know by making a stack of cards they answer incorrectly or hesitantly.

3. Take the stack you made of facts the student had difficulty with, and show the student these facts again for additional practice.

LEARN Post the Facts

Students will add facts through 20 to the Addition Facts Chart. Gather the sticky notes and Addition Facts Chart from the Sums Through 16 lesson. Continue to work on all the facts through 20.

Remember to ask students the facts in a random order. If they are able to quickly recall the fact, have them write the sum on a sticky note and place it on the chart. If not, students will need more practice with finding that sum.

When students are finished placing the facts with sums through 20, the chart will look like the one shown.

Objectives

- Demonstrate automatic recall of addition facts with sums through 20.

Addition Facts Chart

10	10	11	12	13	14	15	16	17	18	19	20
9	9	10	11	12	13	14	15	16	17	18	19
8	8	9	10	11	12	13	14	15	16	17	18
7	7	8	9	10	11	12	13	14	15	16	17
6	6	7	8	9	10	11	12	13	14	15	16
5	5	6	7	8	9	10	11	12	13	14	15
4	4	5	6	7	8	9	10	11	12	13	14
3	3	4	5	6	7	8	9	10	11	12	13
2	2	3	4	5	6	7	8	9	10	11	12
1	1	2	3	4	5	6	7	8	9	10	11
0	0	1	2	3	4	5	6	7	8	9	10
+	0	1	2	3	4	5	6	7	8	9	10

TRY IT All Sums

Students will practice addition facts with sums through 20. Give students the All Sums activity page from their Activity Book and read the directions with them.

Objectives

- Demonstrate automatic recall of addition facts with sums through 20.

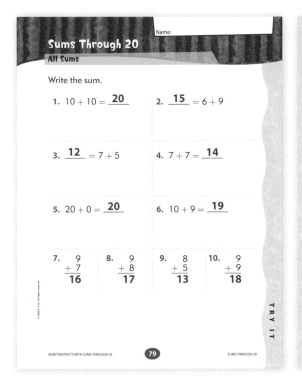

Name: _____

Sums Through 20

All Sums

Write the sum.

1. $10 + 10 =$ **20**

2. **15** $= 6 + 9$

3. **12** $= 7 + 5$

4. $7 + 7 =$ **14**

5. $20 + 0 =$ **20**

6. $10 + 9 =$ **19**

7. $\begin{array}{r} 9 \\ + 7 \\ \hline 16 \end{array}$

8. $\begin{array}{r} 9 \\ + 8 \\ \hline 17 \end{array}$

9. $\begin{array}{r} 8 \\ + 5 \\ \hline 13 \end{array}$

10. $\begin{array}{r} 9 \\ + 9 \\ \hline 18 \end{array}$

ADDITION FACTS WITH SUMS THROUGH 20   **79**   SUMS THROUGH 20

TRY IT

Circle the answer.

11. $5 + 10 =$?

   A. 5   B. 14
   (C.) 15   D. 16

12. $9 + 6 =$?

   (A.) 15   B. 16
   C. 14   D. 13

13. $10 + 7 =$?

   A. 8   B. 12
   C. 15   (D.) 17

14. $7 + 0 =$?

   A. 8   (B.) 7
   C. 6   D. 0

Write the sum.

15. $\begin{array}{r} 10 \\ + 6 \\ \hline 16 \end{array}$

16. $\begin{array}{r} 9 \\ + 5 \\ \hline 14 \end{array}$

17. $\begin{array}{r} 8 \\ + 5 \\ \hline 13 \end{array}$

18. $\begin{array}{r} 5 \\ + 5 \\ \hline 10 \end{array}$

TRY IT

ADDITION FACTS WITH SUMS THROUGH 20   **80**   SUMS THROUGH 20

CHECKPOINT

Objectives

- Demonstrate automatic recall of addition facts with sums through 20.

Print the Checkpoint and have students complete it on their own. Read the directions, problems, and answer choices to students if necessary. Use the answer key to score the Checkpoint, and then enter the results online.

Name   Date

Checkpoint Answer Key

Part 1: Solve.

(1 point)
1. $8 + 0 = 8$

(1 point)
2. $10 + 2 = 12$

(1 point)
3. $10 + 9 = 19$

(1 point)
4. $7 + 8 = 15$

(1 point)
5. $9 + 9 = 18$

(1 point)
6. $6 + 5 = 11$

(1 point)
7. $8 + 9 = 17$

(1 point)
8. $9 + 6 = 15$

(1 point)
9. $3 + 10 = 13$

(1 point)
10. $7 + 4 = 11$

(1 point)
11. $9 + 7 = 16$

(1 point)
12. $10 + 5 = 15$

(1 point)
13. $7 + 3 = 10$

(1 point)
14. $8 + 8 = 16$

(1 point)
15. $4 + 9 = 13$

(1 point)
16. $6 + 8 = 14$

(1 point)
17. $7 + 3 =$ **10**

(1 point)
18. $5 + 8 =$ **13**

(1 point)
19. $7 + 6 =$ **13**

(1 point)
20. $10 + 10 =$ **20**

Name   Date

Part 2: Solve.

(1 point)
21. $10 + 9 =$ **19**

(1 point)
22. $7 + 9 =$ **16**

(1 point)
23. $9 + 9 = 18$

(1 point)
24. $10 + 0 = 10$

(1 point)
25. $7 + 2 = 9$

Circle the answer.

(1 point)
26. $6 + 8 =$ _____
   A. 12   (B.) 14
   C. 16   D. 18

(1 point)
27. $3 + 7 =$ _____
   (A.) 10   B. 11
   C. 9   D. 8

(1 point)
28. $8 + 7 =$ _____
   A. 14   (B.) 15
   C. 16   D. 17

(1 point)
29. $8 + 1 =$ _____
   A. 18   (B.) 9
   C. 19   D. 10

(1 point)
30. $4 + 6 =$ _____
   A. 12   B. 11   (C.) 10   D. 9

(1 point)
Solve.

31. $6 + 9 = 15$

(1 point)
32. $7 + 2 = 9$

Unit Review

Lesson Overview

UNIT REVIEW Look Back	20 minutes	ONLINE
UNIT REVIEW Checkpoint Practice	20 minutes	OFFLINE
▶ **UNIT REVIEW** Prepare for the Checkpoint		

▶ Unit Objectives

- Demonstrate automatic recall of addition facts with sums through 16.
- Demonstrate automatic recall of addition facts with sums through 20.

▶ Advance Preparation

In this lesson, students will have an opportunity to review previous activities in the Addition Facts with Sums Through 20 unit. Look at the suggested activities in Unit Review: Prepare for the Checkpoint online and gather any needed materials.

Materials to Gather

SUPPLIED
Checkpoint Practice activity page

Keywords

addend	number sentence
addition facts	pattern
expression	sum

UNIT REVIEW Look Back

ONLINE 20min

Students have learned to quickly recall addition facts with sums through 20 without the use of models. They will review these facts in preparation for the Unit Checkpoint.

Objectives

- Review unit objectives.

UNIT REVIEW Checkpoint Practice

OFFLINE 20min

Students will complete a Checkpoint Practice activity page to prepare for the Unit Checkpoint. If necessary, read the directions, problems, and answer choices to students. Have students answer the problems on their own. Carefully review the answers with students.

Problems 1–20 are timed. Students will have 3 minutes and 30 seconds to find 20 sums. Problems 1–36 are untimed.

Objectives

- Review unit objectives.

Unit Review
Checkpoint Practice

Problems 1–20 are timed. You will have 3 minutes and 30 seconds to complete this section. Write the sum.

1. $\begin{array}{r} 8 \\ +6 \\ \hline 14 \end{array}$ 2. $\begin{array}{r} 9 \\ +6 \\ \hline 15 \end{array}$ 3. $\begin{array}{r} 3 \\ +0 \\ \hline 3 \end{array}$ 4. $\begin{array}{r} 8 \\ +4 \\ \hline 12 \end{array}$ 5. $\begin{array}{r} 8 \\ +2 \\ \hline 10 \end{array}$

6. $5 + 7 = \underline{12}$ 7. $5 + 3 = \underline{8}$

8. $0 + 4 = \underline{4}$ 9. $9 + 0 = \underline{9}$

10. $6 + 4 = \underline{10}$ 11. $9 + 1 = \underline{10}$

12. $10 + 0 = \underline{10}$ 13. $7 + 2 = \underline{9}$

14. $6 + 8 = \underline{14}$ 15. $3 + 5 = \underline{8}$

16. $\begin{array}{r} 10 \\ +4 \\ \hline 14 \end{array}$ 17. $\begin{array}{r} 9 \\ +7 \\ \hline 16 \end{array}$ 18. $\begin{array}{r} 8 \\ +7 \\ \hline 15 \end{array}$ 19. $\begin{array}{r} 9 \\ +9 \\ \hline 18 \end{array}$ 20. $\begin{array}{r} 8 \\ +0 \\ \hline 8 \end{array}$

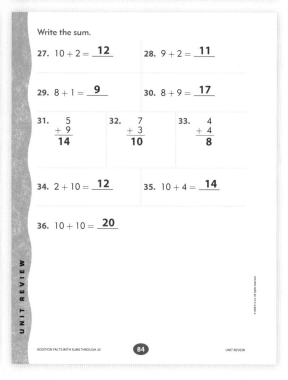

This section is untimed. Write the sum.

1. $7 + 9 = \underline{16}$ 2. $\underline{9} = 6 + 3$

3. $\underline{10} = 9 + 1$ 4. $5 + 5 = \underline{10}$

5. $\begin{array}{r} 6 \\ +5 \\ \hline 11 \end{array}$ 6. $\begin{array}{r} 7 \\ +7 \\ \hline 14 \end{array}$

7. $\begin{array}{r} 3 \\ +8 \\ \hline 11 \end{array}$ 8. $\begin{array}{r} 8 \\ +6 \\ \hline 14 \end{array}$

9. $4 + 8 = \underline{12}$ 10. $\underline{20} = 10 + 10$

11. $\underline{12} = 9 + 3$ 12. $7 + 8 = \underline{15}$

13. $\begin{array}{r} 6 \\ +9 \\ \hline 15 \end{array}$ 14. $\begin{array}{r} 8 \\ +8 \\ \hline 16 \end{array}$

15. $\begin{array}{r} 9 \\ +8 \\ \hline 17 \end{array}$ 16. $\begin{array}{r} 9 \\ +9 \\ \hline 18 \end{array}$

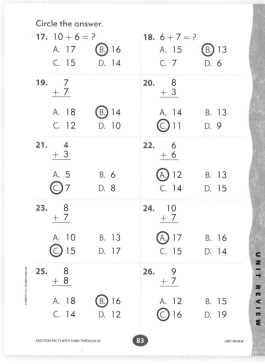

Circle the answer.

17. $10 + 6 = ?$
   A. 17   **(B.) 16**
   C. 15   D. 14

18. $6 + 7 = ?$
   A. 15   **(B.) 13**
   C. 7   D. 6

19. $\begin{array}{r} 7 \\ +7 \end{array}$
   A. 18   **(B.) 14**
   C. 12   D. 10

20. $\begin{array}{r} 8 \\ +3 \end{array}$
   A. 14   B. 13
   (C.) 11   D. 9

21. $\begin{array}{r} 4 \\ +3 \end{array}$
   A. 5   B. 6
   (C.) 7   D. 8

22. $\begin{array}{r} 6 \\ +6 \end{array}$
   (A.) 12   B. 13
   C. 14   D. 15

23. $\begin{array}{r} 8 \\ +7 \end{array}$
   A. 10   B. 13
   (C.) 15   D. 17

24. $\begin{array}{r} 10 \\ +7 \end{array}$
   (A.) 17   B. 16
   C. 15   D. 14

25. $\begin{array}{r} 8 \\ +8 \end{array}$
   A. 18   **(B.) 16**
   C. 14   D. 12

26. $\begin{array}{r} 9 \\ +7 \end{array}$
   A. 12   B. 15
   (C.) 16   D. 19

Write the sum.

27. $10 + 2 = \underline{12}$ 28. $9 + 2 = \underline{11}$

29. $8 + 1 = \underline{9}$ 30. $8 + 9 = \underline{17}$

31. $\begin{array}{r} 5 \\ +9 \\ \hline 14 \end{array}$ 32. $\begin{array}{r} 7 \\ +3 \\ \hline 10 \end{array}$ 33. $\begin{array}{r} 4 \\ +4 \\ \hline 8 \end{array}$

34. $2 + 10 = \underline{12}$ 35. $10 + 4 = \underline{14}$

36. $10 + 10 = \underline{20}$

→ UNIT REVIEW Prepare for the Checkpoint

What you do next depends on how students performed in the previous activity, Unit Review: Checkpoint Practice. If students had difficulty with any of the problems, complete the appropriate review activity listed in the table online.

Unit Checkpoint

UNIT CHECKPOINT Offline	60 minutes	**OFFLINE**

▶ Unit Objectives

This lesson assesses the following objectives:

- Demonstrate automatic recall of addition facts with sums through 16.
- Demonstrate automatic recall of addition facts with sums through 20.

Materials to Gather

SUPPLIED

Unit Checkpoint (printout)

UNIT CHECKPOINT Offline

Objectives

- Assess unit objectives.

Print the Checkpoint. Read the directions, questions, and answer choices to students if necessary. After students have completed both Parts 1 and 2, use the answer key to score the Checkpoint, and then to to the next screen to enter the results.

Students may take a break between completing Part 1 and Part 2. (It's not necessary that they complete these parts back-to-back.) Be sure to wait until students have completed Part 2 before entering the results online.

○ Checkpoint   Math | Addition Facts with Sums Through 20 | Unit Checkpoint

Name _____   Date _____

Unit Checkpoint Answer Key

Part 1
Solve.   **Each answer is worth 1 point.**

1. 4 + 1 = **5**
2. 7 + 0 = **7**
3. 1 + 3 = **4**
4. 4 + 6 = **10**
5. 3 + 4 = **7**
6. 3 + 5 = **8**
7. 4 + 7 = **11**
8. 10 + 2 = **12**
9. 3 + 3 = **6**
10. 7 + 2 = **9**
11. 3 + 2 = **5**
12. 5 + 4 = **9**
13. 2 + 5 = **7**
14. 10 + 0 = **10**
15. 3 + 6 = **9**
16. **11** = 6 + 5
17. 2 + 6 = **8**
18. 5 + 3 = **8**
19. **4** = 2 + 2
20. **12** = 8 + 4

○ Checkpoint   Math | Addition Facts with Sums Through 20 | Unit Checkpoint

Name _____   Date _____

Part 2
Solve.   **Each answer is worth 1 point.**

1. 6 + 7 = **13**
2. 5 + 9 = **14**
3. 7 + 8 = **15**
4. 7 + 9 = **16**
5. 4 + 9 = **13**
6. 9 + 8 = **17**
7. 9 + 9 = **18**
8. 7 + 7 = **14**
9. 9 + 6 = **15**
10. 10 + 9 = **19**
11. 9 + 7 = **16**
12. 10 + 10 = **20**
13. 8 + 8 = **16**
14. **19** = 9 + 10
15. **16** = 10 + 6
16. 10 + 8 = **18**
17. 8 + 9 = **17**
18. **13** = 5 + 8
19. 6 + 8 = **14**
20. 9 + 4 = **13**

Addition Strategies

Look at all the ways I can add numbers.

$$5 + (6 + 4) = 15$$

$$(5 + 6) + 4 = 15$$

$$(2 + 7) + 7 = 16$$

$$2 + (7 + 7) = 16$$

▶ Unit Objectives

- Identify one more than or one less than a given number.
- Identify 10 more than or 10 less than a given number.
- Use "counting on" to solve addition problems.
- Use "counting on from the greatest number" to solve addition problems.
- Combine memorized facts with counting strategies to solve addition problems.
- Given a number of objects up through 20, show how those objects can be grouped and regrouped to illustrate the associative property.
- Find the sum of three one-digit numbers, with sums through 20.

▶ Big Ideas

- Counting principles and numbers can be used to solve addition and subtraction problems.
- The commutative and associative properties can be used to simplify expressions.

▶ Unit Introduction

Students will begin by learning to find one more than and 10 more than another number. They will learn this concept using hundred charts and number lines—eventually they should be able to find one more or 10 more without using these tools.

Next students will learn how to add two numbers by counting on. Students will use blocks and number lines as they practice this skill. They will learn that counting on from the greater addend is easier than counting on from the lesser addend.

Students will be introduced to the associative property, learning that they can group three numbers in different ways to make it easier to find their sum.

Finally, students will use the various addition strategies they will have learned— counting on, using doubles, using memorized facts and similar facts, and grouping to solve addition problems with sums through 30.

One More, 10 More

Lesson Overview

Skills Update	5 minutes	ONLINE
GET READY Use a Hundred Chart	5 minutes	ONLINE
LEARN 10 More on a Hundred Chart	15 minutes	ONLINE
LEARN One More on a Number Line	15 minutes	OFFLINE
TRY IT One More and 10 More	10 minutes	OFFLINE
CHECKPOINT	10 minutes	OFFLINE

▶ Lesson Objectives

- Identify one more than or one less than a given number.
- Identify 10 more than or 10 less than a given number.

▶ Prerequisite Skills

- Count aloud whole numbers through 100.
- Count by 10s through 100.

▶ Advance Preparation

Print the Number Line 0–100. Cut out the number lines and tape them together to form one number line from 0 to 100.

▶ Content Background

Students will learn how to find one more and 10 more than a given number. They will use a number line and hundred chart to learn this concept. As students practice finding one more and 10 more, they should begin to see patterns, which will eventually lead them being able to find one more and 10 more without the assistance of tools.

Materials to Gather

SUPPLIED

One More on a Number Line activity page

One More and 10 More activity page

Number Line – 0–100 (printout)

Checkpoint (printout)

Keywords

column – a list of numbers or group of objects arranged in a vertical format

hundred chart – a 10-by-10 grid displaying the numbers from 1 to 100 in order from left to right

number line – a line consisting of points equally spaced, each of which corresponds to a unique number

pattern – a sequence of objects and/or numbers with attributes that are repeated in a predictable way

row – a list of numbers or group of objects arranged in a horizontal format

GET READY Use a Hundred Chart

Students will use an online hundred chart to count by ones and tens.

DIRECTIONS FOR USING THE HUNDRED CHART LEARNING TOOL

1. Turn off the audio by clicking the ON/OFF button.
2. Have students choose a tool and count by ones through 100 on the chart. Students should click each number as they count it. If students say a number incorrectly, have them listen to the audio for that number.
3. **Say:** Point to the 10s on the chart.
   Students should point to the numbers in the right column.
4. Have students choose a new tool and count by 10s through 100 on the chart. Students should click each number as they count it. Emphasize to students that they should look down the column to find the next 10.

Objectives

- Count aloud whole numbers through 100.
- Count by 10s through 100.

Tips

You may want to review the terms *row* and *column* with students.

LEARN 10 More on a Hundred Chart

Students will use an online hundred chart and number patterns to find a number that is 10 more than a given number.

To find a number that is 10 more than a given number, students can count on 10 from the number. The number students land on is 10 more than the starting number. A hundred chart helps students quickly identify this number because the number that is 10 more is in the box directly below the given number.

Students can also use number patterns to find the number that is 10 more than a given number. To find the number that is 10 more, students increase the tens digit by 1. The ones digit stays the same.

Objectives

- Identify 10 more than or 10 less than a given number.

DIRECTIONS FOR USING THE HUNDRED CHART LEARNING TOOL

1. Turn off the audio by clicking the ON/OFF button.
2. Have students choose a counting tool. Tell students they will use the hundred chart to find 10 more than a given number.
   Say: Let's find 10 more than 47. Click 47, and count on 10 numbers.
   Be sure that students count to the right and move to the beginning of the next row when they reach the end of a row.
3. Ask students what number they landed on. (57) Point out that 57 is directly below 47 on the hundred chart.
4. Have students use the hundred chart to find the number that is 10 more than the following numbers: 35, 90, 21, 12, and 68. Help them see that they do not need to count on 10 to find the number that is 10 more—they can find the number directly below the starting number.
5. **Ask:** 78 is 10 more than 68. What is the same about the numbers 68 and 78?
   ANSWER: Both numbers have the same ones digit (8). The tens digits is one more.
6. Have students tell the numbers that are 10 more than the following numbers: 9, 45, 77, 64, and 80. If students have difficulty, remind them that the tens digit is one more and the ones digit is the same. You may also tell them one of the digits. Students should use the hundred chart to check their answers.

LEARN One More on a Number Line

Objectives

* Identify one more than or one less than a given number.

Students will use a number line to find a number that is one more than a given number. Gather the Number Line 0–100 and One More on a Number Line activity page from the Activity Book. Read the directions on the activity page with students.

1. Point to the first number line on the activity page.

   Ask: What numbers does this number line show?
   ANSWER: 0 through 10

2. Tell students to start at 0 and point to each number and count aloud to 10.

3. **Ask:** In which direction do you move as you count?
   ANSWER: to the right

4. Explain to students that as they move right on the number line, each number is one more than the number before it.
   Ask: Point to 1. Move right one number. What number are you on?
   ANSWER: 2

   Say: 2 is one more than 1.

5. Have students complete the activity page. For each problem, students should point to the starting number and move their finger one number to the right.

6. Give students the Number Line 0–100.
   Say: Now tell me the number that is one more than each number I say. Use counting or the number line if you need help.

   Ask: What is one more than 19? (20)

   Ask: What is one more than 70? (71)

   Ask: What is one more than 83? (84)

   Ask: What is one more than 49? (50)

   Ask: What is one more than 66? (67)

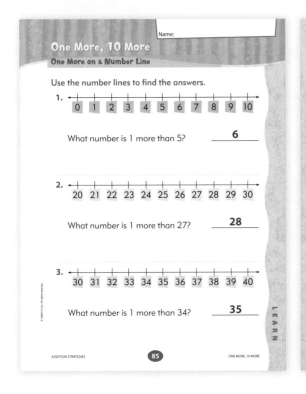

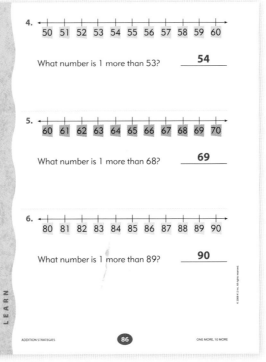

TRY IT One More and 10 More

Objectives

- Identify one more than or one less than a given number.
- Identify 10 more than or 10 less than a given number.

Students will practice finding the number that is one more or 10 more than a given number. Give students the One More and 10 More activity page from their Activity Book and read the directions with them.

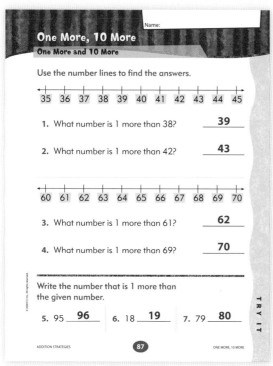

Name: _____

One More, 10 More
One More and 10 More

Use the number lines to find the answers.

35 36 37 38 39 40 41 42 43 44 45

1. What number is 1 more than 38?   **39**

2. What number is 1 more than 42?   **43**

60 61 62 63 64 65 66 67 68 69 70

3. What number is 1 more than 61?   **62**

4. What number is 1 more than 69?   **70**

Write the number that is 1 more than the given number.

5. 95 __**96**__   6. 18 __**19**__   7. 79 __**80**__

Circle the answer.

8. What number is 1 more than 15?
    A. 12   (B.) 16   C. 14   D. 19

9. What number is 1 more than 37?
    A. 36   (B.) 38   C. 40   D. 42

10. What number is 1 more than 12?
    A. 10   B. 11   C. 12   (D.) 13

11. What number is 1 more than 19?
    (A.) 20   B. 21   C. 18   D. 17

12. What number is 1 more than 7?
    A. 7   (B.) 8   C. 9   D. 10

13. What number is 1 more than 23?
    (A.) 24   B. 26   C. 27   D. 28

Use this half of the hundred chart for Problems 14–17.

1	2	3	4	5	6	7	8	9	10
11	12	13	14	15	16	17	18	19	20
21	22	23	24	25	26	27	28	29	30
31	32	33	34	35	36	37	38	39	40
41	42	43	44	45	46	47	48	49	50

14. What number is 10 more than 39?   **49**

15. What number is 10 more than 26?   **36**

16. What number is 10 more than 4?   **14**

17. What number is 10 more than 40?   **50**

Write the number that is 10 more than the given number.

18. 44 __**54**__   19. 8 __**18**__   20. 79 __**89**__

Use the number lines to find the answers.

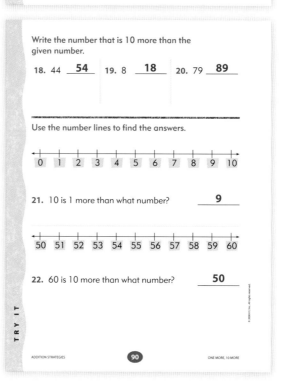

0 1 2 3 4 5 6 7 8 9 10

21. 10 is 1 more than what number?   **9**

50 51 52 53 54 55 56 57 58 59 60

22. 60 is 10 more than what number?   **50**

Print the Checkpoint and have students complete it on their own. Read the directions, problems, and answer choices to students if necessary. Use the answer key to score the Checkpoint, and then enter the results online.

- Identify one more than or one less than a given number.
- Identify 10 more than or 10 less than a given number.

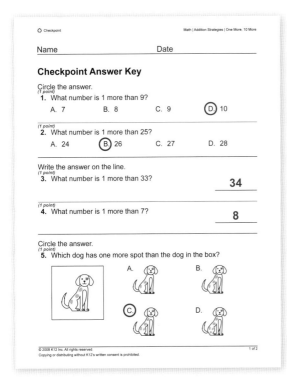

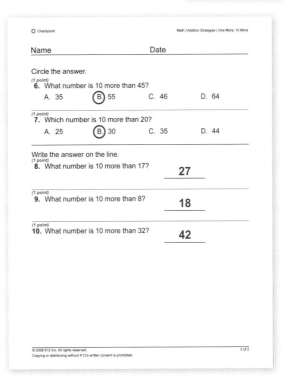

Count On to Add

Lesson Overview

Skills Update	5 minutes	ONLINE
GET READY Review Addition	5 minutes	ONLINE
LEARN Use a Number Line to Count On	5 minutes	ONLINE
TRY IT Practice Counting on a Number Line	10 minutes	OFFLINE
LEARN Use Blocks to Count On	15 minutes	OFFLINE
LEARN Use Strategies to Add	10 minutes	OFFLINE
TRY IT Solve Addition Problems	10 minutes	OFFLINE

▶ Lesson Objectives

- Use "counting on" to solve addition problems.
- Use "counting on from the largest number" to solve addition problems.
- Combine memorized facts with counting strategies to solve addition problems.

▶ Prerequisite Skills

- Demonstrate and explain the meaning of addition as putting together or combining sets.
- Use concrete objects or sketches to represent a quantity up through 30.
- Demonstrate automatic recall of addition facts with sums through 20.
- Identify one more than or one less than a given number.
- Identify 10 more than or 10 less than a given number.

▶ Common Errors and Misconceptions

- Students might start counting before or after pointing to the first object in a group. Or they might stop counting before or after they point to the last object. Students should point to each object as they count it.
- Students might say more than one number for each object when counting objects in a group. Or they might skip objects. Students should point to each object and say exactly one number. Then they should point to the next object and say exactly one number, and so on.
- Students might use an incorrect counting sequence, such as "one, two, four, six, ten."

Materials to Gather

SUPPLIED

blocks – B (red, blue)

Practice Counting on a Number Line activity page

Use Blocks to Count On activity page

Use Strategies to Add activity page

Solve Addition Problems activity page

ALSO NEEDED

index card

▶ Advance Preparation

On the index card, write the following questions:

- Do you have the fact memorized?
- Does it help to switch the addends around?
- Can you count on?
- Can you make a 10?
- Can you use another fact you know?

▶ Content Background

To find one more than a number, students have learned how to *count on*. For example, they can start with 10 and count on one to reach 11. In this lesson, students will learn to count on to add. Students can combine counting on with any other strategy they have learned to add.

Keywords	
	add – to combine, or put together, groups of objects or numbers
	addend – one of the two or more numbers that are added to determine a sum
	addition – the process of combining, or putting together, groups of objects or numbers; a mathematical operation
	addition facts – simple addition problems that usually have addends less than or equal to 10 and sums through 20
	count on – to add two groups by starting with the number of objects in one group and then counting up, in order, the number of objects in the other group
	expression – a number or a combination of numbers and symbols that represents a given value, such as $2 + 3$ or $10 - 4 + 1$
	sum – the solution to an addition problem

ONLINE
5 min

GET READY Review Addition

Students will use objects to show that addition is putting groups together. They will also demonstrate the automatic recall of addition facts with sums through 20 by using online flash cards.

Gather the circles. On the first screen, students will use the circles to model an addition expression. After students complete the questions on this screen, collect the circles.

Objectives

- Demonstrate and explain the meaning of addition as putting together or combining sets.
- Use concrete objects or sketches to represent a quantity up through 30.
- Demonstrate automatic recall of addition facts with sums through 20.

LEARN Use a Number Line to Count On

Students will learn to use a number line to count on to add by watching an animation.

- Use "counting on" to solve addition problems.
- Use "counting on from the largest number" to solve addition problems.
- Combine memorized facts with counting strategies to solve addition problems.

TRY IT Practice Counting on a Number Line

Students will practice counting on a number line to add. Give students the Practice Counting on a Number Line activity page from their Activity Book and read the directions with them.

- Use "counting on" to solve addition problems.
- Use "counting on from the largest number" to solve addition problems.
- Combine memorized facts with counting strategies to solve addition problems.

Count On to Add

Practice Counting on a Number Line

Name:

Use the number line to count on to find the sum.

1. $5 + 3 = $ __8__

2. $4 + 9 = $ __13__

3. $11 + 8 = $ __19__

4. $0 + 16 = $ __16__

5. $2 + 13 = $ __15__

6. $15 + 5 = $ __20__

7. $12 + 7 = $ __19__

8. $4 + 12 = $ __16__

9. $9 + 4 = $ __13__

TRY IT

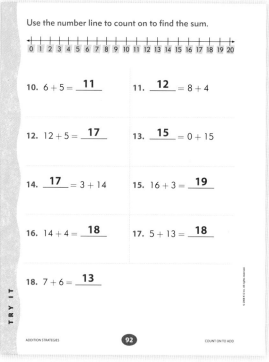

Use the number line to count on to find the sum.

10. $6 + 5 = $ __11__

11. __12__ $ = 8 + 4$

12. $12 + 5 = $ __17__

13. __15__ $ = 0 + 15$

14. __17__ $ = 3 + 14$

15. $16 + 3 = $ __19__

16. $14 + 4 = $ __18__

17. $5 + 13 = $ __18__

18. $7 + 6 = $ __13__

LEARN Use Blocks to Count On

OFFLINE
15 min

Students will use circle blocks to count on from the greater addend to solve addition problems.

Give students the circles and the Use Blocks to Count On activity page from their Activity Book. Read the directions with them.

1. Point to Problem 1, and explain to students that you'll find the first sum together.

2. Display 5 red circles and 2 blue circles.

   Ask: Which addend is greater, 5 or 2?
   ANSWER: 5

3. **Say:** 5 is the greater addend. When counting on, start with the greater addend, and then count on the number of the lesser addend.

4. Point to the 5 red circles and say, "five." Move one of the blue circles to the group of red circles and say, "six." Move the other blue circle and say, "seven."

   Say: The last number I said was 7. So the sum of 5 and 2 is 7.

5. Repeat Steps 2–4 with Problem 2. Have students move the circles and count.

6. Have students complete the remaining problems. Assist students as needed.

Objectives

- Use "counting on" to solve addition problems.
- Use "counting on from the largest number" to solve addition problems.
- Combine memorized facts with counting strategies to solve addition problems.

Name: _____

Count On to Add
Use Blocks to Count On

Count on to find the sum.
Use circles to help you.

1. $5 + 2 = \underline{7}$ 2. $4 + 5 = \underline{9}$

3. $7 + 8 = \underline{15}$ 4. $0 + 9 = \underline{9}$

5. $2 + 12 = \underline{14}$ 6. $16 + 3 = \underline{19}$

7. $10 + 7 = \underline{17}$ 8. $4 + 15 = \underline{19}$

9. $7 + 2 = \underline{9}$ 10. $\underline{17} = 12 + 5$

11. $\underline{11} = 7 + 4$ 12. $1 + 8 = \underline{9}$

13. $3 + 13 = \underline{16}$ 14. $15 + 4 = \underline{19}$

15. $\underline{19} = 10 + 9$ 16. $3 + 14 = \underline{17}$

ADDITION STRATEGIES   93   COUNT ON TO ADD

ADDITION STRATEGIES   94   COUNT ON TO ADD

LEARN Use Strategies to Add

Objectives

- Use "counting on" to solve addition problems.
- Use "counting on from the largest number" to solve addition problems.
- Combine memorized facts with counting strategies to solve addition problems.

Students will learn that there are many strategies they can use to solve addition problems. They will choose the most appropriate strategy to solve different addition problems.

Give students the circle blocks, the question index card, and the Use Strategies to Add activity page from their Activity Book. Read the directions with them.

1. **Say:** You know many strategies, or ways, to help you add. What strategies do you know?
   ANSWERS: memorizing the facts, counting on, using a number line, and so on

2. Give students the activity page and index card.
   Say: Look at the first problem, $6 + 7$. Before finding the sum, ask yourself the questions on the index card.

   Read aloud the questions on the card:
   - Do you have the fact memorized?
   - Does it help to switch the addends around?
   - Can you count on?
   - Can you make a 10?
   - Can you use another fact you know?

3. **Say:** For which questions did you answer Yes? Use one of those strategies to find the sum.

4. Have students continue solving the problems in this way. For each problem, have them explain what strategy they used.

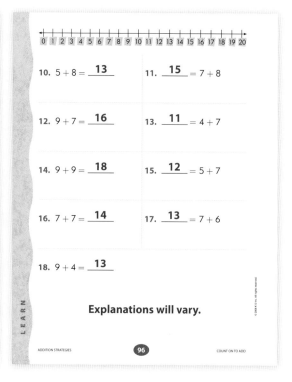

Count On to Add

Use Strategies to Add

Name:

Choose a strategy to find the sum.
Explain which strategy you chose for the problem.

0 1 2 3 4 5 6 7 8 9 10 11 12 13 14 15 16 17 18 19 20

1. $6 + 7 = $ __13__   2. $6 + 9 = $ __15__

3. $10 + 8 = $ __18__   4. $3 + 5 = $ __8__

5. $8 + 9 = $ __17__   6. $8 + 7 = $ __15__

7. $5 + 5 = $ __10__   8. $8 + 6 = $ __14__

9. $9 + 5 = $ __14__

Explanations will vary.

0 1 2 3 4 5 6 7 8 9 10 11 12 13 14 15 16 17 18 19 20

10. $5 + 8 = $ __13__   11. __15__ $= 7 + 8$

12. $9 + 7 = $ __16__   13. __11__ $= 4 + 7$

14. $9 + 9 = $ __18__   15. __12__ $= 5 + 7$

16. $7 + 7 = $ __14__   17. __13__ $= 7 + 6$

18. $9 + 4 = $ __13__

Explanations will vary.

TRY IT Solve Addition Problems

Students will practice using different adding strategies. Give students the Solve Addition Problems activity page from their Activity Book and read the directions with them.

Objectives

- Use "counting on" to solve addition problems.
- Use "counting on from the largest number" to solve addition problems.
- Combine memorized facts with counting strategies to solve addition problems.

Count On to Add
Solve Addition Problems

Name: _____

Use the number line to count on to find the sum.

1 2 3 4 5 6 7 8 9 10 11 12 13 14 15 16 17 18 19 20

1. $2 + 8 =$ __10__ **2.** $11 + 6 =$ __17__

3. $7 + 4 =$ __11__ **4.** $14 + 5 =$ __19__

Count on to find the sum.

5. $16 + 4 =$ __20__ **6.** $5 + 7 =$ __12__

7. $10 + 5 =$ __15__

Use any strategy you have learned to find the sum.

8. $6 + 9 =$ __15__ **9.** $18 + 3 =$ __21__

10. $25 + 4 =$ __29__

T R Y   I T

Use the number line to count on to find the sum.

10 11 12 13 14 15 16 17 18 19 20 21 22 23 24 25 26 27 28 29 30

11. $17 + 10 =$ __27__

12. $13 + 5 =$ __18__

13. $16 + 5 =$ __21__

14. Use a strategy you have learned, or math facts, to solve this problem. Then explain how you solved the problem. **See below.**

$9 + 6 =$ __15__

15. Use a strategy you have learned, or math facts, to solve this problem. Circle the answer.

$7 + 4 = ?$

A. 13   B. 12   C. 11   D. 10

16. Count on 9 from 13 to find the sum of $13 + 9$.

$13 + 9 =$ __22__

T R Y   I T

Additional Answers
14. Explanations will vary. **Example:** I used math facts. I know that $9 + 6$ is 15.

Different Ways to Add

Skills Update	5 minutes	ONLINE
GET READY Review Basic Facts	10 minutes	ONLINE
LEARN Find Sums Through 30	25 minutes	ONLINE
TRY IT Addition Strategies	10 minutes	OFFLINE
CHECKPOINT	10 minutes	OFFLINE

▶ Lesson Objectives

- Use "counting on" to solve addition problems.
- Use "counting on from the greatest number" to solve addition problems.
- Combine memorized facts with counting strategies to solve addition problems.

▶ Prerequisite Skills

- Demonstrate and explain the meaning of addition as putting together or combining sets.
- Use concrete objects or sketches to represent a quantity up through 30.
- Demonstrate automatic recall of addition facts with sums through 20.

▶ Common Errors and Misconceptions

- Students might start counting before or after pointing to the first object in a group. Or they might stop counting before or after they point to the last object. Students should point to each object as they count it.
- Students might say more than one number for each object when counting objects in a group. Or they might skip objects. Students should point to each object and say exactly one number. Then they should point to the next object and say exactly one number, and so on.
- Students might use an incorrect counting sequence, such as "one, two, four, six, ten."

▶ Advance Preparation

Print the Number Line 0–100. Cut out the first two sections, and tape them together to make a number line from 0 to 40.

▶ Content Background

In this lesson, students will use different strategies to add.

Materials to Gather

SUPPLIED

Number Line 0–100 (printout)

Addition Strategies activity page

Checkpoint (printout)

GET READY Review Basic Facts

Students will use online flash cards to recall basic addition facts.

Deck 1 has facts with sums through 10. Deck 2 has facts with sums through 15. Deck 3 has facts with sums through 20.

Have students complete flash card facts as time allows.

Objectives

- Demonstrate automatic recall of addition facts with sums through 20.

LEARN Find Sums Through 30

Students will use addition strategies to find sums through 30.

Gather the number line you prepared. As students work through the problems online, do the following:

- Ask them to describe the addition strategies they use for each problem. Accept all appropriate strategies that give the correct sum. Remind them that having the sum memorized is also a strategy.
- If students have trouble describing a strategy, have them roll the mouse over the hint button.
- On the last screen, give students the number line you prepared. They can use that or any other strategy to find the sums.

Objectives

- Use "counting on" to solve addition problems.
- Use "counting on from the greatest number" to solve addition problems.
- Combine memorized facts with counting strategies to solve addition problems.

TRY IT Addition Strategies

Students will practice using different addition strategies. Give students the Addition Strategies activity page from their Activity Book and read the directions with them.

Objectives

- Use "counting on" to solve addition problems.
- Use "counting on from the greatest number" to solve addition problems.
- Combine memorized facts with counting strategies to solve addition problems.

Tips

Review with students that when counting on, they should start with the greater number and count on the lesser number.

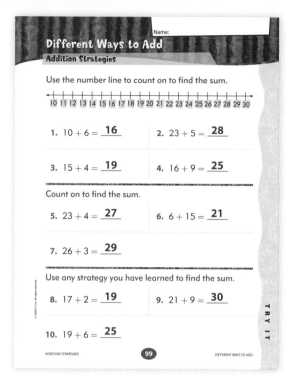

Different Ways to Add
Addition Strategies

Name:

Use the number line to count on to find the sum.

10 11 12 13 14 15 16 17 18 19 20 21 22 23 24 25 26 27 28 29 30

1. $10 + 6 = $ **16**

2. $23 + 5 = $ **28**

3. $15 + 4 = $ **19**

4. $16 + 9 = $ **25**

Count on to find the sum.

5. $23 + 4 = $ **27**

6. $6 + 15 = $ **21**

7. $26 + 3 = $ **29**

Use any strategy you have learned to find the sum.

8. $17 + 2 = $ **19**

9. $21 + 9 = $ **30**

10. $19 + 6 = $ **25**

T R Y   I T

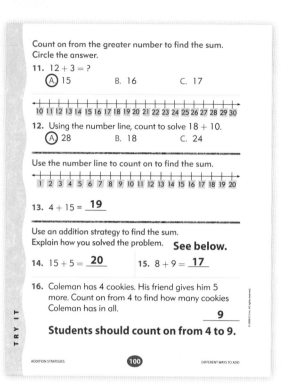

Count on from the greater number to find the sum. Circle the answer.

11. $12 + 3 = ?$
   (A) 15   B. 16   C. 17

10 11 12 13 14 15 16 17 18 19 20 21 22 23 24 25 26 27 28 29 30

12. Using the number line, count to solve $18 + 10$.
   (A) 28   B. 18   C. 24

Use the number line to count on to find the sum.

1 2 3 4 5 6 7 8 9 10 11 12 13 14 15 16 17 18 19 20

13. $4 + 15 = $ **19**

Use an addition strategy to find the sum.
Explain how you solved the problem.   **See below.**

14. $15 + 5 = $ **20**

15. $8 + 9 = $ **17**

16. Coleman has 4 cookies. His friend gives him 5 more. Count on from 4 to find how many cookies Coleman has in all.   **9**

Students should count on from 4 to 9.

T R Y   I T

Additional Answers

14–15. Explanations will vary. **Example:** I started at 15 and counted on 5.

OFFLINE
10 min

CHECKPOINT

Print the Checkpoint and have students complete it on their own. Read the directions, problems, and answer choices to students if necessary. Use the answer key to score the Checkpoint, and then enter the results online.

Objectives

- Use "counting on" to solve addition problems.
- Use "counting on from the greatest number" to solve addition problems.
- Combine memorized facts with counting strategies to solve addition problems.

Name _____ Date _____

Checkpoint Answer Key

Count on from the greater number to add. Circle the sum.

(1 point)
1. $9 + 4$

  A. 12

  Ⓑ 13

  C. 14

(1 point)
2. $18 + 6$

  A. 22

  B. 23

  Ⓒ 24

Count on aloud from the greater number to add. Say the sum.

(1 point)
3. $8 + 3$

Students should count aloud from 8 to 11.

(1 point)
4. $5 + 18$

Students should count aloud from 18 to 23.

Use any strategy to add. Circle the answer.

(1 point)
5. $5 + 15 = ?$

  Ⓐ 20   B. 15

  C. 10   D. 5

(1 point)
6. $3 + 3 = ?$

  A. 3   Ⓑ 6

  C. 13   D. 33

(1 point)
7. $4 + 3 = ?$

  Ⓐ 7   B. 8

  C. 9   D. 10

(1 point)
8. $2 + 8 = ?$

  A. 12   Ⓑ 10

  C. 9   D. 8

Name _____ Date _____

Use the number line for Problems 9–12.

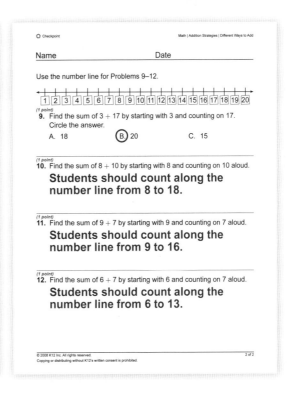

(1 point)
9. Find the sum of $3 + 17$ by starting with 3 and counting on 17. Circle the answer.

  A. 18   Ⓑ 20   C. 15

(1 point)
10. Find the sum of $8 + 10$ by starting with 8 and counting on 10 aloud.

Students should count along the number line from 8 to 18.

(1 point)
11. Find the sum of $9 + 7$ by starting with 9 and counting on 7 aloud.

Students should count along the number line from 9 to 16.

(1 point)
12. Find the sum of $6 + 7$ by starting with 6 and counting on 7 aloud.

Students should count along the number line from 6 to 13.

Grouping to Add

Skills Update	5 minutes	ONLINE
GET READY Addition Number Sentences	5 minutes	ONLINE
LEARN Plate Addition	15 minutes	OFFLINE
TRY IT Group to Add	10 minutes	OFFLINE
LEARN Add Three Numbers	15 minutes	OFFLINE
TRY IT Three Addends	10 minutes	OFFLINE

▶ Lesson Objectives

- Given a number of objects up through 20, show how those objects can be grouped and regrouped to illustrate the associative property.
- Find the sum of three one-digit numbers, with sums through 20.

▶ Prerequisite Skills

- Use models and math symbols to represent addition.
- Combine memorized facts with counting strategies to solve addition problems.

▶ Advance Preparation

For the Learn: Plate Addition activity, lay out the plates as shown.

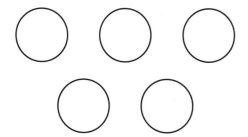

▶ Content Background

Students will learn that when adding three numbers, they may regroup the addends to simplify the problem. The way they group the addends does not affect the sum. For example, given the problem $2 + 9 + 8$, students may first add $2 + 8$ to make 10, and then add $9 + 10$. Students will use counting objects as they begin learning this concept. Then they will apply the concept to abstract problems.

Materials to Gather

SUPPLIED

Plate Addition activity page

blocks – O (all colors)

Group to Add activity page

Add Three Numbers activity page

Three Addends activity page

ALSO NEEDED

paper plates – 5

GET READY Addition Number Sentences

ONLINE 5 min

Students will solve addition problems using online flash cards.

Objectives

- Use models and math symbols to represent addition.
- Combine memorized facts with counting strategies to solve addition problems.

LEARN Plate Addition

OFFLINE 15 min

Students will use cubes to model addition sentences with three one-digit addends. They will group and regroup the cubes to make the sums easier to find.

If you haven't done so, lay out the plates as described in Advance Preparation. Give students the cubes and the Plate Addition activity page from their Activity Book.

1. **Say:** Place a group of 2 cubes on one plate, a group of 3 cubes on another plate, and a group of 4 cubes on the third plate. On the activity page, below the cubes in Way 1 in the example, write the addition expression for the cubes.
   ANSWER: $2 + 3 + 4$

2. **Say:** You can combine these cubes in different ways to find the total. First combine 2 cubes and 3 cubes. Move them to an empty plate.

   Ask: How many cubes are there?
   ANSWER: 5

   Say: Put the remaining group of 4 cubes on the other empty plate. Write the addition expression below the cubes in Way 2 in the example.
   ANSWER: $5 + 4$

3. **Say:** Now combine the groups of 5 cubes and 4 cubes to show the total.
   Ask: What is the total?
   ANSWER: 9

   Say: Remember, the total is the sum. Write the sum on the activity page.

4. **Say:** Now let's combine the cubes in a different way. Put the 2, 3, and 4 cubes back on the three plates. Now combine the groups of 3 and 4 cubes and move them to an empty plate. Move the 2 cubes to the other empty plate.
   Ask: How many cubes are there in all?
   ANSWER: 9

   Explain to students that they can group the addends in different ways, and the sum will stay the same.

Objectives

- Given a number of objects up through 20, show how those objects can be grouped and regrouped to illustrate the associative property.

Tips

Have students use different colored cubes for each group. When students sketch their cubes, they may color them with crayons to match their models.

5. Repeat Steps 1–4 to have students complete the activity page. Have them show the addition with cubes and sketch the cubes in the circles to show their work. They can represent the cubes with dots. Supply students with the following number sentences to model for Way 1 of each problem:

- Problem 1: $6 + 2 + 8$
- Problem 2: $3 + 4 + 6$
- Problem 3: $5 + 4 + 6$

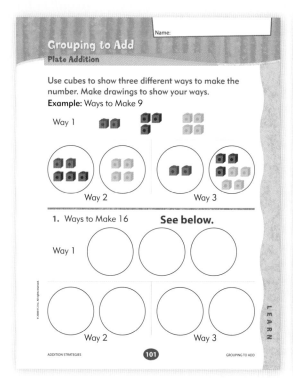

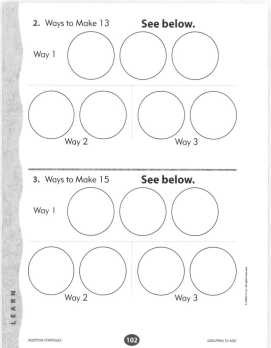

Additional Answers

1. Drawings will vary. **Example drawings:** 6 (circle 1) + 2 (circle 2) + 8 (circle 3) = $(6 + 2) + 8 = 8 + 8 = 16$, or $6 + 2 + 8 = 6 + (2 + 8) = 6 + 10 = 16$

2. Drawings will vary. **Example drawings:** $3 + 4 + 6 = (3 + 4) + 6 = 7 + 6 = 13$, or $3 + 4 + 6 = 3 + (4 + 6) = 3 + 10 = 13$

3. Drawings will vary. **Example drawings:** $5 + 4 + 6 = (5 + 4) + 6 = 9 + 6 = 15$, or $5 + 4 + 6 = 5 + (4 + 6) = 5 + 10 = 15$

TRY IT Group to Add

Objectives

- Given a number of objects up through 20, show how those objects can be grouped and regrouped to illustrate the associative property.

- Find the sum of three one-digit numbers, with sums through 20.

Students will practice grouping addends in different ways to find the sum of three one-digit numbers. Give students the cubes and the Group to Add activity page from their Activity Book. Read the directions with them.

Tips

Students may draw circles if drawing hearts and stars is too difficult.

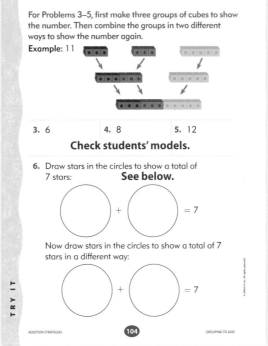

Additional Answers

6. Drawings may vary. **Possible drawings:** 2 stars + 5 stars; 3 stars + 4 stars; 6 stars + 1 star

LEARN Add Three Numbers

Students will add three one-digit numbers. They will learn that they can group numbers so that the sum is easier to find. Give students the Add Three Numbers activity page from their Activity Book and read the directions with them.

1. **Say:** Look at the example problem, $9 + 1 + 2$. In this problem, $9 + 1$ were added first to make 10. Then 2 was added to 10 to make 12. Now look at Problem 1. Add $1 + 2$ first. Then add 9. Write the sum.

2. **Say:** We can choose which way to group numbers to make the problem easier.

   Ask: Which way of grouping do you think is easier, the example or Problem 1?
   ANSWER: Either answer is correct. Students may say Problem 1 is easier because they prefer adding the lesser numbers first. Explain that many people find the grouping in the example easier because they can make a 10.

3. Have students complete Problems 2 and 3. Discuss which grouping they found easier.

4. Have students complete the remaining problems. After each problem, ask students to explain how they chose to group the addends.

Objectives

- Find the sum of three one-digit numbers, with sums through 20.

Tips

Students may use cubes to model the number sentence if needed.

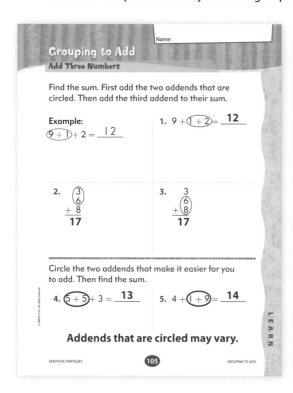

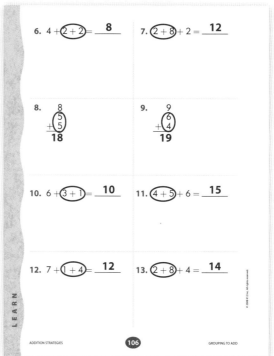

TRY IT Three Addends

Students will practice grouping addends in different ways to find the sum of three one-digit numbers. Give students the Three Addends activity page from their Activity Book and read the directions with them.

Objectives

- Given a number of objects up through 20, show how those objects can be grouped and regrouped to illustrate the associative property.

Tips

Students do not need to regroup the addends to find the sum. They may wish to just add the numbers from left to right. However, if they choose to group the numbers, have them circle the numbers that they grouped and tell you why they grouped in that way.

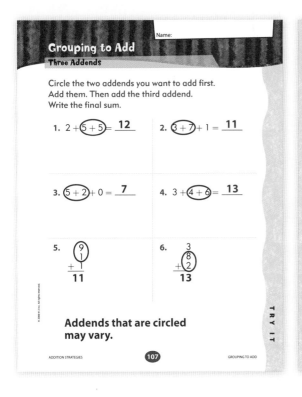

Grouping to Add
Three Addends

Name:

Circle the two addends you want to add first. Add them. Then add the third addend. Write the final sum.

1. $2 + \boxed{5 + 5} = $ **12**   2. $\boxed{3 + 7} + 1 = $ **11**

3. $\boxed{5 + 2} + 0 = $ **7**   4. $3 + \boxed{4 + 6} = $ **13**

5. $\boxed{9 \atop 1}$
    $+ \; 1$
    ——
    11

6. $\boxed{3 \atop 8}$
    $+ \boxed{2}$
    ——
    13

Addends that are circled may vary.

TRY IT

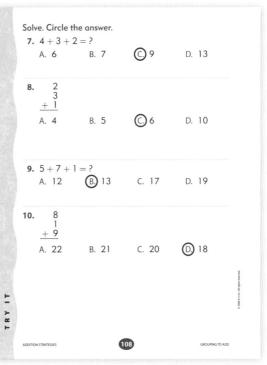

Solve. Circle the answer.

7. $4 + 3 + 2 = ?$

   A. 6   B. 7   C. 9   D. 13

8.   2
       3
    $+ \; 1$

   A. 4   B. 5   C. 6   D. 10

9. $5 + 7 + 1 = ?$

   A. 12   B. 13   C. 17   D. 19

10.   8
       1
    $+ \; 9$

   A. 22   B. 21   C. 20   D. 18

TRY IT

Grouping Addends

Lesson Overview

Skills Update	5 minutes	ONLINE
GET READY Use Objects and Symbols to Add	5 minutes	OFFLINE
LEARN Group Objects Different Ways	10 minutes	OFFLINE
LEARN Three Addends in a Number Sentence	15 minutes	ONLINE
TRY IT Group and Regroup	10 minutes	OFFLINE
TRY IT Sum of Three Addends	5 minutes	OFFLINE
CHECKPOINT	10 minutes	OFFLINE

▶ Lesson Objectives

- Given a number of objects up through 20, show how those objects can be grouped and regrouped to illustrate the associative property
- Find the sum of three one-digit numbers, with sums through 20.

▶ Prerequisite Skills

- Use models and math symbols to represent addition.
- Combine memorized facts with counting strategies to solve addition problems.

▶ Content Background

Students will add three numbers, regrouping the addends to simplify the problem. The way they group the addends does not affect the sum. For example, given the problem $2 + 9 + 8$, students may first add $2 + 8$ to make 10, and then add $9 + 10$. Students will use counting objects as they begin learning this concept. Then they will apply the concept to abstract problems.

Students will use models, then drawings, and then expressions to transition from the concrete to the abstract.

Materials to Gather

SUPPLIED

blocks – B (all colors)

blocks – O (all colors)

Group Objects Different Ways activity page

Group and Regroup activity page

Sum of Three Addends activity page

Checkpoint (printout)

Keywords	
	addition sentence – a number sentence that involves addition only
	number sentence – two expressions related by an equals symbol ($=$), a not-equal-to symbol ($\neq$), or an inequality symbol; for example, $7 - 2 = 4 + 1$; $5 \neq 4 + 4$; $6 + 2 > 1 + 4$
	parentheses – a type of grouping symbol used in expressions and equations

GET READY Use Objects and Symbols to Add

Objectives

- Use models and math symbols to represent addition.

Students will read, interpret, and model number sentences.
   Give students the circle blocks.

1. Explain to students that they will use circles to show adding. Ask them to use the circles to show $16 = 5 + 11$. (Students should make a group of 5 circles of one color and a separate group of 11 circles of another color. Then they should combine the groups.)

2. **Say:** Now let's write a number sentence for the model.
   Ask: What symbols will you use in the number sentence? Why?
   ANSWER: I will use the plus symbol because it shows addition and the equals symbol because it shows that two amounts are the same.

3. Have students write the number sentence on a sheet of paper. ($16 = 5 + 11$)

4. Explain that now you will write a different number sentence and that students will model it using the circles.

5. Write $7 + 9 = 16$.

6. Have students use circles to model the number sentence. Then have them explain what they did. (They may say, "A group of 7 circles combined with a group of 9 circles is the same as 16 circles.")

7. Have students write a number sentence of their choosing. Then have them model the sentence with circles and explain what they did.

LEARN Group Objects Different Ways

Objectives

- Given a number of objects up through 20, show how those objects can be grouped and regrouped to illustrate the associative property.

Students will use cubes to model addition sentences with three one-digit addends. They will group and regroup the cubes to make the sums easier to find.
   Give students the cubes and the Group Objects Different Ways activity page from their Activity Book.

1. Show students 10 red cubes. Explain that there are many ways to make a group of 10 cubes.

2. Using the 10 cubes, make a train of 2 cubes, a train of 5 cubes, and a train of 3 cubes. Have students tell how many cubes are in each group.

3. Point to Way 1 in the example on the activity page, and explain that 2 plus 5 plus 3 is one way to make 10.

4. Connect the 2-train and the 5-train. Have students tell how many cubes are in the new train. (7)

5. Point to Way 2 on the activity page, and explain that 7 plus 3 is another way to make 10.

6. Separate the 2-train and 5-train. Now connect the 5-train and 3-train. Have students tell how many cubes are in the new train. (8)

7. Point to Way 3 on the activity page, and explain that 2 plus 8 is another way to make 10.

8. Take the trains apart, and ask students how many cubes there are. (10) Explain that because you did not add any cubes or take any cubes away, there are still 10 cubes.

9. Repeat the activity with the numbers 12, 16, and 20 as indicated on the activity page. Have students decide how to group the addends.

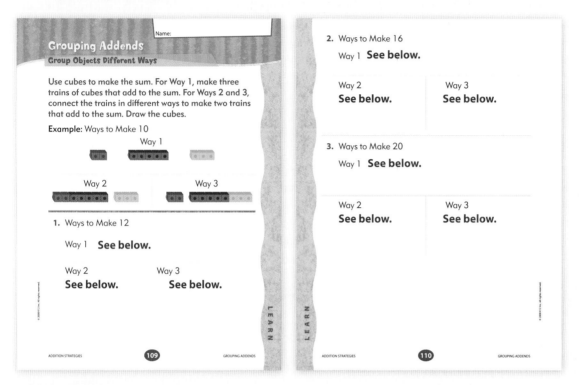

Additional Answers

1. Drawings will vary. **Example drawing for Way 1:** 3 cubes + 7 cubes + 2 cubes; **Example drawing for Way 2:** 10 cubes + 2 cubes; **Example drawing for Way 3:** 3 cubes + 9 cubes

2. Drawings will vary. **Example drawing for Way 1:** 5 cubes + 5 cubes + 6 cubes; **Example drawing for Way 2:** 10 cubes + 6 cubes; **Example drawing for Way 3:** 5 cubes + 11 cubes

3. Drawings will vary. **Example drawing for Way 1:** 10 cubes + 6 cubes + 4 cubes; **Example drawing for Way 2:** 16 cubes + 4 cubes; **Example drawing for Way 3:** 10 cubes + 10 cubes

LEARN Three Addends in a Number Sentence

Students will watch ways to add three one-digit numbers. They will learn to decide which way of grouping makes the sum easier to find. They will also learn how to use parentheses to show grouping.

Objectives

- Find the sum of three one-digit numbers, with sums through 20.

TRY IT Group and Regroup

This Try It activity has two parts.

Objectives

- Given a number of objects up through 20, show how those objects can be grouped and regrouped to illustrate the associative property.

PART 1

Gather the cubes.

1. Show students 10 red cubes.

   Say: Use the cubes to show three groups that add to 10.
   Students may use one group of 4 cubes and two groups of 3 cubes each.

   Say: Combine two of the groups to make two groups that add to 10.
   Students may use one group of 4 cubes and one group of 6.

2. **Say:** Now use the cubes to show three groups that have a sum of 18 cubes.
   SAMPLE ANSWERS: groups of 5, 6, and 7 cubes; 3, 6, and 9 cubes; 2, 6, and 10 cubes

3. Repeat Step 2 with the numbers 15, 13, and 16.
   SAMPLE ANSWERS:
   15: groups of 4, 5, and 6 cubes; 3, 5, and 7 cubes; 2, 4, and 9 cubes
   13: groups of 2, 5, and 6 cubes; 3, 4, and 6 cubes; 2, 4, and 7 cubes
   16: groups of 4, 5, and 7 cubes; 5, 5, and 6 cubes; 2, 6, and 8 cubes

4. **Say:** Now I want you to show me two different ways to make the number 14. First, make two groups that add to 14. Then make three groups that add to 14.
   SAMPLE ANSWERS:
   2 groups: groups of 7 and 7 cubes; 6 and 8 cubes
   3 groups: groups of 4, 4, and 6 cubes; 7, 4, and 3 cubes

PART 2

Students will practice grouping addends in different ways to find the sum of three one-digit numbers. Give students the Group and Regroup activity page from their Activity Book and read the directions with them.

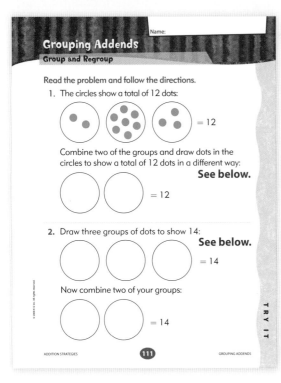

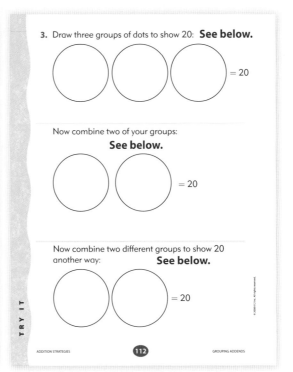

Additional Answers

1. Drawings will vary. **Example drawings:** 2 dots + 10 dots; 5 dots + 7 dots; 9 dots + 3 dots

2. Drawings will vary. **Example drawing for first row:** 3 dots + 4 dots + 7 dots; **Example drawings for second row:** 7 dots + 7 dots; 3 dots + 11 dots; 10 dots + 4 dots

3. Drawings will vary. **Example drawing for first row:** 8 dots + 3 dots + 9 dots; **Example drawings for second and third rows:** 12 dots + 8 dots; 11 dots + 9 dots; 17 dots + 3 dots

TRY IT Sum of Three Addends

OFFLINE
5 min

Objectives

- Find the sum of three one-digit numbers, with sums through 20.

Students will practice grouping addends to find the sum of three one-digit numbers. They will need to decide which two addends to group. Give students the Sum of Three Addends activity page from their Activity Book and read the directions with them.

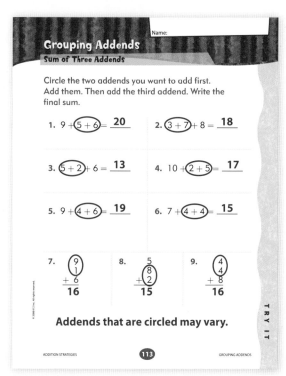

Grouping Addends

Sum of Three Addends

Name:

Circle the two addends you want to add first. Add them. Then add the third addend. Write the final sum.

1. $9 + (5 + 6) =$ __20__   2. $(3 + 7) + 8 =$ __18__

3. $(5 + 2) + 6 =$ __13__   4. $10 + (2 + 5) =$ __17__

5. $9 + (4 + 6) =$ __19__   6. $7 + (4 + 4) =$ __15__

7. 9
    1
    $+ 6$ (9 and 1 circled)
    __16__

8. 5
    8
    $+ 2$ (8 and 2 circled)
    __15__

9. 4
    4
    $+ 8$ (4 and 4 circled)
    __16__

Addends that are circled may vary.

TRY IT

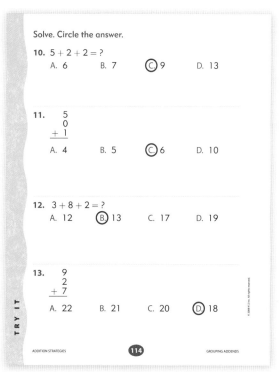

TRY IT

Solve. Circle the answer.

10. $5 + 2 + 2 = ?$
    A. 6   B. 7   C. 9 ⟲   D. 13

11. 5
     0
     $+ 1$
    A. 4   B. 5   C. 6 ⟲   D. 10

12. $3 + 8 + 2 = ?$
    A. 12   B. 13 ⟲   C. 17   D. 19

13. 9
     2
     $+ 7$
    A. 22   B. 21   C. 20   D. 18 ⟲

OFFLINE
10 min

CHECKPOINT

Print the Checkpoint. In Part 1, students will take a performance-based assessment. In Part 2, students will complete the problems on their own. Read the directions, problems, and answer choices to students if necessary. Use the answer key to score the Checkpoint, and then enter the results online.

Gather the circles. Follow the directions on the Checkpoint to use them for Problems 1 and 2.

Objectives

- Given a number of objects up through 20, show how those objects can be grouped and regrouped to illustrate the associative property.

- Find the sum of three one-digit numbers, with sums through 20.

Name _____ Date _____

Checkpoint Answer Key

Part 1

Follow the instructions for Problems 1 and 2. Choose the response that best describes how the student performs on the task. When you have finished, enter the results online.

Place 5 blue circles, 2 red circles, and 8 green circles in three separate piles by color.

1. Say, "Add the blue circles and the red circles together. Then add the green circles. How many circles do you have in all?"
(1 point)
Did the student say that there are 15 circles in all?

  A. Yes   B. No

---

2. Say, "If you add the green and red circles first, and then add the blue circles, will you get the same answer? Explain why."
(1 point)
Did the student say that the answer will stay the same because grouping addends differently does not change the sum?

  A. Yes   B. No

Give students Part 2 of the assessment.

Name _____ Date _____

Part 2

Circle the answer for Problems 3–14.
(1 point)

3. ○○○○   +   ●●●   =   ●●●●●●●

    ●●●   +   ●●●●●●●   +   ○○○○ = ?

The top row shows that the 4 white circles plus the 3 gray circles equals 7 black circles. What is the sum of the circles in the bottom row?

  A. 12   B. 17   (C.) 14

(1 point)
4. The top row shows that the sum of the three groups of flowers is 14. The bottom row shows these groups added in a different order. What is the sum of the flowers in the bottom row?

✿ + ✿✿✿✿✿ + ✿✿✿✿✿✿✿✿ = 14 flowers

✿✿✿✿✿ + ✿✿✿✿✿✿✿✿ + ✿ = ?

  A. 15   B. 17   (C.) 14

Name _____ Date _____

(1 point)
5. Look at the pictures below. The picture on the top row shows 18 squares in all. When you add the numbers in a different order by using the picture on the bottom row, do you get the same number of squares in all?

□□□□ + □□□□□ + □□□□□□□□□ = 18 squares

□□□□□□ + □□□□ + □□□□□□□□ = ?

  (A.) Yes, you get the same number of squares.

  B. No, you do not get the same number of squares.

(1 point) **6.** $4 + 3 + 2 =$	*(1 point)* **7.** $5 + 7 + 1 =$
A. 6	A. 12
B. 7	(B.) 13
(C.) 9	C. 17
D. 13	D. 19

(1 point) **8.** $\begin{array}{r} 2 \\ 3 \\ +\,1 \\ \hline \end{array}$	*(1 point)* **9.** $\begin{array}{r} 8 \\ 1 \\ +\,9 \\ \hline \end{array}$
A. 4	A. 22
B. 5	B. 21
(C.) 6	C. 20
D. 10	(D.) 18

Name _____ Date _____

(1 point) **10.** $\begin{array}{r} 1 \\ 0 \\ +\,8 \\ \hline \end{array}$	*(1 point)* **11.** $\begin{array}{r} 6 \\ 7 \\ +\,7 \\ \hline \end{array}$
A. 18	A. 22
B. 12	B. 21
(C.) 9	(C.) 20
D. 7	D. 18

(1 point) **12.** $\begin{array}{r} 4 \\ 5 \\ +\,3 \\ \hline \end{array}$	*(1 point)* **13.** $\begin{array}{r} 2 \\ 5 \\ +\,6 \\ \hline \end{array}$
A. 15	A. 11
B. 14	B. 12
C. 13	(C.) 13
(D.) 12	D. 14

(1 point) **14.** $8 + 4 + 3 =$	*(1 point)* Write the sum.
A. 16	
(B.) 15	**15.** $9 + 7 + 4 = $ __**20**__
C. 14	
D. 13	

174 ADDITION STRATEGIES

Unit Review

Lesson Overview

UNIT REVIEW Look Back	20 minutes	ONLINE
UNIT REVIEW Checkpoint Practice	20 minutes	OFFLINE
⏩ **UNIT REVIEW** Prepare for the Checkpoint		

▶ Unit Objectives

This lesson reviews the following objectives:

- Identify one more than or one less than a given number.
- Identify 10 more than or 10 less than a given number.
- Use "counting on" to solve addition problems.
- Use "counting on from the greatest number" to solve addition problems.
- Combine memorized facts with counting strategies to solve addition problems.
- Given a number of objects up through 20, show how those objects can be grouped and regrouped to illustrate the associative property.
- Find the sum of three one-digit numbers, with sums through 20.

▶ Advance Preparation

In this lesson, students will have an opportunity to review previous activities in the Addition Strategies unit. Look at the suggested activities in Unit Review: Prepare for the Checkpoint online and gather any needed materials.

Materials to Gather

SUPPLIED
Checkpoint Practice (printout)
blocks – O (red, yellow, blue)

Keywords

add	grouping property of
addend	addition
addition	hundred chart
addition facts	number line
addition sentence	number sentence
associative	parentheses
property of addition	pattern
column	row
count on	sum
expression	

UNIT REVIEW Look Back

ONLINE 20min

Objectives

- Review unit objectives.

In this unit, students began by learning to find one more than and 10 more than another number. They learned this concept using hundred charts and number lines—they should now be able to find one more or 10 more without using these tools.

Next students learned how to add two numbers by counting on. Students used blocks and number lines as they practiced this skill. They learned that counting on from the greater addend is easier than counting on from the lesser addend.

Students were introduced to the associative property, learning that they can group three numbers in different ways to make it easier to find their sum.

Finally, students used the various addition strategies they learned—counting on, using doubles, using memorized facts and similar facts, and grouping to solve addition problems with sums through 30. Students will review these concepts to prepare for the Unit Checkpoint.

UNIT REVIEW Checkpoint Practice

OFFLINE **20**min

Objectives

• Review unit objectives.

Students will complete a Checkpoint Practice activity page to prepare for the Unit Checkpoint. If necessary, read the directions, problems, and answer choices to students. Have students answer the problems on their own. Carefully review the answers with students.

Gather the cubes. Students will need the cubes for Problem 10. If they wish, they may also use the cubes for problems that call for using any strategy.

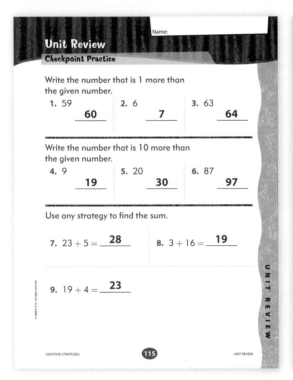

Unit Review
Checkpoint Practice

Name:

Write the number that is 1 more than the given number.

1. 59 __60__   2. 6 __7__   3. 63 __64__

Write the number that is 10 more than the given number.

4. 9 __19__   5. 20 __30__   6. 87 __97__

Use any strategy to find the sum.

7. 23 + 5 = __28__   8. 3 + 16 = __19__

9. 19 + 4 = __23__

ADDITION STRATEGIES   115   UNIT REVIEW

Use cubes to make three groups to show the number. Then combine the groups in two different ways to find the sum. Draw all the groups.

10. 14

Check students' models and drawings. Answers will vary.
Example: ⊡⊡⊡⊡ ⊡⊡⊡ ⊡⊡⊡⊡⊡⊡⊡

⊡⊡⊡⊡ ⊡⊡⊡⊡⊡⊡⊡⊡⊡⊡

⊡⊡⊡⊡⊡⊡⊡ ⊡⊡⊡⊡⊡⊡⊡

Find the sum. Circle the two numbers you added first. Explain your reasons for grouping those numbers.

11. 9 + ⑤ + ⑥ = __20__   12. ③ + ⑦ + 8 = __18__

13. ⑤ + ② + 6 = __13__

14. ⑨
    ①
    + 6

    16

15. 5
    ⑧
    + ②

    15

16. ④
    ④
    + 8

    16

Addends that are circled and explanations will vary.

ADDITION STRATEGIES   116   UNIT REVIEW

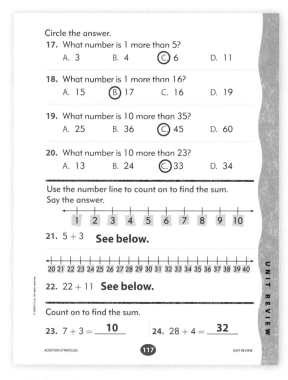

Circle the answer.

17. What number is 1 more than 5?
    A. 3   B. 4   (C.) 6   D. 11

18. What number is 1 more than 16?
    A. 15   (B.) 17   C. 16   D. 19

19. What number is 10 more than 35?
    A. 25   B. 36   (C.) 45   D. 60

20. What number is 10 more than 23?
    A. 13   B. 24   (C.) 33   D. 34

Use the number line to count on to find the sum. Say the answer.

21. $5 + 3$ **See below.**

22. $22 + 11$ **See below.**

Count on to find the sum.

23. $7 + 3 = $ __10__   **24.** $28 + 4 = $ __32__

ADDITION STRATEGIES   117   UNIT REVIEW

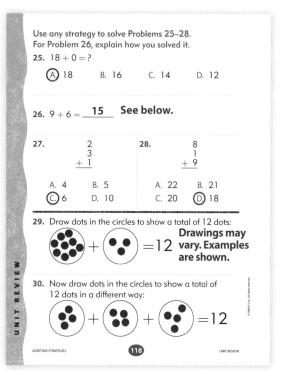

Use any strategy to solve Problems 25–28. For Problem 26, explain how you solved it.

25. $18 + 0 = ?$
    (A.) 18   B. 16   C. 14   D. 12

26. $9 + 6 = $ __15__   **See below.**

27.
$$\begin{array}{r} 2 \\ 3 \\ +\ 1 \\ \hline \end{array}$$
    A. 4   B. 5
    (C.) 6   D. 10

28.
$$\begin{array}{r} 8 \\ 1 \\ +\ 9 \\ \hline \end{array}$$
    A. 22   B. 21
    C. 20   (D.) 18

29. Draw dots in the circles to show a total of 12 dots:
Drawings may vary. Examples are shown.

30. Now draw dots in the circles to show a total of 12 dots in a different way:

ADDITION STRATEGIES   118   UNIT REVIEW

Additional Answers

21. Students should start at 5 and count on 3 to 8. They should state that $5 + 3 = 8$.

22. Students should start at 22 and count on 11 to 33. They should state that $22 + 11 = 33$.

26. **Possible answer:** Start at 9 and count on 6 to 15.

⤵ UNIT REVIEW Prepare for the Checkpoint

What you do next depends on how students performed in the previous activity, Unit Review: Checkpoint Practice. If students had difficulty with any of the problems, complete the appropriate review activity listed in the table online.

Unit Checkpoint

Lesson Overview

UNIT CHECKPOINT Online	25 minutes	**ONLINE**
UNIT CHECKPOINT Offline	35 minutes	**OFFLINE**

▶ Unit Objectives

This lesson assesses the following objectives:

- Identify one more than or one less than a given number.
- Identify 10 more than or 10 less than a given number.
- Use "counting on" to solve addition problems.
- Use "counting on from the greatest number" to solve addition problems.
- Combine memorized facts with counting strategies to solve addition problems.
- Given a number of objects up through 20, show how those objects can be grouped and regrouped to illustrate the associative property.
- Find the sum of three one-digit numbers, with sums through 20.

Materials to Gather

SUPPLIED
Unit Checkpoint (printout)
blocks – O (red, blue)

UNIT CHECKPOINT Online

ONLINE 25 min

Students will complete this part of the Unit Checkpoint online. Read the directions, problems, and answer choices to students. If necessary, help students with keyboard or mouse operations.

Objectives

- Assess unit objectives.

UNIT CHECKPOINT Offline

OFFLINE 35 min

Students will complete this part of the Unit Checkpoint offline. In Part 1, students will take a performance-based assessment. In Part 2, students will complete the problems on their own. Print the Unit Checkpoint. Read the directions, problems, and answer choices to students if necessary. Use the answer key to score the Checkpoint, and then enter the results online.

Gather the cubes. Students will use the cubes for Problems 18–21.

Objectives

- Assess unit objectives.

Name _____ Date _____

Unit Checkpoint Answer Key

Part 1

Follow the instructions for each problem. Choose the response that best describes how the student performs on the task. When you have finished, enter the results online.

1. Show the student this problem on a sheet of paper: $15 + 5 =$ _____.
Say, "Use a strategy you have learned, or math facts, to solve this problem. Then explain how you solved it."
(1 point)
Did the student answer 20 and explain the strategy or math fact used to solve the problem?

  A. Yes   B. No

2. Show the student this problem on a sheet of paper: $9 + 6 =$ _____.
Say, "Use a strategy you have learned, or math facts, to solve this problem."
(1 point)
Did the student answer 15 and explain the strategy or math fact used to solve the problem?

  A. Yes   B. No

Give students Part 2 of the assessment.

Name _____ Date _____

Part 2
(1 point)
3. Find the sum.

$9 + 3 + 7 =$ **19**

Count on to find the sum.

(1 point)
4. $7 + 3 =$ **10**   *(1 point)* **5.** $28 + 4 =$ **32**

Add to find the sum.

(1 point)
6. $10 + 6 =$ **16**   *(1 point)* **7.** $16 + 5 =$ **21**

(1 point)
8. What number is 10 more than 23? **33**

(1 point)
9. What number is 1 more than 49? **50**

(1 point)
10. Count on 11 from 22 to find the sum of $22 + 11$. **33**

(1 point)
11. Count on 9 from 13 to find the sum of $13 + 9$. **22**

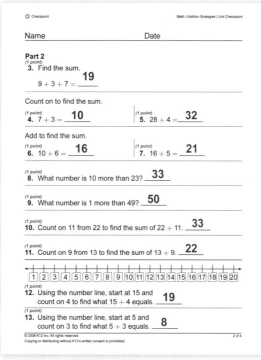

(1 point)
12. Using the number line, start at 15 and count on 4 to find what $15 + 4$ equals. **19**

(1 point)
13. Using the number line, start at 5 and count on 3 to find what $5 + 3$ equals. **8**

Name _____ Date _____

(1 point)
14. Draw balloons in the circles to show a total of 7 balloons.

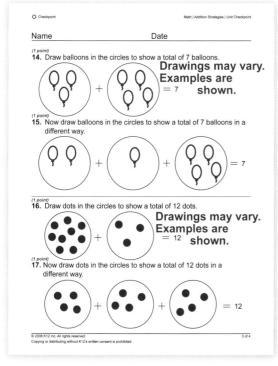

Drawings may vary. Examples are shown.

(1 point)
15. Now draw balloons in the circles to show a total of 7 balloons in a different way.

(1 point)
16. Draw dots in the circles to show a total of 12 dots.

Drawings may vary. Examples are shown.

(1 point)
17. Now draw dots in the circles to show a total of 12 dots in a different way.

Name _____ Date _____

For Problems 18–21, follow the directions, and then sketch your models.
(1 point)
18. Use two groups of cubes to show one way to make 10.

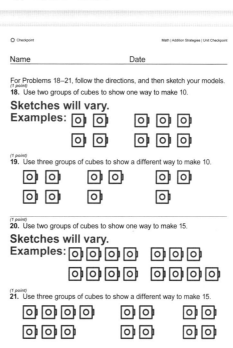

Sketches will vary. Examples:

(1 point)
19. Use three groups of cubes to show a different way to make 10.

(1 point)
20. Use two groups of cubes to show one way to make 15.

Sketches will vary. Examples:

(1 point)
21. Use three groups of cubes to show a different way to make 15.

Addition Number Sentences

▶ Unit Objectives

- Represent equivalent forms of the same number through the use of physical models such as tens rods and ones cubes through 20, such as $7 = 4 + 3$, or $5 + 2$, or $1 + 2 + 4$, or $9 - 2$, or $20 - 13$.

- Represent equivalent forms of the same number through the use of diagrams through 20, such as $7 = 4 + 3$, or $5 + 2$, or $1 + 2 + 4$, or $9 - 2$, or $20 - 13$.

- Represent equivalent forms of the same number through 20 through the use of number expressions, such as $7 = 4 + 3$, or $5 + 2$, or $1 + 2 + 4$, or $9 - 2$, or $20 - 13$.

- Solve addition problems by filling in a missing number or numbers in a given number sentence.

▶ Big Ideas

Models and mathematical symbols can represent addition and subtraction.

▶ Unit Introduction

Students will identify and practice showing numbers in various ways—with models, sketches, and addition expressions. Then they will represent equivalent forms of the same number, such as 2 and $1 + 1$, in these various ways.

Students will use a balance to help identify equivalent forms of a number, including equal expressions, such as $3 + 5$ and $4 + 4$. Then they will use the balance to find the missing number in an addition sentence; first they will find missing sums, and then they will find missing addends.

Students will learn that they can add two numbers in any order and the sum will not change. They will explore this property using the balance and blocks, and then they will use this knowledge to find missing addends in number sentences with addition expressions on each side.

Different Forms of Numbers

Lesson Overview

Skills Update	5 minutes	ONLINE
GET READY Show Amounts	5 minutes	OFFLINE
LEARN Show Numbers with Objects	15 minutes	OFFLINE
LEARN Show Numbers with Drawings	10 minutes	OFFLINE
LEARN Show Numbers with Expressions	15 minutes	OFFLINE
TRY IT Show Numbers Different Ways	10 minutes	OFFLINE

▶ Lesson Objectives

- Represent equivalent forms of the same number through the use of physical models such as tens rods and ones cubes through 20.
- Represent equivalent forms of the same number through the use of diagrams through 20.
- Represent equivalent forms of the same number through 20 through the use of number expressions, such as $7 = 4 + 3$, or $5 + 2$, or $1 + 2 + 4$.

▶ Prerequisite Skills

Use concrete objects or sketches to represent a quantity up through 30.

▶ Content Background

Students will identify different ways to show a number.

Although the phrase *equals sign* is often used in everyday language, *equals symbol* is more accurate as a mathematical term. In math, *sign* refers specifically to positive signs and negative signs.

Materials to Gather

SUPPLIED

blocks – B (all colors)

blocks – O (10 of each color)

Show Numbers Different Ways activity page

ALSO NEEDED

paper, construction – 1 light-colored sheet

crayons

Keywords

addend – one of the two or more numbers that are added to determine a sum

equals symbol ($=$) – a symbol that shows the relationship between two equal values

equivalent – having the same value

expression – a number or a combination of numbers and symbols that represents a given value, such as $2 + 3$ or $10 - 4 + 1$

model (noun) – a physical object, diagram, or picture that represents an amount, an expression, an equation, or a problem situation

plus symbol ($+$) – the symbol that signals addition

sum – the solution to an addition problem

GET READY Show Amounts

- Use concrete objects or sketches to represent a quantity up through 30.

Students will use circle blocks to represent numbers through 30.
Gather the circles and construction paper.

1. Place the circles in the workspace. Place the construction paper in front of students. Place 15 circles on the paper.

   Say: These circles show 15.

2. **Ask:** How can you check the amount?
   ANSWER: You can count the circles.

3. Put the circles back in the pile.

4. **Say:** Use the circles to show me 23. Put the circles on the paper.

5. Check that students have placed 23 circles on the paper. If necessary, have students place the circles on the paper one at a time as they count.

6. Watch for students who miss circles when they count or who double-count circles. Explain that they have to say one number for each circle.

7. **Say:** Put the circles back in the pile. Now we are going to use the circles to show other amounts.

8. Repeat with other amounts through 30.

Tips

To prevent students from skipping an object or counting an object twice, have students move exactly one circle as they count it.

LEARN Show Numbers with Objects

- Represent equivalent forms of the same number through the use of physical models such as tens rods and ones cubes through 20.

Students will use models to represent equivalent forms of the same numbers.
Gather the cubes.

1. Make a train of 2 red cubes and 3 blue cubes. Then make a train of 1 red cube and 4 blue cubes.

2. **Ask:** What number do both of the trains show?
   ANSWER: 5

   Say: Make a train of 5 green cubes. Put it next to the other trains. Are all the trains the same length?
   ANSWER: Yes

3. **Say:** These are all ways to show 5.

4. Make a train of 4 red cubes and 3 blue cubes. Then make a train of 1 red cube, 4 blue cubes, and 2 yellow cubes.

5. **Ask:** What number do both of the trains show?
   ANSWER: 7

   Say: Make a train of 7 green cubes. Put it next to the other trains. Are all the trains the same length?
   ANSWER: Yes

   Say: These are all ways to show 7.

6. **Say:** Now it is your turn to show numbers with cubes. Use the cubes to model the number 9 two different ways.

   Check students' models. Accept any train that has 9 cubes in it.

7. **Say:** Make a train of 9 cubes of one color. Compare it to the other trains you made.

   Ask: Do all of these trains show 9? How do you know?
   ANSWER: Yes. They are all the same length. They all have 9 cubes.

8. **Say:** Now I will make a train, and you will make another train to show the same number in a different way.

9. Make a train with 3 red cubes and 5 blue cubes.

   Say: Use cubes to show the same number in a different way.

   Accept any train with 8 cubes.

10. Repeat Step 9 with numbers through 10. Make a train with 2 or 3 different-colored cubes, and have students make a different train that shows the same number. Students can use 2 or 3 different-colored cubes to show each number.

OFFLINE
10min

LEARN Show Numbers with Drawings

Students will use drawings to represent equivalent forms of the same with numbers.
   Gather the crayons.

1. Draw 3 blue stars, a plus symbol, and then 3 red stars.

2. **Ask:** How many blue stars are there?
   ANSWER: 3

   Ask: What is after the 3 blue stars?
   ANSWER: a plus symbol

   Ask: How many red stars are there?
   ANSWER: 3

3. Draw 4 red stars, a plus symbol, 1 blue star, another plus symbol, and 1 yellow star. Draw an equals symbol after the last star on each drawing.

4. **Ask:** What number do these pictures show?
   ANSWER: 6

   Say: Both of these pictures show the number 6. Write a 6 after each equals symbol.

5. **Say:** Now it is your turn to draw pictures to show numbers. Draw 2 pictures to show the number 4. You can use any simple shape or object in your picture, such as a circle, square, or star. Write a plus symbol between each group to show the addition.

6. Help students write two equals symbols with a 4 after each one, being sure to leave space before the equals symbol for the pictures.

   Accept any drawing that shows a total of 4 objects.

7. Write 9 =. Then draw 5 red dots and 4 blue dots after the equals symbol.

8. **Say:** Look at my picture. Draw a picture that shows the same number a different way.

9. Have students write 9 = and then have them draw their own pictures.

   Accept any drawing that shows a total of 9 objects.

10. Repeat Steps 7–9 with numbers through 10. Have students draw 2 diagrams for given numbers for some problems. Be sure to vary where you place the equals symbol and the sum. Write the equals symbol after the sum for some problems. Write the equals symbol before the sum for other problems.

Objectives

- Represent equivalent forms of the same number through the use of diagrams through 20.

Tips

Remind students to use simple shapes for sketches.

LEARN Show Numbers with Expressions

Objectives

- Represent equivalent forms of the same number through the use of diagrams through 20.

Students will use expressions to represent equivalent forms of a given number.

1. **Say:** You can use expressions to show a number. Your number expression can have two or three addends.

2. Write $2 + 1$ and $1 + 1 + 1$ on a sheet of paper.

   Ask: What is the sum of these expressions?
   ANSWER: They are both equal to 3.

3. **Say:** Both expressions have a sum of 3, so both of these expressions show the number 3.

4. **Say:** On your paper, write 2 expressions to show the number 5.

5. Check students' work. Accept any expression with a sum of 5.

6. Repeat Steps 4–5 with 5 other numbers through 10. Tell students to write more than 2 expressions, and to use 3 addends for some of their expressions.

7. Write $3 + 4$ on a sheet of paper.

   Say: Write another expression that shows the same number as $3 + 4$.

   Check students' work. Accept any expression that has a value of 7.

8. Give students other expressions with sums through 10 in random order, and have them write an expression showing the same number for each.

Tips

Watch for students who cannot find other ways to represent a number or an expression. Suggest that they choose one of the numbers used in their first expression and break it apart. For example, if they write $1 + 7$, they can break the 7 apart and make $1 + 3 + 4$.

TRY IT Show Numbers Different Ways

Objectives

- Represent equivalent forms of the same number through the use of physical models such as tens rods and ones cubes through 20.

- Represent equivalent forms of the same number through the use of diagrams through 20.

- Represent equivalent forms of the same number through 20 through the use of number expressions, such as $7 = 4 + 3$, or $5 + 2$, or $1 + 2 + 4$.

Students will practice representing numbers in different ways. Give students the cubes and the Show Numbers Different Ways activity page from their Activity Books. Read the directions with them.

For Problems 3 and 4, show students the following cube trains. Have them make a different train that shows the same number.

Problem 3: Show students 4 blue cubes and 1 red cube.
Problem 4: Show students 2 blue cubes and 7 red cubes.

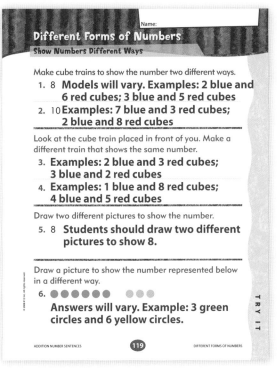

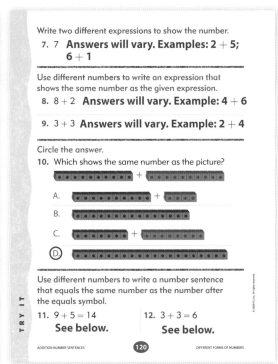

Additional Answers

11. Students should write any other expression that equals 14. Answers will vary. Accept any reasonable answer.

Examples:

$7 + 7$

$8 + 6$

$13 + 1$

$5 + 5 + 4$

12. Students should write any other expression that equals 6. Answers will vary. Accept any reasonable answer.

Examples:

$5 + 1$

$2 + 4$

$6 + 0$

$3 + 2 + 1$

Ways to Show Numbers

Skills Update	5 minutes	ONLINE
GET READY Show Amounts Through 30	5 minutes	OFFLINE
LEARN Show Numbers Other Ways	15 minutes	OFFLINE
LEARN Show Numbers Three Ways	15 minutes	OFFLINE
TRY IT Sum It Up	10 minutes	OFFLINE
CHECKPOINT	10 minutes	OFFLINE

▶ Lesson Objectives

- Represent equivalent forms of the same number through the use of physical models such as tens rods and ones cubes through 20.
- Represent equivalent forms of the same number through the use of diagrams through 20.
- Represent equivalent forms of the same number through 20 through the use of number expressions, such as $7 = 4 + 3$, or $5 + 2$, or $1 + 2 + 4$, or $9 - 2$.

▶ Prerequisite Skills

Use concrete objects or sketches to represent a quantity up through 30.

▶ Content Background

Students will show numbers in different ways in this lesson.

The word *expression* is defined as a combination of number(s) and symbol(s) that represents a given value. An expression does not include an equals symbol ($=$) or other relational symbols, such as a not-equal-to symbol ($\neq$), a less-than symbol ($<$), or a greater-than symbol ($>$).

The term *number sentence* is defined as two expressions that are related to one another by an equals symbol ($=$), a not-equal-to symbol ($\neq$), a less-than symbol ($<$), or a greater-than symbol ($>$).

Materials to Gather

SUPPLIED

blocks – O (10 of each color)

Sum It Up activity page

Checkpoint (printout)

ALSO NEEDED

crayons

counting objects – 30 each of three types

glue

paper, construction – 6 light-colored sheets

GET READY Show Amounts Through 30

Students will use drawings to represent quantities up through 30.
  Gather the crayons.

1. Show students how to fold a sheet of paper into four sections, unfold it, and flatten it out. Write one of these numbers—14, 17, 21, 30—in the top left corner of each section.

2. Point to the section labeled 14. Ask students to draw 14 dots in that section. If students have difficulty, have them count aloud each dot as they draw it.

3. **Say:** When you are drawing pictures to show amounts, you can use any simple object or shape, as long as you can count it.

4. Repeat Step 2 for the numbers 17, 21, and 30.

Objectives

Use concrete objects or sketches to represent a quantity up through 30.

Tips

Remind students to use simple shapes for sketches.

LEARN Show Numbers Other Ways

Students will represent equivalent forms of the same number by using models, pictures, and expressions.
  Gather the cubes and crayons.

1. Show students a train of 8 red cubes and 7 blue cubes.

    Say: There are many ways to show the same number. These cubes represent a number. Let's make a picture to show the same number.

2. Give students a sheet of paper and crayons.

    Say: Draw a picture that shows the cubes. We can use any simple drawings to represent the cubes. Let's use a red circle for each red cube. Use a blue circle for each blue cube. Write a plus symbol between the groups of circles.

    Students should draw 8 red circles, a plus symbol, and then 7 blue circles.

    Ask: What number do the cubes and picture show?
    ANSWER: 15.

3. **Say:** Write an equals symbol after the circles, and then write 15.

4. **Say:** Now write an addition expression to match the picture and the cube train.

    Students should write $8 + 7$.

5. **Say:** The cubes, the picture, and the expression all show the number 15.

6. Take the cube train apart. Draw a picture of 3 red squares, 7 blue squares, and 9 yellow squares. Write an equals symbol before the squares and a plus symbol between each group of squares.

    Ask: What number does this picture show?
    ANSWER: 19.

    Have students write 19 in front of the equals symbol.

7. **Say:** Use cubes to show the picture. Use red, blue, and yellow cubes to show the red, blue, and yellow squares.

    Students should use 3 red, 7 blue, and 9 yellow cubes to make a train.

8. **Say:** Now write an expression to match the picture and the cube train.

    Students should write $3 + 7 + 9$.

Objectives

- Represent equivalent forms of the same number through the use of physical models such as tens rods and ones cubes through 20.

- Represent equivalent forms of the same number through the use of diagrams through 20.

- Represent equivalent forms of the same number through 20 through the use of number expressions, such as $7 = 4 + 3$, or $5 + 2$, or $1 + 2 + 4$.

9. **Say:** The picture, the cube train, and the expression all show the number 19.

10. Take the cube train apart. Write $6 + 8$.

    Ask: What number does this expression show?
    ANSWER: 14.

11. **Say:** Make a cube train to show the expression. Use a different color to show each addend.

    Students should make a cube train with 6 cubes of one color and 8 cubes of another color.

12. **Say:** Now draw a picture to match the train. Remember to use a plus symbol and an equals symbol.

    Students should draw a group of 6 objects and a group of 8 objects with a plus symbol in between. Students may write the equals symbol and 14 on either side of the expression.

13. **Say:** The expression, the cube train, and the picture all show the number 14.

14. Show students a cube train with 6 red, 8 blue, and 2 yellow cubes. Repeat Steps 1–5 with this train.

15. Show students a picture of 5 red stars and 6 blue stars. Repeat Steps 6–9 with this picture.

16. Show students the expression $9 + 3$. Repeat Steps 10–13 with this expression.

17. If time permits, have students complete additional examples with numbers 11 through 20.

LEARN Show Numbers Three Ways

Students will represent equivalent forms of a given number using models, pictures, and expressions.

Gather the counting objects (for example, dry macaroni, beans, and buttons), glue, and construction paper.

1. **Say:** Show the number 17 two different ways, using these counting objects. You can use 2 or 3 different objects for each way. Line them up in rows like trains.

2. Lay a sheet of construction paper on the table horizontally.

3. **Say:** Make a picture for each of your object trains by gluing them on the construction paper. Write the number 17 at the top of the paper. Then lay your objects out on the paper where you want them and write plus symbols and equal symbols between the different groups. Leave space between the groups of objects so you can write the expressions below them. Then glue the objects in place.

   Check students' work before allowing them to glue.

4. Below each train, have students write the equivalent expression.

   Here is a sample of what a completed project may look like:

5. Have students repeat the activity to show 15, 20, 18, 11, and 14.

Tips

Watch for students who cannot find a second way to represent a number with models. Suggest that they take the numbers used in their first train and break one of the numbers apart. For example, if they made a train with 5 and 7, they can break the 7 apart and make $5 + 3 + 4$. Explain that this method would work for pictures and expressions as well.

Tips

If students are ready for a challenge, offer them 4 types of counting objects and have them try to show the sums with 4 addends.

Objectives

Students will practice representing equivalent forms of numbers. Give students the cubes, crayons, and the Sum It Up activity page from their Activity Book. Read the directions with them.

For Problem 1, show students a cube train with 5 red cubes, 2 blue cubes, and 8 yellow cubes.

- Represent equivalent forms of the same number through the use of physical models such as tens rods and ones cubes through 20.

- Represent equivalent forms of the same number through the use of diagrams through 20.

- Represent equivalent forms of the same number through 20 through the use of number expressions, such as $7 = 4 + 3$, or $5 + 2$, or $1 + 2 + 4$, or $9 - 2$, or $20 - 13$.

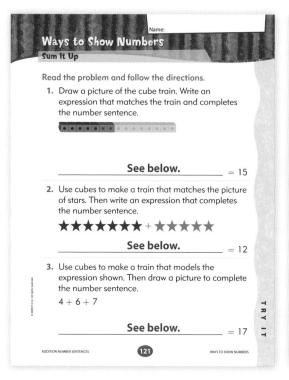

Ways to Show Numbers

Sum It Up

Read the problem and follow the directions.

1. Draw a picture of the cube train. Write an expression that matches the train and completes the number sentence.

   _____**See below.**_____ $= 15$

2. Use cubes to make a train that matches the picture of stars. Then write an expression that completes the number sentence.

   ★★★★★★★ + ★★★★★

   _____**See below.**_____ $= 12$

3. Use cubes to make a train that models the expression shown. Then draw a picture to complete the number sentence.

   $4 + 6 + 7$

   _____**See below.**_____ $= 17$

ADDITION NUMBER SENTENCES   **121**   WAYS TO SHOW NUMBERS

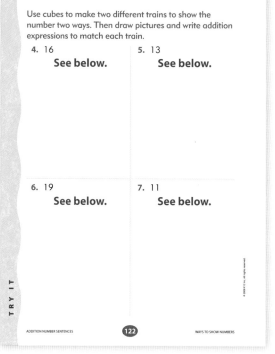

Use cubes to make two different trains to show the number two ways. Then draw pictures and write addition expressions to match each train.

4. 16
   See below.

5. 13
   See below.

6. 19
   See below.

7. 11
   See below.

ADDITION NUMBER SENTENCES   **122**   WAYS TO SHOW NUMBERS

Additional Answers

1. Students should draw 5 red shapes, 2 blue shapes, and 8 yellow shapes and write $5 + 2 + 8$ on the line.

2. Students should make a train of 7 red cubes and 5 blue cubes and write $7 + 5$ on the line.

3. Students should make a train. They should draw a picture on the line. The train and drawing should have 4 cubes of one color, 6 of another, and 7 of a third color.

4–7. Check students' work to be sure that the numbers are represented correctly and that each train matches a drawing and a number sentence.

Read the problem and follow the directions.

8. Draw two models for the number 13.

See below.

9. Use cubes to model the number 15 two different ways. Write the expressions for each way.

See below.

_____

_____

10. The picture uses addition to show 12. Using dots, draw another addition picture that shows 12.

●●●●●●●●●● + ●●

See below.

ADDITION NUMBER SENTENCES (123) WAYS TO SHOW NUMBERS

TRY IT

TRY IT

Read the problem and follow the directions.

11. Which two pictures show 10? Circle the answer.

A. ●● + ●●●●●
●●● + ●●●●

(B.) ●●●●● + ●●●●●
●●● + ●●●●●●●

C. ●●●● + ●●●●●●
●●●●●●●●● + ●●●

12. Write four expressions to show the number 8.

_____ **See below.** _____

_____   _____

13. 7 + 2 = 9. Write three other expressions to show 9.

_____ **See below.** _____

_____

ADDITION NUMBER SENTENCES (124) WAYS TO SHOW NUMBERS

8. Drawings will vary.
Examples:
a set of 7 cubes and a set of 6 cubes
a set of 10 cubes and a set of 3 cubes

9. Students should create two models and write two expressions to match their models for the number 15. Models and expressions will vary.
Examples:
a set of 9 cubes and a set of 6 cubes and an expression of $9 + 6$
a set of 10 cubes and a set of 5 cubes and an expression of $10 + 5$

10. Drawings will vary. Accept any reasonable answer.
Examples:
6 dots + 6 dots
11 dots + 1 dot

12. Students should write four expressions that equal 8. Accept any reasonable answer.
Examples:
$1 + 1 + 1 + 1 + 1 + 1 + 1 + 1$
$2 + 2 + 2 + 2$
$3 + 5$
$4 + 4$
$1 + 7$

13. Students should write three other expressions that equal 9. Accept any reasonable answer.
Examples:
$8 + 1$
$4 + 5$
$9 + 0$

CHECKPOINT

Objectives

- Represent equivalent forms of the same number through the use of physical models such as tens rods and ones cubes through 20.

- Represent equivalent forms of the same number through the use of diagrams through 20.

- Represent equivalent forms of the same number through 20 through the use of number expressions, such as $7 = 4 + 3$, or $5 + 2$, or $1 + 2 + 4$.

Print the Checkpoint. In Part 1, students will take a performance-based assessment. In Part 2, students will complete the problems on their own. Read the directions, problems, and answer choices to students if necessary. Use the answer key to score the Checkpoint, and then enter the results online.

Gather the cubes. Students will use the cubes for Problems 1 and 2.

Name _____ Date _____

Checkpoint Answer Key

Part 1

Follow the instructions for each item. Choose the response that best describes how the student performs on the task. When you have finished, enter the results online.

1. Use the cubes to model the number 11 two different ways.

   Examples: Set of 10 cubes and 1 cube. Set of 11 cubes. Models will vary.
   (1 point)
   Did the student model the number 11?

   A. Yes   B. No
   (1 point)
   Did the student model the number 11 a different way?

   A. Yes   B. No

2. Use the cubes to model the number 18 two different ways.

   Examples: Set of 10 cubes and set of 8 cubes. Two sets of 9 cubes each. Models will vary.
   (1 point)
   Did the student model the number 18?

   A. Yes   B. No
   (1 point)
   Did the student model the number 18 a different way?

   A. Yes   B. No

Give students Part 2 of the assessment.

Name _____ Date _____

Part 2

Circle the answer.
(1 point)
3. Which shows a way to represent the number 16?

   (A) [model]

   B. [model]

   C. [model]

(1 point)
4. This picture uses addition to show 5.   ●+●●●●
   Which answer choice also shows 5?

   A. ●●+●●   (B) ●●+●●●

   C. ●●●●●+●   D. ●●●●+●●

(1 point)
5. The picture uses addition to show 14. Which answer choice also shows 14?

   ☆☆☆☆☆☆☆☆☆+☆☆☆☆☆

   A. ★★★★+★★★★★

   B. ★+★★★★★

   (C) ★★★★★★★+★★★★★★★

   D. ★★★★★★★★★★★★★+★

Name _____ Date _____

(1 point)
6. Which two pictures show 6?

(A.) ♥♥♥ + ♥♥♥   and   ♥♥♥♥♥ + ♥

B. ♥♥♥♥ + ♥   and   ♥♥♥ + ♥♥

C. ♥♥♥♥ + ♥♥♥   and   ♥♥ + ♥♥♥♥♥

(1 point)
7. Which two pictures show 11?

A. ♥♥♥♥♥♥♥♥ + ♥♥♥   and   ♥♥♥♥♥ + ♥
♥♥♥♥♥♥♥   ♥♥♥♥

B. ♥ + ♥   and   ♥♥ + ♥

(C.) ♥♥♥♥ + ♥   and   ♥♥♥♥ + ♥♥♥
♥♥♥♥   ♥♥♥

(1 point)
8. What is another way to write 6 + 6?

A. 3 + 3 + 3   (B) 4 + 4 + 4
C. 2 + 2 + 2   D. 5 + 5 + 9

Name _____ Date _____

(1 point)
9. Which of the following is equal to 6 + 6?

A. 5 + 1   (B.) 10 + 2   C. 6 + 3

(3 points)
10. 7 + 9 = 16. Write three other ways to show 16.

**Award 1 point for each correct
expression for a total of 3 points.
Answers will vary.**

Examples:
16 + 0
8 + 8
4 + 4 + 8
10 + 6

Missing Numbers in Addition

Lesson Overview

Skills Update	5 minutes	ONLINE
GET READY Balance Model	5 minutes	ONLINE
LEARN Balance Number Sentences	15 minutes	ONLINE
LEARN Find Missing Numbers	10 minutes	OFFLINE
TRY IT What Is Missing?	15 minutes	OFFLINE

▶ Lesson Objectives

Solve addition problems by filling in a missing number or numbers in a given number sentence.

▶ Content Background

Students will learn that they can find a missing part of an addition problem.

In an addition number sentence, there are often three numbers: two addends and the sum. Students have learned to add the addends to find the sum. Some addition problems may have more than two addends.

Students also can write an addition number sentence with a missing addend—for example, $3 + ? = 7$. In this lesson, students will learn how to find the missing addend by asking themselves, "3 plus what number is the same as 7?"

Materials to Gather

SUPPLIED
blocks – O (10 of each color)
Find Missing Numbers activity page
What Is Missing? activity page
Missing Numbers activity page

Keywords

addition sentence – a number sentence that involves addition only
number sentence – two expressions related by an equals symbol ($=$), a not-equal-to symbol ($\neq$), or an inequality symbol; for example, $7 - 2 = 4 + 1$; $5 \neq 4 + 4$; $6 + 2 > 1 + 4$

GET READY Balance Model

ONLINE
5 min

Students will use a balance to decide if expressions are equal and to find a sum.

Objectives

• Solve addition problems by filling in a missing number or numbers in a given number sentence.

LEARN Balance Number Sentences

ONLINE 15 min

Students will learn to use a balance to find a missing number in an addition sentence.
Explain that the missing number can be on either side of the expression and can be the first number or the second number. Remind students that when the missing number is an addend, the missing number can be added to the given addend and it will equal the given sum.

Objectives
- Solve addition problems by filling in a missing number or numbers in a given number sentence.

LEARN Find Missing Numbers

OFFLINE 10 min

Students will use cubes to find missing numbers in addition sentences.
Gather the cubes and the Find Missing Numbers activity page from the Activity Book.

Objectives
- Solve addition problems by filling in a missing number or numbers in a given number sentence.

PROBLEM 1

1. Make a train with 8 red cubes and 4 yellow cubes.

   Say: Look at Problem 1 on your activity page. The addition sentence has two addends. The sum is missing. How can we use this cube train to find the missing sum?
   ANSWER: Find the total number of cubes in the train.

2. **Ask:** How many cubes are in the train?
   ANSWER: 12

   Say: So 8 plus 4 equals 12, and 12 is the missing number in the addition sentence.

PROBLEM 2

3. Take the 4 yellow cubes off the train so it is a train with 8 red cubes.

4. **Say:** Look at Problem 2. The addition sentence has one addend (8) and a sum (13). The other addend is missing. We can use this cube train to find this missing addend.

5. **Say:** Look at the cube train (with 8 red cubes). It is part of a 13-train, but it has only 8 cubes. We need more cubes to make the rest of the train. Let's find out how many cubes to add. Let's add yellow cubes, one at a time, until we have 13 cubes in the train.

6. Have students count with you as you add cubes to the train until you get to 13 cubes.

   Ask: How many yellow cubes did we add?
   ANSWER: 5

   Say: Write 5 on the line. So the missing number is 5. 8 plus 5 equals 13.

7. Have students complete the activity page. For problems with missing sums, use Steps 1 and 2 as a guide. For problems with missing addends, use Steps 4–6.

Missing Numbers in Addition
Find Missing Numbers

Name:

Use cubes to model the number sentence.
Write the missing number.

1. $8 + 4 = \underline{12}$ 2. $8 + \underline{5} = 13$

3. $8 + \underline{6} = 14$ 4. $8 + \underline{7} = 15$

5. $8 + \underline{8} = 16$ 6. $8 + \underline{9} = 17$

7. $15 = 10 + \underline{5}$ 8. $15 = 9 + \underline{6}$

9. $15 = 8 + \underline{7}$ 10. $15 = 7 + \underline{8}$

11. $15 = 6 + \underline{9}$ 12. $15 = 5 + \underline{10}$

L E A R N

L E A R N

13. $\underline{4} + 5 = 9$ 14. $7 + \underline{5} = 12$

15. $\underline{20} = 16 + 4$ 16. $8 + \underline{9} = 17$

17. $\underline{12} = 9 + 3$ 18. $\underline{5} + 14 = 19$

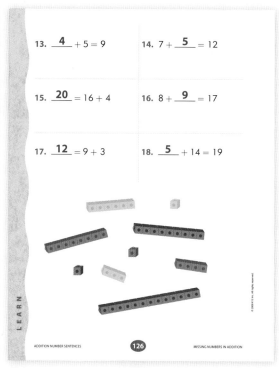

OFFLINE
15 min

TRY IT What Is Missing?

Objectives

Students will practice finding the missing number in an addition sentence. Give students the What Is Missing? activity page from their Activity Book and read the directions with them. Use the answer key to check students' answers, and then enter the results online.

- Solve addition problems by filling in a missing number or numbers in a given number sentence.

Missing Numbers in Addition
What Is Missing?

Name:

Write the missing number.

1. $7 + \underline{4} = 11$ 2. $9 + \underline{4} = 13$

3. $\underline{7} + 7 = 14$ 4. $12 = 8 + \underline{4}$

Circle the missing number.

5. $9 = ? + 4$
   A. 9   B. 7   Ⓒ 5   D. 3

Write the missing number.

6. $14 = 5 + \underline{9}$

T R Y I T

T R Y I T

Circle the missing number.

7. $12 = ? + 6$
   A. 18   B. 12   Ⓒ 6   D. 3

8. $13 + ? = 18$
   A. 4   Ⓑ 5   C. 8   D. 13

9. $19 = 10 + ?$
   Ⓐ 9   B. 12   C. 21   D. 27

10. $? + 9 = 12$
   A. 2   Ⓑ 3   C. 15   D. 21

Write the missing number.

11. $8 + \underline{9} = 17$ 12. $\underline{9} = 2 + 7$

13. $9 + \underline{6} = 15$ 14. $12 = 8 + \underline{4}$

15. $5 + \underline{7} = 12$ 16. $5 + 8 = \underline{13}$

17. $\underline{8} + 6 = 14$ 18. $14 = 5 + \underline{9}$

Circle the missing number.

19. $? + 5 = 9$

Ⓐ 4   B. 7   C. 12   D. 14

20. $19 = 10 + ?$

Ⓐ 9   B. 12   C. 21   D. 27

TRY IT

Missing Numbers in Addition Sentences

Lesson Overview

Skills Update	5 minutes	ONLINE
GET READY Add Frogs	5 minutes	ONLINE
LEARN Does Order Matter?	15 minutes	OFFLINE
TRY IT What Number Is Missing?	15 minutes	OFFLINE
TRY IT Fill In the Number	10 minutes	OFFLINE
CHECKPOINT	10 minutes	OFFLINE

▶ Lesson Objectives

Solve addition problems by filling in a missing number or numbers in a given number sentence.

▶ Advance Preparation

Label an index card with the = symbol, or gather the symbol card you created previously.

▶ Content Background

In this lesson, students will learn how to find the missing addend in an addition sentence.

The commutative property of addition states that you can add numbers in any order and the sum does not change. For example, $5 + 3 = 8$ and $3 + 5 = 8$. So $5 + 3 = 3 + 5$. This means that addition is commutative. Without using the term commutative property, students will add numbers in different orders to learn that the sum is the same.

An addition sentence is a sentence that involves addition and can be restated by using mathematical symbols. For example: Five and four equals nine; $5 + 4 = 9$.

Keywords	**commutative property of addition** – a rule stating that changing the order of two addends does not change their sum

Tips

SUPPLIED

blocks – O (10 of each color)

What Number Is Missing? activity page

Fill In the Number activity page

Checkpoint (printout)

ALSO NEEDED

index card – labeled with = symbol

GET READY Add Frogs

ONLINE
5 min

Students will solve addition problems by adding numbers in any order to get the same sum.

Objectives

- Solve addition problems by filling in a missing number or numbers in a given number sentence.

LEARN Does Order Matter?

- Solve addition problems by filling in a missing number or numbers in a given number sentence.

Students will add numbers and find missing numbers in addition sentences. They will learn that the order in which the numbers are added does not change the sum.

Gather the cubes and equals symbol card.

1. Make a train of 9 red cubes and a train of 7 blue cubes. Place the red train to the right of the blue train. Have students count how many cubes are in each train. Then ask them how many cubes there are in all. (16)

2. Have students watch as you move the red train to the left of the blue train.

3. Ask students how many cubes are in each train.

   Ask: Did you have to count to find the answer? Why or why not?
   ANSWER: No, moving the cubes does not change how many.

   If students counted the cubes again, explain that because you did not add not take away cubes, the number of cubes in each train has not changed.

4. Now ask students how many cubes there are in all. (16) Ask if the sum changed. (No)

   Say: Switching the order of the trains does not change the total number of cubes.

5. Write $9 + 7 = 16$ on a sheet of paper.

   Say: These trains show 9 plus 7 equals 16. You can write $9 + 7 = 16$ to show the addition.

6. Move the red train to the right of the blue train. Write $7 + 9 = 16$ on a sheet of paper.

   Say: These trains show 7 plus 9 equals 16. You can write $7 + 9 = 16$ to show the addition.

7. Point to the trains and the number sentences.

   Say: You can switch the order of the trains and get the same total. You can also switch the order of addends and get the same sum.

8. Have students make a 7-train with yellow cubes and a 9-train with green cubes. Place the trains from left to right in this order: red 9-train, blue 7-train, some space, yellow 7-train, green 9-train.

9. Ask students the sum of the red and blue cubes. (16) Ask them the sum of the yellow and green cubes. (16).

   Say: So these two groups are equal. Place the equals symbol card between the two groups.

10. Write $9 + 7 = 7 + 9$ on paper. Point to the trains and the equals symbol, and have students say, "9 plus 7 equals 7 plus 9."

11. Repeat Steps 1–10 for the following number sentences: $6 + 8 = 8 + 6$ and $5 + 7 = 7 + 5$. Make sure students use a different color for each addend.

12. Write $4 + 7 = \underline{\quad} + 4$.

    Say: You know you can add numbers in any order and get the same sum. This math idea can help you find a missing number in a number sentence. Look at this number sentence. Use trains and the equals symbol card to show this number sentence. Leave a space for the missing train.

    Students should show a 4-train, a 7-train, the equals symbol card, a space, and a 4-train. Make sure students use a different color for each addend.

Watch for students counting the cubes or adding to find the missing number in an addition sentence.

Work with them on using the cubes. As you switch the order of the cubes, ask questions such as: "Did I take any cubes away? Did I add any cubes? Will the amount change if I slide them over here? Do I need to recount, or will the number stay the same?"

13. Ask students how many cubes they need to put in the missing train to make the sides equal. (7) Have students explain how they found the answer. If students counted, say the following:

Say: Look at the number sentence. The 7 is an addend in both expressions. This means that the other addend must also be the same. You can add in any order, so 4 plus 7 is equal to 7 plus 4.

14. Repeat Steps 12 and 13 for the number sentence $5 + 6 = 6 + \underline{\hspace{1cm}}$. This missing addend is 5.

15. Write the following problems for students to solve:

- $6 + 7 = 7 + \underline{\hspace{1cm}}$ (6)
- $9 + \underline{\hspace{1cm}} = 6 + 9$ (6)
- $8 + 9 = \underline{\hspace{1cm}} + 8$ (9)

Have students solve the problems without using cubes. Remind them that if the same addend appears on both sides of the equals symbol, the other addend must also be the same.

16. Write the following problems for students to solve:

- $84 + 47 = 47 + \underline{\hspace{1cm}}$ (84)
- $176 + 193 = \underline{\hspace{1cm}} + 176$ (193)
- $\underline{\hspace{1cm}} + 66 = 66 + 59$ (59)

Explain that students will now solve the same types of problems but with much greater numbers. Remind students that they don't need to know how to add the numbers to find the missing addend.

TRY IT What Number Is Missing?

OFFLINE

15min

Objectives

Students will practice finding the missing numbers in addition sentences. Give students the What Number Is Missing? activity page from their Activity Book and read the directions with them. Use the answer key to check students' answers, and then enter the results online.

- Solve addition problems by filling in a missing number or numbers in a given number sentence.

Name:

Missing Numbers in Addition Sentences
What Number Is Missing?

Write the missing number.

1. $5 + 9 = \underline{9} + 5$

2. $8 + 2 = 2 + \underline{8}$

3. $7 + \underline{10} = 10 + 7$

4. $7 + 5 = \underline{5} + 7$

5. $\underline{8} + 3 = 3 + 8$

6. $\underline{7} + 4 = 4 + 7$

7. $6 + \underline{3} = 3 + 6$

8. $6 + 9 = \underline{9} + 6$

9. $8 + 9 = 9 + \underline{8}$

10. $40 + \underline{32} = 32 + 40$

11. $67 + 45 = \underline{45} + 67$

12. $118 + 79 = 79 + \underline{118}$

ADDITION NUMBER SENTENCES   131   MISSING NUMBERS IN ADDITION SENTENCES

TRY IT

13. $4 + 5 = \underline{5} + 4$

14. $5 + \underline{10} = 10 + 5$

15. $7 + 3 = 3 + \underline{7}$

16. $\underline{2} + 4 = 4 + 2$

17. Look at the addition sentence below.
Do you need to add to find the missing number?
Explain why or why not.

$$43 + 74 = \underline{74} + 43$$

See below.

TRY IT

ADDITION NUMBER SENTENCES   132   MISSING NUMBERS IN ADDITION SENTENCES

Additional Answers

17. No; 43 is an addend on both sides of the equals symbol, so the other addends must be the same. The missing number must be 74.

MISSING NUMBERS IN ADDITION SENTENCES **203**

OFFLINE
10 min

TRY IT Fill In the Number

Objectives

- Solve addition problems by filling in a missing number or numbers in a given number sentence.

Students will practice finding the missing numbers in addition sentences. Give students the Fill In the Number activity page from their Activity Book and read the directions with them.

Missing Numbers in Addition Sentences
Fill In the Number

Name:

Write the missing number.

1. $2 + 10 = \underline{10} + 2$ 2. $8 + 3 = 3 + \underline{8}$

3. $1 + \underline{6} = 6 + 1$ 4. $8 + 9 = \underline{9} + 8$

5. $\underline{4} + 6 = 6 + 4$ 6. $\underline{7} + 2 = 2 + 7$

7. $7 + \underline{3} = 3 + 7$ 8. $10 + 9 = \underline{9} + 10$

9. $9 + 3 = 3 + \underline{9}$ 10. $9 + 8 = \underline{8} + 9$

11. $45 + \underline{112} = 112 + 45$

12. $23 + 54 = \underline{54} + 23$

13. $167 + 70 = 70 + \underline{167}$

ADDITION NUMBER SENTENCES (133) MISSING NUMBERS IN ADDITION SENTENCES

TRY IT

---

14. Look at the addition sentence below. Do you need to add the numbers to find the missing number? Explain why or why not. **See below.**

$$66 + 113 = 113 + \underline{66}$$

Circle the missing number.

15. $6 + 6 = ? + 6$
 A. 18   B. 12   (C) 6   D. 3

16. $8 + 5 = ? + 8$
 (A) 5   B. 8   C. 13   D. 3

17. $2 + 9 = ? + 9$
 A. 11   B. 9   C. 7   (D) 2

Write the missing numbers.

18. $20 + 40 = \underline{\quad} + \underline{\quad} + 40$
Write any two numbers whose sum is 20; for example, $10 + 10$ or $5 + 15$

ADDITION NUMBER SENTENCES (134) MISSING NUMBERS IN ADDITION SENTENCES

TRY IT

Additional Answers

14. No; 113 is an addend on both sides of the equals symbol, so the other addends must be the same. The missing number must be 66.

CHECKPOINT

Objectives

Print the Checkpoint and have students complete it on their own. Read the directions, problems, and answer choices to students, if necessary. Use the answer key to score the Checkpoint, and then enter the results online.

- Solve addition problems by filling in a missing number or numbers in a given number sentence.

○ Checkpoint   Math | Addition Number Sentences | Missing Numbers in Addition Sentences

Name _____ Date _____

Checkpoint Answer Key

Write the missing number.

(1 point)
1. $7 + 4 = \underline{\textbf{4}} + 7$

(1 point)
2. $\underline{\textbf{3}} + 5 = 8$

(1 point)
3. $8 + 6 = \underline{\textbf{5}} + 9$

(1 point)
4. $7 + \underline{\textbf{4}} = 11$

(1 point)
5. $14 = \underline{\textbf{7}} + 7$

(1 point)
6. $30 = 10 + \underline{\textbf{20}}$

(1 point)
7. $81 + 22 = \underline{\textbf{22}} + 81$

(1 point)
8. $\underline{\textbf{10}} = 7 + 3$

1 of 1

Unit Review

UNIT REVIEW Look Back	20 minutes	**ONLINE**
UNIT REVIEW Checkpoint Practice	20 minutes	**OFFLINE**
⏩ **UNIT REVIEW** Prepare for the Checkpoint		

▶ Unit Objectives

This lesson reviews the following objectives:

- Represent equivalent forms of the same number through the use of physical models such as tens rods and ones cubes through 20.
- Represent equivalent forms of the same number through the use of diagrams through 20.
- Represent equivalent forms of the same number through 20 through the use of number expressions, such as $7 = 4 + 3$, or $5 + 2$, or $1 + 2 + 4$.
- Solve addition problems by filling in a missing number or numbers in a given number sentence.

▶ Advance Preparation

In this lesson, students will have an opportunity to review previous activities in the Addition Number Sentences unit. Look at the suggested activities in Unit Review: Prepare for the Checkpoint online and gather any needed materials.

Materials to Gather

SUPPLIED
Checkpoint Practice activity page
blocks – O (all colors)

ALSO NEEDED
paper, drawing – 1 sheet

Keywords		
	addend	expression
	addition sentence	model (noun)
	commutative property	number sentence
	of addition	plus symbol ($+$)
	equals symbol ($=$)	sum
	equivalent	

UNIT REVIEW Look Back

ONLINE 20 min

Objectives

- Review unit objectives.

In this unit, students have and practiced showing numbers in various ways—with models, sketches, and expressions. Then they represented equivalent forms of the same number, such as 2 and $1 + 1$, in these various ways.

Students used a balance to help identify equivalent forms of a number, including equal expressions, such as $3 + 5$ and $4 + 4$. Then they used the balance to find the missing number in an addition sentence; first they found missing sums, and then they found missing addends.

Students learned that they can add two numbers in any order and the sum will not change. They explored this property using the balance and blocks, and then they used this knowledge to find missing addends in number sentences with addition expressions on each side. Students will review these concepts to prepare for the Unit Checkpoint.

UNIT REVIEW Checkpoint Practice

Students will complete a Checkpoint Practice activity page to prepare for the Unit Checkpoint. If necessary, read the directions, problems, and answer choices to students. Have students answer the problems on their own. Carefully review the answers with students.

Give students the cubes to use for Problems 1, 2, 6, and 15. Give them the drawing paper for Problems 6 and 16.

Objectives

* Review unit objectives.

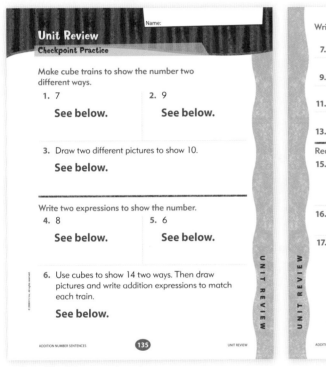

Name: _____

Unit Review
Checkpoint Practice

Make cube trains to show the number two different ways.

1. 7   2. 9
   See below.   **See below.**

3. Draw two different pictures to show 10.
   See below.

Write two expressions to show the number.
4. 8   5. 6
   See below.   **See below.**

6. Use cubes to show 14 two ways. Then draw pictures and write addition expressions to match each train.
   See below.

ADDITION NUMBER SENTENCES   135   UNIT REVIEW

Write the missing number for the addition sentence.

7. __8__ + 4 = 12   8. 6 + __9__ = 15

9. 8 + 9 = __9__ + 8   10. 8 + __3__ = 3 + 8

11. __7__ + 8 = 15   12. 5 + 9 = __7__ + 7

13. 25 = __20__ + 5   14. __12__ = 9 + 3

Read the problem and follow the directions.

15. Use the cubes to model the number 17 two different ways. Use more than one group of cubes for at least one of your models.
    See below.

16. Draw two pictures to show the number 20.
    See below.

17. Which answer choice shows the same number as the picture below? Circle the answer.
    7 = ☺☺ + ☺☺☺☺☺
    A. 7 = ●●●● + ●●●●
    B. 7 = ●●●●●●
    C. 7 = ●●●●●● + ●●●
    (D) 7 = ●●●●●● + ●

ADDITION NUMBER SENTENCES   136   UNIT REVIEW

Additional Answers

1. Students should make two different cube trains that both show 7.

2. Students should make two different cube trains that both show 9.

3. Students should draw two different pictures to show 10.

4. Students should write two expressions with a value of 8.

5. Students should write two expressions with a value of 6.

6. Check students' work to be sure that the numbers are represented correctly and that each train matches a drawing and a number sentence.

15. Students should create two models for the number 17. Models will vary.
    Examples:
    model for a set of 17 cubes
    model for a set of 10 cubes and a set of 7 cubes

16. Students should draw two different pictures to show 20.

⟶ UNIT REVIEW Prepare for the Checkpoint

What you do next depends on how students performed in the previous activity, Unit Review: Checkpoint Practice. If students had difficulty with any of the problems, complete the appropriate review activity listed in the table online.

Unit Checkpoint

| UNIT CHECKPOINT Offline | 60 minutes | OFFLINE |

▶ Unit Objectives

This lesson assesses the following objectives:

- Represent equivalent forms of the same number through the use of physical models such as tens rods and ones cubes through 20.
- Represent equivalent forms of the same number through the use of diagrams through 20.
- Represent equivalent forms of the same number through 20 through the use of number expressions, such as $7 = 4 + 3$, or $5 + 2$, or $1 + 2 + 4$.
- Solve addition problems by filling in a missing number or numbers in a given number sentence.

Materials to Gather

SUPPLIED

Unit Checkpoint (printout)

UNIT CHECKPOINT Offline

OFFLINE
60 min

Students will complete the Unit Checkpoint offline. Print the Checkpoint and have students complete it on their own. Read the directions, problems, and answer choices to students, if necessary. Use the answer key to score the Checkpoint, and then enter the results online.

Objectives

- Assess unit objectives.

Name   Date

Unit Checkpoint Answer Key

Circle the missing number.

(1 point)
1. $6 + 3 = \underline{\hspace{1cm}} + 2$

  A. 5   B. 6   (C.) 7   D. 11

(1 point)
2. $15 = \underline{\hspace{1cm}} + 5$

  A. 5   B. 8   (C.) 10   D. 20

(1 point)
3. $\underline{\hspace{1cm}} = 5 + 1$

  (A.) 6   B. 7   C. 4   D. 3

(1 point)
4. $4 + 6 = \underline{\hspace{1cm}} + 7$

  A. 17   B. 10   C. 8   (D.) 3

(1 point)
5. $3 + 2 = \underline{\hspace{1cm}} + 1$

  A. 5   (B.) 4   C. 3   D. 2

(1 point)
6. $8 + \underline{\hspace{1cm}} = 11$

  A. 19   B. 11   C. 8   (D.) 3

Write the missing number.

(1 point)
7. $5 + 5 = \underline{\textbf{3}} + 7$

Name   Date

Circle the answer.

(1 point)
8. Which shows a way to represent the number 14?

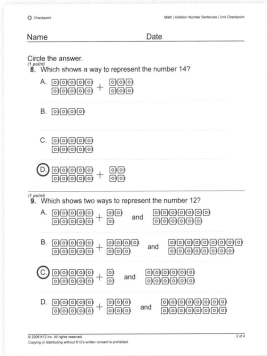

(1 point)
9. Which shows two ways to represent the number 12?

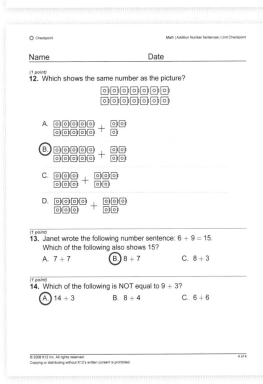

Name   Date

(1 point)
10. Which answer choice also shows 10?

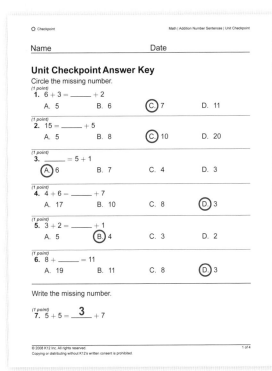

(1 point)
11. Which two pictures show 10?

  A. ●●●● + ●●●   and   ●●● + ●●●●●●

  (B.) ●●●●● + ●●●●●   and   ●●●●●●●●● + ●

  C. ●●●●●●●●● + ●●   and   ●●●● + ●●●●●●●●

Name   Date

(1 point)
12. Which shows the same number as the picture?

  A.
  (B.)
  C.
  D.

(1 point)
13. Janet wrote the following number sentence: $6 + 9 = 15$.
  Which of the following also shows 15?

  A. $7 + 7$ (B.) $8 + 7$ C. $8 + 3$

(1 point)
14. Which of the following is NOT equal to $9 + 3$?

  (A.) $14 + 3$ B. $8 + 4$ C. $6 + 6$

Introduction to Subtraction

▶ Unit Objectives

- Demonstrate and explain the meaning of subtraction as taking away.
- Use concrete objects or sketches to model and solve addition or subtraction computation problems with sums and minuends up through 30.
- Recognize that the − symbol refers to subtraction.
- Correctly use the − symbol.
- Use models and math symbols to represent subtraction.
- Recognize that the equals symbol shows an equality between two expressions.
- Given concrete objects, show how two sets can be added together, and then reverse the operation to show how a number can be subtracted from the whole.
- Use models to demonstrate that the order in which numbers are subtracted changes the solution.
- Demonstrate understanding of the result of subtracting zero from a given quantity.
- Demonstrate the meaning of subtraction as comparing two quantities.

▶ Big Ideas

- Models and mathematical symbols can represent addition and subtraction.
- Subtraction represents taking away.
- Subtraction can show the finding of a mystery addend.

▶ Unit Introduction

Students will learn that to subtract means to take away, and they will use models to show subtraction. They will learn that when they subtract, the number that is left is the difference. They will learn the meaning of the minus symbol (−) and review the meaning of the equals symbol (=) so they can read and write subtraction sentences.

Students will explore the relationship between addition and subtraction, learning that they are opposite operations. They will demonstrate the opposite operations with objects and drawings. They will learn that subtraction is not commutative, and that subtracting zero from a given number results in a difference of the original number.

Students will then learn about using subtraction in comparing numbers, which will allow them to find how much greater or lesser a number is than another number. They will use pairing, modeling, and drawings to compare numbers.

Understand Subtraction

Lesson Overview

Skills Update	5 minutes	ONLINE
GET READY Take Away	5 minutes	ONLINE
LEARN Animals in Action	15 minutes	ONLINE
LEARN Circle Subtraction	15 minutes	OFFLINE
TRY IT Show Subtraction	10 minutes	OFFLINE
CHECKPOINT	10 minutes	OFFLINE

▶ **Lesson Objectives**

- Demonstrate and explain the meaning of subtraction as taking away.
- Use concrete objects or sketches to model and solve addition or subtraction computation problems with sums and minuends up through 30.

▶ **Prerequisite Skills**

- Demonstrate the meaning of subtraction as taking away an amount from a given quantity (with minuends up through 20).
- Use concrete objects or sketches to model and solve addition or subtraction computation problems involving sums or minuends up through 20.

▶ **Content Background**

Students will learn that to subtract means to take away. They will use drawings and objects to show and explain what it means to subtract.

The answer to a subtraction problem is called the *difference*. When subtracting objects, the difference is the number of objects left in a group after some objects have been taken away. Encourage students to use the term *difference* as they explore subtraction.

Materials to Gather

SUPPLIED

blocks – B (30 of any color)

Show Subtraction activity page

Checkpoint (printout)

ALSO NEEDED

paper, construction – 1 light-colored sheet

Keywords

difference – the solution to a subtraction problem

subtract – to take away objects from a group or to find a difference between two groups

subtraction – the process of taking away objects from a group or finding the difference between two groups; a mathematical operation

take away – in subtraction, to separate a group from the total

GET READY Take Away

ONLINE 5 min

Objectives

Students learn that subtraction means taking away. They will watch blocks fall from block towers and count the blocks that remain.

- Demonstrate the meaning of subtraction as taking away an amount from a given quantity (with minuends up through 20).
- Use concrete objects or sketches to model and solve addition or subtraction computation problems involving sums or minuends up through 20.

LEARN Animals in Action

ONLINE 15 min

Objectives

Students will solve subtraction problems that are modeled by animals. They will watch animals walk, fly, or swim away from a group, and they will connect their leaving to subtraction. Then they will count the animals that remain.

- Demonstrate the meaning of subtraction as taking away an amount from a given quantity (with minuends up through 20).

LEARN Circle Subtraction

OFFLINE 15 min

Objectives

Students will use circle blocks and drawings to model and explain subtraction. Gather the circles and construction paper.

- Use concrete objects or sketches to model and solve addition or subtraction computation problems with sums and minuends up through 30.

1. Place the construction paper in front of students. Place 9 circles on the paper.
   Say: There are 9 circles.

2. Take 1 circle off the paper.
   Say: I take away 1 circle.

   Ask: How many circles are on the paper now?
   ANSWER: 8

   If students have difficulty, tell them to count the circles left on the paper.

3. **Say:** 9 take away 1 equals 8. When you take circles away, you subtract them. Subtract means "take away."

4. Place 25 circles on the paper. Repeat Steps 1–3 with the number sentence "25 take away 18 equals 7."

5. **Say:** Now it's your turn to use the circles to show subtraction. Place 10 circles on the paper.

6. **Say:** Take 4 circles off the paper.

   Ask: How many circles are left?
   ANSWER: 6

   If students have difficulty, tell them to count the circles left on the paper.

7. **Say:** Tell me what number sentence you showed. Use the words take away.
   ANSWER: 10 take away 4 equals 6.

8. Repeat Steps 5–7 with the following number sentences: 13 take away 9 equals 4; 12 take away 5 equals 7; 17 take away 8 equals 9; and 20 take away 5 equals 15.

9. **Say:** You can also draw pictures to show subtraction. Draw 7 squares on a sheet of paper.

10. **Say:** I have 7 squares. I will show subtraction with X's. Draw X's over 3 of the squares.

11. **Say:** The number of squares without X's is the number left. It is the difference.

    Ask: How many squares are not crossed out?

    ANSWER: 4

    Say: 7 take away 3 equals 4.

12. Repeat Steps 9–11 with the following number sentences: 13 take away 7 equals 6; 12 take away 9 equals 3; and 6 take away 5 equals 1. When repeating Step 11, have students say the number sentence for each picture.

13. **Say:** Now it's your turn to draw pictures to show subtraction. Draw 8 squares.

14. Cross out 2.

    Ask: How many squares are not crossed out?

    ANSWER: 6

    If students have difficulty, tell them to count the squares that are not crossed out.

15. **Ask:** What number sentence does the picture show?

    ANSWER: 8 take away 2 equals 6.

16. Repeats Steps 13–15 with the following number sentences: 10 take away 5 equals 5, 8 take away 3 equals 5, and 11 take away 3 equals 8.

Tips

Tell students that they can draw any shape or object to show subtraction.

Explain that they can shade in or cross out an object to show that it was subtracted.

TRY IT Show Subtraction

Objectives

Students will practice modeling and solving subtraction problems. Give students the circle blocks and the Show Subtraction activity page from their Activity Book. Read the directions with them.

For Problems 3 and 4, students may draw any simple shapes to represent the objects in the problems. They may shade in or cross out the objects they are subtracting.

- Demonstrate and explain the meaning of subtraction as taking away.
- Use concrete objects or sketches to model and solve addition or subtraction computation problems with sums and minuends up through 30.

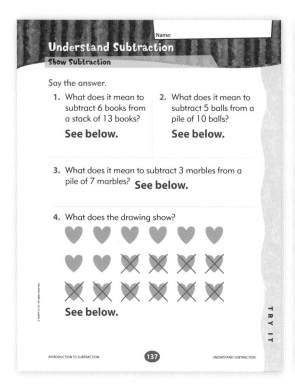

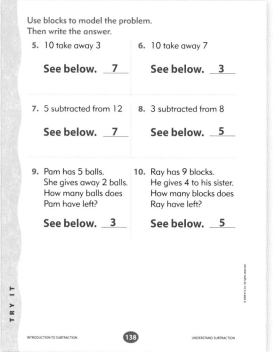

Additional Answers

1. Answers will vary. **Example:** Students should say that it means to take 6 books away from 13 books.

2. Answers will vary. **Example:** Students say that if you have 10 balls and you subtract 5, you are taking 5 balls away and you will be left with 5 balls.

3. Answers will vary. **Example:** To subtract 3 marbles from 7 marbles means to take 3 marbles away from the 7 marbles.

4. Answers will vary. **Example:** It shows subtraction: 18 take away 10 equals 8, or 10 subtracted from 18 equals 8.

5. Students should start with 10 circles and take away 3, leaving 7.

6. Students should start with 10 circles and take away 7, leaving 3.

7. Students should show a group of 12 circles and take away 5, leaving 7.

8. Students should show 8 circles and then take 3 away, leaving 5.

9. Students should show 5 circles. They should take 2 circles away, showing 3 circles left.

10. Students should show 9 circles. They should take 4 circles away, showing 5 circles left.

Draw a picture to model the problem.
Then write the answer.

11. 6 subtracted from 11. __5__

12. 11 take away 3. __8__

13. There are 11 heart stickers.
Tina uses 4 of them.

How many stickers are left? __7__

14. Adam has 6 stamps.
He uses 4 stamps.
How many stamps does he have left? __2__

TRY IT

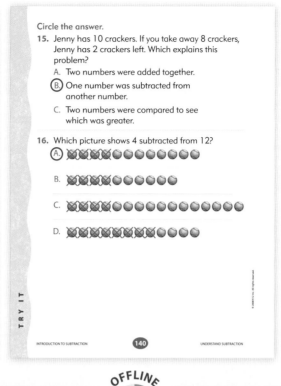

TRY IT

Circle the answer.

15. Jenny has 10 crackers. If you take away 8 crackers, Jenny has 2 crackers left. Which explains this problem?

A. Two numbers were added together.

(B.) One number was subtracted from another number.

C. Two numbers were compared to see which was greater.

16. Which picture shows 4 subtracted from 12?

(A)

B.

C.

D.

OFFLINE

10 min

CHECKPOINT

Objectives

Print the Checkpoint. In Part 1, students will take a performance-based assessment. In Part 2, students will complete the problems on their own. Read the directions, problems, and answer choices to students, if necessary. Use the answer key to score the Checkpoint, and then enter the results online.

Gather the circle blocks, and give them to students to use for Problem 3.

- Demonstrate and explain the meaning of subtraction as taking away.

- Use concrete objects or sketches to model and solve addition or subtraction computation problems with sums and minuends up through 30.

Name _____ Date _____

Checkpoint Answer Key

Part 1

Follow the instructions for each item. Choose the response that best describes how the student performs on the task. When you have finished, enter the results online.

Give students paper for drawing their answers to Problems 1 and 4.

1. Say, "Maria sees 15 butterflies in the garden. A bird scares 6 away. How many butterflies are left? Draw a picture to find the answer. Then explain what your picture shows."

   Example: A drawing of 15 butterflies or symbols with 6 of them crossed out. Students should say that they drew 15 butterflies and crossed out 6, and there are 9 left.
   (2 points)
   Did the student draw and explain correctly?

   A. Yes   B. No

2. Say, "Explain what it means to subtract 5 balls from a pile of 10 balls."

   Example: Students explain that to subtract 5 balls from 10 balls means to take 5 balls away from 10 balls.
   (1 point)
   Did the student explain correctly?

   A. Yes   B. No

Name _____ Date _____

3. Say, "Use circles to show 6 take away 2."
   (1 point)
   Example: Students show 6 circles and then take away 2, leaving 4 circles.

   Did the student model correctly?

   A. Yes   B. No

4. Say, "Draw a picture to show 4 subtracted from 9."

   Example: Students draw 9 objects and then cross out 4, leaving 5 objects.
   (1 point)
   Did the student draw correctly?

   A. Yes   B. No

Give students Part 2 of the assessment.

Name _____ Date _____

Part 2

Circle the answer.
(1 point)
5. Which best describes subtraction?

   A. put together

   (B.) take away

   C. make greater

   D. combine sets

(1 point)
6. Whitney had 19 marbles. She took away 11 marbles. What should you do to find how many marbles Whitney has left?

   (A.) Subtract 11 from 19.

   B. Add 11 and 19.

   C. Compare 11 and 29.

(1 point)
7. Which shows 3 subtracted from 10?

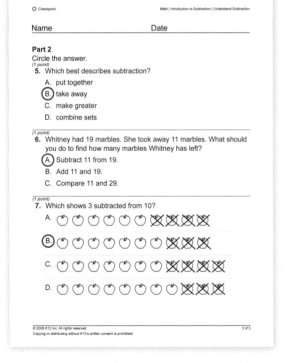

218 INTRODUCTION TO SUBTRACTION

The Minus Symbol

Skills Update	5 minutes	**ONLINE**
GET READY Subtract Fruit	5 minutes	**ONLINE**
LEARN Model Subtraction	15 minutes	**OFFLINE**
LEARN Use the Minus Symbol	15 minutes	**OFFLINE**
TRY IT Write the Subtraction	10 minutes	**OFFLINE**
CHECKPOINT	10 minutes	**OFFLINE**

▶ Lesson Objectives

- Recognize that the − symbol refers to subtraction.
- Correctly use the − symbol.
- Use models and math symbols to represent subtraction.

▶ Prerequisite Skills

- Demonstrate the meaning of subtraction as taking away an amount from a given quantity (with minuends up through 20).
- Demonstrate the meaning of subtraction as comparing the difference between two quantities (with minuends up through 20).
- Recognize that the equals symbol shows an equality between two expressions.

▶ Advance Preparation

Number index cards 0 through 30, or gather the number cards you created previously. Label two other cards with the following symbols: = and −. Save cards for use in future lessons.

▶ Content Background

Students have learned that *subtraction* means "take away." In this lesson, they will learn the minus symbol (−). They will use the minus symbol, equals symbol, and numbers to write number sentences to represent subtraction models.

Although the phrases *equals sign* and *minus sign* are often used in everyday language, *equals symbol* and *minus symbol* are more accurate as a mathematical terms. In math, *sign* refers specifically to positive signs and negative signs.

The answer to a subtraction problem is called the *difference*. When subtracting objects, the difference is the number of objects left in a group after some objects have been taken away. Encourage students to use the term *difference* as they explore subtraction.

Materials to Gather

SUPPLIED

blocks – O (20 of any color)
Write the Subtraction activity page
Checkpoint (printout)

ALSO NEEDED

index cards – numbered 0 through 30
index cards – labeled with = and − symbols

GET READY Subtract Fruit

ONLINE
5 min

Objectives

Students will subtract using models. They will watch fruit fall from trees and count the pieces of fruit that remain.

- Demonstrate the meaning of subtraction as taking away an amount from a given quantity (with minuends up through 20).

LEARN Model Subtraction

OFFLINE
15 min

Objectives

Students will model subtraction with objects and drawings. Then they will write number sentences to represent the models.

Gather the cubes.

- Recognize that the − symbol refers to subtraction.
- Correctly use the − symbol.
- Use models and math symbols to represent subtraction.

1. **Say:** We can use objects, drawings, and symbols to show subtraction. Let's start with objects.

2. Display 9 cubes. Have students take away 1 cube. Ask how many cubes are left. (8)

   Say: 9 take away 1 equals 8.

3. Repeat Step 2 with the following number sentences: 10 take away 4 equals 6; 8 take away 5 equals 3; and 11 take away 3 equals 8.

4. **Say:** Now let's use drawings to show subtraction.

5. Have students draw 6 circles on a sheet of paper. Have them cross out 4 circles. Ask how many circles are not crossed out. (2)

6. **Say:** Tell me what number sentence you showed.
   ANSWER: 6 take away 4 equals 2.

7. **Say:** The math word *minus* means "subtract" or "take away." So another way to say the number sentence for the picture is "6 minus 4 equals 2."

8. Repeat Steps 5 and 6 with the following number sentences: 12 minus 9 equals 3; 8 minus 3 equals 5; and 16 minus 10 equals 6. Have students use the word *minus* when stating the number sentence for each picture.

9. Under students' first picture, write the matching subtraction sentence using the minus symbol: $6 - 4 = 2$. Point to the minus symbol.

    Say: This symbol means *minus*. It tells us to subtract. It is called the *minus symbol*.

    Point to each number and symbol in the number sentence as you read it: "6 minus 4 equals 2."

10. Under students' second drawing write 12   9   3 with spaces as shown. Have students write the minus symbol and equals symbol in the appropriate spaces, assisting them as needed. ($12 - 9 = 3$)

11. Have students read the number sentence, pointing to each number and symbol as they read it. (12 minus 9 equals 3.)

12. Repeat Steps 10 and 11 for each subtraction picture.

LEARN Use the Minus Symbol

Students will model subtraction problems with drawings. Then they will use number and symbol cards to create number sentences to represent the drawings. Finally they will use the cards to make number sentences without first using drawings. Gather the number and symbol cards.

1. Point to the minus symbol on the computer keyboard.

    Say: This is the minus symbol. We use the minus symbol to show subtraction.

2. Draw a picture of 5 stars. Cross out 4 of the stars.

    Ask: What number sentence does this picture show?
    ANSWER: 5 minus 4 equals 1.

3. Write 5   4   1 under the drawing. Then write a minus symbol between the 5 and 4. Point to the minus symbol.

    Say: This is the minus symbol. When you see this symbol between two numbers, it means "take away" or "subtract." Look at where the symbol is. It is near the middle of the numbers, not the bottom or the top.

4. **Ask:** What symbol belongs between the 4 and 1? How do you know?
    ANSWER: equals symbol; The numbers on each side of the equals symbol are the same: $5 - 4$ is the same as 1.

5. **Say:** This number sentence shows my picture. We can read this sentence different ways: 5 take away 4 equals 1, 5 minus 4 equals 1, and 4 subtracted from 5 equals 1.

6. Have students draw 9 hearts and cross out 3 of them.

7. Give students the number and symbol cards. Have students use the cards to make a number sentence to match their picture. ($9 - 3 = 6$)

Objectives

*   Recognize that the — symbol refers to subtraction.
*   Correctly use the — symbol.
*   Use models and math symbols to represent subtraction.

Tips

Remind students that to find the difference, they should count only the objects that are NOT crossed out. If students need help, have them cover those objects with their hand or a sheet of paper.

8. **Say:** Read your number sentence and explain what it means.
   ANSWER: 9 minus 3 equals 6. There were 9 hearts and 3 were taken away. There are 6 left.

9. Rearrange the cards to show $6 = 9 - 3$. Explain that this number sentence also matches the picture.

10. Repeat Steps 6–9 with the following number sentences: $13 - 3 = 10$; $22 - 15 = 7$; and $6 - 0 = 6$.

11. Have students use only the cards to show the following number sentences: $9 - 7 = 2$; $8 - 1 = 7$; $10 - 0 = 10$; and $7 - 4 = 3$.

OFFLINE
10 min

TRY IT Write the Subtraction

Objectives

Students will practice using the minus symbol. Give students the Write the Subtraction activity page from their Activity Book and read the directions with them.

- Recognize that the $-$ symbol refers to subtraction.
- Correctly use the $-$ symbol.
- Use models and math symbols to represent subtraction.

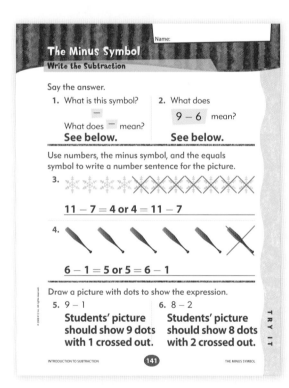

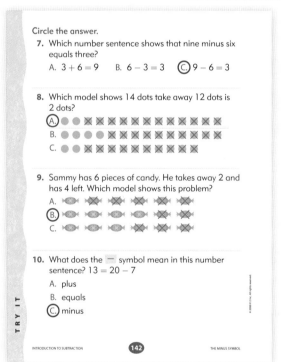

Additional Answers

1. Students should say, "minus symbol."
   Students should say, "to subtract" or "to take away."

2. Students should say, "9 minus 6" or "9 take away 6."

CHECKPOINT

Objectives

- Recognize that the − symbol refers to subtraction.
- Correctly use the − symbol.
- Use models and math symbols to represent subtraction.

Print the Checkpoint and have students complete it on their own. Read the directions, problems, and answer choices to students if necessary. Use the answer key to score the Checkpoint, and then enter the results online.

⚙ Checkpoint   Math | Introduction to Subtraction | The Minus Symbol

Name _____   Date _____

Checkpoint Answer Key

(1 point)
1. Which number sentence shows ten minus two equals eight?

   (A.) $10 - 2 = 8$ B. $8 + 2 = 10$ C. $10 - 8 = 2$

(1 point)
2. Which number sentence shows twenty minus three equals seventeen?

   A. $17 + 3 = 20$ B. $20 - 17 = 3$ (C.) $20 - 3 = 17$

(1 point)
3. What does the symbol in the box mean? $16 \boxed{-} 7 = 9$

   A. equals   B. add   (C.) subtract

(1 point)
4. When you see the ▢ symbol, what do you do?

   (A.) subtract   B. add   C. multiply

(1 point)
5. A new student does not know what to do when he sees the ▢ symbol. What would you tell him it means?

   A. guess   (B.) subtract   C. add

(1 point)
6. Choose the correct symbol to complete the number sentence.

   $20 \square 10 = 10$

   (A.) −   B. +   C. =

(1 point)
7. What symbol would make the number sentence true?

   $10 \square 7 = 3$

   (A.) −   B. +   C. =

Equal Expressions

Lesson Overview

Skills Update	5 minutes	ONLINE
TRY IT Understand the Minus Symbol	5 minutes	ONLINE
LEARN Balance Subtraction Sentences	15 minutes	ONLINE
TRY IT Understand the Equals Symbol	10 minutes	ONLINE
LEARN Number Card Subtraction	15 minutes	OFFLINE
TRY IT Subtraction and the Equals Symbol	10 minutes	OFFLINE

▶ Lesson Objectives

Recognize that the equals symbol shows an equality between two expressions.

▶ Common Errors and Misconceptions

- Students might misinterpret the equals symbol ($=$) as a signal they should "do" something. For example, in the number sentence $5 + 3 =$ ___, students might think the equals symbol means "adds up to" or "produces." So they might view $8 = 5 + 3$ or $8 = 8$ as unacceptable or wrong because they believe the equals symbol must be followed by the answer to a problem.
- Students might not be familiar with number sentences of the form $2 +$ ___ $= 3$. They might see the plus symbol and mistakenly add 2 and 3.
- Students might have difficulty with number sentences of the form $4 + 5 = 3 + 6$. They might wish to rewrite the number sentence with the "answer" after the equals symbol: $4 + 5 = 9$.

▶ Advance Preparation

Number index cards 0 through 30. Label three other cards with the following symbols: $-$, $=$, and $\neq$. Or gather the number and symbol cards you created previously.

▶ Content Background

In this lesson, students will compare expressions to see if they are equal. An expression can be one number or a combination of numbers and symbols.

The word *expression* is defined as a combination of number(s) and symbol(s) that represents a given value. An expression does not include an equals symbol ($=$) or other relational symbol, such as a not-equal-to symbol ($\neq$), a less-than symbol ($<$), or a greater-than symbol ($>$).

The term *number sentence* is defined as two expressions related to each other by an equals symbol ($=$) or other relational symbol, such as a not-equal-to symbol ($\neq$), a less-than symbol ($<$), or a greater-than symbol ($>$).

Materials to Gather

SUPPLIED

blocks – B (red, blue)

Subtraction and the Equals Symbol activity page

ALSO NEEDED

index cards – numbered 0 through 30

index cards – labeled with $-$, $=$, and $\neq$ symbols

TRY IT Understand the Minus Symbol

ONLINE 5 min

Students will complete an online Try It. Read the directions, problems, and answer choices to students. If necessary, help students with keyboard or mouse operations.

Objectives

- Recognize that the — symbol refers to subtraction.

LEARN Balance Subtraction Sentences

ONLINE 15 min

A number sentence is like a level balance—just as the objects on each side of a balance have the same weight, the expressions on each side of the equals symbol have the same value. By removing blocks from the "heavier" side of a balance, students will learn about equality in subtraction number sentences. They will learn that by subtracting a given number of blocks, the balance becomes level, and the expressions become equal.

Objectives

- Recognize that the equals symbol shows an equality between two expressions.

TRY IT Understand the Equals Symbol

ONLINE 10 min

Students will complete an online Try It. Read the directions, problems, and answer choices to students. If necessary, help students with keyboard or mouse operations.

Objectives

- Recognize that the equals symbol shows an equality between two expressions.

LEARN Number Card Subtraction

OFFLINE 15 min

Students will use number and symbol cards to show subtraction sentences. They will decide if two expressions are equal or not equal and whether they should place the equals symbol or not-equal-to symbol between them.
    Gather the circle blocks, number cards, and symbol cards.

Objectives

- Recognize that the equals symbol shows an equality between two expressions.

1. Show students the equals symbol card.

   Say: This card is the equals symbol. It shows that two expressions are equal.

2. Show students the not-equal-to symbol card.

   Say: This card is the not-equal-to symbol. It shows that two expressions are not equal.

3. Put out cards to show $8 - 2$ and 6. Place the equals symbol and the not-equal-to symbol cards above the number cards.

   Say: Look at the two expressions: 8 minus 2, and 6.

4. **Ask:** Are the expressions equal? If you want, use circles to model the expressions.
   ANSWER: Yes

5. Place the the equals symbol card between the expressions.

   Say: Because the sides are equal, we can place an equals symbol between them. Read the number sentence.
   ANSWER: 8 minus 2 equals 6.

6. Put out cards to show 7 and $10 - 2$. Place the equals symbol and the not-equal-to symbol cards above the number cards.

   Say: Look at the expressions: 7, and 10 minus 2.

7. **Ask:** Are the expressions equal? If you want, use circles to model the expressions.
   ANSWER: No

8. Place the not-equal-to symbol card between the expressions.

   Say: If the sides are not equal, then we can place the not-equal-to symbol card between them. Read the number sentence.
   ANSWER: 7 is not equal to 10 minus 2.

9. Repeat with the following subtraction sentences. Have students place either the equals symbol card or the not-equal-to symbol card between the expressions.

   $9 - 6$ and 3 $(=)$

   11 and $12 - 2$ $(\neq)$

   $12 - 3$ and 7 $(\neq)$

   7 and $13 - 5$ $(\neq)$

TRY IT Subtraction and the Equals Symbol

OFFLINE
10min

Objectives

Students will practice deciding if expressions are equal. Give students the Subtraction and the Equals Symbol activity page from their Activity Book and read the directions with them.

- Recognize that the equals symbol shows an equality between two expressions.

Name:

Equal Expressions
Subtraction and the Equals Symbol

Tell what the = symbol means in the number sentences.

1. $8 - 4 = 4$

8 − 4 is the same as 4.

2. $6 = 6 - 0$

6 is the same as 6 − 0.

3. $7 = 13 - 6$

7 is the same as 13 − 6.

4. $3 = 8 - 5$

3 is the same as 8 − 5.

Write the missing symbol.

5. $12 - 4 \boxed{=} 8$

6. $3 = 11 \boxed{-} 8$

7. $6 - 2 \boxed{=} 7 - 3$

Tell whether the equals symbol or not-equal-to symbol belongs between the cards.

8. $\boxed{5-2}$ $\boxed{3}$ **equals symbol**

9. $\boxed{6}$ $\boxed{11-5}$ **equals symbol**

10. $\boxed{10-6}$ $\boxed{3}$ **not-equal-to symbol**

INTRODUCTION TO SUBTRACTION · 143 · EQUAL EXPRESSIONS

TRY IT

TRY IT

Circle the answer.

11. John writes $4 + 2$ on the left-hand side of a paper and then writes $7 - 1$ to the right of it.
Which is the correct symbol to write between the two sets of numbers?

A. $+$ B. $-$ Ⓒ $=$ D. $\neq$

12. Elisa writes $7 - 2$ on the left-hand side of a paper and then writes 4 to the right of it.
Which is the correct symbol to write between the two sets of numbers?

A. $+$ B. $-$ Ⓒ $\neq$ D. $=$

13. What does the symbol the arrow is pointing to mean?

$$11 - 7 \overset{\downarrow}{=} 4$$

Ⓐ equals   B. not equal to
C. add   D. subtract

Circle the missing symbol.

14. $4 \boxed{} 10 - 6$

A. $+$ B. $-$ Ⓒ $=$ D. $\neq$

15. $5 - 1 \boxed{} 8 - 4$

A. $+$ B. $-$ Ⓒ $=$ D. $\neq$

INTRODUCTION TO SUBTRACTION · 144 · EQUAL EXPRESSIONS

EQUAL EXPRESSIONS **227**

More Equal Expressions

Lesson Overview

TRY IT Equivalent Expressions	5 minutes	ONLINE
LEARN Build Expressions	40 minutes	ONLINE
TRY IT Complex Expressions	5 minutes	ONLINE
CHECKPOINT	10 minutes	ONLINE

▶ Lesson Objectives

Recognize that the equals symbol shows an equality between two expressions.

▶ Content Background

In this lesson, students will compare expressions to see if they are equal. An expression can be one number or a combination of numbers and symbols.

Materials to Gather

There are no materials to gather for this lesson.

TRY IT Equivalent Expressions

ONLINE 5 min

Students will complete an online Try It. Read the directions, problems, and answer choices to students. If necessary, help students with keyboard or mouse operations.

Objectives

- Recognize that the equals symbol shows an equality between two expressions.

LEARN Build Expressions

ONLINE 40 min

Students will practice building addition and subtraction expressions.

Objectives

- Recognize that the equals symbol shows an equality between two expressions.

DIRECTIONS FOR USING THE BUILDING EXPRESSIONS LEARNING TOOL

1. Click Begin and choose the following:
   - Problem Type: Addition $(+)$
   - Problem Format: $2 + 2 = ?$
2. Click Next and choose the following:
   - Use Numbers: 0–20
   - Equals Symbol Placement: Both Ways
   - Timer Speed: Medium
3. Have students complete the problems. If students are unable to answer a problem correctly in the given time, the correct answer will appear. Review the answer with students before moving on to the next problem.
4. Click Play Again and choose the following:
   - Problem Type: Subtraction $(-)$
   - Problem Format: $4 - 2 = ?$
5. Click Next and choose the options described in Step 2.

6. Have students complete the problems. Review any missed problems with students.

If time permits, complete Steps 7–12.

7. Click Play Again and choose the following:
   - Problem Type: Addition ($+$)
   - Problem Format: $2 + 2 = ?, 2 + ? = 4, ? + 2 = 4$

8. Click Next and choose the options described in Step 2.

9. Have students complete the problems. Review any missed problems with students.

10. Click Play Again and choose the following:
    - Problem Type: Subtraction ($-$)
    - Problem Format: $4 - 2 = ?, 4 - ? = 2, ? - 2 = 2$

11. Click Next and choose the options described in Step 2.

12. Have students complete the problems. Review any missed problems with students.

ONLINE
5 min

TRY IT **Complex Expressions**

Objectives

- Recognize that the equals symbol shows an equality between two expressions.

Students will complete an online Try It. Read the directions, problems, and answer choices to students. If necessary, help students with keyboard or mouse operations.

ONLINE
10 min

CHECKPOINT

Objectives

- Recognize that the equals symbol shows an equality between two expressions.

Students will complete an online Checkpoint. Read the directions, problems, and answer choices to students. If necessary, help students with keyboard or mouse operations.

Put Together, Take Away

Lesson Overview

Skills Update	5 minutes	ONLINE
GET READY Orchard Operations	10 minutes	ONLINE
LEARN Opposites: Add and Subtract	20 minutes	ONLINE
LEARN Add and Take Away Cubes	15 minutes	OFFLINE
TRY IT Show Subtraction	10 minutes	OFFLINE

▶ Lesson Objectives

Given concrete objects, show how two sets can be added together, and then reverse the operation to show how a number can be subtracted from the whole.

▶ Prerequisite Skills

- Use models and math symbols to represent addition.
- Use models and math symbols to represent subtraction.

▶ Common Errors and Misconceptions

Students might have difficulty understanding that addition and subtraction are opposite, or inverse, operations. It might not be obvious to them that addition "undoes" subtraction.

▶ Advance Preparation

Cut a piece of yarn about 3 feet long.

▶ Safety

Be sure to keep the yarn away from students' necks.

▶ Content Background

Students will learn that addition and subtraction are opposite operations. They will use various models as they practice this concept.

Inverse, or opposite, operations "undo" each other. Addition and subtraction are opposite operations, as are multiplication and division. For example, suppose students have a group of 8 blocks. If students add 2 blocks to the group, the sum is 10 blocks: $8 + 2 = 10$. If they remove the 2 blocks, the difference is 8 blocks: $10 - 2 = 8$. Subtracting 2 blocks undoes adding 2 blocks. Students are left with the same number of blocks they started with, 8. Understanding opposite operations will help students with arithmetic, and later on, algebra.

Materials to Gather

SUPPLIED

blocks – O (red, yellow)

Show Subtraction activity page

ALSO NEEDED

scissors, adult

yarn

Keywords

addition – the process of combining, or putting together, groups of objects or numbers; a mathematical operation
opposite operations – mathematical operations that reverse or undo each other, often called inverse operations; subtraction and addition are opposite operations; division and multiplication are opposite operations
sum – the solution to an addition problem

GET READY Orchard Operations

ONLINE 10min

Students will choose the addition or subtraction sentence that represents a picture.

Objectives

- Use models and math symbols to represent addition.
- Use models and math symbols to represent subtraction.

LEARN Opposites: Add and Subtract

ONLINE 20min

Students will add and subtract animals with Johnny. As animals leave and come back to the same group, students will learn that addition and subtraction are opposite operations. For example, suppose 2 squirrels join a group of 6 squirrels, making 8 squirrels: $2 + 6 = 8$. Then the 2 squirrels leave the group, making 6 squirrels again: $8 - 2 = 6$. The subtraction "undid" the addition.

Objectives

- Given concrete objects, show how two sets can be added together, and then reverse the operation to show how a number can be subtracted from the whole.

Tips

Explain that opposite operations undo each other. For example, tell students that turning on a light "undoes" the light being off. Cleaning their room "undoes" it being dirty.

LEARN Add and Take Away Cubes

OFFLINE 15min

Students will use cubes to show that addition and subtraction are opposite operations.

Gather the cubes and yarn.

Objectives

- Given concrete objects, show how two sets can be added together, and then reverse the operation to show how a number can be subtracted from the whole.

SUBTRACTION UNDOES ADDITION

1. Make a circle with the yarn. Place 4 red cubes inside the circle. Then place 7 yellow cubes in the circle.

   Ask: What did I do with the cubes? How many are there in all?
   ANSWER: You added 7 cubes to 4 cubes. There are 11 in all.

2. Remove the yellow cubes from the circle.

Ask: What did I do with the cubes now? How many are left in the circle?
ANSWER: You subtracted 7 cubes from the 11 cubes. There are 4 cubes left.

3. Explain to students that you added 7 cubes and then took 7 cubes away. The 4 cubes left are the same cubes they started with. Subtracting 7 cubes undoes adding 7 cubes. Subtraction and addition are opposite operations.

4. Repeat Steps 1–3 with 2 red cubes and 6 yellow cubes.

5. Place 8 red cubes in the circle. Add 4 yellow cubes.

Ask: What should I do so that there are only 8 cubes in the circle again? Explain.
ANSWER: Subtract 4 cubes; subtracting 4 cubes undoes adding 4 cubes.

ADDITION UNDOES SUBTRACTION

6. Place 9 cubes in the circle. Take away 4 cubes.

Ask: What did I do with the cubes? How many cubes are left?
ANSWER: You subtracted 4 cubes from 9 cubes. There are 5 cubes left.

7. Place the 4 cubes back in the circle.

Ask: How many cubes are there now? Did addition undo subtraction?
ANSWER: 9; Yes

8. **Say:** We took away 4 cubes, and then added 4 cubes. We had the same 9 cubes in the end. Adding undoes subtracting.

9. Have students show you the following examples. They should explain how each example shows that addition and subtraction are opposite operations.

- Add 6 cubes to 7 cubes. Then take away 6 cubes.
- Add 1 cube to 8 cubes. Then take away 1 cube.
- Take away 6 cubes from 13 cubes. Then add 6 cubes.
- Take away 7 cubes from 7 cubes. Then add 7 cubes.

10. Have students place 8 cubes in the circle and then take away 6 cubes.

Ask: What should you do so that there are 8 cubes in the circle again? Explain.
ANSWER: Add 6 cubes; adding 6 cubes undoes subtracting 6 cubes.

Say: Yes. When you add a number and then subtract the same number, you get the number you started with. When you subtract a number and then add the same number, you get the number you started with.

OFFLINE
10 min

TRY IT Show Subtraction

Students will practice showing that addition and subtraction "undo" each other. Give students the cubes and the Show Subtraction activity page from their Activity Book. Read the directions with them.

Objectives

- Given concrete objects, show how two sets can be added together, and then reverse the operation to show how a number can be subtracted from the whole.

Put Together, Take Away
Show Subtraction

Use cubes for Problems 1–5. Read each problem, make the model, and answer the questions.

1. Add 10 red cubes and 4 yellow cubes.
   Subtract 4 yellow cubes.
   How many cubes are left? <u>10</u>

2. Subtract 3 cubes from 7 cubes.
   Add 3 cubes.
   How many cubes are there? <u>7</u>

3. Add 7 cubes to 9 cubes.
   What is the total? <u>16</u>
   How do you get 9 cubes again as the total?
   Subtract 7 cubes to get 9 cubes again.

4. Subtract 5 cubes from 12 cubes.
   How many cubes are left? <u>7</u>
   How do you get 12 cubes again as the total?
   Add 5 cubes to get 12 cubes again.

5. Johnny added 9 to a number. Then he subtracted 9 from the total.
   What number was left? Use cubes to explain.
   The number Johnny got was the same number he started with.

TRY IT

Answer the questions.

6. How many cubes are there altogether? <u>12</u>
   If you subtract the yellow cubes, how many cubes will you have left? <u>7</u>

7. How many cubes are there altogether? <u>18</u>
   If you subtract the orange cubes, how many cubes will you have left? <u>10</u>

8. How many cubes are there altogether? <u>11</u>
   If you subtract the yellow cubes, how many cubes will you have left? <u>9</u>

9. Add the circles and the squares.
   How many are there in all? <u>16</u>
   Draw an X over all the circles.
   How many squares are left? <u>10</u>

TRY IT

Order and Zero in Subtraction

Lesson Overview

Skills Update	5 minutes	ONLINE
GET READY Subtraction Number Sentences	5 minutes	ONLINE
LEARN Does Order Matter?	20 minutes	OFFLINE
LEARN Subtract Zero	15 minutes	OFFLINE
TRY IT Subtraction Rules	10 minutes	OFFLINE
CHECKPOINT	5 minutes	OFFLINE

▶ Lesson Objectives

- Use models to demonstrate that the order in which numbers are subtracted changes the solution.
- Demonstrate understanding of the result of subtracting zero from a given quantity.

▶ Prerequisite Skills

- Demonstrate the meaning of subtraction as taking away an amount from a given quantity (with minuends up through 20).
- Demonstrate the meaning of subtraction as comparing the difference between two quantities (with minuends up through 20).
- Use models and math symbols to represent subtraction.

▶ Content Background

In this lesson, students will learn that the order of numbers in a subtraction problem does affect the difference. They will also learn that subtracting zero from a number does not change the number.

   Although it may be tempting to tell students that they cannot subtract a greater number from a lesser one, the concept of negative numbers does exist in later courses. Therefore, in this lesson, explain the concept in this way: "If you start with 4 circles, you cannot take away 7 circles because there are not enough circles. So 7 minus 4 is not equal to 4 minus 7." In this lesson, students will NOT find differences if they are negative. They will simply learn that changing the order of the numbers in a subtraction sentence changes the difference.

Materials to Gather

SUPPLIED

blocks – B (10 red, 10 yellow)

Subtraction Rules activity page

Checkpoint (printout)

Keywords

minuend – in subtraction, the quantity or number from which another number is subtracted; 8 is the minuend in the problem $8 - 7 = ?$

negative number – a number that is less than zero

subtrahend – the number that is subtracted in a subtraction problem; 7 is the subtrahend in the problem $8 - 7 = ?$

GET READY Subtraction Number Sentences

Students will write subtraction sentences to show the number of animals left in a group after some of the animals move away.

- Demonstrate the meaning of subtraction as taking away an amount from a given quantity (with minuends up through 20).
- Demonstrate the meaning of subtraction as comparing the difference between two quantities (with minuends up through 20).
- Use models and math symbols to represent subtraction.

Tips

Have students use circles to model and solve the problems if they are having trouble.

LEARN Does Order Matter?

Students will model subtraction expressions to determine if the order in which the numbers are subtracted changes the difference.

Gather the circle blocks.

Objectives

- Use models to demonstrate that the order in which numbers are subtracted changes the solution.

1. Show a group of 5 red circles to the left of a group of 3 yellow circles. Ask students how many circles there are altogether. (8)

2. Move the red circles to the right of the yellow circles. Explain that you changed the order of the groups. Ask students how many circles there are altogether now. (8)

   Say: 3 plus 5 is 8. 5 plus 3 is also 8. We can add numbers in any order and get the same sum. So 5 plus 3 equals 3 plus 5.

3. **Say:** Can we subtract numbers in any order and get the same difference? Let's use circles to find out.

   Show a group of 7 circles. Take away 2 circles to show 7 minus 2. Ask students how many circles are left. (5)

4. **Say:** Now let's switch the order. We'll start with 2 and subtract 7.

   Show a group of 2 circles. Count each of the 2 circles as you take it away.

   Say: We don't have any more circles to take away. The answer to 2 minus 7 is not 2. So 7 minus 2 is not equal to 2 minus 7.

5. Have students use circles to show the following expressions. Have them tell you if the expressions in each pair are equal or not equal.

   - $4 - 1$ and $1 - 4$ $(\neq)$
   - $10 - 3$ and $3 - 10$ $(\neq)$
   - $9 - 7$ and $7 - 9$ $(\neq)$
   - $6 - 5$ and $5 - 6$ $(\neq)$

6. Have students use circles to show $8 - 2$ and $2 - 8$. Ask if the expressions are equal. (No) Write $8 - 2 \neq 2 - 8$ on a sheet of paper. Explain that the not-equal-to symbol shows that the two expressions are not the same.

7. Write the following pairs of expressions, leaving a space between the expressions for students to write $=$ or $\neq$. Ask students to write the correct symbol in the space. If students have difficulty, have them model the expressions with circles.

   • $10 - 8$ and $8 - 10$ ($\neq$)
   • $12 - 5$ and $5 - 12$ ($\neq$)
   • $9 - 6$ and $6 - 9$ ($\neq$)
   • $6 - 14$ and $14 - 6$ ($\neq$)
   • $5 - 11$ and $11 - 5$ ($\neq$)

8. Write the following pairs of expressions, leaving a space between the expressions for students to write $=$ or $\neq$. Ask students to write the correct symbol in the space. Students should not use models.

   • $78 - 43$ and $43 - 78$ ($\neq$)
   • $109 - 79$ and $79 - 109$ ($\neq$)

9. Have students explain how they knew the expressions in Step 8 weren't equal. (Changing the order of numbers in subtraction sentences changes the difference. You can't subtract numbers in any order.)

OFFLINE
15 min

LEARN Subtract Zero

Objectives

• Demonstrate understanding of the result of subtracting zero from a given quantity.

Students will use models to learn that the difference of a number and zero is the number itself.

Gather the circle blocks.

1. To review the concept of zero, place a sheet of paper with 0 circles on it in front of students.

   Say: There are zero circles on the paper.

2. Then model taking away zero by placing 5 circles on the paper and writing $5 - 0 = $ ___ under the circles.

   Say: To take away zero circles, I remove no circles. $5 - 0 = 5$.

3. Write the answer to $5 - 0$. Then write $6 - 0 = $ ___ on the paper, and ask students to use circles to show $6 - 0$. Have them write the answer after they model. (6)

4. Write these problems. Have students write the answers. If students have difficulty, have them model the problems with circles.

   • $12 - 0 = $ (12)
   • $4 - 0 = $ (4)
   • $7 - 0 = $ (7)
   • $15 - 0 = $ (15)
   • $20 - 0 = $ (20)
   • $16 - 0 = $ (16)
   • $3 - 0 = $ (3)
   • $9 - 0 = $ (9)

5. Once students have answered the problems in Step 4 correctly, ask them to explain what they notice about the answers. (Each answer is the same as the first number in the problem.)

6. Write these problems. Have students write the answers. Have them explain how they figured out the answers.
   - $56 - 0 =$ (56)
   - $239 - 0 =$ (239)

OFFLINE
10 min

TRY IT Subtraction Rules

Students will practice subtracting zero and deciding if two subtraction expressions are equal. Give students the circle blocks and Subtraction Rules activity page from their Activity Book. Read the directions with them.

Objectives

- Use models to demonstrate that the order in which numbers are subtracted changes the solution.
- Demonstrate understanding of the result of subtracting zero from a given quantity.

Tips

Students may use models to help them subtract.

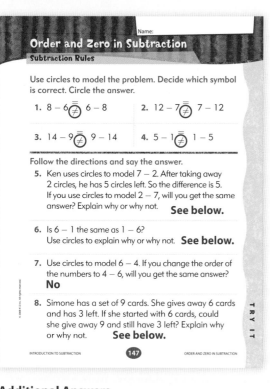

Order and Zero in Subtraction
Subtraction Rules

Use circles to model the problem. Decide which symbol is correct. Circle the answer.

1. $8 - 6 \; \fbox{$\neq$} \; 6 - 8$ 2. $12 - 7 \; \fbox{$\neq$} \; 7 - 12$

3. $14 - 9 \; \fbox{$\neq$} \; 9 - 14$ 4. $5 - 1 \; \fbox{$\neq$} \; 1 - 5$

Follow the directions and say the answer.

5. Ken uses circles to model $7 - 2$. After taking away 2 circles, he has 5 circles left. So the difference is 5. If you use circles to model $2 - 7$, will you get the same answer? Explain why or why not. **See below.**

6. Is $6 - 1$ the same as $1 - 6$? Use circles to explain why or why not. **See below.**

7. Use circles to model $6 - 4$. If you change the order of the numbers to $4 - 6$, will you get the same answer? **No**

8. Simone has a set of 9 cards. She gives away 6 cards and has 3 left. If she started with 6 cards, could she give away 9 and still have 3 left? Explain why or why not. **See below.**

9. Use circles to show that $8 - 3$ is not the same as $3 - 8$. **See below.**

10. Jack has a set of 7 pens. He gives away 3 pens and has 4 left. If he started with 3 pens, could he give away 7 and still have 4 left? Explain why or why not. **See below.**

Write the answer.

11. $8 - 0 = \underline{\textbf{8}}$ 12. $18 - 0 = \underline{\textbf{18}}$

13. $79 - 0 = \underline{\textbf{79}}$ 14. $318 - 0 = \underline{\textbf{318}}$

15. Mark had 12 stickers. He gave away zero stickers. How many stickers does Mark have left?

   $\underline{\textbf{12}}$ stickers

16. What happens to a number when you subtract zero from it?

   You get the same number.

17. When you subtract 0 from 11, how many are left? **11**

18. What number goes in the box?

   $14 - \fbox{\textbf{0}} = 14$

TRY IT

Additional Answers

5. No; You can't take away 7 circles from only 2 circles.

6. No; If you start with 6 circles and take away 1 circle, you have 5 circles. But if you start with 1 circle, there are not enough circles to take away 6 circles. The answers are not the same, so $6 - 1$ does not equal $1 - 6$.

8. No; Students should give a valid explanation, such as $9 - 6$ is not the same as $6 - 9$.

9. Students may first model 8 and take 3 away, and then model 3 and show that it isn't possible to take away 8.

10. No; Students should give a valid explanation, such as $7 - 3$ is not the same as $3 - 7$.

CHECKPOINT

Print the Checkpoint. In Part 1, students will take a performance-based assessment. In Part 2, students will complete the problems on their own. Read the directions, problems, and answer choices to students if necessary. Use the answer key to score the Checkpoint, and then enter the results online.

Gather the circle blocks. Sudents will use the circle blocks for Problems 1–5.

- Use models to demonstrate that the order in which numbers are subtracted changes the solution.
- Demonstrate understanding of the result of subtracting zero from a given quantity.

⚙ Checkpoint   Math | Introduction to Subtraction | Order and Zero in Subtraction

Name _____ Date _____

Checkpoint Answer Key

Part 1

Follow the instructions for each item. Choose the response that best describes how the student performs on the task. When you have finished, enter the results online. Have students use blocks to model problems as they answer questions and explain.

1. Say, "Show how to subtract $7 - 3$. If you turn these numbers around so that you have $3 - 7$, will you get the same answer? Explain why or why not."

    Example: No, you can't take 7 circles away from 3 circles. When you switch the numbers in a subtraction problem, you don't get the same answer.
    (1 point)
    Did the student model and answer correctly?

    A. Yes   B. No

2. Say, "Show how to subtract $8 - 4$. If you turn these numbers around so that you have $4 - 8$, will you get the same answer? Explain why or why not."

    Example: No, you can't take 8 circles from 4 circles. When you switch the numbers in a subtraction problem, you don't get the same answer.
    (1 point)
    Did the student model and answer correctly?

    A. Yes   B. No

⚙ Checkpoint   Math | Introduction to Subtraction | Order and Zero in Subtraction

Name _____ Date _____

3. Say, "Andrew has a set of 6 balls. He gives away 4 balls and has 2 left. If he started with 4 balls, could he give away 6 and still have 2 left? Explain why or why not."
    (1 point)
    Did the student say that starting with 4, giving away 6, and having 2 left is not possible?

    A. Yes   B. No
    (1 point)
    Did the student give a valid explanation, such as when you switch the numbers in a subtraction problem, you don't get the same answer?

    A. Yes   B. No

---

4. Ask, "Is $10 - 2$ the same as $2 - 10$? Explain why or why not."

    Example: No, 10 circles take away 2 circles is 8 circles, but if there are 2 circles to start with, then there are not enough circles to take away 10 circles.
    (1 point)
    Did the student model and answer correctly?

    A. Yes   B. No

---

5. Say, "Show that $15 - 2$ is not the same as $2 - 15$."

    Example: Model 15 and take 2 away, and then model 2 and show that you cannot take away 15.
    (1 point)
    Did the student model and answer correctly?

    A. Yes   B. No

Give students Part 2 of the assessment.

⚙ Checkpoint   Math | Introduction to Subtraction | Order and Zero in Subtraction

Name _____ Date _____

Part 2
Write the answer.
(1 point)
6. Susie has 17 cards.
    She gives away 0 of them.
    How many cards does she have now?   **17**

(1 point)
7. Simon has 7 cookies.
    He eats 0 of them.
    How many cookies does he have now?   **7**

(1 point)
8. $16 - 0 =$ **16**

(1 point)
9. When you subtract 0 from 9, how many are left?   **9**

(1 point)
10. What number goes in the box? $19 - \boxed{0} = 19$

Subtract to Compare

Lesson Overview

Skills Update	5 minutes	ONLINE
GET READY Take Some Away	5 minutes	OFFLINE
LEARN Model Subtraction	20 minutes	ONLINE
LEARN Animal Subtraction	20 minutes	ONLINE
TRY IT How Many Greater or Less?	10 minutes	OFFLINE

▶ Lesson Objectives

- Demonstrate the meaning of subtraction as comparing two quantities.
- Use concrete objects or sketches to model and solve addition or subtraction computation problems with sums and minuends up through 30.

▶ Prerequisite Skills

- Demonstrate the meaning of subtraction as comparing the difference between two quantities (with minuends up through 20).
- Use concrete objects or sketches to model and solve addition or subtraction computation problems involving sums or minuends up through 20.

▶ Common Errors and Misconceptions

- Students might add rather than subtract numbers in a compare problem. For example, when asked how many greater 5 is than 4, students might write the number sentence $5 + 4 = 9$ rather than $5 - 4 = 1$.
- When using objects to model a problem with an unknown difference, such as $9 - 2$, students might combine the groups of objects.

▶ Advance Preparation

Print the Inch Grid Paper.

▶ Content Background

In this lesson, students will learn that they can subtract to find how much greater or how much less one number is than another number. They will also use one-to-one correspondence as they make pairs of objects in two groups.

Students have demonstrated one-to-one correspondence by pointing to exactly one object as they count exactly one number. As they learn to use models to subtract, it's important that they've mastered one-to-one correspondence.

Materials to Gather

SUPPLIED

blocks – B (red, blue)

blocks – O (red, blue)

Inch Grid Paper (printout)

How Many Greater or Less? activity page

Keywords	
	compare – to find the similarities or differences among sizes, values, or amounts
	greater – larger in number or amount than another
	lesser – smaller in number or amount than another
	row – a list of numbers or group of objects arranged in a horizontal format

OFFLINE

5 min

GET READY Take Some Away

Objectives

- Demonstrate the meaning of subtraction as comparing the difference between two quantities (with minuends up through 20).
- Use concrete objects or sketches to model and solve addition or subtraction computation problems involving sums or minuends up through 20.

Students will use models to solve subtraction problems.
Gather the circle blocks.

1. **Say:** Let's use circles to solve subtraction problems. Put 4 circles in front of you.

2. **Say:** Now take away 1 circle.

3. **Say:** You used the circles to show 4 minus 1. The number of circles left is the difference.

    Ask: What is 4 minus 1?
    ANSWER: 3

4. Repeat Steps 1–3 for 7 take away 4.

5. **Say:** Now let's solve subtraction problems with pictures. Draw 9 objects.

6. **Say:** Now cross out 2 objects. When you use a drawing to show subtraction, you can shade the objects or cross them out to show that you are subtracting them.

7. **Say:** Your picture shows 9 minus 2. The number of objects not crossed out is the difference.

    Ask: What is 9 minus 2?
    ANSWER: 7

8. Repeat Steps 5–7 for 6 take away 3.

9. Write the following problems on paper: $8 - 2$; $10 - 1$; and $14 - 9$.

    Say: Use drawings or objects to solve the problems. As you work, explain what you are doing. Tell me which model you used and why.

    Watch for students who do not take away the correct number of objects. Explain that the second number in the problem tells how many to take away.

    Watch for students who count the objects taken away, instead of the objects left, to find the difference. Explain that the number of objects left in the group is the difference.

Tips

Have students use simple drawings, such as circles, squares, or hearts.

LEARN Model Subtraction

Students will use blocks and grid paper to compare two numbers. Gather the circle blocks and Inch Grid Paper.

Follow the directions on each screen. The last screen will direct students to model several problems with the blocks and grid paper.

Objectives

- Demonstrate the meaning of subtraction as comparing two quantities.

Tips

There are many ways to set up a "subtract to compare" problem. Students can use any way they choose. What is important is that blocks are aligned, pairs are marked with connecting lines, and blocks left over are circled.

LEARN Animal Subtraction

Students will draw pictures to compare to solve subtraction problems.

Follow the directions on each screen. Students will make drawings to model problems online.

Objectives

- Use concrete objects or sketches to model and solve addition or subtraction computation problems with sums and minuends up through 30.

TRY IT How Many Greater or Less?

Students will practice comparing to solve subtraction problems. Give students the cubes, grid paper, and How Many Greater or Less? activity page from their Activity Book. Read the directions with them.

Objectives

- Demonstrate the meaning of subtraction as comparing two quantities.
- Use concrete objects or sketches to model and solve addition or subtraction computation problems with sums and minuends up through 30.

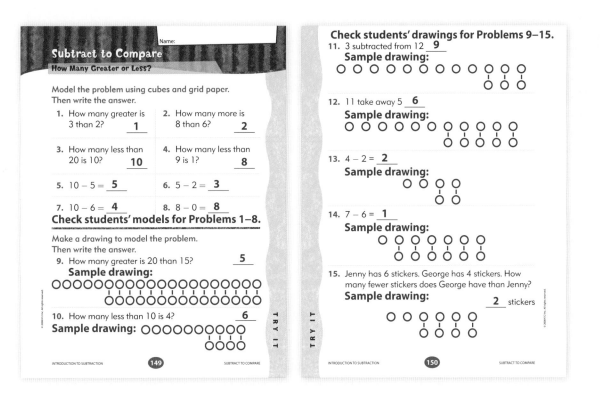

Subtract to Compare
How Many Greater or Less?

Model the problem using cubes and grid paper.
Then write the answer.

1. How many greater is 3 than 2? **1**

2. How many more is 8 than 6? **2**

3. How many less than 20 is 10? **10**

4. How many less than 9 is 1? **8**

5. $10 - 5 =$ **5**

6. $5 - 2 =$ **3**

7. $10 - 6 =$ **4**

8. $8 - 0 =$ **8**

Check students' models for Problems 1–8.

Make a drawing to model the problem.
Then write the answer.

9. How many greater is 20 than 15? **5**
Sample drawing:

10. How many less than 10 is 4? **6**
Sample drawing:

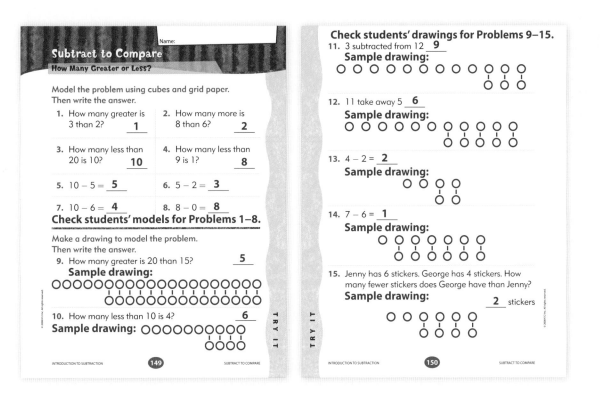

Check students' drawings for Problems 9–15.

11. 3 subtracted from 12 **9**
Sample drawing:

12. 11 take away 5 **6**
Sample drawing:

13. $4 - 2 =$ **2**
Sample drawing:

14. $7 - 6 =$ **1**
Sample drawing:

15. Jenny has 6 stickers. George has 4 stickers. How many fewer stickers does George have than Jenny?
Sample drawing: **2** stickers

TRY IT

Use Pairs to Subtract

Lesson Overview		
Skills Update	5 minutes	ONLINE
GET READY Subtraction Models	5 minutes	ONLINE
LEARN Animal Lineup	10 minutes	ONLINE
TRY IT Line Up to Subtract	5 minutes	OFFLINE
LEARN Match to Subtract	15 minutes	OFFLINE
TRY IT Sketch Objects to Subtract	10 minutes	OFFLINE
CHECKPOINT	10 minutes	OFFLINE

▶ Lesson Objectives

- Demonstrate the meaning of subtraction as comparing two quantities.
- Use concrete objects or sketches to model and solve addition or subtraction computation problems with sums and minuends up through 30.

▶ Prerequisite Skills

- Demonstrate the meaning of subtraction as comparing the difference between two quantities (with minuends up through 20).
- Use concrete objects or sketches to model and solve addition or subtraction computation problems involving sums or minuends up through 20.

▶ Common Errors and Misconceptions

- Students might add rather than subtract numbers in a compare problem. For example, when asked how many greater 5 is than 4, students might write the number sentence $5 + 4 = 9$ rather than $5 - 4 = 1$.
- When using objects to model a problem with an unknown difference, such as $9 - 2$, students might combine the groups of objects.

▶ Advance Preparation

Print the Inch Grid Paper.

▶ Content Background

In this lesson, students will compare groups of objects to solve subtraction problems.

Materials to Gather

SUPPLIED

blocks – B (green, blue)

Line Up to Subtract activity page

blocks – O (red, yellow)

Inch Grid Paper (printout)

Sketch Objects to Subtract activity page

Checkpoint (printout)

GET READY Subtraction Models

Students will learn how to use cubes and pictures to solve subtraction problems.

Objectives

- Demonstrate the meaning of subtraction as comparing the difference between two quantities (with minuends up through 20).
- Use concrete objects or sketches to model and solve addition or subtraction computation problems involving sums or minuends up through 20.

LEARN Animal Lineup

Students will use a picture to compare to solve a subtraction problem.

Objectives

- Demonstrate the meaning of subtraction as comparing two quantities.

TRY IT Line Up to Subtract

Students will practice using pairing to subtract. Give students the Line Up to Subtract activity page from their Activity Book and read the directions with them.

Objectives

- Demonstrate the meaning of subtraction as comparing two quantities.

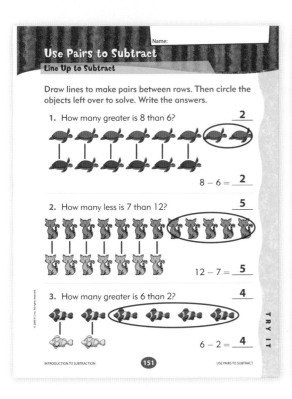

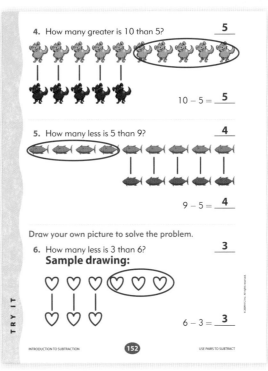

LEARN Match to Subtract

Students will compare to find how many greater or less a given number is than another number by placing blocks on grid paper.

Gather the circles and Inch Grid Paper, and give them to students.

1. Tell students that they will use the circles and grid paper to find how many greater 8 is than 3. Have them place 8 circles in a row (side by side) on the grid paper.

2. Have them place 3 circles in the row below the first row so that the rows are aligned on the left. (You may want to leave a blank row between the rows of circles.)

3. **Ask:** How could you use your model to find how many greater 8 is than 3?
   ANSWER: I see that 3 pairs of circles match up. There are 5 circles left over that are not part of a matched pair.

   Ask: So how many greater is 8 than 3?
   ANSWER: 5

   If students have difficulty, show them how to draw a line joining each circle to the one below it. Have them circle those that are left over and count them.

4. Repeat Steps 1–3 with the following questions:
   - How many less is 7 than 11?   (4)
   - How many less is 6 than 12?   (6)
   - How many greater is 13 than 5? (8)
   - How many greater is 12 than 9? (3)

Objectives

- Use concrete objects or sketches to model and solve addition or subtraction computation problems with sums and minuends up through 30.

Tips

Students may align the objects in columns or rows, and they may align on the right, left, top, or bottom.

TRY IT Sketch Objects to Subtract

Students will practice using pictures and objects to compare to subtract. Give students the cubes, Inch Grid Paper, and Sketch Objects to Subtract activity page from their Activity Book. Read the directions with them.

Objectives

- Demonstrate the meaning of subtraction as comparing two quantities.
- Use concrete objects or sketches to model and solve addition or subtraction computation problems with sums and minuends up through 30.

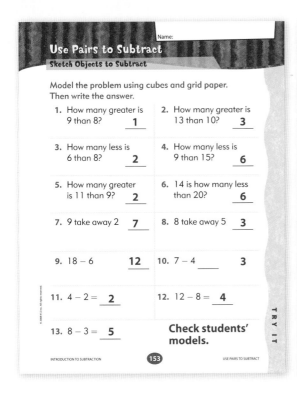

Use Pairs to Subtract

Sketch Objects to Subtract

Model the problem using cubes and grid paper. Then write the answer.

1. How many greater is 9 than 8? __1__

2. How many greater is 13 than 10? __3__

3. How many less is 6 than 8? __2__

4. How many less is 9 than 15? __6__

5. How many greater is 11 than 9? __2__

6. 14 is how many less than 20? __6__

7. 9 take away 2 __7__

8. 8 take away 5 __3__

9. 18 − 6 __12__

10. 7 − 4 __3__

11. 4 − 2 = __2__

12. 12 − 8 = __4__

13. 8 − 3 = __5__

Check students' models.

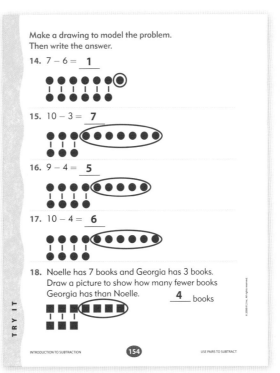

Make a drawing to model the problem. Then write the answer.

14. 7 − 6 = __1__

15. 10 − 3 = __7__

16. 9 − 4 = __5__

17. 10 − 4 = __6__

18. Noelle has 7 books and Georgia has 3 books. Draw a picture to show how many fewer books Georgia has than Noelle. __4__ books

---

OFFLINE **10**min

CHECKPOINT

Print the Checkpoint. Students will take a performance-based assessment. Read the directions and problems to students. Use the answer key to score the Checkpoint, and then enter the results online.

Gather the cubes. Students will use the cubes for Problems 3, 4, and 6.

Objectives

- Demonstrate the meaning of subtraction as comparing two quantities.

- Use concrete objects or sketches to model and solve addition or subtraction computation problems with sums and minuends up through 30.

Name _____   Date _____

Checkpoint Answer Key

Follow the instructions for each item. Choose the response that bests describes how the students performed on the task. When you have finished, enter the results online.

1. Say, "What is the difference between 12 and 6? Draw a picture to show how to solve the problem."
(1 point)
Did students draw correctly?

A. Yes   B. No
(1 point)
Did students find that the difference between 12 and 6 is 6?

A. Yes   B. No

2. Say, "Janice has 10 crayons and Katrina has 11 crayons. How many more crayons does Katrina have than Janice? Draw a picture to show how to solve this problem."
(1 point)
Did students draw correctly?

A. Yes   B. No
(1 point)
Did your student find that Katrina has 1 more crayon than Janice?

A. Yes   B. No

Name _____   Date _____

3. Say, "How much less is 7 than 10? Use cubes to show how to solve the problem."
(1 point)
Did students use cubes to show 10 take away 7?

A. Yes   B. No
(1 point)
Did students find that 7 is 3 less than 10?

A. Yes   B. No

Give students 15 red and 15 yellow cubes. Read directions aloud.

4. Say, "Use cubes to show 7 take away 7."
(1 point)
Did students use counting chips to show 7 take away 7?

A. Yes   B. No

5. Say, "Draw a picture to show 5 subtracted from 6."
(1 point)
Did students draw correctly?

A. Yes   B. No

6. Use cubes to show 7 take away 2.
(1 point)
Did your student use cubes to show 7 take away 2?

A. Yes   B. No

Unit Review

Lesson Overview

UNIT REVIEW Look Back	20 minutes	**ONLINE**
UNIT REVIEW Checkpoint Practice	20 minutes	**OFFLINE**
⏩ **UNIT REVIEW** Prepare for the Checkpoint		

▶ Unit Objectives

This lesson reviews the following objectives:

- Demonstrate and explain the meaning of subtraction as taking away.
- Use concrete objects or sketches to model and solve addition or subtraction computation problems with sums and minuends up through 30.
- Recognize that the − symbol refers to subtraction.
- Correctly use the − symbol.
- Use models and math symbols to represent subtraction.
- Recognize that the equals symbol shows an equality between two expressions.
- Given concrete objects, show how two sets can be added together, and then reverse the operation to show how a number can be subtracted from the whole.
- Use models to demonstrate that the order in which numbers are subtracted changes the solution.
- Demonstrate understanding of the result of subtracting zero from a given quantity.
- Demonstrate the meaning of subtraction as comparing two quantities.

▶ Advance Preparation

In this lesson, students will have an opportunity to review previous activities in the Introduction to Subtraction unit. Look at the suggested activities in Unit Review: Prepare for the Checkpoint online and gather any needed materials.

Print the Inch Grid Paper.

Materials to Gather

SUPPLIED

Checkpoint Practice activity page

Inch Grid Paper (printout)

blocks – B (red, blue)

Keywords

addition	negative number
compare	not-equal-to symbol ($\neq$)
difference	number sentence
equal	opposite operations
equals symbol ($=$)	row
expression	subtract
greater	subtraction
lesser	subtraction sentence
minuend	subtrahend
minus	sum
minus symbol ($-$)	take away

UNIT REVIEW Look Back

- Review unit objectives.

Students learned that subtraction means to take away, and they used models to show subtraction. They learned that when they subtract, the number that is left is the difference. They learned the meaning of the minus symbol ($-$) and reviewed the meaning of the equals symbol ($=$) so they could read and write subtraction sentences.

Students explored the relationship between addition and subtraction; they learned that they are opposite operations. They demonstrated the opposite operations with objects and drawings. They learned that subtraction is not commutative, and that subtracting zero from a given number results in a difference of the original number.

Students then learned about using subtraction in comparing numbers, which allowed them to find how much greater or lesser a number is than another number. They used pairing, modeling, and drawings to compare numbers.

UNIT REVIEW Checkpoint Practice

- Review unit objectives.

Students will complete a Checkpoint Practice activity page to prepare for the Unit Checkpoint. If necessary, read the directions, problems, and answer choices to students. Have students answer the problems on their own. Carefully review the answers with students.

Gather the circle blocks and grid paper. Have students use the materials as described on the activity page.

Name:

Unit Review
Checkpoint Practice

Draw a picture to show the subtraction.
Write the answer.
1. Nick has 10 marbles.
   He gives 4 to his brother.
   How many marbles does Nick have left?

   ⊠ ⊠ ○ ○ ○
   ⊠ ⊠ ○ ○ ○   **6** marbles

Write a subtraction number sentence to match the picture or words.

2. [cars] $8 - 5 = 3$

3. 12 take away 6 is 6 $12 - 6 = 6$

Write the missing symbol.

4. $7 - 5 \boxed{=} 2$ 5. $11 \boxed{-} 5 = 6$

Write $=$ if the expressions are equal.
Write $\neq$ if the expressions are not equal.

6. $6 - 2 \boxed{=} 4$ 7. $8 \boxed{\neq} 12 - 3$

8. $3 - 1 \boxed{=} 4 - 2$ 9. $9 - 4 \boxed{\neq} 4 - 9$

Use circle blocks to model the problem. Write the answer.

10. Add 8 circles to 6 circles.
    What is the total?   **14**
    What do you have to do to get back to 8 circles?
    Subtract 6.

11. Curtis added 5 to a number.
    Then he subtracted 5 from the total.
    What number was left? **the number he started with**

12. Jenny had 15 photos.
    She gave away 0 photos.
    How many photos does Jenny have left?   **15**

Use circle blocks and grid paper to model the problem. Write the answer.

13. How many greater is 10 than 7?   **3**

14. How many less is 6 than 7?   **1**

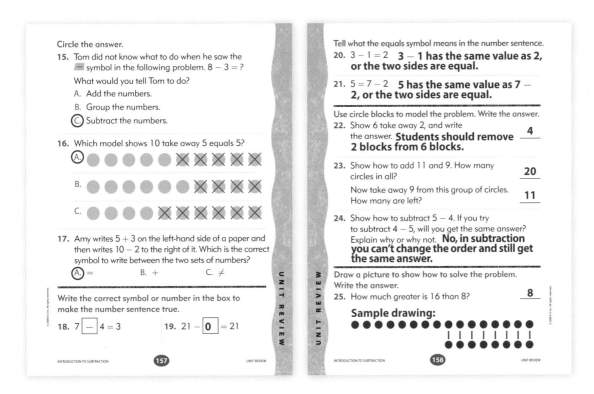

Circle the answer.

15. Tom did not know what to do when he saw the
━ symbol in the following problem. $8 - 3 = ?$

What would you tell Tom to do?

A. Add the numbers.

B. Group the numbers.

(C) Subtract the numbers.

16. Which model shows 10 take away 5 equals 5?

Ⓐ ●●●●● ✕✕✕✕✕

B. ●●●●●● ✕✕✕✕

C. ●●●● ✕✕✕✕✕✕

17. Amy writes $5 + 3$ on the left-hand side of a paper and
then writes $10 - 2$ to the right of it. Which is the correct
symbol to write between the two sets of numbers?

Ⓐ =   B. +   C. ≠

Write the correct symbol or number in the box to
make the number sentence true.

18. $7 \boxed{-} 4 = 3$ **19.** $21 - \boxed{0} = 21$

Tell what the equals symbol means in the number sentence.

20. $3 - 1 = 2$ **3 − 1 has the same value as 2,
or the two sides are equal.**

21. $5 = 7 - 2$ **5 has the same value as 7 −
2, or the two sides are equal.**

Use circle blocks to model the problem. Write the answer.

22. Show 6 take away 2, and write
the answer. **Students should remove
2 blocks from 6 blocks.**   4

23. Show how to add 11 and 9. How many
circles in all?   20

Now take away 9 from this group of circles.
How many are left?   11

24. Show how to subtract $5 - 4$. If you try
to subtract $4 - 5$, will you get the same answer?
Explain why or why not. **No, in subtraction
you can't change the order and still get
the same answer.**

Draw a picture to show how to solve the problem.
Write the answer.

25. How much greater is 16 than 8?   8

Sample drawing:

●●●●●●●●●●●●●●●●
     | | | | | | | |
     ●●●●●●●●

→ UNIT REVIEW Prepare for the Checkpoint

What you do next depends on how students performed in the previous activity,
Unit Review: Checkpoint Practice. If students had difficulty with any of the
problems, complete the appropriate review activity listed in the table online.

Unit Checkpoint

UNIT CHECKPOINT Offline | 60 minutes | **OFFLINE**

▶ Unit Objectives

This lesson assesses the following objectives:

- Demonstrate and explain the meaning of subtraction as taking away.
- Use concrete objects or sketches to model and solve addition or subtraction computation problems with sums and minuends up through 30.
- Recognize that the − symbol refers to subtraction.
- Correctly use the − symbol.
- Use models and math symbols to represent subtraction.
- Recognize that the equals symbol shows an equality between two expressions.
- Given concrete objects, show how two sets can be added together, and then reverse the operation to show how a number can be subtracted from the whole.
- Use models to demonstrate that the order in which numbers are subtracted changes the solution.
- Demonstrate understanding of the result of subtracting zero from a given quantity.
- Demonstrate the meaning of subtraction as comparing two quantities.

Materials to Gather

SUPPLIED

blocks – B (red, blue)
blocks – O (any color)
Unit Checkpoint (printout)

ALSO NEEDED

paper, drawing – 2 sheets

UNIT CHECKPOINT Offline

OFFLINE 60 min

Objectives

- Assess unit objectives.

Students will complete the Unit Checkpoint offline. In Part 1, students will take a performance-based assessment. In Part 2, students will complete the problems on their own. Print the Unit Checkpoint. Read the directions, problems, and answer choices to students if necessary. Use the answer key to score the Checkpoint, and then enter the results online.

Gather the blocks and drawing paper. Students will use them as directed in the Unit Checkpoint.

Name _____ Date _____

Unit Checkpoint Answer Key

Part 1

Follow the instructions for each item. Choose the response that best describes how the student performed on the task. When you have finished, enter the results online.

1. Say, "You look in a math book and see this number sentence: $4 - 1 = 3$. What does the equals symbol mean in this number sentence?"
(1 point)
Did the student say the equals symbol means that $4 - 1$ has the same value as 3, or the two sides are the same or equal?

  A. Yes   B. No

2. Say, "You look in a math book and see this number sentence: $7 = 9 - 2$. What does the equals symbol mean in this number sentence?"
(1 point)
Did the student say the equals symbol means that 7 has the same value as $9 - 2$, or the two sides are the same or equal?

  A. Yes   B. No

3. Say, "You look in a math book and see this number sentence: $7 = 7$. What does the equals symbol mean in this number sentence?"
(1 point)
Did the student say the equals symbol means that 7 has the same value as 7, or the two sides are the same or equal?

  A. Yes   B. No

Name _____ Date _____

4. Say, "Use circles to show 10 take away 5."
(1 point)
Did the student use circles to show 10 take away 5? (A sample model is to show 10 circles and then remove 5.)

  A. Yes   B. No

5. Say, "Draw a picture to show 4 subtracted from 9."
(1 point)
Did the student draw a picture to show 4 subtracted from 9? (A sample picture is to draw 9 circles with 4 crossed out.)

  A. Yes   B. No

6. Say, "Place 4 red cubes and 4 blue cubes on the table. Use the cubes to show if you can add 4 and 4 to make 8. What happens if you take away 4 blue cubes? How many cubes do you have left?"
(1 point)
Did the student use the cubes to show how to combine the two groups of cubes to make 8?

  A. Yes   B. No
(1 point)
Did the student say that if they take away 4 blue cubes, they will be left with 4 red cubes?

  A. Yes   B. No

Name _____ Date _____

7. Say, "Place 5 red cubes and 5 blue cubes on the table. Use the cubes to show how you can add 5 and 5 to make 10. What happens if you take away 5 blue cubes? How many cubes do you have left?"
(1 point)
Did the student use the cubes to show how to combine the two groups of cubes to make 10?

  A. Yes   B. No
(1 point)
Did the student then say that taking away 5 blue cubes leaves 5 red cubes?

  A. Yes   B. No

8. Say, "Simone subtracted 7 from 10 to get 3. If she subtracts 10 from 7, will she also get 3? Explain why or why not."
(1 point)
Did the student say she will not get 3 if she subtracts 10 from 7?

  A. Yes   B. No
(1 point)
Did the student give a valid explanation? (Example: The order in which you subtract changes the solution; in this case, $10 - 7$ is not the same as $7 - 10$.)

  A. Yes   B. No

9. Say, "Use the cubes to show that $8 - 3$ is not the same thing as $3 - 8$."
(1 point)
Did the student use the cubes to show that $8 - 3$ is not the same as $3 - 8$? (Students may first model 8 and take away 3, and then model 3 and show that you cannot take away 8.)

  A. Yes   B. No

Name _____ Date _____

10. Say, "Use the cubes to show that $7 - 3$ is not the same as $3 - 7$."
(1 point)
Did the student use the cubes to show that $7 - 3$ is not the same as $3 - 7$? (Students may first model 7 and take 3 away, and then model 3 and show that you cannot take away 7.)

  A. Yes   B. No

11. Say, "Use the cubes to show that $10 - 5$ is not the same as $5 - 10$."
(1 point)
Did the student use the cubes to show that $10 - 5$ is not the same as $5 - 10$? (Students may first model 10 and take 5 away, and then model 5 and show that you cannot take away 10.)

  A. Yes   B. No

12. Ask, "How many greater is 20 than 10? Draw a picture to show how to solve this problem."
(1 point)
Did the student draw correctly? (Students may draw 20 squares and then 10 squares underneath, and then draw a line from each of the 10 underneath squares to 10 of the 20 squares, leaving 10 squares without lines.)

  A. Yes   B. No

Give students Part 2 of the assessment.

Name _____ Date _____

Part 2
For Problems 13–15, write the symbol in the box that makes the
number sentence true.

(1 point)
13. $6 - 1 \boxed{=} 9 - 4$

_____

(1 point)
14. $7 \boxed{-} 3 = 4$

_____

(1 point)
15. $10 \boxed{-} 4 = 6$

_____

For Problems 16–26, circle the answer.
(1 point)
16. What does the symbol the
arrow is pointing to mean? $10 \overset{\downarrow}{-} 2 = 8$

   (A) subtract   B. equals   C. add

_____

(1 point)
17. Which number goes in the box?

   $12 = 12 - \boxed{}$

   (A) 0   B. 11   C. 12

Name _____ Date _____

(1 point)
18. Which number sentence shows that when five is subtracted from
nine, the difference is four?

   A. $5 + 4 = 9$ B. $6 - 4 = 2$ (C) $9 - 5 = 4$

(1 point)
19. How would you subtract 2 stars from this group of 9 stars?

   ☆ ☆ ☆ ☆ ☆ ☆ ☆ ☆ ☆

   (A) cross out 2 stars

   B. draw two more stars

   C. cross out 9 stars

_____

(1 point)
20. The $-$ symbol is in the math problem $6 - 4 = \boxed{}$. What should
you do when you see it?

   A. combine two numbers

   (B) subtract two numbers

   C. add two numbers

_____

(1 point)
21. Which symbol goes in the box?

   $7 - 1 \boxed{} 10 - 4$

   A. $<$ B. $+$ (C) $=$

_____

(1 point)
22. Which number goes in the box?

   $18 - \boxed{} = 18$

   (A) 0   B. 18   C. 9

Name _____ Date _____

(1 point)
23. Shilpa has 10 cookies. She gives 6 cookies to her friends. What
do you need to do to find out how many cookies she has left?

   (A) subtract 6 from 10

   B. subtract 10 from 6

   C. add 6 and 10

_____

(1 point)
24. Which shows $11 - 5 = 6$?

   A. ★ ★ ★ ★ ★ ★ ✕ ✕ ✕ ✕

   B. ★ ★ ★ ★ ★ ✕ ✕ ✕ ✕ ✕

   C. ★ ★ ★ ★ ★ ★ ★ ★ ✕ ✕ ✕

   (D) ★ ★ ★ ★ ★ ★ ✕ ✕ ✕ ✕ ✕

_____

(1 point)
25. Which shows $16 - 5 = 11$?

   A. ⬤ ⬤ ⬤ ⬤ ⬤ ✕ ✕ ✕ ✕ ✕ ✕ ✕ ✕ ✕ ✕ ✕

   (B) ⬤ ⬤ ⬤ ⬤ ⬤ ⬤ ⬤ ⬤ ⬤ ⬤ ⬤ ✕ ✕ ✕ ✕ ✕

   C. ⬤ ⬤ ⬤ ⬤ ⬤ ⬤ ✕ ✕ ✕ ✕ ✕

   D. ⬤ ⬤ ⬤ ⬤ ⬤ ✕ ✕ ✕ ✕ ✕ ✕

Name _____ Date _____

(1 point)
26. Which shows ten take away three is seven?

   A. ♥ ♥ ♥ ♥ ✕ ✕ ✕ ✕ ✕ ✕ ✕

   B. ♥ ♥ ♥ ♥ ✕ ✕ ✕

   C. ♥ ♥ ♥ ♥ ♥ ✕ ✕ ✕

   (D) ♥ ♥ ♥ ♥ ♥ ♥ ♥ ✕ ✕ ✕

_____

(1 point)
27. Write a number sentence for this model.

   ⬤ ⬤ ⬤ ⬤ ⬤ ⬤ ⬤ ⬤ ✕ ✕

   $10 - 2 = 8$

_____

(1 point)
28. What does the $-$ symbol mean in this number sentence?

   $12 = 13 - 1$

   subtract 1 from 13

Subtraction Facts Through 20

compare

take away

subtraction

count back from a number

fact families

5 - 1 =

▶ Unit Objectives

- Demonstrate automatic recall of subtraction facts with minuends through 8.

- Demonstrate understanding of the result of subtracting zero from a given quantity.

- Given concrete objects, show how two sets can be added together, and then reverse the operation to show how a number can be subtracted from the whole.

- Demonstrate automatic recall of subtraction facts with minuends through 12.

- Demonstrate automatic recall of subtraction facts with minuends through 16.

- Demonstrate automatic recall of subtraction facts with minuends through 20.

▶ Unit Introduction

Students will explore different strategies to solve subtraction problems with minuends through 20, including using models, counting back, using patterns, and using addition facts and fact families.

They will practice the subtraction facts, working toward automatic recall: first through 12, then through 16, and finally through 20. Their practice will include online and offline activities, and timed and untimed activities.

Subtraction Facts Through 8

Lesson Overview

Skills Update	5 minutes	ONLINE
GET READY Minus Symbol for Subtraction	15 minutes	ONLINE
LEARN Use Addition Facts to Subtract	20 minutes	ONLINE
TRY IT Practice Facts	20 minutes	OFFLINE

▶ Lesson Objectives

Demonstrate automatic recall of subtraction facts with minuends through 8.

▶ Prerequisite Skills

- Recognize that the − symbol refers to subtraction.
- Recognize that the equals symbol shows an equality between two expressions.

▶ Content Background

The three parts of a subtraction sentence are the *minuend*, the *subtrahend*, and the *difference*. The number you are subtracting from is the minuend. The number you are subtracting is the subtrahend. The answer is the difference.

4	−	1	=	3
minuend		subtrahend		difference

　　Inverse, or opposite, operations "undo" each other. Addition and subtraction are opposite operations, as are multiplication and division. For example, suppose students have a group of 8 blocks. If students add 2 blocks to the group, the sum is 10 blocks: $8 + 2 = 10$. If they remove the 2 blocks, the difference is 8 blocks: $10 − 2 = 8$. Subtracting 2 blocks undoes adding 2 blocks. Students are left with the same number of blocks they started with, 8. Understanding opposite operations will help students with arithmetic, and later on, algebra.

　　The term *symbol* is used in this lesson. Although *equals sign* is used often in everyday language, *equals symbol* is more accurate as a mathematical term. The same can be said of *minus symbol* and *minus sign*. In math, *sign* specifically refers to the positive signs and negative signs.

difference – the solution to a subtraction problem
minuend – in subtraction, the quantity or number from which another number is subtracted; 8 is the minuend in the problem $8 - 7 = ?$
opposite operations – mathematical operations that reverse or undo each other, often called inverse operations; subtraction and addition are opposite operations; division and multiplication are opposite operations
subtraction – the process of taking away objects from a group or finding the difference between two groups; a mathematical operation
subtrahend – the number that is subtracted in a subtraction problem; 7 is the subtrahend in the problem $8 - 7 = ?$
take away – in subtraction, to separate a group from the total

ONLINE
15 min

GET READY Minus Symbol for Subtraction

Students will use models and symbols to show subtraction.

Gather the circle blocks. If necessary, encourage students to use the circles as they work through the activity.

Objectives

- Recognize that the − symbol refers to subtraction.

ONLINE
20 min

LEARN Use Addition Facts to Subtract

Students will use addition facts to solve subtraction problems.

Gather the circle blocks. If necessary, encourage students to use the circles as they work through the activity.

Help students understand that addition can be used to help solve subtraction problems since addition and subtraction are opposite operations.

Objectives

- Demonstrate automatic recall of subtraction facts with minuends through 8.

Tips

If students use circle blocks to show subtraction, point out that there are two ways to use the circles. They can make pairs, or they can take away one group of circles from a total number of circles.

TRY IT Practice Facts

Objectives

Students will practice solving subtraction facts through 8. Give students the circle blocks and Practice Facts activity page from their Activity Book. Read the directions with them.

- Demonstrate automatic recall of subtraction facts with minuends through 8.

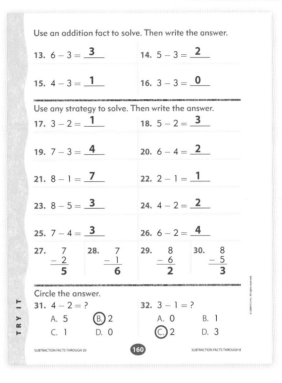

Relate Addition and Subtraction

Skills Update	5 minutes	ONLINE
GET READY Addition and Subtraction Practice	5 minutes	ONLINE
LEARN Fact Families	10 minutes	ONLINE
LEARN Use Addition Facts	10 minutes	ONLINE
LEARN Where's Jojo?	10 minutes	ONLINE
TRY IT Subtraction Facts	10 minutes	OFFLINE
CHECKPOINT	10 minutes	OFFLINE

▶ Lesson Objectives

- Demonstrate automatic recall of subtraction facts with minuends through 8.
- Demonstrate understanding of the result of subtracting zero from a given quantity.
- Given concrete objects, show how two sets can be added together, and then reverse the operation to show how a number can be subtracted from the whole.

▶ Prerequisite Skills

- Use models and math symbols to represent addition.
- Use models and math symbols to represent subtraction.

▶ Common Errors and Misconceptions

Students might have difficulty understanding that addition and subtraction are opposite, or inverse, operations. It might not be obvious to them that addition "undoes" subtraction.

▶ Content Background

Students have learned that addition and subtraction are opposite operations. In this lesson, they will learn about fact families. They will then use the related addition sentences to solve subtraction problems.

Fact families are related number sentences. Because you can add addends in any order and get the same sum, each addition sentence has a related addition sentence. For example, $5 + 3 = 8$ is related to $3 + 5 = 8$. The addends and the sums are the same. Since addition and subtraction are inverse operations, every addition sentence also has a related subtraction sentence. For example, $5 + 3 = 8$ and $8 - 3 = 5$ are related. Also, $3 + 5 = 8$ and $8 - 5 = 3$ are related. The two addition sentences and their related subtraction sentences make up the fact family for 3, 5, and 8.

Materials to Gather

SUPPLIED

blocks – O (10 red, 10 blue)

Subtraction Facts activity page

Checkpoint (printout)

There are four number sentences in most fact families, two addition sentences and two subtraction sentences. The exceptions to this rule are the doubles facts. Since the addends in a doubles fact are the same, there is only one addition fact in the fact family. Since there is only one addition fact, there is only one related subtraction fact in the family. For example, $5 + 5 = 10$ and $10 - 5 = 5$ make up the fact family for 5, 5, and 10.

Keywords

fact family – a complete set of related number sentences, usually four (e.g., $3 + 4 = 7$, $4 + 3 = 7$, $7 - 3 = 4$, $7 - 4 = 3$), but only two in the case of doubles facts (e.g., $5 + 5 = 10$, $10 - 5 = 5$)

ONLINE
5min

GET READY Addition and Subtraction Practice

Students will practice writing addition and subtraction sentences to represent everyday situations.

Objectives

- Use models and math symbols to represent addition.
- Use models and math symbols to represent subtraction.

ONLINE
10min

LEARN Fact Families

Students will model and write fact families.

Objectives

- Given concrete objects, show how two sets can be added together, and then reverse the operation to show how a number can be subtracted from the whole.

Tips

Point out that you can add numbers in any order, so that every cube train really shows two addition facts. As an example, make a train with 3 red cubes to the left of 4 blue cubes to show $3 + 4$. Then turn the train over so that the blue cubes are on the left. Explain that it is the same train, but now it shows $4 + 3$.

LEARN Use Addition Facts

Students will use addition facts to find the difference in a related subtraction problem.

Objectives

- Given concrete objects, show how two sets can be added together, and then reverse the operation to show how a number can be subtracted from the whole.

Tips

Remind students that in the subtraction sentences, the greater number is always written first.

LEARN Where's Jojo?

Students will play a game to practice solving subtraction problems.

Objectives

- Demonstrate the automatic recall of subtraction facts with minuends through 8.
- Demonstrate understanding of the result of subtracting zero from a given quantity.

Tips

Students can use cubes to model the problems shown and find the related addition fact.

TRY IT Subtraction Facts

Objectives

Students will practice solving subtraction facts by using related addition facts. Give students the cubes and Subtraction Facts activity page from their Activity Book. Read the directions with them.

For Problems 10–17, students should explain how they got their answer. Students may have memorized the facts, so the answer "I just knew it" is acceptable.

- Demonstrate automatic recall of subtraction facts with minuends through 8.
- Demonstrate understanding of the result of subtracting zero from a given quantity.
- Given concrete objects, show how two sets can be added together, and then reverse the operation to show how a number can be subtracted from the whole.

Name: _____

Relate Addition and Subtraction
Subtraction Facts

Complete the fact family.

1. 2, 5, 7

$2 + 5 = 7$

$7 - 5 = 2$

$\underline{5} + \underline{2} = \underline{7}$

$\underline{7} - \underline{2} = \underline{5}$

2. 1, 3, 4

$1 + 3 = 4$

$4 - 3 = 1$

$\underline{3} + \underline{1} = \underline{4}$

$\underline{4} - \underline{1} = \underline{3}$

3. 6, 2, 8

$\underline{6} + \underline{2} = \underline{8}$

$\underline{2} + \underline{6} = \underline{8}$

$\underline{8} - \underline{6} = \underline{2}$

$\underline{8} - \underline{2} = \underline{6}$

4. 2, 2, 4

$\underline{2} + \underline{2} = \underline{4}$

$\underline{4} - \underline{2} = \underline{2}$

TRY IT

TRY IT

Solve the addition facts for the subtraction sentence. Then find the difference.

5. $8 - 5 = ?$

$5 + \underline{3} = 8$

$\underline{3} + 5 = 8$

$8 - 5 = \underline{3}$

6. $5 - 0 = ?$

$0 + \underline{5} = 5$

$\underline{5} + 0 = 5$

$5 - 0 = \underline{5}$

7. $6 - 4 = ?$

$4 + \underline{2} = 6$

$\underline{2} + 4 = 6$

$6 - 4 = \underline{2}$

8. $7 - 1 = ?$

$1 + \underline{6} = 7$

$\underline{6} + 1 = 7$

$7 - 1 = \underline{6}$

9. Place 6 red cubes in a group and 2 blue cubes in a separate group. How many cubes are there in all? If you take away the blue cubes, how many cubes will be left? **Students should place the red and blue cubes in one group and say that there are 8 cubes in all. They should then remove the 2 blue cubes and say that there are 6 cubes left.**

Write the difference. Explain how you found the answer.

10. $8 - 5 = \underline{\textbf{3}}$ 11. $5 - 0 = \underline{\textbf{5}}$

12. $8 - 3 = \underline{\textbf{5}}$ 13. $7 - 0 = \underline{\textbf{7}}$

14. $\begin{array}{r} 8 \\ -\ 4 \\ \hline \textbf{4} \end{array}$ 15. $\begin{array}{r} 7 \\ -\ 1 \\ \hline \textbf{6} \end{array}$

16. $\begin{array}{r} 3 \\ -\ 3 \\ \hline \textbf{0} \end{array}$ 17. $\begin{array}{r} 6 \\ -\ 4 \\ \hline \textbf{2} \end{array}$

Accept reasonable explanations.

T R Y   I T

T R Y   I T

Circle the answer.
18. $6 - 0 = ?$
Ⓐ 6   B. 5   C. 8

Write the difference.

19. $7 - 3 = \underline{\textbf{4}}$ 20. $6 - 4 = \underline{\textbf{2}}$

21. $7 - 4 = \underline{\textbf{3}}$ 22. $3 - 2 = \underline{\textbf{1}}$

23. $\begin{array}{r} 8 \\ -\ 3 \\ \hline \textbf{5} \end{array}$ 24. $\begin{array}{r} 7 \\ -\ 5 \\ \hline \textbf{2} \end{array}$ 25. $\begin{array}{r} 8 \\ -\ 1 \\ \hline \textbf{7} \end{array}$

OFFLINE
10 min

CHECKPOINT

Print the Checkpoint. In Part 1, students will take a performance-based assessment. In Part 2, students will complete the problems on their own. Read the directions, problems, and answer choices to students if necessary. Use the answer key to score the Checkpoint, and then enter the results online.

Gather the cubes for Part 1.

Objectives

- Demonstrate automatic recall of subtraction facts with minuends through 8.
- Demonstrate understanding of the result of subtracting zero from a given quantity.
- Given concrete objects, show how two sets can be added together, and then reverse the operation to show how a number can be subtracted from the whole.

Name _____ Date _____

Checkpoint Answer Key

Part 1

Gather the cubes. Read each problem aloud.

1. Place 5 red cubes in a group on the table. Have students place 3 blue cubes in a separate group on the table and show how they would add together the blue and red cubes.

   Ask, "How many cubes are there in all? If you take away the red cubes, how many cubes will be left?"

   (1 point)
   Did the student place the red and blue cubes in one group together and say that there are 8 cubes in all?

   A. Yes   B. No

   (1 point)
   Did the student remove the 5 red cubes and say that there are 3 cubes left?

   A. Yes   B. No

2. Place 4 red cubes in a group on the table. Have students place 3 blue cubes in a separate group on the table and show how they would add together the blue and red cubes.

   Ask, "How many red and blue cubes are there in all? If you remove the blue cubes, how many cubes will be left?"

   Students should place the red and blue cubes in one group together and say that there are 7 cubes altogether.

   (1 point)
   Did the student model and answer correctly?

   A. Yes   B. No

   Students should then remove the 3 blue cubes and say that there are 4 cubes left.

   (1 point)
   Did the students model and answer correctly?

   A. Yes   B. No

Name _____ Date _____

3. Have students place 2 red cubes in a group on the table and place 5 blue cubes in another group.

   Ask, "Show how you would add together the blue and red cubes. How many cubes are there in all? If you take away the blue cubes, how many cubes will be left?"

   Students should place the red and blue cubes in one group together and say that there are 7 cubes in all.

   (1 point)
   Did the student model and answer correctly?

   A. Yes   B. No

   Students should then remove the 5 blue cubes and say that there are 2 cubes left.

   (1 point)
   Did the student model and answer correctly?

   A. Yes   B. No

4. Have students make a group of 4 cubes and a group of 2 cubes, and then add the two groups.

   Ask, "How many are there altogether? Subtract 2 of the cubes and tell me how many are left."

   After combining the cubes, students should say that there are 6 altogether.

   (1 point)
   Did the student model and answer correctly?

   A. Yes   B. No

   After subtracting 2 cubes, students should say that there are 4 left.

   (1 point)
   Did the student model and answer correctly?

   A. Yes   B. No

Give students Part 2 of the assessment.

Name _____ Date _____

Part 2

Circle the answer.

(1 point)
5. $8 - 0 = ?$

   A. 0   (B.) 8   C. 6   D. 5

(1 point)
6. $6 - 2 = ?$

   A. 1   B. 2   C. 3   (D.) 4

(1 point)
7. $5 - 4 = ?$

   A. 3   B. 2   (C.) 1   D. 0

Write the answer.

(1 point)
8. $7 - 2 =$ __5__

(1 point)
9. $6 - 3 =$ __3__

(1 point)
10. $7 - 0 =$ __7__

(1 point) 11.	*(1 point)* 12.	*(1 point)* 13.	*(1 point)* 14.
$\begin{array}{r} 8 \\ -6 \\ \hline 2 \end{array}$	$\begin{array}{r} 7 \\ -6 \\ \hline 1 \end{array}$	$\begin{array}{r} 6 \\ -2 \\ \hline 4 \end{array}$	$\begin{array}{r} 5 \\ -1 \\ \hline 4 \end{array}$

Subtraction Facts Through 12

Lesson Overview

Skills Update	5 minutes	ONLINE
GET READY Subtraction Facts Through 8	5 minutes	ONLINE
LEARN Subtraction Patterns	20 minutes	OFFLINE
LEARN Let's Subtract	15 minutes	OFFLINE
TRY IT Find the Difference	15 minutes	OFFLINE

▶ Lesson Objectives

Demonstrate automatic recall of subtraction facts with minuends through 12.

▶ Prerequisite Skills

Demonstrate automatic recall of subtraction facts with minuends through 8.

▶ Content Background

Students will look at a subtraction facts and review the three strategies (model the problem, use an addition facts, and find a pattern) that could be used to find the difference.

All of these strategies can help students learn subtraction facts through 12.

Materials to Gather

SUPPLIED

blocks – O (all colors)
Subtraction Patterns activity page
Let's Subtract activity page
Find the Difference activity page

Keywords

pattern – a sequence of objects and/or numbers with attributes that are repeated in a predictable way
strategy – a method or approach to solve a problem

GET READY Subtraction Facts Through 8

ONLINE
5 min

Objectives

- Demonstrate automatic recall of subtraction facts with minuends through 8.

Students will solve subtraction facts with minuends through 8.

LEARN Subtraction Patterns

OFFLINE
20 min

Objectives

- Demonstrate automatic recall of subtraction facts with minuends through 12.

Students will model and solve subtraction facts. They will also recognize and use patterns to find differences. Give students the Subtraction Patterns activity page from their Activity Book and read the directions with them.

Name:

Subtraction Facts Through 12
Subtraction Patterns

Look for a pattern or use cubes to find each difference.

1.
9 – 0 = **9**
9 – 1 = **8**
9 – 2 = **7**
9 – 3 = **6**
9 – 4 = **5**
9 – 5 = **4**
9 – 6 = **3**
9 – 7 = **2**
9 – 8 = **1**
9 – 9 = **0**

2.
10 – 0 = **10**
10 – 1 = **9**
10 – 2 = **8**
10 – 3 = **7**
10 – 4 = **6**
10 – 5 = **5**
10 – 6 = **4**
10 – 7 = **3**
10 – 8 = **2**
10 – 9 = **1**
10 – 10 = **0**

3.
11 – 1 = **10**
11 – 2 = **9**
11 – 3 = **8**
11 – 4 = **7**
11 – 5 = **6**
11 – 6 = **5**
11 – 7 = **4**
11 – 8 = **3**
11 – 9 = **2**
11 – 10 = **1**

4.
12 – 2 = **10**
12 – 3 = **9**
12 – 4 = **8**
12 – 5 = **7**
12 – 6 = **6**
12 – 7 = **5**
12 – 8 = **4**
12 – 9 = **3**
12 – 10 = **2**

L E A R N

OFFLINE

15 min

LEARN Let's Subtract

Objectives

Students will find, use, and explain patterns to solve subtraction facts.
   Give students the cubes and the Let's Subtract activity page from their Activity Book.

1. Explain that there are many ways to find the answer to a subtraction problem. Students may model the problem, use a related addition fact, find and use a pattern, or use the rule for zero.

2. Have students find the answers to Problems 1–4 on the activity page and explain any patterns they see. Students should explain that the first number stays the same, the second number decreases by 1, and the difference increases by 1.

3. Repeat for Problems 5–8. Have students explain the patterns they see. Students should explain that the first number stays the same, the second number decreases by 1, and the difference increases by 1.

4. Repeat for Problems 9–12. Have students explain the patterns they see. Students should explain that the first number decreases by 1, the second number stays the same, and the difference decreases by 1.

5. Have students complete the rest of the activity page.

- Demonstrate automatic recall of subtraction facts with minuends through 12.

Subtraction Facts Through 12
Let's Subtract

Name:

Write the difference. Describe any patterns you see. **Patterns may vary.**

1. $5 - 5 = 0$	2. $5 - 4 = 1$	3. $5 - 3 = 2$	4. $5 - 2 = 3$
5. $9 - 7 = 2$	6. $9 - 6 = 3$	7. $9 - 5 = 4$	8. $9 - 4 = 5$
9. $7 - 4 = 3$	10. $6 - 4 = 2$	11. $5 - 4 = 1$	12. $4 - 4 = 0$
13. $12 - 6 = 6$	14. $12 - 7 = 5$	15. $12 - 8 = 4$	16. $12 - 9 = 3$

17. $8 - 8 = 0$	18. $8 - 7 = 1$	19. $8 - 6 = 2$	20. $8 - 3 = 5$
21. $11 - 9 = 2$	22. $11 - 8 = 3$	23. $11 - 7 = 4$	24. $11 - 6 = 5$
25. $12 - 4 = 8$	26. $12 - 5 = 7$	27. $12 - 6 = 6$	28. $12 - 7 = 5$
29. $8 - 2 = 6$	30. $10 - 4 = 6$	31. $9 - 5 = 4$	32. $12 - 5 = 7$

LEARN

167 168

OFFLINE **15 min**

TRY IT Find the Difference

Objectives

Students will choose the best strategy to solve subtraction problems with minuends through 12. Give students the Find the Difference activity page from their Activity Book and read the directions with them.

Students may choose any strategy—including looking for and using patterns—for each problem.

- Demonstrate automatic recall of subtraction facts with minuends through 12.

Subtraction Facts Through 12
Find the Difference

Name:

Write the difference.

1. $11 - 9 = 2$	2. $11 - 8 = 3$	3. $11 - 7 = 4$	4. $11 - 6 = 5$
5. $12 - 7 = 5$	6. $12 - 6 = 6$	7. $12 - 5 = 7$	8. $12 - 4 = 8$
9. $8 - 3 = 5$	10. $7 - 3 = 4$	11. $6 - 3 = 3$	12. $5 - 3 = 2$
13. $7 - 1 = 6$	14. $7 - 2 = 5$		

15. $7 - 3 = 4$	16. $7 - 4 = 3$	17. $12 - 5 = 7$	18. $4 - 3 = 1$
19. $11 - 7 = 4$	20. $7 - 5 = 2$	21. $11 - 4 = 7$	22. $11 - 5 = 6$
23. $10 - 5 = 5$	24. $10 - 3 = 7$	25. $12 - 8 = 4$	26. $12 - 9 = 3$

Circle the answer.

27. $12 - 3 = ?$
(A) 9
B. 8
C. 10

28. $11 - 2 = ?$
(A) 9
B. 7
C. 8

TRY IT

169 170

Count Back Subtraction Facts

Skills Update	5 minutes	ONLINE
GET READY Subtract with Patterns	5 minutes	ONLINE
LEARN Count Back 1 or 2	5 minutes	ONLINE
LEARN Subtraction Blocks	10 minutes	OFFLINE
LEARN Post the Facts	15 minutes	OFFLINE
TRY IT Subtract, Subtract	10 minutes	OFFLINE
CHECKPOINT	10 minutes	OFFLINE

▶ Lesson Objectives

Demonstrate automatic recall of subtraction facts with minuends through 12.

▶ Prerequisite Skills

Demonstrate automatic recall of subtraction facts with minuends through 8.

▶ Advance Preparation

CREATE SUBTRACTION BLOCKS

- Label the top of the first sheet of construction paper **9**, the second sheet **10**, the third sheet **11**, and the fourth sheet **12**.
- Write each of the following facts, without the answer, on a separate yellow sticky note. Leave room for students to write the answer (e.g., $12 - 2 =$).

Materials to Gather

SUPPLIED

Subtraction Facts Chart (printout)

Subtract, Subtract activity page

Checkpoint (printout)

ALSO NEEDED

paper, construction – 4 light-colored sheets

glue stick

timer

marker, permanent

poster board – 2 sheets, standard size (22 in. by 28 in.)

sticky notes, small rectangular (2 in. by 1.5 in.) – 78 yellow, 88 orange

tape, clear

meterstick or yardstick

	$12 - 5 = 7$	$11 - 5 = 6$
$12 - 2 = 10$	$11 - 4 = 7$	$12 - 10 = 2$
$12 - 6 = 6$	$11 - 2 = 9$	$9 - 9 = 0$
$12 - 4 = 8$	$11 - 9 = 2$	$12 - 11 = 1$
$11 - 0 = 11$	$10 - 1 = 9$	$10 - 10 = 0$
$11 - 1 = 10$	$10 - 6 = 4$	$12 - 12 = 0$
$11 - 7 = 4$	$10 - 7 = 3$	$10 - 4 = 6$
$11 - 6 = 5$	$9 - 0 = 9$	$11 - 11 = 0$
$9 - 5 = 4$	$9 - 2 = 7$	$11 - 8 = 3$
$9 - 6 = 3$	$9 - 4 = 5$	$11 - 10 = 1$
$9 - 1 = 8$	$9 - 3 = 6$	$12 - 1 = 11$
$10 - 3 = 7$	$9 - 7 = 2$	$12 - 7 = 5$
$10 - 2 = 8$	$10 - 9 = 1$	$9 - 8 = 1$
$10 - 5 = 5$	$11 - 3 = 8$	$12 - 9 = 3$
$10 - 0 = 10$	$12 - 3 = 9$	$10 - 8 = 2$
$12 - 0 = 12$	$12 - 8 = 4$	

POST THE FACTS

Print the Subtraction Facts Chart. Follow the instructions on the printout to set up the chart. Students will use the chart to keep track of the subtraction facts they have mastered. Find a place to display the chart so students can see their progress.

▶ **Content Background**

Students will solve subtraction facts. They will learn the strategy of counting back 1 or 2 on a number line to subtract. Students will also complete a chart of the subtraction facts they have mastered.

Keywords	**count back** – to subtract by starting with the number of objects in one group and then counting back, in order, the number of objects in the other group

GET READY Subtract with Patterns

ONLINE 5 min

Objectives

- Demonstrate automatic recall of subtraction facts with minuends through 8.

Students will solve subtraction facts with minuends through 8. The facts will be organized in patterns, such as $4 - 1 = 3$, $4 - 2 = 2$, $4 - 3 = 1$, and $4 - 4 = 0$.

Review the subtraction strategies students have learned:

- Use objects to model subtraction.
- Use a related addition fact to subtract.
- Use the zero rule to subtract.
- Find and use a pattern to subtract.

As students progress through the activity, have them explain how they found their answers.

LEARN Count Back 1 or 2

ONLINE 5 min

Objectives

- Demonstrate automatic recall of subtraction facts with minuends through 12.

Tips

Remind students not to count the starting number as 1.

Students will subtract 1 and 2 from a given number using a number line.

- As students progress through the activity, ask questions such as, "At what number did you start? How many numbers did the arrow move back? Where did the arrow land?"
- Continually point out to students that the difference is the number on which the arrow lands.
- Help students realize they can count back 1 or 2 without the number line.

LEARN Subtraction Blocks

OFFLINE 10 min

Objectives

- Demonstrate automatic recall of subtraction facts with minuends through 12.

Students will sort subtraction facts by the minuend (first number), solve the problem, and look for patterns in subtraction facts with minuends 9, 10, 11, and 12.

Gather the construction paper and sticky notes you prepared. Also gather the marker, glue stick, and timer. Place the paper in front of students. Give them all the fact sticky notes.

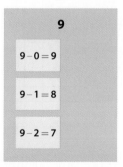

1. Ask students to work first with the paper labeled 9. Have students separate out all the sticky notes with subtraction facts that begin with 9.
2. Have them make a "subtraction block tower" by placing sticky notes in order from the top to the bottom of the paper, with $9 - 0$ on top, followed by $9 - 1$, $9 - 2$, and so on.
3. Have students write the answers on each sticky note in the tower. Then have them look for a pattern and study the facts.
4. Have students repeat Steps 1–3 for 10, 11, and 12.
5. Make sure that students have arranged all the facts correctly. They may wish to make permanent towers by gluing the sticky notes onto the paper.
6. Check students' answers. Help students correct any incorrect answers.
7. Next, pick up the completed tower sheets. Set a timer for 1 minute. Say each fact for students (in any order) and listen to their answers. Keep track of how many facts students answer correctly in 1 minute.
8. Repeat until all facts have been timed at least once.

Tips

Timed challenges help students increase the ability to quickly recall subtraction facts.

LEARN Post the Facts

- Demonstrate automatic recall of subtraction facts with minuends through 12.

Show students the Subtraction Facts Chart that you made earlier. Students will work on facts with minuends through 12.

Gather the remaining orange sticky notes.

1. **Say:** The Subtraction Facts Chart will help you keep track of the subtraction facts that you know and the ones you still need to learn.

2. Explain that $12 - 3 = 9$. As you say 12, point to the 12 row, and as you say 3, move along the row to the 3 column. Tell students that when they have shown you that they know $12 - 3$ by saying it quickly and often, they will be able to write 9 on a sticky note and place it in the square where the row meets the column.

3. **Ask:** What is $1 - 0$?

4. If students are able to quickly recall the difference, have them write the difference (1) on a sticky note and place it in the square that is 1 up and 0 over. If not, tell them that they will need to practice $1 - 0$ some more, and then they can put the difference on the chart.

5. Have students repeat these steps for all the facts with minuends through 12. Give students the facts in random order.

Tips

You can use tape to secure the sticky notes to the facts chart, if necessary.

Subtraction Facts Chart

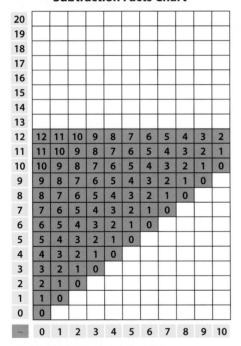

	0	1	2	3	4	5	6	7	8	9	10
20											
19											
18											
17											
16											
15											
14											
13											
12	12	11	10	9	8	7	6	5	4	3	2
11	11	10	9	8	7	6	5	4	3	2	1
10	10	9	8	7	6	5	4	3	2	1	0
9	9	8	7	6	5	4	3	2	1	0	
8	8	7	6	5	4	3	2	1	0		
7	7	6	5	4	3	2	1	0			
6	6	5	4	3	2	1	0				
5	5	4	3	2	1	0					
4	4	3	2	1	0						
3	3	2	1	0							
2	2	1	0								
1	1	0									
0	0										

Note: Save the chart. You will use it again in other lessons.

TRY IT Subtract, Subtract

Objectives

Students will practice counting back to solve subtraction facts. Give students the Subtract, Subtract activity page from their Activity Book and read the directions with them.

For Problems 1–12 in Part 1, have students tell you the strategy they used to solve each problem.

- Demonstrate automatic recall of subtraction facts with minuends through 12.

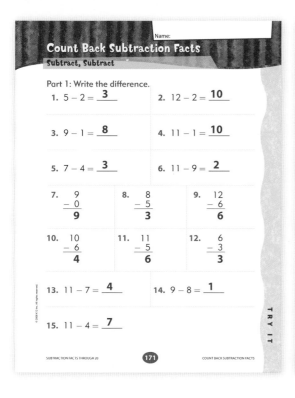

Count Back Subtraction Facts

Subtract, Subtract

Part 1: Write the difference.

1. $5 - 2 = $ **3**   2. $12 - 2 = $ **10**

3. $9 - 1 = $ **8**   4. $11 - 1 = $ **10**

5. $7 - 4 = $ **3**   6. $11 - 9 = $ **2**

7. $\begin{array}{r} 9 \\ -0 \\ \hline 9 \end{array}$ 8. $\begin{array}{r} 8 \\ -5 \\ \hline 3 \end{array}$ 9. $\begin{array}{r} 12 \\ -6 \\ \hline 6 \end{array}$

10. $\begin{array}{r} 10 \\ -6 \\ \hline 4 \end{array}$ 11. $\begin{array}{r} 11 \\ -5 \\ \hline 6 \end{array}$ 12. $\begin{array}{r} 6 \\ -3 \\ \hline 3 \end{array}$

13. $11 - 7 = $ **4**   14. $9 - 8 = $ **1**

15. $11 - 4 = $ **7**

SUBTRACTION FACTS THROUGH 20   **171**   COUNT BACK SUBTRACTION FACTS

Part 2: Write the difference.

1. $10 - 5 = $ **5**   2. $11 - 9 = $ **2**

3. $9 - 9 = $ **0**   4. $11 - 5 = $ **6**

5. $9 - 4 = $ **5**   6. $12 - 3 = $ **9**

7. $11 - 6 = $ **5**   8. $9 - 5 = $ **4**

9. $12 - 7 = $ **5**   10. $11 - 7 = $ **4**

11. $\begin{array}{r} 12 \\ -6 \\ \hline 6 \end{array}$ 12. $\begin{array}{r} 10 \\ -4 \\ \hline 6 \end{array}$ 13. $\begin{array}{r} 11 \\ -1 \\ \hline 10 \end{array}$ 14. $\begin{array}{r} 12 \\ -4 \\ \hline 8 \end{array}$

15. $\begin{array}{r} 10 \\ -9 \\ \hline 1 \end{array}$ 16. $\begin{array}{r} 12 \\ -2 \\ \hline 10 \end{array}$ 17. $\begin{array}{r} 10 \\ -7 \\ \hline 3 \end{array}$ 18. $\begin{array}{r} 12 \\ -7 \\ \hline 5 \end{array}$

19. $12 - 9 = $ **3**   20. $11 - 7 = $ **4**

21. $10 - 4 = $ **6**

SUBTRACTION FACTS THROUGH 20   **172**   COUNT BACK SUBTRACTION FACTS

TRY IT

CHECKPOINT

OFFLINE
10 min

Objectives

Print the Checkpoint and have students complete it on their own. Read the directions, problems, and answer choices to students if necessary. Use the answer key to score the Checkpoint, and then enter the results online.

- Demonstrate automatic recall of subtraction facts with minuends through 12.

○ Checkpoint   Math | Subtraction Facts Through 20 | Count Back Subtraction Facts

Name   Date

Checkpoint Answer Key

Part 1: Solve.

(1 point)
1. $12 - 2 =$ **10**

(1 point)
2. $8 - 0 =$ **8**

(1 point)
3. $\begin{array}{r} 11 \\ -\ 7 \\ \hline \mathbf{4} \end{array}$

(1 point)
4. $\begin{array}{r} 9 \\ -\ 1 \\ \hline \mathbf{8} \end{array}$

(1 point)
5. $\begin{array}{r} 8 \\ -\ 3 \\ \hline \mathbf{5} \end{array}$

(1 point)
6. $\begin{array}{r} 10 \\ -\ 3 \\ \hline \mathbf{7} \end{array}$

(1 point)
7. $3 - 2 =$ **1**

(1 point)
8. $5 - 4 =$ **1**

(1 point)
9. $\begin{array}{r} 9 \\ -\ 9 \\ \hline \mathbf{0} \end{array}$

(1 point)
10. $\begin{array}{r} 12 \\ -\ 8 \\ \hline \mathbf{4} \end{array}$

(1 point)
11. $\begin{array}{r} 12 \\ -\ 10 \\ \hline \mathbf{2} \end{array}$

(1 point)
12. $\begin{array}{r} 9 \\ -\ 3 \\ \hline \mathbf{6} \end{array}$

(1 point)
13. $12 - 5 =$ **7**

(1 point)
14. $4 - 0 =$ **4**

(1 point)
15. $\begin{array}{r} 4 \\ -\ 1 \\ \hline \mathbf{3} \end{array}$

(1 point)
16. $\begin{array}{r} 12 \\ -\ 9 \\ \hline \mathbf{3} \end{array}$

1 of 2

○ Checkpoint   Math | Subtraction Facts Through 20 | Count Back Subtraction Facts

Name   Date

Part 2: Solve.

(1 point)
1. $9 - 6 =$ **3**

(1 point)
2. $5 - 0 =$ **5**

(1 point)
3. $\begin{array}{r} 12 \\ -\ 7 \\ \hline \mathbf{5} \end{array}$

(1 point)
4. $\begin{array}{r} 9 \\ -\ 1 \\ \hline \mathbf{8} \end{array}$

(1 point)
5. $\begin{array}{r} 12 \\ -\ 3 \\ \hline \mathbf{9} \end{array}$

(1 point)
6. $\begin{array}{r} 11 \\ -\ 5 \\ \hline \mathbf{6} \end{array}$

(1 point)
7. $10 - 2 =$ **8**

(1 point)
8. $12 - 4 =$ **8**

(1 point)
9. $\begin{array}{r} 10 \\ -\ 9 \\ \hline \mathbf{1} \end{array}$

(1 point)
10. $\begin{array}{r} 7 \\ -\ 3 \\ \hline \mathbf{4} \end{array}$

(1 point)
11. $\begin{array}{r} 11 \\ -\ 8 \\ \hline \mathbf{3} \end{array}$

(1 point)
12. $\begin{array}{r} 9 \\ -\ 9 \\ \hline \mathbf{0} \end{array}$

(1 point)
13. $10 - 5 =$ **5**

(1 point)
14. $12 - 9 =$ **3**

(1 point)
15. $\begin{array}{r} 4 \\ -\ 2 \\ \hline \mathbf{2} \end{array}$

(1 point)
16. $\begin{array}{r} 10 \\ -\ 7 \\ \hline \mathbf{3} \end{array}$

(1 point)
17. $\begin{array}{r} 12 \\ -\ 6 \\ \hline \mathbf{6} \end{array}$

(1 point)
18. $\begin{array}{r} 8 \\ -\ 8 \\ \hline \mathbf{0} \end{array}$

(1 point)
19. $1 - 1 =$ **0**

(1 point)
20. $10 - 6 =$ **4**

2 of 2

Subtraction Facts Through 16

Lesson Overview

Skills Update	5 minutes	ONLINE
GET READY Fact Bingo	10 minutes	ONLINE
LEARN Subtraction Machine	20 minutes	ONLINE
LEARN Color Facts	15 minutes	OFFLINE
TRY IT Practice Subtraction Facts	10 minutes	OFFLINE

▶ Lesson Objectives

Demonstrate automatic recall of subtraction facts with minuends through 16.

▶ Prerequisite Skills

Demonstrate automatic recall of subtraction facts with minuends through 12.

▶ Content Background

Students will recall subtraction facts with minuends through 16.

Materials to Gather

SUPPLIED
Color Facts activity page
Practice Subtraction Facts activity page

ALSO NEEDED
crayons

ONLINE
10 min

GET READY Fact Bingo

Students will play a game to help them recall addition and subtraction facts.

Objectives

Demonstrate automatic recall of subtraction facts with minuends through 12.

Tips

If students need help, allow them to use cubes to model the problem.

LEARN Subtraction Machine

Objectives

Demonstrate automatic recall of subtraction facts with minuends through 16.

Students will sort subtraction facts by their differences. It may be helpful to write the strategies that students have learned on an index card for them to use.

LEARN Color Facts

Objectives

Demonstrate automatic recall of subtraction facts with minuends through 16.

Students will solve subtraction facts and use a color key to color a picture. Give students the crayons and Color Facts activity page from their Activity Book. Read the directions with them.

Tips

Have students use strategies other than using objects to model a fact. Encourage them to think of a related addition fact or count back if they don't know an answer.

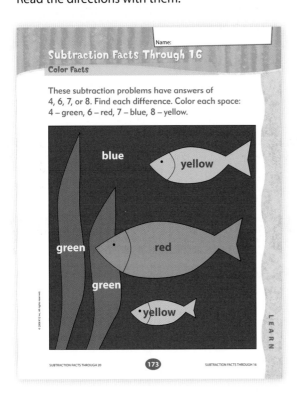

Name:

Subtraction Facts Through 16

Color Facts

These subtraction problems have answers of 4, 6, 7, or 8. Find each difference. Color each space: 4 – green, 6 – red, 7 – blue, 8 – yellow.

blue
yellow
green
red
green
yellow

SUBTRACTION FACTS THROUGH 20   173   SUBTRACTION FACTS THROUGH 16

LEARN

TRY IT Practice Subtraction Facts

Students will practice solving subtractions facts with minuends through 16. Give students the Practice Subtraction Facts activity page from their Activity Book and read the directions with them.

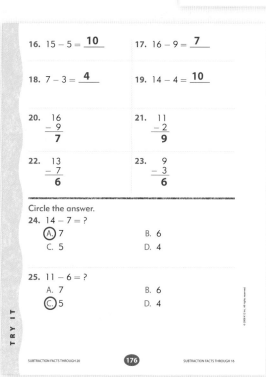

Subtraction Facts Through 16
Practice Subtraction Facts

Write the difference.

1. $15 - 8 = \underline{7}$

2. $1 - 0 = \underline{1}$

3. $16 - 8 = \underline{8}$

4. $14 - 5 = \underline{9}$

5. $16 - 9 = \underline{7}$

6. $11 - 10 = \underline{1}$

7. $15 - 7 = \underline{8}$

8. $13 - 4 = \underline{9}$

9. $10 - 9 = \underline{1}$

10. $\begin{array}{r} 8 \\ -5 \\ \hline 3 \end{array}$

11. $\begin{array}{r} 13 \\ -6 \\ \hline 7 \end{array}$

12. $\begin{array}{r} 15 \\ -9 \\ \hline 6 \end{array}$

13. $\begin{array}{r} 9 \\ -7 \\ \hline 2 \end{array}$

14. $\begin{array}{r} 13 \\ -8 \\ \hline 5 \end{array}$

15. $\begin{array}{r} 15 \\ -6 \\ \hline 9 \end{array}$

16. $15 - 5 = \underline{10}$

17. $16 - 9 = \underline{7}$

18. $7 - 3 = \underline{4}$

19. $14 - 4 = \underline{10}$

20. $\begin{array}{r} 16 \\ -9 \\ \hline 7 \end{array}$

21. $\begin{array}{r} 11 \\ -2 \\ \hline 9 \end{array}$

22. $\begin{array}{r} 13 \\ -7 \\ \hline 6 \end{array}$

23. $\begin{array}{r} 9 \\ -3 \\ \hline 6 \end{array}$

Circle the answer.

24. $14 - 7 = ?$
   - Ⓐ 7
   - B. 6
   - C. 5
   - D. 4

25. $11 - 6 = ?$
   - A. 7
   - B. 6
   - Ⓒ 5
   - D. 4

TRY IT

TRY IT

Facts Using Subtraction

Skills Update	5 minutes	ONLINE
GET READY Make a Subtraction Sentence	5 minutes	ONLINE
LEARN Bunny Facts	10 minutes	ONLINE
LEARN Fact Flash	10 minutes	OFFLINE
LEARN Post the Facts	10 minutes	OFFLINE
TRY IT Know Subtraction Facts	10 minutes	OFFLINE
CHECKPOINT	10 minutes	OFFLINE
CHECKPOINT	10 minutes	ONLINE

▶ Lesson Objectives

Demonstrate automatic recall of subtraction facts with minuends through 16.

▶ Prerequisite Skills

Demonstrate automatic recall of subtraction facts with minuends through 12.

▶ Advance Preparation

Use index cards to make flash cards for subtraction facts with minuends 13–16. One side of the card should have the difference. The other side should have the subtraction expression. You should have the following cards:

- minuend of 13: $13 - 0$; $13 - 1$; $13 - 2$; $13 - 3$; $13 - 4$; $13 - 5$; $13 - 6$; $13 - 7$; $13 - 8$; $13 - 9$; $13 - 10$; $13 - 11$; $13 - 12$; $13 - 13$
- minuend of 14: $14 - 0$; $14 - 1$; $14 - 2$; $14 - 3$; $14 - 4$; $14 - 5$; $14 - 6$; $14 - 7$; $14 - 8$; $14 - 9$; $14 - 10$; $14 - 11$; $14 - 12$; $14 - 13$; $14 - 14$
- minuend of 15: $15 - 0$; $15 - 1$; $15 - 2$; $15 - 3$; $15 - 4$; $15 - 5$; $15 - 6$; $15 - 7$; $15 - 8$; $15 - 9$; $15 - 10$; $15 - 11$; $15 - 12$; $15 - 13$; $15 - 14$; $15 - 15$
- minuend of 16: $16 - 0$; $16 - 1$; $16 - 2$; $16 - 3$; $16 - 4$; $16 - 5$; $16 - 6$; $16 - 7$; $16 - 8$; $16 - 9$; $16 - 10$; $16 - 11$; $16 - 12$; $16 - 13$; $16 - 14$; $16 - 15$; $16 - 16$

$16 - 16$	0
Front of Flash Card	Back of Flash Card

Gather the Subtraction Facts Chart you created in the Count Back Subtraction Facts lesson. If you do not have this chart, follow the instructions in the Subtraction Facts Chart printout.

▶ Content Background

Students will solve subtraction facts with minuends through 16.

Materials to Gather

SUPPLIED

Know Subtraction Facts activity page

Checkpoint (printout)

ALSO NEEDED

completed Subtraction Facts Chart from Count Back Subtraction Facts lesson

sticky notes, small rectangular (2 in. by 1.5 in.) – 44 orange

index cards – 62

timer

GET READY Make a Subtraction Sentence

Objectives

- Demonstrate automatic recall of subtraction facts with minuends through 12.

Students will solve subtraction facts with minuends through 12.
   Encourage students to ask themselves questions such as the following:

- Do I have this fact memorized?
- Do I need a model?
- Should I use an addition fact?
- Can I use another subtraction fact I know?
- Should I count back?
- Can I make pairs?

LEARN Bunny Facts

Objectives

- Demonstrate automatic recall of subtraction facts with minuends through 16.

Students will match subtraction facts with the correct differences.

- Review with students the strategies that they can use: use the zero rule, make pairs, find a pattern, use a related addition fact, count back, and so on.
- Remind students that they can use any strategy, or combination of strategies, to solve the problems.
- Ask questions such as the following: What strategy can you use to solve this problem? What is the difference?

LEARN Fact Flash

Objectives

- Demonstrate automatic recall of subtraction facts with minuends through 16.

Students will solve subtraction facts shown on flash cards. Part of the activity is untimed. Part of the activity is timed.
   Gather the flash cards and timer.

1. **Say:** I am going to hold up a flash card with a subtraction fact. When you see the fact, say the difference.
2. Explain that you will make a pile of the facts that students know and another pile of the facts they still need to work on.
3. After they have gone through the deck of flash cards, give students the facts they missed. Have them use a strategy to help them find the differences to these facts. Strategies could include use objects to model, use a pattern, use a related addition fact, and count back.
4. **Say:** Let's play again. This time I am going to give you 1 minute. Let's see how many subtraction facts you can complete this time.

   Have students play a few rounds and encourage them to try to beat their previous scores each time.

Tips

Timed challenges help students increase the ability to quickly recall subtraction facts.

LEARN Post the Facts

Objectives

- Demonstrate automatic recall of subtraction facts with minuends through 16.

Students will add facts through 16 to the Subtraction Facts Chart. Gather the sticky notes and Subtraction Facts Chart from the Count Back Subtraction Facts lesson. Make sure they have completed all the facts through 12. Then continue to work on all the facts through 16.
   Remember to ask students the facts in a random order. If they are able to quickly recall the fact, have them write the difference on a sticky note and place it on the chart. If not, students will need more practice with finding that difference.

When students have mastered all the differences with minuends through 16, the chart should look like the one shown.

Subtraction Facts Chart

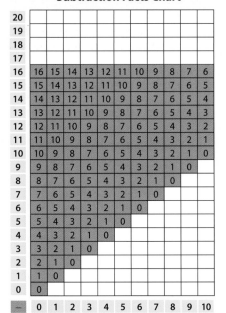

	0	1	2	3	4	5	6	7	8	9	10
20											
19											
18											
17											
16	16	15	14	13	12	11	10	9	8	7	6
15	15	14	13	12	11	10	9	8	7	6	5
14	14	13	12	11	10	9	8	7	6	5	4
13	13	12	11	10	9	8	7	6	5	4	3
12	12	11	10	9	8	7	6	5	4	3	2
11	11	10	9	8	7	6	5	4	3	2	1
10	10	9	8	7	6	5	4	3	2	1	0
9	9	8	7	6	5	4	3	2	1	0	
8	8	7	6	5	4	3	2	1	0		
7	7	6	5	4	3	2	1	0			
6	6	5	4	3	2	1	0				
5	5	4	3	2	1	0					
4	4	3	2	1	0						
3	3	2	1	0							
2	2	1	0								
1	1	0									
0	0										
−	0	1	2	3	4	5	6	7	8	9	10

Tips

You can use tape to secure the sticky notes to the facts chart, if necessary.

OFFLINE 10 min

TRY IT Know Subtraction Facts

Students will practice solving subtraction facts. Give students the Know Subtraction Facts activity page from their Activity Book and read the directions with them.

Objectives

- Demonstrate automatic recall of subtraction facts with minuends through 16.

Name:

Facts Using Subtraction
Know Subtraction Facts

Part 1: Write the difference.

1. 14 − 7 = **7**
2. 9 − 5 = **4**
3. 16 − 6 = **10**
4. 13 − 5 = **8**

5. 7 − 0 = **7**
6. 14 − 5 = **9**
7. 16 − 6 = **10**
8. 15 − 6 = **9**

9. 13 − 7 = **6**
10. 5 − 5 = **0**

11. 13 − 10 = **3**
12. 16 − 7 = **9**

Circle the answer.
13. 13 − 9 = ?
   A. 3   (B.) 4
   C. 5   D. 6

14. 14 − 5 = ?
   A. 5   B. 7
   (C.) 9   D. 10

TRY IT

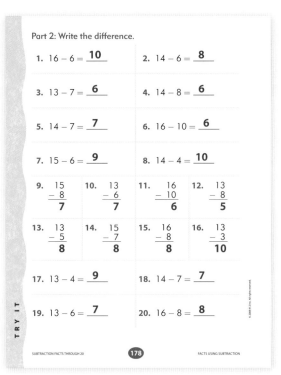

Part 2: Write the difference.

1. 16 − 6 = **10**
2. 14 − 6 = **8**

3. 13 − 7 = **6**
4. 14 − 8 = **6**

5. 14 − 7 = **7**
6. 16 − 10 = **6**

7. 15 − 6 = **9**
8. 14 − 4 = **10**

9. 15 − 8 = **7**
10. 13 − 6 = **7**
11. 16 − 10 = **6**
12. 13 − 8 = **5**

13. 13 − 5 = **8**
14. 15 − 7 = **8**
15. 16 − 8 = **8**
16. 13 − 3 = **10**

17. 13 − 4 = **9**
18. 14 − 7 = **7**

19. 13 − 6 = **7**
20. 16 − 8 = **8**

TRY IT

CHECKPOINT

Objectives

- Demonstrate automatic recall of subtraction facts with minuends through 16.

Print the Checkpoint and have students complete it on their own. Read the directions, problems, and answer choices to students if necessary. Use the answer key to score the Checkpoint, and then enter the results online.

○ Checkpoint   Math | Subtraction Facts Through 20 | Facts Using Subtraction

Name   Date

Checkpoint Answer Key

Part 1: Solve.

(1 point)
1. $16 - 6 = \underline{10}$

(1 point)
2. $12 - 10 = \underline{2}$

(1 point)
3. $\begin{array}{r} 11 \\ -\ 9 \\ \hline 2 \end{array}$

(1 point)
4. $\begin{array}{r} 15 \\ -\ 8 \\ \hline 7 \end{array}$

(1 point)
5. $\begin{array}{r} 8 \\ -\ 5 \\ \hline 3 \end{array}$

(1 point)
6. $\begin{array}{r} 13 \\ -\ 7 \\ \hline 6 \end{array}$

(1 point)
7. $13 - 4 = \underline{9}$

(1 point)
8. $15 - 6 = \underline{9}$

(1 point)
9. $\begin{array}{r} 10 \\ -\ 10 \\ \hline 0 \end{array}$

(1 point)
10. $\begin{array}{r} 12 \\ -\ 3 \\ \hline 9 \end{array}$

(1 point)
11. $\begin{array}{r} 13 \\ -\ 3 \\ \hline 10 \end{array}$

(1 point)
12. $\begin{array}{r} 6 \\ -\ 3 \\ \hline 3 \end{array}$

(1 point)
13. $11 - 5 = \underline{6}$

(1 point)
14. $16 - 8 = \underline{8}$

(1 point)
15. $\begin{array}{r} 15 \\ -\ 7 \\ \hline 8 \end{array}$

(1 point)
16. $\begin{array}{r} 12 \\ -\ 5 \\ \hline 7 \end{array}$

CHECKPOINT

Objectives

- Demonstrate automatic recall of subtraction facts with minuends through 16.

Students will complete this part of the Checkpoint online. Read the directions, problems, and answer choices to students. If necessary, help students with keyboard or mouse operations.

Subtraction Through 20

Lesson Overview

Skills Update	5 minutes	ONLINE
GET READY Card Subtraction	10 minutes	ONLINE
LEARN Find the Difference	20 minutes	ONLINE
LEARN Choose a Strategy	15 minutes	OFFLINE
TRY IT All the Facts	10 minutes	OFFLINE

▶ Lesson Objectives

Demonstrate automatic recall of subtraction facts with minuends through 20.

▶ Prerequisite Skills

Demonstrate automatic recall of subtraction facts with minuends through 16.

▶ Content Background

Students will recall subtraction facts with minuends through 20.

Materials to Gather

SUPPLIED

Choose a Strategy activity page

All the Facts activity page

ONLINE
10min

GET READY Card Subtraction

Students will complete a subtraction sentence with the correct minuend and subtrahend when given the difference.

As students work through the problems, encourage them to ask themselves the following questions:

- What is the difference?
- Can the first number in my subtraction sentence be less than the difference?
- How can I decide what the second number in the subtraction sentence should be?

Objectives

- Demonstrate automatic recall of subtraction facts with minuends through 16.

LEARN Find the Difference

ONLINE 20 min

Objectives

- Demonstrate automatic recall of subtraction facts with minuends through 20.

Students will solve subtraction facts with minuends through 20.

As students work through the problems, encourage them to ask themselves the following questions:

- Have I memorized this subtraction fact?
- Is counting back the easiest way to find the difference?
- Do I know a related addition fact that will help me solve this problem?
- Should I model the problem by lining up circles to make pairs and counting the circles that are not part of a matched pair?
- Should I model the take-away strategy?
- Does the zero rule apply here?
- Is there a pattern I can use to make the problem simpler?

LEARN Choose a Strategy

OFFLINE 15 min

Objectives

- Demonstrate automatic recall of subtraction facts with minuends through 20.

Students will solve subtraction facts and name the strategy they used. Accept all reasonable answers, which may include the following: I counted back, I memorized it, I used the zero rule, I used patterns, I used a related addition fact, and I made a model.

Give students the Choose a Strategy activity page from their Activity Book and read the directions with them.

Name: _____

Subtraction Through 20
Choose a Strategy

Write the difference. Tell what strategy you used.

1. 9 − 3 = **6**
2. 11 − 1 = **10**
3. 12 − 6 = **6**
4. 7 − 1 = **6**

5. 16 − 8 = **8**
6. 15 − 5 = **10**

7. 13 − 9 = **4**
8. 18 − 10 = **8**

9. 12 − 5 = **7**
10. 13 − 6 = **7**

11. 17 − 8 = **9**
12. 5 − 4 = **1**

13. 11 − 3 = **8**
14. 13 − 8 = **5**
15. 14 − 8 = **6**
16. 17 − 8 = **9**

---

17. 16 − 7 = **9**
18. 15 − 6 = **9**
19. 7 − 5 = **2**
20. 9 − 8 = **1**

21. 16 − 8 = **8**
22. 15 − 5 = **10**

23. 17 − 9 = **8**
24. 11 − 8 = **3**
25. 14 − 7 = **7**
26. 10 − 8 = **2**

27. 8 − 2 = **6**
28. 15 − 7 = **8**
29. 17 − 8 = **9**
30. 16 − 8 = **8**

Accept all reasonable strategies.

TRY IT All the Facts

Objectives

Students will practice solving subtraction facts with minuends through 20. Give students the All the Facts activity page from their Activity Book and read the directions with them.

• Demonstrate automatic recall of subtraction facts with minuends through 20.

Subtraction Through 20

All the Facts

Name:

Write the difference.

1.	2.	3.	4.
9 − 2 = **7**	6 − 1 = **5**	12 − 2 = **10**	5 − 1 = **4**

5.	6.	7.	8.
15 − 2 = **13**	15 − 7 = **8**	15 − 6 = **9**	15 − 5 = **10**

9. 11 − 8 = **3**   10. 13 − 5 = **8**

11. 17 − 8 = **9**   12. 20 − 10 = **10**

SUBTRACTION FACTS THROUGH 20   **181**   SUBTRACTION THROUGH 20

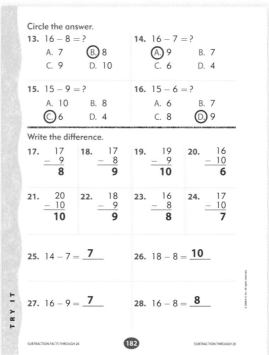

Circle the answer.

13. 16 − 8 = ?
A. 7   (B.) 8
C. 9   D. 10

14. 16 − 7 = ?
(A.) 9   B. 7
C. 6   D. 4

15. 15 − 9 = ?
A. 10   B. 8
(C.) 6   D. 4

16. 15 − 6 = ?
A. 6   B. 7
C. 8   (D.) 9

Write the difference.

17.	18.	19.	20.
17 − 9 = **8**	17 − 8 = **9**	19 − 9 = **10**	16 − 10 = **6**

21.	22.	23.	24.
20 − 10 = **10**	18 − 9 = **9**	16 − 8 = **8**	17 − 10 = **7**

25. 14 − 7 = **7**   26. 18 − 8 = **10**

27. 16 − 9 = **7**   28. 16 − 8 = **8**

SUBTRACTION FACTS THROUGH 20   **182**   SUBTRACTION THROUGH 20

TRY IT

All the Subtraction Facts

Lesson Overview

Skills Update	5 minutes	ONLINE
GET READY Subtraction Facts	10 minutes	ONLINE
LEARN Flash Card Subtraction	10 minutes	ONLINE
LEARN Quilt Facts	10 minutes	OFFLINE
LEARN Post the Facts	5 minutes	OFFLINE
TRY IT Subtract the Facts	10 minutes	OFFLINE
CHECKPOINT	10 minutes	OFFLINE

▶ Lesson Objectives

Demonstrate automatic recall of subtraction facts with minuends through 20.

▶ Prerequisite Skills

Demonstrate automatic recall of subtraction facts with minuends through 16.

▶ Advance Preparation

Cut each sheet of construction paper into three 1 in.-by-8 in. strips and six 1 in.-by-4 in. strips.

Gather the Subtraction Facts Chart you created in the Facts Using Subtraction lesson. If you do not have this chart, follow the instructions in the Subtraction Facts Chart printout to create it.

▶ Content Background

In this lesson, students will recall subtraction facts with minuends through 20.

Although the phrase *minus sign* is often used in everyday language, *minus symbol* is more accurate as a mathematical term. In math, *sign* refers specifically to positive signs and negative signs.

Materials to Gather

SUPPLIED

Subtract the Facts activity page

Checkpoint (printout)

ALSO NEEDED

paper, construction – 4 sheets (1 red, 1 green, 1 blue, 1 yellow)

glue stick

completed Subtraction Facts Chart from Facts Using Subtraction lesson

scissors, adult

sticky notes, small rectangular (2 in. by 1.5 in.) – 44 orange

poster board – 1 sheet (22 in. by 28 in.)

timer

GET READY Subtraction Facts

ONLINE 10min

Students will create subtraction facts when given a difference.

As students work through the activity, have them ask themselves the following questions:

- What number do you want to be first in the number sentence?
- Can the first number be less than the target difference?
- What is the difference?
- How can you decide what the next number in the subtraction sentence should be?

Objectives

- Demonstrate automatic recall of subtraction facts with minuends through 16.

Tips

If needed, students may use cubes to model the problems.

LEARN Flash Card Subtraction

ONLINE 10min

Students will solve subtraction facts with minuends through 20. Students will use 3 decks of flash cards.

Deck 1 has facts with minuends less than or equal to 8. Deck 2 has facts with minuends greater than 8 and less than or equal to 12. Deck 3 has facts with minuends greater than 12 and less than or equal to 20.

1. Have students practice the facts without a timer.
2. Time students to see how many facts they can answer in 1 minute. Then have them repeat and try to improve their performance. Be sure students answer facts from all 3 decks.
3. Record the facts students know and the facts they do not know.
4. Use the appropriate deck to give students additional practice on the facts with which they have difficulty.

Objectives

- Demonstrate automatic recall of subtraction facts with minuends through 20.

Tips

If students need extra practice, they may practice their subtraction facts by using their flash cards offline.

LEARN Quilt Facts

OFFLINE 10min

Students will write subtraction facts for a given difference.

Gather the construction paper strips, glue stick, and poster board.

1. Have students write 9 on each red strip, 8 on each blue strip, 7 on each green strip, and 6 on each yellow strip.
2. Tell students that they are going to make a fact quilt. They can lay out the strips to make a color pattern.

Objectives

- Demonstrate automatic recall of subtraction facts with minuends through 20.

Here is an example of a pattern that students may design:

7	7
8	8
9	9
6	6
7	7
8	8
9	9
6	6
7	
8	
9	
6	
7	
8	
9	
6	
7	
8	
9	
7	7
8	8
9	9
6	6

3. Tell students that each number represents the difference to a subtraction fact. Have them write a different subtraction fact on each strip. Check students' facts as they write them.

4. After students have written all the facts for all the strips, have students glue the strips onto a separate sheet of paper to create their fact quilt.

LEARN Post the Facts

Objectives

- Demonstrate automatic recall of subtraction facts with minuends through 20.

Students will add facts through 20 to the Subtraction Facts Chart. Gather the sticky notes and Subtraction Facts Chart from the Facts Using Subtraction lesson. Make sure they have completed all the facts through 16. Then continue to work on all the facts through 20.

Remember to ask students the facts in a random order. If they are able to quickly recall the fact, have them write the difference on a sticky note and place it on the chart. If not, students will need more practice with finding that difference.

When students have mastered all the differences with minuends through 20, the chart should look like the one shown.

Tips

You can use tape to secure the sticky notes to the facts chart, if necessary.

Subtraction Facts Chart

	0	1	2	3	4	5	6	7	8	9	10
20	20	19	18	17	16	15	14	13	12	11	10
19	19	18	17	16	15	14	13	12	11	10	9
18	18	17	16	15	14	13	12	11	10	9	8
17	17	16	15	14	13	12	11	10	9	8	7
16	16	15	14	13	12	11	10	9	8	7	6
15	15	14	13	12	11	10	9	8	7	6	5
14	14	13	12	11	10	9	8	7	6	5	4
13	13	12	11	10	9	8	7	6	5	4	3
12	12	11	10	9	8	7	6	5	4	3	2
11	11	10	9	8	7	6	5	4	3	2	1
10	10	9	8	7	6	5	4	3	2	1	0
9	9	8	7	6	5	4	3	2	1	0	
8	8	7	6	5	4	3	2	1	0		
7	7	6	5	4	3	2	1	0			
6	6	5	4	3	2	1	0				
5	5	4	3	2	1	0					
4	4	3	2	1	0						
3	3	2	1	0							
2	2	1	0								
1	1	0									
0	0										
−	0	1	2	3	4	5	6	7	8	9	10

TRY IT Subtract the Facts

Objectives

- Demonstrate automatic recall of subtraction facts with minuends through 20.

Students will practice solving subtraction facts with minuends through 20. Give students the Subtract the Facts activity page from their Activity Book and read the directions with them.

All the Subtraction Facts
Subtract the Facts

Name:

Part 1: Write the difference.

1. $20 - 10 = \underline{10}$ 2. $5 - 5 = \underline{0}$

3. $10 - 1 = \underline{9}$ 4. $13 - 7 = \underline{6}$

5. $\begin{array}{r} 18 \\ -\ 8 \\ \hline 10 \end{array}$ 6. $\begin{array}{r} 15 \\ -\ 7 \\ \hline 8 \end{array}$ 7. $\begin{array}{r} 16 \\ -\ 8 \\ \hline 8 \end{array}$ 8. $\begin{array}{r} 14 \\ -\ 5 \\ \hline 9 \end{array}$

9. $\begin{array}{r} 16 \\ -\ 9 \\ \hline 7 \end{array}$ 10. $\begin{array}{r} 17 \\ -\ 9 \\ \hline 8 \end{array}$ 11. $\begin{array}{r} 7 \\ -\ 0 \\ \hline 7 \end{array}$ 12. $\begin{array}{r} 19 \\ -\ 10 \\ \hline 9 \end{array}$

13. $\begin{array}{r} 20 \\ -\ 10 \\ \hline 10 \end{array}$ 14. $\begin{array}{r} 19 \\ -\ 9 \\ \hline 10 \end{array}$ 15. $\begin{array}{r} 12 \\ -\ 9 \\ \hline 3 \end{array}$ 16. $\begin{array}{r} 17 \\ -\ 8 \\ \hline 9 \end{array}$

Part 2: Write the difference.

17. $\begin{array}{r} 16 \\ -\ 9 \\ \hline 7 \end{array}$ 18. $\begin{array}{r} 20 \\ -\ 10 \\ \hline 10 \end{array}$ 19. $\begin{array}{r} 17 \\ -\ 8 \\ \hline 9 \end{array}$ 20. $\begin{array}{r} 19 \\ -\ 9 \\ \hline 10 \end{array}$

21. $16 - 8 = \underline{8}$ 22. $15 - 9 = \underline{6}$

23. $16 - 6 = \underline{10}$ 24. $15 - 10 = \underline{5}$

25. $\begin{array}{r} 18 \\ -\ 10 \\ \hline 8 \end{array}$ 26. $\begin{array}{r} 17 \\ -\ 9 \\ \hline 8 \end{array}$ 27. $\begin{array}{r} 19 \\ -\ 8 \\ \hline 11 \end{array}$ 28. $\begin{array}{r} 16 \\ -\ 10 \\ \hline 6 \end{array}$

29. $\begin{array}{r} 12 \\ -\ 2 \\ \hline 10 \end{array}$ 30. $\begin{array}{r} 19 \\ -\ 10 \\ \hline 9 \end{array}$ 31. $\begin{array}{r} 17 \\ -\ 10 \\ \hline 7 \end{array}$ 32. $\begin{array}{r} 15 \\ -\ 8 \\ \hline 7 \end{array}$

33. $\begin{array}{r} 15 \\ -\ 9 \\ \hline 6 \end{array}$ 34. $\begin{array}{r} 15 \\ -\ 5 \\ \hline 10 \end{array}$ 35. $\begin{array}{r} 18 \\ -\ 9 \\ \hline 9 \end{array}$ 36. $\begin{array}{r} 17 \\ -\ 7 \\ \hline 10 \end{array}$

TRY IT

OFFLINE
10 min

CHECKPOINT

Objectives

Print the Checkpoint and have students complete it on their own. Read the directions, problems, and answer choices to students if necessary. Use the answer key to score the Checkpoint, and then enter the results online.

- Demonstrate automatic recall of subtraction facts with minuends through 20.

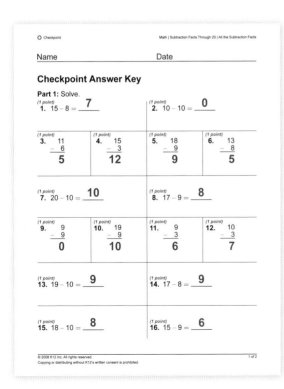

Checkpoint   Math | Subtraction Facts Through 20 | All the Subtraction Facts

Name _____   Date _____

Checkpoint Answer Key

Part 1: Solve.

(1 point)
1. $15 - 8 = \underline{7}$ *(1 point)*
2. $10 - 10 = \underline{0}$

(1 point)
3. $\begin{array}{r} 11 \\ -\ 6 \\ \hline 5 \end{array}$ *(1 point)*
4. $\begin{array}{r} 15 \\ -\ 3 \\ \hline 12 \end{array}$ *(1 point)*
5. $\begin{array}{r} 18 \\ -\ 9 \\ \hline 9 \end{array}$ *(1 point)*
6. $\begin{array}{r} 13 \\ -\ 8 \\ \hline 5 \end{array}$

(1 point)
7. $20 - 10 = \underline{10}$ *(1 point)*
8. $17 - 9 = \underline{8}$

(1 point)
9. $\begin{array}{r} 9 \\ -\ 9 \\ \hline 0 \end{array}$ *(1 point)*
10. $\begin{array}{r} 19 \\ -\ 9 \\ \hline 10 \end{array}$ *(1 point)*
11. $\begin{array}{r} 9 \\ -\ 3 \\ \hline 6 \end{array}$ *(1 point)*
12. $\begin{array}{r} 10 \\ -\ 3 \\ \hline 7 \end{array}$

(1 point)
13. $19 - 10 = \underline{9}$ *(1 point)*
14. $17 - 8 = \underline{9}$

(1 point)
15. $18 - 10 = \underline{8}$ *(1 point)*
16. $15 - 9 = \underline{6}$

Checkpoint   Math | Subtraction Facts Through 20 | All the Subtraction Facts

Name _____   Date _____

Part 2: Solve.

(1 point)
17. $20 - 6 = \underline{14}$ *(1 point)*
18. $12 - 5 = \underline{7}$

(1 point)
19. $\begin{array}{r} 16 \\ -\ 7 \\ \hline 9 \end{array}$ *(1 point)*
20. $\begin{array}{r} 14 \\ -\ 9 \\ \hline 5 \end{array}$ *(1 point)*
21. $\begin{array}{r} 7 \\ -\ 3 \\ \hline 4 \end{array}$ *(1 point)*
22. $\begin{array}{r} 15 \\ -\ 7 \\ \hline 8 \end{array}$

(1 point)
23. $11 - 7 = \underline{4}$ *(1 point)*
24. $16 - 9 = \underline{7}$

(1 point)
25. $\begin{array}{r} 19 \\ -\ 2 \\ \hline 17 \end{array}$ *(1 point)*
26. $\begin{array}{r} 14 \\ -\ 4 \\ \hline 10 \end{array}$ *(1 point)*
27. $\begin{array}{r} 12 \\ -\ 8 \\ \hline 4 \end{array}$ *(1 point)*
28. $\begin{array}{r} 13 \\ -\ 10 \\ \hline 3 \end{array}$

(1 point)
29. $7 - 5 = \underline{2}$ *(1 point)*
30. $16 - 8 = \underline{8}$

(1 point)
31. $\begin{array}{r} 11 \\ -\ 2 \\ \hline 9 \end{array}$ *(1 point)*
32. $\begin{array}{r} 14 \\ -\ 6 \\ \hline 8 \end{array}$ *(1 point)*
33. $\begin{array}{r} 17 \\ -\ 7 \\ \hline 10 \end{array}$ *(1 point)*
34. $\begin{array}{r} 10 \\ -\ 7 \\ \hline 3 \end{array}$

(1 point)
35. $10 - 8 = \underline{2}$ *(1 point)*
36. $20 - 7 = \underline{13}$

Unit Review

UNIT REVIEW Look Back	20 minutes	ONLINE
UNIT REVIEW Checkpoint Practice	20 minutes	OFFLINE
⏩ UNIT REVIEW Prepare for the Checkpoint		

▶ Unit Objectives

This lesson reviews the following objectives:

- Demonstrate automatic recall of subtraction facts with minuends through 8.
- Demonstrate understanding of the result of subtracting zero from a given quantity.
- Given concrete objects, show how two sets can be added together, and then reverse the operation to show how a number can be subtracted from the whole.
- Demonstrate automatic recall of subtraction facts with minuends through 12.
- Demonstrate automatic recall of subtraction facts with minuends through 16.
- Demonstrate automatic recall of subtraction facts with minuends through 20.

▶ Advance Preparation

In this lesson, students will have an opportunity to review previous activities in the Subtraction Facts Through 20 unit. Look at the suggested activities in Unit Review: Prepare for the Checkpoint online and gather any needed materials.

Materials to Gather

SUPPLIED
blocks – B (red, green)
Checkpoint Practice activity page

ALSO NEEDED
timer

Keywords		
count back	pattern
difference	strategy
fact family	subtraction
minuend	subtrahend
opposite operations	take away

UNIT REVIEW Look Back

ONLINE
20 min

Objectives

- Review unit objectives.

In this unit, students worked toward automatic recall of subtraction facts through 20. Students will review these facts to prepare for the Unit Checkpoint.

UNIT REVIEW Checkpoint Practice

OFFLINE
20 min

Objectives

- Review unit objectives.

Students will complete a Checkpoint Practice activity page to prepare for the Unit Checkpoint. If necessary, read the directions, problems, and answer choices to students. Have students answer the problems on their own. Carefully review the answers with students. Gather the circle blocks for Problems 17–22. Part 1 is untimed. Part 2 is timed. Students have 2 minutes to complete the 20 problems.

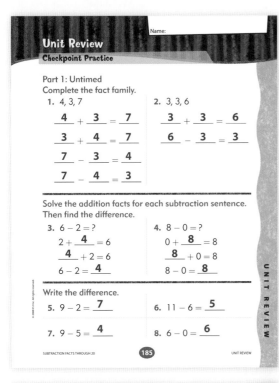

Unit Review
Checkpoint Practice

Name:

Part 1: Untimed
Complete the fact family.

1. 4, 3, 7

$\underline{4} + \underline{3} = \underline{7}$

$\underline{3} + \underline{4} = \underline{7}$

$\underline{7} - \underline{3} = \underline{4}$

$\underline{7} - \underline{4} = \underline{3}$

2. 3, 3, 6

$\underline{3} + \underline{3} = \underline{6}$

$\underline{6} - \underline{3} = \underline{3}$

Solve the addition facts for each subtraction sentence. Then find the difference.

3. $6 - 2 = ?$

$2 + \underline{4} = 6$

$\underline{4} + 2 = 6$

$6 - 2 = \underline{4}$

4. $8 - 0 = ?$

$0 + \underline{8} = 8$

$\underline{8} + 0 = 8$

$8 - 0 = \underline{8}$

Write the difference.

5. $9 - 2 = \underline{7}$

6. $11 - 6 = \underline{5}$

7. $9 - 5 = \underline{4}$

8. $6 - 0 = \underline{6}$

---

9. $13 - 5 = \underline{8}$

10. $20 - 10 = \underline{10}$

11. $14 - 5 = \underline{9}$

12. $15 - 7 = \underline{8}$

13. $\begin{array}{r} 15 \\ -10 \\ \hline 5 \end{array}$

14. $\begin{array}{r} 18 \\ -8 \\ \hline 10 \end{array}$

15. $\begin{array}{r} 16 \\ -7 \\ \hline 9 \end{array}$

16. $\begin{array}{r} 18 \\ -9 \\ \hline 9 \end{array}$

For Problems 17–19, place 8 red circles in a group. Then place 4 green circles in a separate group.

17. How would you add together the green and red circles? **Students should put the red and green circles in one group together.**

18. How many red and green circles are there in all? $\underline{12}$

19. If you remove the 4 green circles, how many circles will be left? $\underline{8}$

For Problems 20–22, place 7 red circles in a group. Then place 2 green circles in a separate group.

20. How would you add together the green and red circles? **Students should put the red and green circles in one group together.**

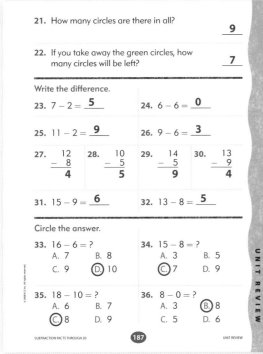

21. How many circles are there in all? $\underline{9}$

22. If you take away the green circles, how many circles will be left? $\underline{7}$

Write the difference.

23. $7 - 2 = \underline{5}$

24. $6 - 6 = \underline{0}$

25. $11 - 2 = \underline{9}$

26. $9 - 6 = \underline{3}$

27. $\begin{array}{r} 12 \\ -8 \\ \hline 4 \end{array}$

28. $\begin{array}{r} 10 \\ -5 \\ \hline 5 \end{array}$

29. $\begin{array}{r} 14 \\ -5 \\ \hline 9 \end{array}$

30. $\begin{array}{r} 13 \\ -9 \\ \hline 4 \end{array}$

31. $15 - 9 = \underline{6}$

32. $13 - 8 = \underline{5}$

Circle the answer.

33. $16 - 6 = ?$
A. 7　B. 8
C. 9　(D.) 10

34. $15 - 8 = ?$
A. 3　B. 5
(C.) 7　D. 9

35. $18 - 10 = ?$
A. 6　B. 7
(C.) 8　D. 9

36. $8 - 0 = ?$
A. 3　(B.) 8
C. 5　D. 6

Part 2: Timed
Write the difference. You will have 2 minutes to complete these problems.

1. $11 - 2 = \underline{9}$

2. $9 - 6 = \underline{3}$

3. $\begin{array}{r} 5 \\ -3 \\ \hline 2 \end{array}$

4. $\begin{array}{r} 8 \\ -5 \\ \hline 3 \end{array}$

5. $\begin{array}{r} 13 \\ -4 \\ \hline 9 \end{array}$

6. $\begin{array}{r} 14 \\ -6 \\ \hline 8 \end{array}$

7. $\begin{array}{r} 12 \\ -10 \\ \hline 2 \end{array}$

8. $\begin{array}{r} 10 \\ -8 \\ \hline 2 \end{array}$

9. $\begin{array}{r} 14 \\ -6 \\ \hline 8 \end{array}$

10. $\begin{array}{r} 17 \\ -7 \\ \hline 10 \end{array}$

11. $13 - 10 = \underline{3}$

12. $18 - 10 = \underline{8}$

13. $19 - 9 = \underline{10}$

14. $16 - 8 = \underline{8}$

15. $\begin{array}{r} 16 \\ -10 \\ \hline 6 \end{array}$

16. $\begin{array}{r} 9 \\ -0 \\ \hline 9 \end{array}$

17. $\begin{array}{r} 11 \\ -7 \\ \hline 4 \end{array}$

18. $\begin{array}{r} 13 \\ -5 \\ \hline 8 \end{array}$

19. $16 - 9 = \underline{7}$

20. $11 - 10 = \underline{1}$

➜ UNIT REVIEW Prepare for the Checkpoint

What you do next depends on how students performed in the previous activity, Unit Review: Checkpoint Practice. If students had difficulty with any of the problems, complete the appropriate review activity listed in the table online.

Unit Checkpoint

| **UNIT CHECKPOINT** Offline | 60 minutes | **OFFLINE** |

▶ Unit Objectives

This lesson assesses the following objectives:

- Demonstrate automatic recall of subtraction facts with minuends through 8.
- Demonstrate understanding of the result of subtracting zero from a given quantity.
- Given concrete objects, show how two sets can be added together, and then reverse the operation to show how a number can be subtracted from the whole.
- Demonstrate automatic recall of subtraction facts with minuends through 12.
- Demonstrate automatic recall of subtraction facts with minuends through 16.
- Demonstrate automatic recall of subtraction facts with minuends through 20.

Materials to Gather

SUPPLIED

Unit Checkpoint (printout)

UNIT CHECKPOINT Offline

OFFLINE 60 min

Objectives

- Assess unit objectives.

Print the Checkpoint. Read the directions, questions, and answer choices to students if necessary. After students have completed both Parts 1 and 2, use the answer key to score the Checkpoint, and then go to the next screen to enter the results.

Students may take a break between completing Part 1 and Part 2. (It's not necessary that they complete these parts back-to-back.) Be sure to wait until students have completed Part 2 before entering the results online.

Name _____　　　Date _____

Unit Checkpoint Answer Key

Part 1
Solve.
Each answer is worth 1 point.

1. $\begin{array}{r} 10 \\ -3 \\ \hline \mathbf{7} \end{array}$	2. $\begin{array}{r} 9 \\ -2 \\ \hline \mathbf{7} \end{array}$	3. $\begin{array}{r} 8 \\ -5 \\ \hline \mathbf{3} \end{array}$	4. $\begin{array}{r} 9 \\ -6 \\ \hline \mathbf{3} \end{array}$
5. $\begin{array}{r} 5 \\ -3 \\ \hline \mathbf{2} \end{array}$	6. $\begin{array}{r} 6 \\ -3 \\ \hline \mathbf{3} \end{array}$	7. $\begin{array}{r} 7 \\ -5 \\ \hline \mathbf{2} \end{array}$	8. $\begin{array}{r} 8 \\ -8 \\ \hline \mathbf{0} \end{array}$

9. $\begin{array}{r} 10 \\ -0 \\ \hline \mathbf{10} \end{array}$	10. $\begin{array}{r} 10 \\ -8 \\ \hline \mathbf{2} \end{array}$	11. $8 - 1 = \underline{\mathbf{7}}$
		12. $8 - 3 = \underline{\mathbf{5}}$

13. $10 - 5 = \underline{\mathbf{5}}$ 　　　　14. $7 - 4 = \underline{\mathbf{3}}$

15. $9 - 7 = \underline{\mathbf{2}}$ 　　　　16. $9 - 3 = \underline{\mathbf{6}}$

17. $8 - 4 = \underline{\mathbf{4}}$ 　　　　18. $7 - 1 = \underline{\mathbf{6}}$

19. $9 - 5 = \underline{\mathbf{4}}$ 　　　　20. $7 - 3 = \underline{\mathbf{4}}$

Name _____　　　Date _____

Part 2
Solve.
Each answer is worth 1 point.

1. $\begin{array}{r} 12 \\ -2 \\ \hline \mathbf{10} \end{array}$	2. $\begin{array}{r} 11 \\ -4 \\ \hline \mathbf{7} \end{array}$	3. $\begin{array}{r} 16 \\ -8 \\ \hline \mathbf{8} \end{array}$	4. $\begin{array}{r} 15 \\ -6 \\ \hline \mathbf{9} \end{array}$
5. $\begin{array}{r} 20 \\ -10 \\ \hline \mathbf{10} \end{array}$	6. $\begin{array}{r} 14 \\ -6 \\ \hline \mathbf{8} \end{array}$	7. $\begin{array}{r} 17 \\ -10 \\ \hline \mathbf{7} \end{array}$	8. $\begin{array}{r} 16 \\ -9 \\ \hline \mathbf{7} \end{array}$

9. $\begin{array}{r} 13 \\ -8 \\ \hline \mathbf{5} \end{array}$	10. $\begin{array}{r} 19 \\ -10 \\ \hline \mathbf{9} \end{array}$	11. $19 - 9 = \underline{\mathbf{10}}$
		12. $16 - 10 = \underline{\mathbf{6}}$

13. $13 - 5 = \underline{\mathbf{8}}$ 　　　　14. $12 - 10 = \underline{\mathbf{2}}$

15. $14 - 9 = \underline{\mathbf{5}}$ 　　　　16. $14 - 10 = \underline{\mathbf{4}}$

17. $12 - 7 = \underline{\mathbf{5}}$ 　　　　18. $16 - 7 = \underline{\mathbf{9}}$

19. $15 - 9 = \underline{\mathbf{6}}$ 　　　　20. $18 - 9 = \underline{\mathbf{9}}$

Subtraction Strategies

There are many ways to subtract.

8 – 2 = 6

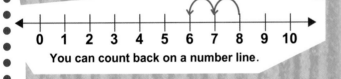

You can count back on a number line.

1	2	3	4	5	6	7	8	9	10
11	12	13	14	15	16	17	18	19	20
21	22	23	24	25	26	27	28	29	30

You can count back on a hundred chart.

You can use circles to subtract.

▶ Unit Objectives

- Identify one more than or one less than a given number.
- Identify 10 more than or 10 less than a given number.
- Use "counting back" to solve subtraction problems.
- Combine memorized facts with counting strategies to solve subtraction problems.

▶ Big Ideas

Counting principles and numbers can be used to solve addition and subtraction problems.

▶ Unit Introduction

Students will learn various subtraction strategies. They will start by learning how to find one less than and 10 less than a given number. Then students will use hundred charts and number lines to count back, use blocks to model subtraction, and use facts that they know to help them find differences.

One Less, 10 Less

Lesson Overview

Skills Update	5 minutes	ONLINE
GET READY Count By Ones and 10s	5 minutes	ONLINE
LEARN One Less on a Number Line	15 minutes	ONLINE
LEARN 10 Less on a Hundred Chart	15 minutes	ONLINE
TRY IT One Less and 10 Less	15 minutes	OFFLINE
CHECKPOINT	5 minutes	OFFLINE

▶ Lesson Objectives
- Identify one more than or one less than a given number.
- Identify 10 more than or 10 less than a given number.

▶ Prerequisite Skills
- Count aloud whole numbers through 100.
- Count by 10s through 100.

▶ Advance Preparation
Print the Hundred Chart.

▶ Content Background
Students will learn to identify and find the numbers that are one less and 10 less than another number.

Keywords	**fewer** – a lesser number than another **hundred chart** – a 10-by-10 grid displaying the numbers from 1 to 100 in order from left to right **number line** – a line consisting of points equally spaced, each of which corresponds to a unique number

GET READY Count by Ones and 10s

ONLINE 5 min

Students will use a hundred chart to count forward and backward by ones. Then they will count forward by 10s.

Objectives
- Count aloud whole numbers through 100.
- Count by 10s through 100.

LEARN One Less on a Number Line

Students will learn how to find one less than a given number using a number line.

LEARN 10 Less on a Hundred Chart

Students will use an online hundred chart to find a number that is 10 less than a given number. First they will count back to find the number that is 10 less. Then they will use the location of the number on the hundred chart to find 10 less. Finally students will identify number patterns to find 10 less.

DIRECTIONS FOR USING THE HUNDRED CHART LEARNING TOOL

1. **Say:** Let's use the hundred chart to find 10 more than 30.

   Have students choose a tool. Have them click 30 and count on by ones 10 more numbers. Make sure students count 31 as the first number.

   Ask: What number did you land on?
   ANSWER: 40

   Say: Look at where 30 is on the hundred chart. Look at where 40 is.

   Ask: What do you notice?
   ANSWER: 40 is in the box just below 30 in the same column.

2. **Say:** Now let's use the hundred chart to find 10 less than a number. Let's find out what number is 10 less than 30.

   Click Clear Chart. Have students click 30 and count back by ones 10 numbers. Make sure students count 29 as the first number.

   Ask: What number did you land on?
   ANSWER: 20

   Say: Look at where 30 is on the hundred chart. Look at where 20 is.

   Ask: What do you notice?
   ANSWER: 20 is in the box just above 30 in the same column.

3. Repeat with the following problems. Students may count forward or back by ones on the hundred chart. Or they may click the answer without counting by ones.

   • What is 10 less than 35?   (25)

   • What is 10 more than 82? (92)

   • What is 10 fewer than 57? (47)

4. Write the following numbers on a sheet of paper:

   20 and 10   75 and 65   43 and 33   97 and 87

   Say: Look at the pairs of numbers. The second number is 10 less than the first number.

   Ask: What pattern do you see when you look at the two numbers together?
   ANSWER: The digits on the right are the same. The digits on the left are one apart. The number that is 10 less than the other number has the lesser digit on the left.

Objectives

• Identify one more than or one less than a given number.

Objectives

• Identify 10 more than or 10 less than a given number.

Tips

Remind students who are *counting back* on the hundred chart that when they reach the beginning of a row, the next number is at the end of the previous row.

TRY IT One Less and 10 Less

OFFLINE
15 min

Students will practice finding one less and 10 less than a number. Give students the Hundred Chart and the One Less and 10 Less activity page from their Activity Book. Read the directions with them.

Objectives

- Identify one more than or one less than a given number.
- Identify 10 more than or 10 less than a given number.

Tips

If students have difficulty using the partial number lines on the activity page, print the Number Line 0–100. Cut each number line and tape them together to make a number line from 0 through 100.

Name:

One Less, 10 Less

One Less and 10 Less

Use the number line for Problems 1–4.

21 22 23 24 25 26 27 28 29 30 31 32 33 34 35 36 37 38 39 40

1. What number is 1 more than 27? **28**

2. What number is 1 less than 27? **26**

3. What number is 1 more than 30? **31**

4. What number is 1 less than 30? **29**

Use the number line for Problems 5 and 6.

61 62 63 64 65 66 67 68 69 70 71 72 73 74 75 76 77 78 79 80

5. What number is 1 less than 74? **73**

6. What number is 1 less than 79? **78**

Write the number that is 1 less than the given number.

7. 83 **82**   8. 44 **43**   9. 16 **15**

SUBTRACTION STRATEGIES   (189)   ONE LESS, 10 LESS

Use the Hundred Chart for Problems 10–13.

10. What number is 10 more than 18? **28**

11. What number is 10 less than 18? **8**

12. What number is 10 less than 41? **31**

13. What number is 10 more than 39? **49**

Write the number that is 10 less than the given number.

14. 59 **49**   15. 21 **11**   16. 94 **84**

Write the answer.

17. What number is 10 less than 39? **29**

18. What number is 10 less than 70? **60**

19. What number is 10 more than 45? **55**

20. What number is 10 more than 33? **43**

SUBTRACTION STRATEGIES   (190)   ONE LESS, 10 LESS

T R Y   I T

ONE LESS, 10 LESS **299**

OFFLINE
5min

Objectives

- Identify one more than or one less than a given number.
- Identify 10 more than or 10 less than a given number.

Print the Checkpoint and have students complete it on their own. Read the directions, problems, and answer choices to students if necessary. Use the answer key to score the Checkpoint, and then enter the results online.

○ Checkpoint   Math | Subtraction Strategies | One Less, 10 Less

Name _____ Date _____

Checkpoint Answer Key

Read each problem and answer the question.

(1 point)
1. What number is 1 less than 29? __**28**__

(1 point)
2. What number is 1 less than 89? __**88**__

(1 point)
3. What number is 1 more than 7? __**8**__

(1 point)
4. What number is 1 more than 29? __**30**__

(1 point)
5. What number is 10 less than 55? __**45**__

(1 point)
6. What number is 10 less than 20? __**10**__

(1 point)
7. What number is 10 more than 55? __**65**__

(1 point)
8. What number is 10 more than 28? __**38**__

1 of 1

Counting Back and Other Strategies

Lesson Overview

Skills Update	5 minutes	**ONLINE**
GET READY Find the Difference	5 minutes	**ONLINE**
LEARN Step Back	15 minutes	**OFFLINE**
LEARN Count Back to Subtract	15 minutes	**OFFLINE**
LEARN Subtraction Strategies	10 minutes	**OFFLINE**
TRY IT Subtract	10 minutes	**OFFLINE**

▶ Lesson Objectives

- Use "counting back" to solve subtraction problems.
- Combine memorized facts with counting strategies to solve subtraction problems.

▶ Prerequisite Skills

- Use "counting on" to solve addition problems.
- Use "counting on from the largest number" to solve addition problems.
- Demonstrate automatic recall of subtraction facts with minuends through 20.
- Identify one more than or one less than a given number.
- Identify 10 more than or 10 less than a given number.

▶ Common Errors and Misconceptions

- Students might start counting before or after pointing to the first object in a group. Or they might stop counting before or after they point to the last object. Students should point to each object as they count it.
- Students might say more than one number for each object when counting objects in a group. Or they might skip objects. Students should point to each object and say exactly one number. Then they should point to the next object and say exactly one number, and so on.
- Students might use an incorrect counting sequence, such as "one, two, four, six, ten."

▶ Advance Preparation

Write the numbers 0–20 on the sticky notes. Place the ribbon on the floor, and evenly space the numbers, to make a "floor" number line. Alternatively, display the number line horizontally on a long wall.

Print the Subtraction Strategy Cards. Cut on dashed lines to make cards.

Materials to Gather

SUPPLIED

blocks – B (20 of any color)
Step Back activity page
Subtraction Strategy Cards (printout)
Subtraction Strategies activity page
Subtract activity page

ALSO NEEDED

sticky notes, small rectangular (2 in. by 1.5 in.) – 21
wide ribbon – 1 strip, about 8 ft long
paper, construction – 1 light-colored sheet
scissors, adult

▶ Safety

You can secure the ends of the ribbon to the floor with tape so that students don't slip on the ribbon.

While students count backward on the number line, they should not walk backward. Make sure students face zero as they step so that they are always walking forward.

▶ Content Background

Students will explore different strategies to solve a subtraction problem.

The three parts of a subtraction sentence are the *minuend*, the *subtrahend*, and the *difference*. In the subtraction sentence $4 - 1 = 3$, the number you are subtracting from (4) is the minuend, the number you are subtracting (1) is the subtrahend, and the answer (3) is the difference.

The term *difference* is used with students and by students, but the terms *minuend* and *subtrahend* will not be formally introduced to students at this time.

Keywords	**count back** – to subtract by starting with the number of objects in one group and then counting back, in order, the number of objects in the other group **strategy** – a method or approach to solve a problem **subtraction** – the process of taking away objects from a group or finding the difference between two groups; a mathematical operation

GET READY Find the Difference — ONLINE 5 min

Students will use online flash cards for subtraction facts with minuends through 20. Students will use three decks of flash cards.

Deck 1 has facts with minuends less than or equal to 8. Deck 2 has facts with minuends greater than 8 and less than or equal to 12. Deck 3 has facts with minuends greater than 12 and less than or equal to 20.

Objectives

- Demonstrate automatic recall of subtraction facts with minuends through 20.
- Identify one more than or one less than a given number.
- Identify 10 more than or 10 less than a given number.

LEARN Step Back — OFFLINE 15 min

Students will use a number line to count back to subtract.

Work near the ribbon number line you prepared earlier. Give students the Step Back activity page from their Activity Book and read the directions with them. Work together to solve the problems. Although students are counting back, have them walk forward toward zero.

Objectives

- Use "counting back" to solve subtraction problems.
- Combine memorized facts with counting strategies to solve subtraction problems.

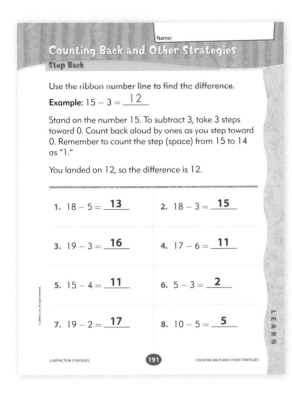

Name:

Counting Back and Other Strategies

Step Back

Use the ribbon number line to find the difference.

Example: 15 − 3 = __12__

Stand on the number 15. To subtract 3, take 3 steps toward 0. Count back aloud by ones as you step toward 0. Remember to count the step (space) from 15 to 14 as "1."

You landed on 12, so the difference is 12.

1. 18 − 5 = __13__   2. 18 − 3 = __15__

3. 19 − 3 = __16__   4. 17 − 6 = __11__

5. 15 − 4 = __11__   6. 5 − 3 = __2__

7. 19 − 2 = __17__   8. 10 − 5 = __5__

SUBTRACTION STRATEGIES   191   COUNTING BACK AND OTHER STRATEGIES

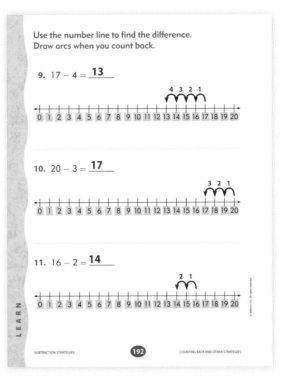

Use the number line to find the difference.
Draw arcs when you count back.

9. 17 − 4 = __13__

10. 20 − 3 = __17__

11. 16 − 2 = __14__

SUBTRACTION STRATEGIES   192   COUNTING BACK AND OTHER STRATEGIES

OFFLINE

15 min

LEARN Count Back to Subtract

Students will use circle blocks to count back to subtract. Gather the construction paper and circles.

SOLVE EXAMPLE

1. **Say:** We can use circles to count back to subtract. Let's count back with circles to solve 12 − 3.

2. Place 12 circles on the paper.

3. **Say:** To subtract 3 from 12, we take away 3 circles.

4. **Say:** Now count back from 12 with me as I take away 3 circles one at a time: 11, 10, 9.

   Remove circles one at a time as you count back.

5. **Ask:** What number did we say when I took away the third circle?
   ANSWER: 9

   Say: We started with 12 circles. We counted back as I took 3 circles away. The last number we said was 9, so 12 minus 3 equals 9.

SOLVE PROBLEMS

6. **Say:** Let's try another problem. Use circles to count back to find 15 − 4.

7. **Ask:** How many circles should you place on the paper?
   ANSWER: 15

8. Have students place the circles.

9. **Ask:** How many should you take away?
   ANSWER: 4

Objectives

- Use "counting back" to solve subtraction problems.
- Combine memorized facts with counting strategies to solve subtraction problems.

10. **Say:** Remove the 4 circles, one at a time, as you count back.

    Students should remove the 4 circles and count back: 14, 13, 12, 11. Remind students that the first number they should say is one less than the starting number.

11. **Ask:** What is 15 − 4?
    ANSWER: 11

    Ask: How do you know?
    ANSWER: The number I said when I took away the fourth circle was 11.

12. Repeat the previous steps for the following problems:
    9 − 4; 17 − 2; 14 − 6; 20 − 7; and 18 − 5.

CREATE PROBLEMS

13. **Say:** It's your turn to make up and solve a subtraction problem.

14. **Say:** Place some circles on the paper and tell how many you plan to take away. Tell the problem that you will solve.

    For example, if students place 13 circles and plan to take away 4, they should say that their problem is 13 − 4.

15. **Say:** Now remove circles and count back to solve. What is the answer? Check students' answers.

16. Repeat as time permits.

OFFLINE
10 min

LEARN Subtraction Strategies

Objectives

Students will learn that there are many strategies that they can use to solve subtraction problems.

   Give students the Subtraction Strategy Cards and Subtraction Strategies activity page from their Activity Book. Read the directions with them. Review the strategies on the cards with students. Provide students with circles if they choose.

- Use "counting back" to solve subtraction problems.
- Combine memorized facts with counting strategies to solve subtraction problems.

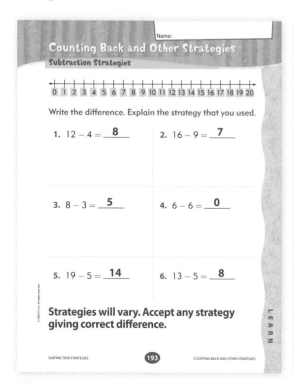

Name:

Counting Back and Other Strategies
Subtraction Strategies

0 1 2 3 4 5 6 7 8 9 10 11 12 13 14 15 16 17 18 19 20

Write the difference. Explain the strategy that you used.

1. 12 − 4 = __8__   2. 16 − 9 = __7__

3. 8 − 3 = __5__   4. 6 − 6 = __0__

5. 19 − 5 = __14__   6. 13 − 5 = __8__

Strategies will vary. Accept any strategy giving correct difference.

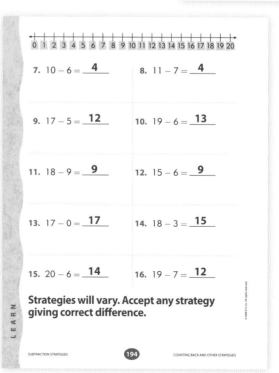

0 1 2 3 4 5 6 7 8 9 10 11 12 13 14 15 16 17 18 19 20

7. 10 − 6 = __4__   8. 11 − 7 = __4__

9. 17 − 5 = __12__   10. 19 − 6 = __13__

11. 18 − 9 = __9__   12. 15 − 6 = __9__

13. 17 − 0 = __17__   14. 18 − 3 = __15__

15. 20 − 6 = __14__   16. 19 − 7 = __12__

Strategies will vary. Accept any strategy giving correct difference.

TRY IT Subtract

Objectives

Students will use various strategies, including counting back, to subtract. Give students the Subtract activity page from their Activity Book and read the directions with them.

- Use "counting back" to solve subtraction problems.
- Combine memorized facts with counting strategies to solve subtraction problems.

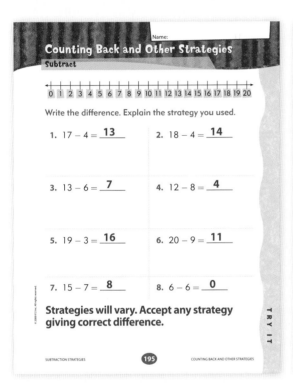

Name:

Counting Back and Other Strategies
Subtract

0 1 2 3 4 5 6 7 8 9 10 11 12 13 14 15 16 17 18 19 20

Write the difference. Explain the strategy you used.

1. $17 - 4 =$ __13__

2. $18 - 4 =$ __14__

3. $13 - 6 =$ __7__

4. $12 - 8 =$ __4__

5. $19 - 3 =$ __16__

6. $20 - 9 =$ __11__

7. $15 - 7 =$ __8__

8. $6 - 6 =$ __0__

Strategies will vary. Accept any strategy giving correct difference.

TRY IT

SUBTRACTION STRATEGIES   195   COUNTING BACK AND OTHER STRATEGIES

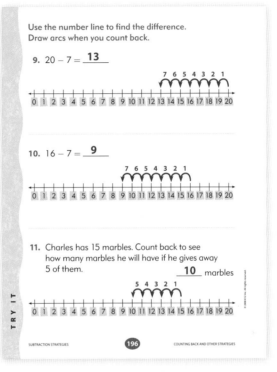

Use the number line to find the difference.
Draw arcs when you count back.

9. $20 - 7 =$ __13__

7 6 5 4 3 2 1
0 1 2 3 4 5 6 7 8 9 10 11 12 13 14 15 16 17 18 19 20

10. $16 - 7 =$ __9__

7 6 5 4 3 2 1
0 1 2 3 4 5 6 7 8 9 10 11 12 13 14 15 16 17 18 19 20

11. Charles has 15 marbles. Count back to see how many marbles he will have if he gives away 5 of them.   __10__ marbles

5 4 3 2 1
0 1 2 3 4 5 6 7 8 9 10 11 12 13 14 15 16 17 18 19 20

TRY IT

SUBTRACTION STRATEGIES   196   COUNTING BACK AND OTHER STRATEGIES

Use Strategies to Subtract

Skills Update	5 minutes	ONLINE
GET READY 10 Less, One Less	5 minutes	ONLINE
LEARN Count Back	15 minutes	ONLINE
LEARN Subtraction Strategies	15 minutes	ONLINE
TRY IT Subtraction	10 minutes	OFFLINE
CHECKPOINT	10 minutes	OFFLINE

▶ Lesson Objectives

- Use "counting back" to solve subtraction problems.
- Combine memorized facts with counting strategies to solve subtraction problems.

▶ Prerequisite Skills

- Demonstrate automatic recall of subtraction facts with minuends through 20.
- Identify one more than or one less than a given number.
- Identify 10 more than or 10 less than a given number.
- Use "counting on" to solve addition problems.
- Use "counting on from the largest number" to solve addition problems.

▶ Common Errors and Misconceptions

- Students might start counting before or after pointing to the first object in a group. Or they might stop counting before or after they point to the last object. Students should point to each object as they count it.
- Students might say more than one number for each object when counting objects in a group. Or they might skip objects. Students should point to each object and say exactly one number. Then they should point to the next object and say exactly one number, and so on.
- Students might use an incorrect counting sequence, such as "one, two, four, six, ten."

▶ Advance Preparation

Print the Number Line 0–20. Cut out and tape together the number lines to make one long number line.

▶ Content Background

Students will explore different strategies to solve subtraction problems.

Materials to Gather

SUPPLIED
blocks – B (red, blue)
Number Line 0–20 (printout)
Subtraction activity page
Checkpoint (printout)

Also Needed
tape, clear
scissors, adult

GET READY 10 Less, One Less

Students will use a hundred chart to identify one less than a number and 10 less than a number.

As students find the differences, have them point to each number on the chart. Remind students that when they get to the beginning of a row, they must continue counting back by moving to the last number in the row above.

Objectives

- Identify one more than or one less than a given number.
- Identify 10 more than or 10 less than a given number.

LEARN Count Back

Students will use a number line to count back to subtract. Because many elevators show the floor numbers above the door, an elevator is like a number line. The movement of an elevator down from floor to floor is like the act of counting back on a number line, or subtracting.

Before completing the activity, have students describe any experiences they have had riding in an elevator. Be sure that students understand that an elevator travels up and down to different floors in a building.

Objectives

- Use "counting back" to solve subtraction problems.
- Combine memorized facts with counting strategies to solve subtraction problems.

Tips

If students have difficulty using the number lines online, have them use the Number Line 0–20 printout you prepared earlier.

LEARN Subtraction Strategies

Students will use different strategies to subtract. Complete these steps before beginning the online activity. Gather the circle blocks.

1. **Say:** There are many strategies for subtracting. Let's see how many ways we can use to find $18 - 11$.

2. Give students the circles.

   Say: Use circles to show $18 - 11$.

   Students may show 18 circles, take 11 away, and say that there are 7 left, so $18 - 11 = 7$. Students may also make lines of 18 and 11 circles, pair circles up, and say that there are 7 circles with no pair. Finally, students may start with 18 circles, count back 11 circles, and say that the last number they said was 7.

3. **Say:** Now let's use a fact that you know to find the difference. Suppose you know that $18 - 10 = 8$. You could subtract $18 - 10$ to get 8, and then add subtract one more from 8, because 11 is one more than 10. The answer is 7.

   Have students explain how they could use a different fact to find the difference.

4. **Ask:** Can you think of other strategies for finding $18 - 11$?

   Students may describe using a number line, using fact families, counting back, and so on.

5. **Say:** Now let's play a computer game to practice subtracting. If you need to, use a strategy to find the answer to each problem.

Objectives

- Use "counting back" to solve subtraction problems.
- Combine memorized facts with counting strategies to solve subtraction problems.

6. Follow the directions to set up the learning tool. When students have difficulty, encourage them to ask themselves the following questions:

- Do I have the fact memorized?
- Can I use a related fact?
- Can I count back?
- Can I use models?
- Can I use another subtraction fact I know?
- Can I make pairs?

DIRECTIONS FOR USING THE BUILDING EXPRESSIONS LEARNING TOOL

7. Click Begin and choose the following:
- Problem Type: Subtraction (−)
- Problem Format: $4 - 2 = ?, 4 - ? = 2, ? - 2 = 2$

8. Click Next and choose the following:
- Use Numbers: 0–20
- Equals Symbol Placement: Both Ways
- Timer Speed: Choose whichever speed you feel is appropriate.

OFFLINE
10min

TRY IT Subtraction

Students will practice using strategies to subtract. Give students the Number Line 0–20 printout you prepared earlier and the Subtraction activity page from their Activity Book. Read the directions with them.

Objectives

- Use "counting back" to solve subtraction problems.
- Combine memorized facts with counting strategies to solve subtraction problems.

Name:
Use Strategies to Subtract
Subtraction

Write the difference. Explain the strategy you used.
Use the number line if you need help.

1. $14 - 3 = \underline{11}$ 2. $18 - 5 = \underline{13}$

3. $16 - 10 = \underline{6}$ 4. $18 - 4 = \underline{14}$

5. $18 - 5 = \underline{13}$ 6. $19 - 6 = \underline{13}$

7. $14 - 9 = \underline{5}$ 8. $20 - 17 = \underline{3}$

Strategies will vary. Accept any strategy giving correct difference.

SUBTRACTION STRATEGIES   197   USE STRATEGIES TO SUBTRACT

TRY IT

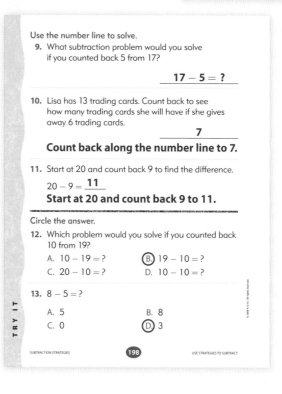

TRY IT

Use the number line to solve.
9. What subtraction problem would you solve if you counted back 5 from 17?

$\underline{17 - 5 = ?}$

10. Lisa has 13 trading cards. Count back to see how many trading cards she will have if she gives away 6 trading cards.

$\underline{7}$
Count back along the number line to 7.

11. Start at 20 and count back 9 to find the difference.

$20 - 9 = \underline{11}$
Start at 20 and count back 9 to 11.

Circle the answer.
12. Which problem would you solve if you counted back 10 from 19?
A. $10 - 19 = ?$ (B) $19 - 10 = ?$
C. $20 - 10 = ?$ D. $10 - 10 = ?$

13. $8 - 5 = ?$
A. 5   B. 8
C. 0   (D) 3

SUBTRACTION STRATEGIES   198   USE STRATEGIES TO SUBTRACT

CHECKPOINT

Print the Checkpoint and have students complete it on their own. Read the directions, problems, and answer choices to students if necessary. Use the answer key to score the Checkpoint, and then enter the results online.

Objectives

- Use "counting back" to solve subtraction problems.
- Combine memorized facts with counting strategies to solve subtraction problems.

○ Checkpoint   Math | Subtraction Strategies | Use Strategies to Subtract

Name _____   Date _____

Checkpoint Answer Key

Read each problem and follow the directions.
(1 point)
1. Count back from 15 to find the difference.

   $15 - 4 = \underline{11}$ **Start at 15 and count back 4 to 11.**

(1 point)
2. There are 13 birds sitting on a wire.

   Then 4 of the birds fly away.
   Count back from 13 to find how many birds are left. $\underline{9}$

   Start at 13 and count back from 4 to 9.

Write the difference. Explain the strategy you used. **Sample answers:**
(1 point)
3. $19 - 11 = \underline{8}$ **I used an addition fact I knew: 11 + 8 = 19; I counted back 11 from 19.**

(1 point)
4. $20 - 10 = \underline{10}$ **I used an addition fact I knew: 10 + 10 = 20; I counted back 10 from 20.**

Circle the answer.
(1 point)
5. Which of the following subtraction problems would you solve if you counted back 7 from 16?

   A. $7 - 16 = ?$ (B.) $16 - 7 = ?$ C. $7 - 7 = ?$ D. $16 - 5 = ?$

(1 point)
6. Use a strategy that you have learned, or math facts, to solve this problem. $12 - 10 = ?$

   A. 22   B. 5   (C.) 2   D. 8

1 of 1

Unit Review

Lesson Overview

UNIT REVIEW Look Back	20 minutes	**ONLINE**
UNIT REVIEW Checkpoint Practice	20 minutes	**OFFLINE**
▶ **UNIT REVIEW** Prepare for the Checkpoint		

▶ Unit Objectives

This lesson reviews the following objectives:

- Identify one more than or one less than a given number.
- Identify 10 more than or 10 less than a given number.
- Use "counting back" to solve subtraction problems.
- Combine memorized facts with counting strategies to solve subtraction problems.

Materials to Gather

SUPPLIED
Checkpoint Practice activity page

▶ Advance Preparation

In this lesson, students will have an opportunity to review previous activities in the Subtraction Strategies unit. Look at the suggested activities in Unit Review: Prepare for the Checkpoint online and gather any needed materials.

Keywords	count back	number line
	fewer	strategy
	hundred chart	subtraction

UNIT REVIEW Look Back

ONLINE **20** min

Students learned various subtraction strategies. They started by learning how to find one less than and 10 less than a given number. Then students used hundred charts and number lines to count back, used blocks to model subtraction, and used facts that they know to help them find differences. Students will review these concepts to prepare for the Unit Checkpoint.

Objectives

- Review unit objectives.

UNIT REVIEW Checkpoint Practice

OFFLINE **20** min

Students will complete a Checkpoint Practice activity page to prepare for the Unit Checkpoint. If necessary, read the directions, problems, and answer choices to students. Have students answer the problems on their own. Carefully review the answers with students.

Objectives

- Review unit objectives.

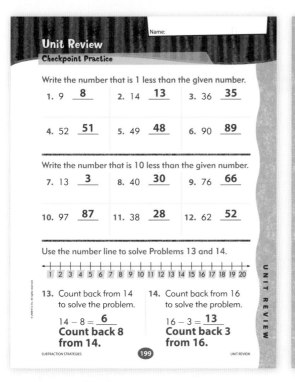

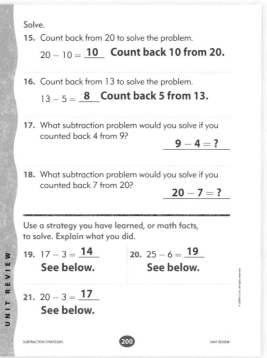

Additional Answers

19. **Sample answers:** counted back 3 from 17; used addition fact I knew:
$14 + 3 = 17$

20. **Sample answers:** counted back 6 from 25; used addition fact I knew:
$19 + 6 = 25$

21. **Sample answers:** counted back 3 from 20; used addition fact I knew:
$17 + 3 = 20$

➡ UNIT REVIEW Prepare for the Checkpoint

What you do next depends on how students performed in the previous activity, Unit Review: Checkpoint Practice. If students had difficulty with any of the problems, complete the appropriate review activity listed in the table online.

Unit Checkpoint

UNIT CHECKPOINT Online	30 minutes	**ONLINE**
UNIT CHECKPOINT Offline	30 minutes	**OFFLINE**

▶ Unit Objectives

This lesson assesses the following objectives:

- Identify one more than or one less than a given number.
- Identify 10 more than or 10 less than a given number.
- Use "counting back" to solve subtraction problems.
- Combine memorized facts with counting strategies to solve subtraction problems.

Materials to Gather

SUPPLIED
Unit Checkpoint (printout)

UNIT CHECKPOINT Online

ONLINE
30 min

Objectives

- Assess unit objectives.

Students will complete this part of the Unit Checkpoint online. Read the directions, problems, and answer choices to students. If necessary, help students with keyboard or mouse operations.

UNIT CHECKPOINT Offline

OFFLINE
30 min

Objectives

- Assess unit objectives.

Students will complete this part of the Unit Checkpoint offline. Print the Checkpoint and have students complete it on their own. Read the directions, problems, and answer choices to students, if necessary. Use the answer key to score the Checkpoint, and then enter the results online.

Name _____ Date _____

Unit Checkpoint Answer Key

Read each problem and solve.

(1 point)
1. What number is 1 less than 89? __**88**__

(1 point)
2. What number is 1 less than 55? __**54**__

(1 point)
3. What number is 1 less than 34? __**33**__

(1 point)
4. What number is 1 less than 57? __**56**__

(1 point)
5. What number is 10 less than 99? __**89**__

(1 point)
6. What number is 10 less than 12? __**2**__

(1 point)
7. What number is 10 less than 34? __**24**__

(1 point)
8. What number is 10 less than 47? __**37**__

Name _____ Date _____

0 1 2 3 4 5 6 7 8 9 10 11 12 13 14 15 16 17 18 19 20

For Problems 9–11, use the number line above.

(1 point)
9. Using the number line, count back from 7 to solve the problem.

$7 - 2 =$ __**5**__

Count back along the number line to 5.

(1 point)
10. Using the number line, count back from 11 to solve the problem.

$11 - 7 =$ __**4**__

Count back along the number line to 4.

(1 point)
11. Using the number line, count back from 13 to solve the problem.

$13 - 6 =$ __**7**__

Count back along the number line to 7.

(1 point)
12. Use a counting strategy you have learned, or math facts, to solve this problem. Explain what you did.

$14 - 4 =$ __**10**__ **Sample answers: I counted back 4 from 14; I just knew that $10 + 4 = 14$. Students should mention at least one counting strategy or fact.**

Name _____ Date _____

(1 point)
13. Use a counting strategy you have learned, or math facts, to solve this problem. Explain what you did.

$19 - 9 =$ __**10**__ **Sample answers: I counted back 9 from 19 to get 10; I just knew that $9 + 10 = 19$. Students should mention at least one counting strategy or fact.**

(1 point)
14. Count back from 13 to solve the problem.

$13 - 5 =$ __**8**__

Count back 5 from 13 to solve $13 - 5 = 8$.

(1 point)
15. Count back from 12 to find the difference.

$12 - 5 =$ __**7**__

Count back 5 from 12 to solve $12 - 5 = 7$.

Circle the answer.

(1 point)
16. Which math fact could you use to solve this problem?

$? = 17 - 6$

A. $17 + 10 = 27$

B. $17 - 1 = 16$

C. $11 + 6 = 17$

Semester Review

Lesson Overview

SEMESTER REVIEW Look Back	20 minutes	**ONLINE**
SEMESTER REVIEW Checkpoint Practice	20 minutes	**OFFLINE**
⏩ **SEMESTER REVIEW** Prepare for the Checkpoint		

▶ Semester Objectives

This lesson reviews the following objectives:

- Write numerals through 100.
- Count by 5s through 100.
- Use the symbols for less than, equal to, or greater than ($<, =, >$) to compare and order whole numbers through 100.
- Use concrete objects or sketches to model and solve addition or subtraction computation problems with sums and minuends up through 30.
- Recognize that the equals symbol shows an equality between two expressions.
- Use the equals symbol in number sentences to express equality.
- Demonstrate automatic recall of addition facts with sums through 20.
- Identify 10 more than or 10 less than a given number.
- Find the sum of three one-digit numbers, with sums through 20.
- Represent equivalent forms of the same number through 20 through the use of number expressions, such as $7 = 4 + 3$, or $5 + 2$, or $1 + 2 + 4$, or $9 - 2$, or $20 - 13$.
- Solve addition problems by filling in a missing number or numbers in a given number sentence.
- Demonstrate automatic recall of subtraction facts with minuends through 20.
- Tell time to the nearest half hour.
- Describe objects in space by direction, such as behind, in front of, next to, left of, or right of.
- Demonstrate understanding that the order in which numbers are added does not affect the sum.
- Use models and math symbols to represent addition.
- Demonstrate understanding of the rule for adding zero.
- Given a number of objects up through 20, show how those objects can be grouped and regrouped to illustrate the associative property.
- Use models and math symbols to represent subtraction.
- Given concrete objects, show how two sets can be added together, and then reverse the operation to show how a number can be subtracted from the whole.
- Use models to demonstrate that the order in which numbers are subtracted changes the solution.
- Demonstrate understanding of the result of subtracting zero from a given quantity.
- Combine memorized facts with counting strategies to solve subtraction problems.

Materials to Gather

SUPPLIED

blocks – B (all colors)

blocks – O (all colors)

Checkpoint Practice activity page

▶ Advance Preparation

In this lesson, students will have an opportunity to review previous activities from the semester. Look at the suggested activities in Semester Review: Prepare for the Checkpoint online and be prepared to gather any needed materials.

SEMESTER REVIEW Look Back

ONLINE 20min

Objectives

- Review semester objectives.

This semester, students learned number concepts for numbers through 100. They also learned the concepts and strategies associated with addition and subtraction of basic facts with sums and minuends through 20. Students will review key concepts from the semester to prepare for the Semester Checkpoint.

To review, students will first play a Number Plunder game. Students should be able to recall all addition facts and subtraction facts they have learned in the semester. If they have not memorized the facts, they will have trouble playing Number Plunder successfully.

Students should play Addition Levels 1 and 2 and Subtraction Level 1. Pay special attention to the facts that students are not able to recall quickly. Help them review those facts with circle blocks and the addition and subtraction flash cards you created this semester. Note that students must use the arrow keys on the computer keyboard to control the Viking's movement in Number Plunder.

Students will then play a Super Genius game. If students answer a problem incorrectly, the correct answer will display. Be sure to help students understand why the answer is correct before students move on to the next problem. If they miss several problems, have students play the game again.

SEMESTER REVIEW Checkpoint Practice

OFFLINE 20min

Objectives

- Review semester objectives.

This activity has two parts.

PART 1

Give students the blocks.

1. **Say:** Use the circles to show how to add $5 + 10$.

   Students should make a group of 5 circles and a group of 10 circles and combine them to find the total of 15.

2. **Say:** Draw a picture to show 5 subtracted from 8.

   Drawings will vary. Accept reasonable drawings.

3. **Ask:** Show me $3 + 5$ and $5 + 3$ by using cubes. Are the results the same or different?

   Students should show by using cubes that $3 + 5$ is the same as $5 + 3$.

4. **Say:** Use circles to make a model for this number sentence: $5 + 5 = 10$.

   Students should arrange two groups of circles, one with 5 and the other with 5. They can then group the circles together to total 10 or count the circles and say there are 10 in all.

5. **Ask:** You look in a math book and see this number sentence: $3 + 1 = 2 + 2$. What does the equals symbol mean in that number sentence?

   Students should say that the equals symbol means that $3 + 1$ has the same value as $2 + 2$.

6. Place 9 red circles in a pile, 6 yellow circles in a pile, and 4 blue circles in a pile.

   Ask: Add the blue circles and the red circles together. Then add the yellow circles. How many circles do you have in all?
   ANSWER: 19

7. **Ask:** If you add the yellow and blue circles together first, and then add the red circles, will you get the same answer? Explain why or why not.

   Students should say they will get the same answer as when they added the blue and red circles first, and then the yellow ones, because no matter what order they add the numbers in, they will get the same answer.

8. **Say:** Use the circles to solve 8 take away 4.

   Students should put down 8 circles, and then take away 4 circles, and say there are 4 circles left.

9. **Ask:** Use 5 cubes of one color and 3 cubes of a different color to show how you can add 5 and 3 to make 8. What happens if you take away the 3 cubes of one color? How many cubes do you have left?

   Students should use the cubes to show how to combine the two groups of cubes to make 8. Students should then say that if they take away 3 cubes, they will be left with 5 cubes.

10. **Say:** Use cubes to show that $7 - 5$ is not the same as $5 - 7$.

    Students may first model 7 and take away 5, and then model 5 and show that they cannot take away 7.

11. **Say:** Gather 15 cubes. If you subtract 0 cubes, how many will you have left?
    ANSWER: 15

12. **Say:** Use a strategy you have learned, or math facts, to solve this problem. Then explain how you solved the problem. $18 - 5 = ?$
    ANSWER: 13.

    Students should explain how they solved the problem. Sample explanation: "I counted back 5 to find the difference."

13. **Ask:** What is the sum when you add any number to zero?
    ANSWER: The sum of any number and zero is always that number.

PART 2

Students will complete a Checkpoint Practice activity page to prepare for the Semester Checkpoint. If necessary, read the directions, problems, and answer choices to students. Have students answer the problems on their own. Carefully review the answers with students.

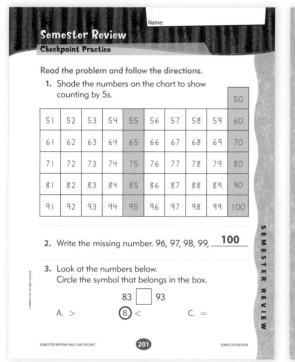

Name:

Semester Review

Checkpoint Practice

Read the problem and follow the directions.

1. Shade the numbers on the chart to show counting by 5s.

									50
51	52	53	54	55	56	57	58	59	60
61	62	63	64	65	66	67	68	69	70
71	72	73	74	75	76	77	78	79	80
81	82	83	84	85	86	87	88	89	90
91	92	93	94	95	96	97	98	99	100

2. Write the missing number. 96, 97, 98, 99, **100**

3. Look at the numbers below.
Circle the symbol that belongs in the box.

83 ☐ 93

A. >   B. <   C. =

SEMESTER REVIEW

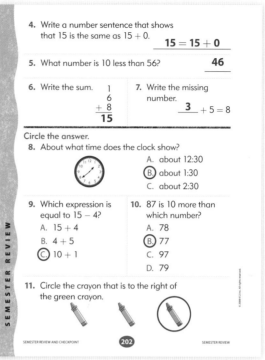

4. Write a number sentence that shows that 15 is the same as $15 + 0$.   **$15 = 15 + 0$**

5. What number is 10 less than 56?   **46**

6. Write the sum.
$$\begin{array}{r} 1 \\ 6 \\ + 8 \\ \hline 15 \end{array}$$

7. Write the missing number.
3 $+ 5 = 8$

Circle the answer.

8. About what time does the clock show?

A. about 12:30
B. about 1:30
C. about 2:30

9. Which expression is equal to $15 - 4$?
A. $15 + 4$
B. $4 + 5$
C. $10 + 1$

10. 87 is 10 more than which number?
A. 78
B. 77
C. 97
D. 79

11. Circle the crayon that is to the right of the green crayon.

SEMESTER REVIEW

→ SEMESTER REVIEW Prepare for the Checkpoint

What you do next depends on how students performed in the previous activity, Checkpoint Practice. If students had difficulty with any of the problems, complete the appropriate review activity listed in the table online.

Because there are many concepts to review, consider using the Your Choice day to continue preparing for the Semester Checkpoint.

Semester Checkpoint

SEMESTER CHECKPOINT Online	30 minutes	ONLINE
SEMESTER CHECKPOINT Offline	30 minutes	OFFLINE

▶ Semester Objectives

This lesson assesses the following objectives:

- Write numerals through 100.
- Count by 5s through 100.
- Use the symbols for less than, equal to, or greater than ($<, =, >$) to compare and order whole numbers through 100.
- Use concrete objects or sketches to model and solve addition or subtraction computation problems with sums and minuends up through 30.
- Recognize that the equals symbol shows an equality between two expressions.
- Use the equals symbol in number sentences to express equality.
- Demonstrate automatic recall of addition facts with sums through 20.
- Identify 10 more than or 10 less than a given number.
- Find the sum of three one-digit numbers, with sums through 20.
- Represent equivalent forms of the same number to 20 through the use of number expressions, such as $7 = 4 + 3$, or $5 + 2$, or $1 + 2 + 4$, or $9 - 2$, or $20 - 13$.
- Solve addition problems by filling in a missing number or numbers in a given number sentence.
- Demonstrate automatic recall of subtraction facts with minuends through 20.

Materials to Gather

SUPPLIED
Semester Checkpoint (printout)
blocks – B (all colors)

ALSO NEEDED
cups – 3

SEMESTER CHECKPOINT Online

ONLINE
30min

Objectives

- Assess semester objectives.

Students will complete this part of the Semester Checkpoint online. Read the directions, problems, and answers choices to students. If necessary, help students with keyboard or mouse operations.

SEMESTER CHECKPOINT Offline

OFFLINE
30min

Objectives

- Assess semester objectives.

Students will complete this part of the Semester Checkpoint offline. Students will take a performance-based assessment. Print the Semester Checkpoint. Read the directions, problems, and answer choices to students if necessary. Use the answer key to score the Checkpoint, and then enter the results online.

Gather the cups and blocks for Problems 4 and 7.

Name _____ Date _____

Semester Checkpoint Answer Key

Follow the instructions for each problem. Choose the response that best describes how the student performs on each task. When you have finished, enter the results online.

1. Say, "Write the number fifty-one."
(1 point)
Did the student write 51?

   A. Yes   B. No

2. Say, "Write the number ninety-eight."
(1 point)
Did the student write 98?

   A. Yes   B. No

3. Write the following on a sheet of paper: 50, 55, 60, _____, _____, 75
Say, "Write the missing numbers."
(1 point)
Did the student write 65, 70?

   A. Yes   B. No

4. Place three cups side by side on a sheet of paper with space between the cups. Draw a large + symbol between the first and second cups and a large = symbol between the second and third cups.
Say, "Use the circles and the cups to solve 12 + 13 = ___."

The student should put 12 circles into the first cup, and should put 13 circles into the second cup. Then the student should pour all circles from the first two cups into the last cup. The student should then count all the circles in last cup to find the answer: 25.
(1 point)
Did the student use the circles and cups to find that 12 + 13 = 25?

   A. Yes   B. No

Name _____ Date _____

5. Write "12 + 4 = _____" on a sheet of paper.
Say, "Make a sketch to solve the problem."

The student could draw 12 dots, then draw another 4 dots, and then count all the dots to find there are 16 in all.
(1 point)
Did the student make a sketch to find 12 + 4 = 16?

   A. Yes   B. No

6. Write "15 − 6 = _____" on a sheet of paper.
Say, "Make a sketch to solve the problem."

The student could draw 15 dots, then cross out 6 dots, and then count the dots left to find there are 9.
(1 point)
Did the student make a sketch to show 15 − 6 = 9?

   A. Yes   B. No

7. Write "20 − 4 = _____" on a sheet of paper.
Say, "Use circles to solve the problem."

The student could count out 20 circles, then take 4 circles away, and then count how many circles are left to find there are 16.
(1 point)
Did the student use circles to find 20 − 4 = 16?

   A. Yes   B. No

Name _____ Date _____

8. Say, "Write a number sentence that uses the numbers 10, 10, and 20, and the equals symbol."

Possible answers: 10 + 10 = 20, 20 = 10 + 10, 20 − 10 = 10, or 10 = 20 − 10.
(1 point)
Did the student write a number sentence by using 10, 10, and 20, and the equals symbol?

   A. Yes   B. No

9. Say, "Byron wrote the number 11 as 18 − 7. Using different numbers, show another way to write 11."

Possible answers: 12 − 1, 5 + 5 + 1, 5 + 6, 13 − 2, or 2 + 2 + 2 + 2 + 2 + 1.
(1 point)
Did the student show another reasonable way to write 11?

   A. Yes   B. No

10. Say, "Lola wrote the number 12 as 10 + 2. Using different numbers, show another way to write 12."

Possible answers: 8 + 4, 6 + 6, 7 + 5, 12 + 0, or 14 − 2.
(1 point)
Did the student show another reasonable way to write 12?

   A. Yes   B. No

Subtraction Number Sentences

▶ Unit Objectives

- Represent equivalent forms of the same number through the use of physical models such as tens rods and ones cubes through 20.

- Represent equivalent forms of the same number through the use of diagrams through 20.

- Represent equivalent forms of the same number to 20 through the use of number expressions, such as $7 = 4 + 3$, or $5 + 2$, or $1 + 2 + 4$.

- Solve subtraction problems by filling in a missing number in a given number sentence, such as $\underline{\ ?\ } = 5 - 4$, or $7 - 3 = \underline{\ ?\ }$, or $9 - \underline{\ ?\ } = 2$.

▶ Big Ideas

Models and mathematical symbols can represent addition and subtraction.

▶ Unit Introduction

Students will begin this unit by modeling and drawing the same number in different ways. They also will write different expressions for the same number. Then they will use various strategies to find the missing number in a subtraction number sentence. The missing number may be a difference or a subtrahend.

Same Number Different Ways

Skills Update	5 minutes	ONLINE
GET READY Egg Carton Models	10 minutes	OFFLINE
LEARN Make Models for Numbers	15 minutes	OFFLINE
LEARN Draw Pictures for Numbers	10 minutes	OFFLINE
LEARN Write Expressions for Numbers	10 minutes	OFFLINE
TRY IT Numbers Different Ways	10 minutes	OFFLINE

▶ Lesson Objectives

- Represent equivalent forms of the same number through the use of physical models such as tens rods and ones cubes through 20.
- Represent equivalent forms of the same number through the use of diagrams through 20.
- Represent equivalent forms of the same number to 20 through the use of number expressions, such as $7 = 4 + 3$, or $5 + 2$, or $1 + 2 + 4$.

▶ Prerequisite Skills

Use concrete objects or sketches to represent a quantity up through 30.

▶ Advance Preparation

Tie one end of the string around the middle of a pencil so that when students string the pasta, it will not fall off the end.

Number index cards 0 through 15, or gather the number cards you created previously.

▶ Safety

Supervise students to make sure they do not choke on small objects.

▶ Content Background

Students will represent a number using models, sketches, and expressions.

Materials to Gather

SUPPLIED

blocks – B (30 of any color)

blocks – O (red, blue)

Numbers Different Ways activity page

ALSO NEEDED

crayons

egg cartons – 3

index cards – 24

index cards – numbered 0 through 15

string or twine – 35-inch piece (stiff twine recommended)

uncooked pasta, tube-shaped – 20 of one size, 20 of another size

Keywords

expression – a number or a combination of numbers and symbols that represents a given value, such as $2 + 3$ or $10 - 4 + 1$

model (noun) – a physical object, diagram, or picture that represents an amount, an expression, an equation, or a problem situation

GET READY Egg Carton Models

Students will place blocks into the cups of egg cartons to model a given number.
  Gather the circle blocks and egg cartons. Open the egg cartons and place them in front of students.

- Use concrete objects or sketches to represent a quantity up through 30.

1. Put 1 circle into each cup of one egg carton and into 5 cups of another egg carton to model the number 17.

2. **Ask:** What number do the circles show?
   ANSWER: 17

   Say: Now it's your turn to show numbers using the circles and egg cartons.

3. **Say:** Show the number 25.

   Students should put 1 circle into each cup of two egg cartons. Then they should put 1 circle in the third carton.

4. Repeat Step 3 with the number 30.

LEARN Make Models for Numbers

Students will use pasta to show different ways to add and subtract to get the same number.
  Gather the pasta and string.

- Represent equivalent forms of the same number through the use of physical models such as tens rods and ones cubes through 20.

1. Put 10 large pieces of pasta on the string as you count. Then count as you put 2 small pieces of pasta on the string.

   Say: Now there are 12 pieces in all. $10 + 2 = 12$. This model is one way to show 12.

2. **Say:** I can also subtract to show 12. To make a subtraction model, I need to think of a subtraction fact that equals 12. Or I can start with a number greater than 12 and count back until I reach 12. Let's start with 17.

3. Put 17 pieces of large pasta on the string. Count back "16, 15, 14, 13, 12" as you take away 5 pieces.

   Say: Now there are 12 pieces left on the string. I took away 5 pieces. $17 - 5 = 12$. My model shows 12.

4. Have students show 12 using a different subtraction fact. If they've memorized a subtraction fact, they can use both sizes of pasta. For example, to show $14 - 2 = 12$, they should put 12 pieces of large pasta and 2 pieces of small pasta on the string. Then they should take away the 2 small pieces to leave 12.

   If they cannot think of a subtraction fact, have them pick a number greater than 12 and put that many pieces of large pasta on the string. Then have them count back as they remove pieces until only 12 are left on the string. Ask them to count how many pieces they removed. Have them tell you the subtraction fact they showed.

5. Have students show and explain addition and subtraction models for the numbers 7 and 14.

Tips

If you wish, use two different colors or shapes of pasta, two different sizes or colors of beads, and so on.

LEARN Draw Pictures for Numbers

Students will draw different pictures to represent numbers. They will draw four sets of two pictures each.

Gather the crayons.

1. Remind students that addition and subtraction are ways to show a number. They can show addition and subtraction by drawing simple objects. They can cross out objects, pair and circle objects, or shade objects to show subtraction.

2. Give students two sheets of paper. Have them fold each sheet into fourths so that there are four sections on the front and four on the back.

3. On one of the sheets, have students write the number 7 at the top of two sections.

4. Have students draw one addition and one subtraction picture to show 7. For the addition picture, they might draw a group of 3 triangles and a group of 4 stars, and circle both groups to show combining. For the subtraction picture, they might draw 9 squares and cross out 2 squares.

5. Repeat Steps 3 and 4 for the numbers 4, 12, and 9. As students work, suggest that they ask themselves the following questions:

   • In my subtraction picture, do I start with a number of objects that is greater than the number I am trying to show?

   • In my addition picture, do I start with a number of objects that is less than the number I am trying to show?

   • How many shall I take away to show the number?

   • How many shall I add to show the number?

   • Does my picture show the correct number?

Objectives

• Represent equivalent forms of the same number through the use of diagrams through 20.

Tips

Remind students to use simple shapes for sketches. They may use color to distinguish the groups being added or subtracted.

LEARN Write Expressions for Numbers

Students will write addition and subtraction expressions to represent numbers. Then they will play a game of concentration to match expressions that equal the same number.

Gather the number cards and blank index cards.

1. Show the 5 card and ask students to think of subtraction and addition expressions that equal 5. As an example, write $11 - 6$ on a blank index card.

2. Have students write two subtraction expressions and one addition expression for 5 on separate blank index cards.

3. Set the 5 card aside. Shuffle and fan out the remaining number cards upside down.

4. Repeat the process, having students pick five more cards and make four expression (index) cards for each number. Students should include only one addition expression for each number.

5. **Say:** Now we are going to use the 24 expression cards you made to play a game of concentration.

6. Mix the expression cards and place them face down in four rows of six each.

Objectives

• Represent equivalent forms of the same number to 20 through the use of number expressions, such as $7 = 4 + 3$, or $5 + 2$, or $1 + 2 + 4$.

7. Students should turn over two cards, looking for a pair of equal expressions. If the expressions are equal, they should take the pair. If not, they should turn the cards over again.

8. **Say:** I am going to check your cards and you check mine. If one of us catches the other taking an incorrect match, we get to take that pair!

9. Check students' work as you play and have them check yours. Take a pair that is not correct at least once to have students catch your mistake.

OFFLINE
10 min

TRY IT Numbers Different Ways

Students will practice showing numbers different ways. Give students the cubes and Numbers Different Ways activity page from their Activity Book. Read the directions with them.

Objectives

- Represent equivalent forms of the same number through the use of physical models such as tens rods and ones cubes through 20.

- Represent equivalent forms of the same number through the use of diagrams through 20.

- Represent equivalent forms of the same number to 20 through the use of number expressions, such as $7 = 4 + 3$, or $5 + 2$, or $1 + 2 + 4$.

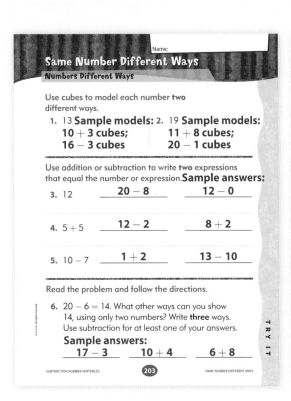

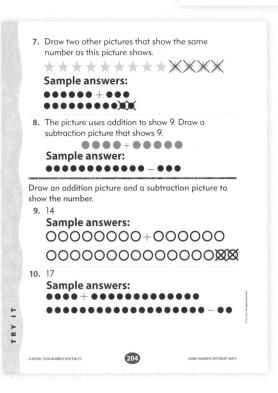

Represent Numbers Different Ways

Lesson Overview

Skills Update	5 minutes	ONLINE
GET READY Draw to Show Numbers	10 minutes	OFFLINE
LEARN Different Ways to Show Numbers	15 minutes	OFFLINE
LEARN Show a Number Three Ways	10 minutes	OFFLINE
TRY IT Show Numbers Different Ways	10 minutes	OFFLINE
CHECKPOINT	10 minutes	OFFLINE

▶ Lesson Objectives
- Represent equivalent forms of the same number through the use of physical models such as tens rods and ones cubes through 20.
- Represent equivalent forms of the same number through the use of diagrams through 20.
- Represent equivalent forms of the same number to 20 through the use of number expressions, such as $7 = 4 + 3$, or $5 + 2$, or $1 + 2 + 4$.

▶ Prerequisite Skills
Use concrete objects or sketches to represent a quantity up through 30.

▶ Advance Preparation
Tie one end of the string around the middle of a pencil so that when students string the pasta, it will not fall off the end.

▶ Safety
Supervise students to make sure they do not choke on small objects.

▶ Content Background
Students will continue to represent a number using models, sketches, and expressions.

Keywords	
	represent – to symbolize or stand for something else

Materials to Gather

SUPPLIED

blocks – B (20 of any color)

blocks – O (red, blue)

Show a Number Three Ways activity page

Show Numbers Different Ways activity page

Checkpoint (printout)

ALSO NEEDED

crayons

egg carton

string or twine – 35-inch piece (stiff twine recommended)

uncooked pasta, tube-shaped – 20 of one size, 20 of another size

GET READY Draw to Show Numbers

Students will draw pictures to show numbers.
  Gather the crayons.

1. Write 18 on a sheet of paper. Ask students to read the number.
  Say: Now I will draw a picture to show this number.

2. Draw 18 triangles in one row.

    Say: I drew 18 triangles. So my picture shows 18.

3. Have students count to check that your picture shows 18.

    Say: I used triangles to show the amount, but I could have used any shape. I drew my shapes in a line, but I could have drawn them in any way. For example, I could have drawn 3 rows of 6.

4. **Say:** Now it's your turn to draw to show a number. Draw two other pictures that each show 18. Your pictures should be different from each other and different from mine.

Objectives

- Use concrete objects or sketches to represent a quantity up through 30.

Tips

Remind students to use simple shapes for sketches.

LEARN Different Ways to Show Numbers

Students will represent numbers in three different ways—with models, pictures, and expressions. They will also represent the same number with equal expressions. Encourage students to use subtraction, rather than addition, for most expressions.
  Gather the crayons, circle blocks, cubes, egg carton, string, and pasta.

1. Display the egg carton. Put 1 circle each into 10 of the cups, counting the circles as you place them. Take out 2 of the circles, counting back "9, 8" as you remove them.

    Ask students what number you showed. (8)

2. Have students make a different model to show 8 using the same expression as you used in your model. They may use any of the available materials. (Students may make a train of 10 cubes and remove 2 cubes.)

3. Have students draw a picture to show 8 using the same expression. (Students may draw 10 stars and cross out 2.)

4. Have students write the expression shown by the models and picture. $(10 - 2)$

5. Have students draw a picture that shows 8 using an expression other than $10 - 2$.

6. Have students write an expression, other than $10 - 2$ and the expression they used for their picture in Step 5, that equals 8.

7. Draw a column of 16 dots. To the right of the column, draw a column of 5 dots. Pair the 5 dots with five of the 16 dots. Circle the 11 dots that aren't paired.

    Ask students what number you showed. (11)

8. Have students make a different picture to show 11 using the same expression as you used in your picture. (Students may draw 16 hearts and cross out 5.)

Objectives

- Represent equivalent forms of the same number through the use of physical models such as tens rods and ones cubes through 20.

- Represent equivalent forms of the same number through the use of diagrams through 20.

- Represent equivalent forms of the same number to 20 through the use of number expressions, such as $7 = 4 + 3$, or $5 + 2$, or $1 + 2 + 4$.

Tips

If you wish, provide any reasonable household items for students to use for their models. Examples include buttons, erasers, and dry beans.

9. Have students make a model to show 11 using the same expression. (Students may make a group of 16 circles and take away 5.)

10. Have students write the expression shown by the pictures and model. (16 − 5)

11. Have students make a model, picture, and expression to show three different ways to make 11. Only one way should use addition.

    (Students may string 20 pieces of pasta and take away 9, draw 12 triangles and cross out 1, and write the expression 15 − 4.)

LEARN Show a Number Three Ways

OFFLINE 10 min

Students will represent numbers in three different ways—with models, pictures, and expressions. Give students the cubes and Show a Number Three Ways activity page from their Activity Book. Read the directions with them.

Instruct students to use a different expression for each model. For example, to show 6, they might make a model of 3 red cubes and 3 blue cubes, a picture of 11 circles with 5 crossed out, and the expression 9 − 3.

Objectives

- Represent equivalent forms of the same number through the use of physical models such as tens rods and ones cubes through 20.
- Represent equivalent forms of the same number through the use of diagrams through 20.
- Represent equivalent forms of the same number to 20 through the use of number expressions, such as $7 = 4 + 3$, or $5 + 2$, or $1 + 2 + 4$.

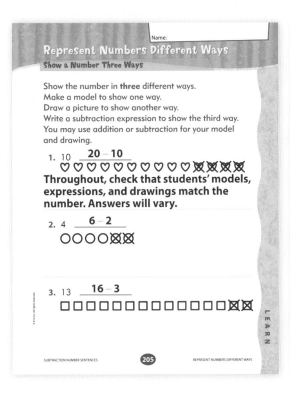

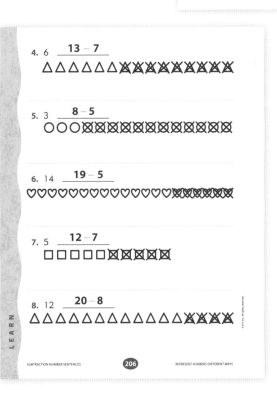

TRY IT Show Numbers Different Ways

Objectives

Students will practice representing numbers in three different ways—with models, pictures, and expressions. Give students the cubes and Show Numbers Different Ways activity page from their Activity Book. Read the directions with them.

- Represent equivalent forms of the same number through the use of physical models such as tens rods and ones cubes through 20.

- Represent equivalent forms of the same number through the use of diagrams through 20.

- Represent equivalent forms of the same number to 20 through the use of number expressions, such as $7 = 4 + 3$, or $5 + 2$, or $1 + 2 + 4$.

Name: _____

Represent Numbers Different Ways

Show Numbers Different Ways

Read the problem and follow the directions.

1. Use cubes to make a model to show the same number as the picture shows. Then write an expression to show the same number.

♥ ♥ ♥ ♥ ♥ ♥ ♥ ♥ ♥ ♥ ✕ ✕ ✕ ✕ _____

Model and expression should show 14.

2. $19 - 5$ is equal to 14.
Write **three** other expressions that show 14.

Sample answers: $15 - 1, 5 + 5 + 4, 5 + 9, 16 - 2, 2 + 2 + 2 + 2 + 2 + 2 + 2$

3. The picture uses subtraction to show 5.
Draw a different subtraction picture that shows 5.

● ● ● ● ● ✕ ✕ ✕ ✕

Sample answer:

○ ○ ○ ○ ○ ✕ ✕ ✕ ✕ ✕

TRY IT

Make a model, draw a picture, and write an expression to show the number. Only one of the three ways should use addition.

4. 16 _____ **Check students' models, pictures, and expressions.**

5. 19 _____

Circle the answer.

6. Which shows the same number as this picture?

▧ ▧ ▧ ▧

A. ▧ ▧ ▧ ✕ ✕ ✕ ✕

B. ▧ ▧ ▧ ✕ ✕ ✕ ✕ ✕ ✕

C. ▧ ▧ ▧ ▧ ▧ ▧ ▧ ✕ ✕ ✕ ✕

Ⓓ ▧ ▧ ▧ ▧ ✕ ✕ ✕ ✕ ✕ ✕

7. Which expression equals $17 - 4$?

A. $17 + 4$

B. $4 + 7$

Ⓒ $12 + 1$

TRY IT

CHECKPOINT

Print the Checkpoint. In Part 1, students will take a performance-based assessment. In Part 2, students will complete the problems on their own. Read the directions, problems, and answer choices to students, if necessary. Use the answer key to score the Checkpoint, and then enter the results online.

Give the circle blocks to students for Problem 1.

- Represent equivalent forms of the same number through the use of physical models such as tens rods and ones cubes through 20.

- Represent equivalent forms of the same number through the use of diagrams through 20.

- Represent equivalent forms of the same number to 20 through the use of number expressions, such as $7 = 4 + 3$, or $5 + 2$, or $1 + 2 + 4$.

Name _____ Date _____

Checkpoint Answer Key

Follow the instructions for each item. Choose the response that best describes how the student performs on the task. When you have finished, enter the results online.

Part 1

Give students 20 circles.

1. Put 4 circles in a row and 5 in a second row. Say, "This is one way to show the number 9. Use the circles to show the number 9 another way, using subtraction."
(1 point)
   Did the student show another way to model the number 9, using subtraction?

   A. Yes   B. No

2. Write $7 - 3 = 4$ on a sheet of paper and say, "Write three other expressions that show 4. One of your expressions must use subtraction."
(1 point)
   Did the student write another way to show 4, using subtraction?

   A. Yes   B. No
(1 point)
   Did the student write another way to show 4, using subtraction or addition?

   A. Yes   B. No
(1 point)
   Did the student write another way to show 4, using subtraction or addition?

   A. Yes   B. No

Give students Part 2 of the Checkpoint.

1 of 2

Name _____ Date _____

Part 2

Circle the answer.
(1 point)
3. Which shows the same number as the picture?

   A.

   B.

   C.

   (D).

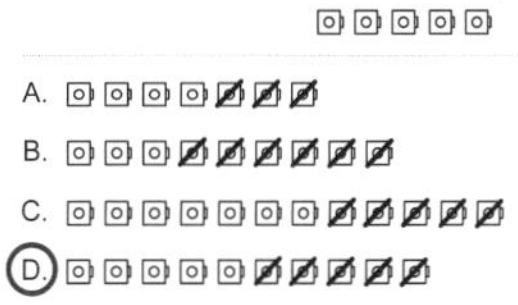

(1 point)
4. This picture uses subtraction to show 13. Which other picture also shows 13?

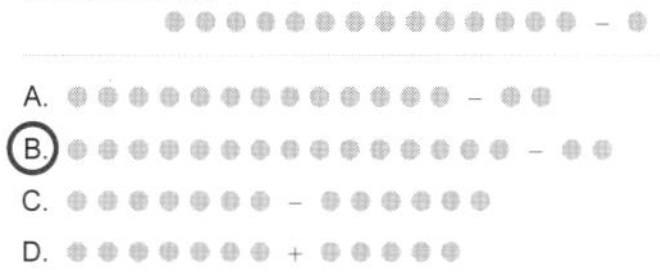

   A.

   (B).

   C.

   D.

(1 point)
5. Which picture shows the same number as the picture below?

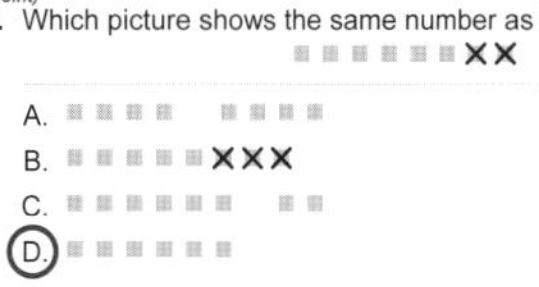

   A.

   B.

   C.

   (D).

2 of 2

Missing Parts in Subtraction Sentences

Lesson Overview

Skills Update	5 minutes	ONLINE
GET READY Model and Draw Subtraction	10 minutes	OFFLINE
LEARN Model Missing Number Problems	15 minutes	OFFLINE
LEARN Find the Missing Bears	15 minutes	OFFLINE
TRY IT What Number Is Missing?	15 minutes	OFFLINE

▶ Lesson Objectives

Solve subtraction problems by filling in a missing number in a given number sentence, such as ___ = 5 − 4, or 7 − 3 = ___, or 9 − ___ = 2.

▶ Prerequisite Skills

Use concrete objects or sketches to model and solve addition or subtraction problems with sums and minuends up through 30.

▶ Common Errors and Misconceptions

Students might not be familiar with number sentences of the form 2 + ___ = 3. They might see the plus symbol and mistakenly add 2 and 3.

▶ Advance Preparation

Make index cards with the following partial subtraction number sentences, one on each card:

- 8 − 5 = ___
- 13 − ___ = 9
- 8 − ___ = 5
- 9 − 7 = ___
- 13 − 4 = ___
- 9 − ___ = 7
- 13 − ___ = 4
- 9 − ___ = 2

▶ Content Background

The three parts of a subtraction sentence are the *minuend*, the *subtrahend*, and the *difference*. The number students are subtracting from is the minuend. The number they are subtracting is the subtrahend. The answer is the difference.

4	−	1	=	3
↓		↓		↓
minuend		subtrahend		difference

The term *difference* is used with students and by students, but the terms *minuend* and *subtrahend* will not be formally introduced to students at this time.

Materials to Gather

SUPPLIED

blocks – B (blue, yellow)

What Number Is Missing? activity page

ALSO NEEDED

index cards – labeled with subtraction number sentences

paper, construction – 1 green sheet

household objects – 2 egg cartons, 1 plastic cup

In the subtraction problems students have solved, the missing number was the difference. However, you can also write a subtraction number sentence with a missing subtrahend, for example $6 - ? = 4$. In this lesson, students will find a missing difference as well as a missing subtrahend in subtraction sentences.

Keywords	**difference** – the solution to a subtraction problem **minuend** – in subtraction, the quantity or number from which another number is subtracted; 8 is the minuend in the problem $8 - 7 = ?$ **subtraction sentence** – a number sentence that involves subtraction only and uses symbols and numbers, such as $8 - 3 = 5$ **subtrahend** – the number that is subtracted in a subtraction problem; 7 is the subtrahend in the problem $8 - 7 = ?$

GET READY Model and Draw Subtraction

OFFLINE
10min

Objectives

- Use concrete objects or sketches to model and solve addition or subtraction problems with sums and minuends up through 30.

Students will model and then write subtraction number sentences.
  Gather the circle blocks and cup.

1. Tell students they will use circles to model subtraction sentences.

2. Place 14 circles in the cup, and tell students how many you placed.

   Say: Take out 3 circles. How many circles are left in the cup?
   ANSWER: 11

   Ask: What is 14 minus 3?
   ANSWER: 11

3. Have students write the matching subtraction sentence. ($14 - 3 = 11$)

4. Repeat Steps 2 and 3 for 20 minus 5.

5. Tell students they will now use drawings to model subtraction sentences.

6. Have students draw 12 shapes and cross out 4 of them.

   Ask: What subtraction problem does your drawing show?
   ANSWER: 12 minus 4

   Ask: What is 12 minus 4?
   ANSWER: 8

7. Have students write the matching subtraction sentence. ($12 - 4 = 8$)

8. Repeat Steps 6 and 7 for 14 minus 7.

9. If time allows, give students more subtraction sentences to model and write.

LEARN Model Missing Number Problems

Students will learn how to find the missing number in a subtraction sentence by counting items in an egg carton. The missing number will be either the difference or the subtrahend, which is the number being subtracted.

Gather the circle blocks and egg cartons. Open the egg cartons and place them in front of students.

DIFFERENCE

1. Have students write the number sentence $9 − 7 =$ ___. Point out that the missing number is the difference.

2. **Say:** Let's model this problem to find the missing number. Place 9 circles in the egg carton—1 circle per cup.

3. Turn the egg carton to face you, lid up, so students cannot see inside it. Remove 7 circles and display them. Close the lid.

4. **Ask:** We need to find the difference. The difference is the number of circles left in the carton. We started with 9 circles, and I took out 7. How many circles are left?
   ANSWER: 2

5. Have students open the lid and count to check their answer. Then have them write the answer in the number sentence.

6. Repeat Steps 1–5 with $18 − 10 =$ ___.

SUBTRAHEND

7. Have students write the number sentence $12 −$ ___ $= 5$. Point out that the missing number is the number being subtracted.

8. **Say:** Place 12 circles in the egg carton. Now hide your eyes while I take out some of the circles.

9. Take out 7 circles and hide them in your hand.

10. Show students the carton.
    Ask: We started with 12 circles. I took some away. There are 5 circles left. How many did I take away?
    ANSWER: 7

11. Have students count the circles in your hand to check their answer. Then have them write the answer in the number sentence.

12. Repeat Steps 7–11 with $19 −$ ___ $= 11$.

13. Have students model and solve the following problems:

    - $12 −$ ___ $= 3$ (9)
    - $15 − 8 =$ ___   (7)
    - $9 = 15 −$ ___   (6)
    - ___ $= 17 − 11$ (6)
    - $13 = 15 −$ ___   (2)
    - $20 −$ ___ $= 8$ (12)

LEARN Find the Missing Bears

OFFLINE 15 min

Students will use models to find missing numbers in subtraction sentences and story problems.

Gather the circle blocks, construction paper, cup, and index cards you prepared.

DIFFERENCE

1. Write $10 - 6 = $ ___. Explain that students will use circles to model this problem and find the difference. Put 10 circles on the paper and ask how many circles need to be taken away. (6) Take away 6 circles and put them in the cup.

2. **Say:** The circles on the paper represent the difference. Write the difference in the subtraction sentence.
   ANSWER: 4

SUBTRAHEND

3. Write $8 - $ ___ $ = 3$. Ask students how many circles they should put on the paper to model the problem. (8) Have them put 8 circles on the paper.

4. **Say:** The difference in this problem is 3. Three circles will be left after some number is taken away.

5. Have students take away circles one at a time and put them into the cup until there are only 3 circles left on the paper.

6. **Ask:** There were 8 circles on the paper, and now there are only 3. How many circles did you take away and put into the cup?
   ANSWER: 5

7. Have students write 5 to complete the subtraction sentence.

8. Give students the index cards and have them solve the problems. Students may model the problems if they choose.

STORY PROBLEMS

Read these story problems to students one at a time. Ask them to model and solve the problem, using the circles, paper, and cup. Then ask them to write a number sentence for the problem.

Explain that the circles can represent bears, the paper can represent grass, and the cup can represent a cave.

Story Problem 1
There are 9 bears outside a cave on the grass.
Some bears go into the cave.
There are 5 bears left outside on the grass.
How many bears went into the cave?

Story Problem 2
There are 14 bears outside a cave on the grass.
Some bears go into the cave.
There are 8 bears left outside on the grass.
How many bears went into the cave?

If students are ready for a challenge, have them make up and model a story problem about bears in a cave. Then have them write the number sentence for the problem.

Objectives

- Solve subtraction problems by filling in a missing number in a given number sentence, such as ___ $= 5 - 4$, or $7 - 3 = $ ___, or $9 - $ ___ $= 2$.

Tips

Write subtraction strategies on index cards and use them to remind students of different ways to find the missing number in a subtraction sentence.

TRY IT What Number Is Missing?

Students will practice finding the missing difference or subtrahend in subtraction sentences. Give students the What Number Is Missing activity page from their Activity Book and read the directions with them.

Students may model the problems if they choose.

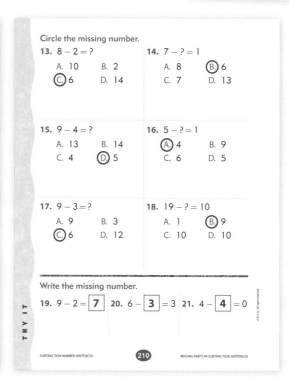

Name: _____

Missing Parts in Subtraction Sentences
What Number Is Missing?

Write the missing number.

1. $13 - 6 = \underline{7}$ 2. $9 - \underline{3} = 6$

3. $12 - 3 = \underline{9}$ 4. $18 - 4 = \underline{14}$

5. $20 - \underline{6} = 14$ 6. $17 - \underline{4} = 13$

7. $6 - \underline{4} = 2$ 8. $14 - 5 = \underline{9}$

9. $16 - \underline{7} = 9$ 10. $14 - \underline{3} = 11$

11. $11 - \underline{6} = 5$ 12. $12 - \underline{5} = 7$

SUBTRACTION NUMBER SENTENCES   209   MISSING PARTS IN SUBTRACTION SENTENCES

TRY IT

Circle the missing number.

13. $8 - 2 = ?$
 A. 10   B. 2
 C. 6   D. 14

14. $7 - ? = 1$
 A. 8   B. 6
 C. 7   D. 13

15. $9 - 4 = ?$
 A. 13   B. 14
 C. 4   D. 5

16. $5 - ? = 1$
 A. 4   B. 9
 C. 6   D. 5

17. $9 - 3 = ?$
 A. 9   B. 3
 C. 6   D. 12

18. $19 - ? = 10$
 A. 1   B. 9
 C. 10   D. 10

Write the missing number.

19. $9 - 2 = \boxed{7}$ 20. $6 - \boxed{3} = 3$ 21. $4 - \boxed{4} = 0$

SUBTRACTION NUMBER SENTENCES   210   MISSING PARTS IN SUBTRACTION SENTENCES

Subtract with Missing Numbers

Lesson Overview

Skills Update	5 minutes	ONLINE
GET READY Subtraction Models	5 minutes	ONLINE
LEARN Shopping Subtraction	15 minutes	ONLINE
LEARN In the Bag	15 minutes	ONLINE
TRY IT Missing Numbers	10 minutes	OFFLINE
CHECKPOINT	10 minutes	OFFLINE

▶ Lesson Objectives

Solve subtraction problems by filling in a missing number in a given number sentence, such as $\underline{?} = 5 - 4$, or $7 - 3 = \underline{?}$, or $9 - \underline{?} = 2$.

▶ Prerequisite Skills

Use concrete objects or sketches to model and solve addition or subtraction problems with sums and minuends up through 30.

▶ Common Errors and Misconceptions

Students might not be familiar with number sentences of the form $2 + \underline{?} = 3$. They might see the plus symbol and mistakenly add 2 and 3.

▶ Content Background

Students will learn how to find a missing number in a subtraction problem.

Materials to Gather

SUPPLIED
Missing Numbers activity page
Checkpoint (printout)

Keywords	**number sentence** – two expressions related by an equals symbol ($=$), a not-equal-to symbol ($\neq$), or an inequality symbol; for example, $7 - 2 = 4 + 1$; $5 \neq 4 + 4$; $6 + 2 > 1 + 4$

GET READY Subtraction Models

ONLINE 5 min

Students will solve a subtraction problem. They will learn how to model the subtraction problem two ways, with circle blocks and with sketches.

Objectives

- Use concrete objects and sketches to model and solve addition or subtraction problems with sums and minuends up through 30.

LEARN Shopping Subtraction

Students will drag produce onto the table to help them find the missing numbers in the subtraction sentences.

Objectives

- Solve subtraction problems by filling in a missing number in a given number sentence, such as $\underline{\ ?\ } = 5 - 4$, or $7 - 3 = \underline{\ ?\ }$, or $9 - \underline{\ ?\ } = 2$.

Tips

Allow students to use pencil and paper to help solve the subtraction problems.

LEARN In the Bag

Students will travel to the bakery, where a baker is filling muffin orders. The baker has taken some muffins from each batch and put them in a bag. Students will complete a subtraction sentence to determine how many muffins were in each batch.

If students have difficulty, encourage them to ask themselves the following questions:

- Can I use the zero rule?
- Can I use a related addition or subtraction fact?
- Can I count back?

Objectives

- Solve subtraction problems by filling in a missing number in a given number sentence, such as $\underline{\ ?\ } = 5 - 4$, or $7 - 3 = \underline{\ ?\ }$, or $9 - \underline{\ ?\ } = 2$.

TRY IT Missing Numbers

Students will practice finding the missing number in subtraction sentences. Give students the Missing Numbers activity page from their Activity Book and read the directions with them.

If students have difficulty, they may model the problems with circle blocks or sketches.

Objectives

- Solve subtraction problems by filling in a missing number in a given number sentence, such as $\underline{\ ?\ } = 5 - 4$, or $7 - 3 = \underline{\ ?\ }$, or $9 - \underline{\ ?\ } = 2$.

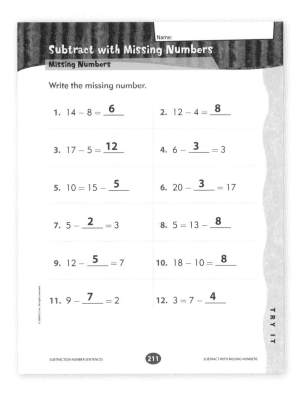

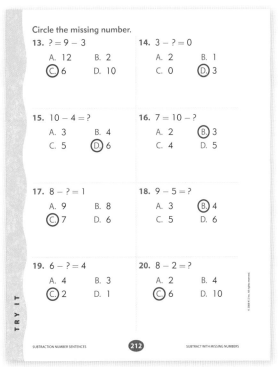

Subtract with Missing Numbers

Missing Numbers

Write the missing number.

1. $14 - 8 = \underline{6}$

2. $12 - 4 = \underline{8}$

3. $17 - 5 = \underline{12}$

4. $6 - \underline{3} = 3$

5. $10 = 15 - \underline{5}$

6. $20 - \underline{3} = 17$

7. $5 - \underline{2} = 3$

8. $5 = 13 - \underline{8}$

9. $12 - \underline{5} = 7$

10. $18 - 10 = \underline{8}$

11. $9 - \underline{7} = 2$

12. $3 = 7 - \underline{4}$

T R Y   I T

Circle the missing number.

13. $? = 9 - 3$

   A. 12   B. 2

   Ⓒ 6   D. 10

14. $3 - ? = 0$

   A. 2   B. 1

   C. 0   Ⓓ 3

15. $10 - 4 = ?$

   A. 3   B. 4

   C. 5   Ⓓ 6

16. $7 = 10 - ?$

   A. 2   Ⓑ 3

   C. 4   D. 5

17. $8 - ? = 1$

   A. 9   B. 8

   Ⓒ 7   D. 6

18. $9 - 5 = ?$

   A. 3   Ⓑ 4

   C. 5   D. 6

19. $6 - ? = 4$

   A. 4   B. 3

   Ⓒ 2   D. 1

20. $8 - 2 = ?$

   A. 2   B. 4

   Ⓒ 6   D. 10

T R Y   I T

OFFLINE
10min

CHECKPOINT

Objectives

Print the Checkpoint and have students complete it on their own. Read the directions, problems, and answer choices to students, if necessary. Use the answer key to score the Checkpoint, and then enter the results online.

- Solve subtraction problems by filling in a missing number in a given number sentence, such as $\underline{?} = 5 - 4$, or $7 - 3 = \underline{?}$, or $9 - \underline{?} = 2$.

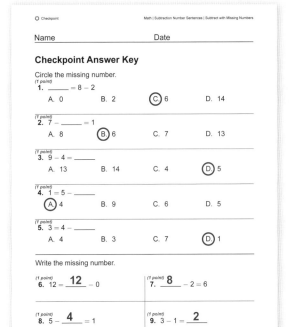

Checkpoint   Math | Subtraction Number Sentences | Subtract with Missing Numbers

Name _____   Date _____

Checkpoint Answer Key

Circle the missing number.

(1 point)
1. $\underline{\quad} = 8 - 2$

   A. 0   B. 2   Ⓒ 6   D. 14

(1 point)
2. $7 - \underline{\quad} = 1$

   A. 8   Ⓑ 6   C. 7   D. 13

(1 point)
3. $9 - 4 = \underline{\quad}$

   A. 13   B. 14   C. 4   Ⓓ 5

(1 point)
4. $1 = 5 - \underline{\quad}$

   Ⓐ 4   B. 9   C. 6   D. 5

(1 point)
5. $3 = 4 - \underline{\quad}$

   A. 4   B. 3   C. 7   Ⓓ 1

Write the missing number.

(1 point)
6. $12 = \underline{12} - 0$

(1 point)
7. $\underline{8} - 2 = 6$

(1 point)
8. $5 - \underline{4} = 1$

(1 point)
9. $3 - 1 = \underline{2}$

1 of 1

Unit Review

Lesson Overview

UNIT REVIEW Look Back	20 minutes	**ONLINE**
UNIT REVIEW Checkpoint Practice	20 minutes	**OFFLINE**
▶ **UNIT REVIEW** Prepare for the Checkpoint		

▶ Unit Objectives

This lesson reviews the following objectives:

- Represent equivalent forms of the same number through the use of physical models such as tens rods and ones cubes through 20.
- Represent equivalent forms of the same number through the use of diagrams through 20.
- Represent equivalent forms of the same number to 20 through the use of number expressions, such as $7 = 4 + 3$, or $5 + 2$, or $1 + 2 + 4$.
- Solve subtraction problems by filling in a missing number in a given number sentence, such as $\underline{\ ?\ } = 5 - 4$, or $7 - 3 = \underline{\ ?\ }$, or $9 - \underline{\ ?\ } = 2$.

Materials to Gather

SUPPLIED

blocks – O (green, blue)

Checkpoint Practice activity page

▶ Advance Preparation

In this lesson, students will have an opportunity to review previous activities in the Subtraction Number Sentences unit. Look at the suggested activities in Unit Review: Prepare for the Checkpoint online and gather any needed materials.

Keywords	difference	number sentence
	expression	represent
	minuend	subtraction sentence
	model (noun)	subtrahend

UNIT REVIEW Look Back

ONLINE 20 min

Objectives

- Review unit objectives.

Students learned how to express the same number in different ways. Then they found the missing number in subtraction sentences. Students will review these concepts to prepare for the Unit Checkpoint.

UNIT REVIEW Checkpoint Practice

OFFLINE 20 min

Objectives

- Review unit objectives.

Students will complete a Checkpoint Practice activity page to prepare for the Unit Checkpoint. If necessary, read the directions, problems, and answer choices to students. Have students answer the problems on their own. Carefully review the answers with students. Give students the cubes for Problems 1–3, 9, and 10.

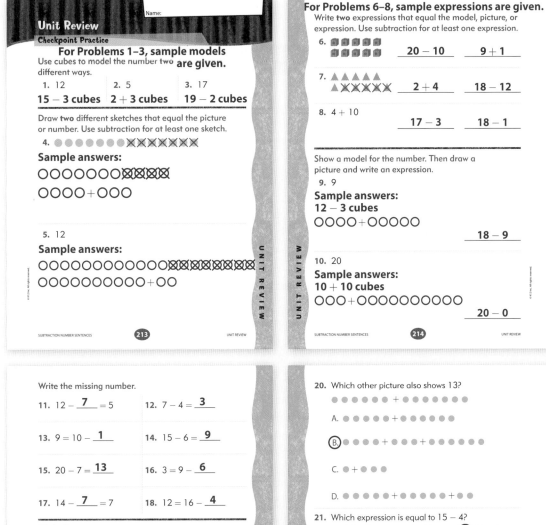

Unit Review

Checkpoint Practice

Name: _____

For Problems 1–3, sample models are given.

Use cubes to model the number two different ways.

1. 12
15 − 3 cubes

2. 5
2 + 3 cubes

3. 17
19 − 2 cubes

Draw **two** different sketches that equal the picture or number. Use subtraction for at least one sketch.

4. ●●●●●●●●●✕✕✕✕✕✕✕

Sample answers:

○○○○○○○⊠⊠⊠⊠

○○○○ + ○○○

5. 12

Sample answers:

○○○○○○○○○○○○○⊠⊠⊠⊠⊠⊠

○○○○○○○○○○ + ○○

For Problems 6–8, sample expressions are given.

Write **two** expressions that equal the model, picture, or expression. Use subtraction for at least one expression.

6. ▦▦▦▦▦
▦▦▦▦▦   20 − 10   9 + 1

7. ▲▲▲▲▲
▲✕✕✕✕✕   2 + 4   18 − 12

8. 4 + 10
17 − 3   18 − 1

Show a model for the number. Then draw a picture and write an expression.

9. 9

Sample answers:

12 − 3 cubes

○○○○ + ○○○○○

18 − 9

10. 20

Sample answers:

10 + 10 cubes

○○○ + ○○○○○○○○○○

20 − 0

Write the missing number.

11. 12 − **7** = 5

12. 7 − 4 = **3**

13. 9 = 10 − **1**

14. 15 − 6 = **9**

15. 20 − 7 = **13**

16. 3 = 9 − **6**

17. 14 − **7** = 7

18. 12 = 16 − **4**

Circle the answer.

19. Which shows the same number as the picture?
▦▦▦▦▦▦▦▦▦

A. ▦▦▦▦▦
▦▦▦▦ − ▦

B. ▦▦▦▦▦
▦▦▦▦▦ − ▦▦

C. ▦▦▦▦▦
▦▦▦▦▦ − ▦▦

D. ▦▦▦▦▦ ▦▦
▦▦▦▦▦ ▦▦

(A is circled)

20. Which other picture also shows 13?
●●●●●●● + ●●●●●●

A. ●●●●● + ●●●●●●●

B. ●●●●● + ●●● + ●●●●●● (B is circled)

C. ● + ●●●

D. ●●●●●● + ●●●●● + ●●

21. Which expression is equal to 15 − 4?
A. 15 + 4   B. 4 + 5   C. 10 + 1 (C is circled)

Read the problem and follow the directions.

22. 9 − 4 = 5. Using different numbers, show another way to write 5.
Sample answer: 16 − 11 = 5

Write or circle the missing number.

23. 9 = 11 − **2**

24. 8 − 2 = ?
A. 8   B. 6 (B is circled)   C. 2

⇥ UNIT REVIEW Prepare for the Checkpoint

What you do next depends on how students performed in the previous activity, Unit Review: Checkpoint Practice. If students had difficulty with any of the problems, complete the appropriate review activity listed in the table online.

Unit Checkpoint

UNIT CHECKPOINT Offline   60 minutes   **OFFLINE**

▶ Unit Objectives

This lesson assesses the following objectives:

- Represent equivalent forms of the same number through the use of physical models such as tens rods and ones cubes through 20.

- Represent equivalent forms of the same number through the use of diagrams through 20.

- Represent equivalent forms of the same number to 20 through the use of number expressions, such as $7 = 4 + 3$, or $5 + 2$, or $1 + 2 + 4$.

- Solve subtraction problems by filling in a missing number in a given number sentence, such as $\underline{\ ?\ } = 5 - 4$, or $7 - 3 = \underline{\ ?\ }$, or $9 - \underline{\ ?\ } = 2$.

Materials to Gather

SUPPLIED

blocks – B (all colors)

Unit Checkpoint (printout)

OFFLINE
60 min

UNIT CHECKPOINT Offline

Objectives

- Assess unit objectives.

Students will complete the Unit Checkpoint offline. In Part 1, students will take a performance-based assessment. In Part 2, students will complete the problems on their own. Print the Unit Checkpoint. Read the directions, problems, and answer choices to students if necessary. Use the answer key to score the Unit Checkpoint, and then enter the results online.

Gather the circle blocks, and use them as directed in Part 1. Then give them to students to use for Problem 5 in Part 2.

⟳ Checkpoint   Math | Subtraction Number Sentences | Unit Checkpoint

Name _____   Date _____

Unit Checkpoint Answer Key

Part 1
Follow the instructions for each item. Choose the response that best describes how the student performs on the task. When you have finished, enter the results online.

1. Make a group of 7 circles and a group of 4 circles. Give students 20 circles.
   Say, "The two groups I made have 11 circles in all. Use your circles to show the number 11 a different way. Use two groups of circles."
   Sample answers: 10 circles and 1 circle; 8 circles and 3 circles
   (1 point) Did the student show another way to model the number 11?
   A. Yes   B. No

2. Write $8 - 4 = 4$ on a sheet of paper.
   Say, "Use subtraction to write three other ways to show 4."
   (1 point) Did the student write a subtraction sentence equal to 4?
   A. Yes   B. No
   (1 point) Did the student write another subtraction sentence equal to 4?
   A. Yes   B. No
   (1 point) Did the student write another subtraction sentence equal to 4?
   A. Yes   B. No

© 2008 K12 Inc. All rights reserved.   1 of 5
Copying or distributing without K12's written consent is prohibited.

⟳ Checkpoint   Math | Subtraction Number Sentences | Unit Checkpoint

Name _____   Date _____

3. Write $18 = 9 + 9$ on a sheet of paper.
   Say, "Using subtraction, write another way to show 18."
   (1 point) Did the student write a subtraction expression that equals 18, such as $20 - 2$, $23 - 5$, or $19 - 1$?
   A. Yes   B. No

4. Write $3 + 5 + 5 = 13$ on a sheet of paper.
   Say, "Using subtraction, write another way to show 13."
   (1 point) Did the student write a subtraction expression that equals 13, such as $20 - 7$, $14 - 1$, or $17 - 4$?
   A. Yes   B. No

Give students Part 2 of the assessment.

© 2008 K12 Inc. All rights reserved.   2 of 5
Copying or distributing without K12's written consent is prohibited.

Name _____ Date _____

Part 2
Read each problem and follow the directions.
(1 point)
5. The picture shows a way to represent the number 9. Use the circles to show 9 another way. Then fill in the blanks.

○ ○ ○ ○ ○ ○ ○ ○ + ○

My model had a group of _____ circles and a group of _____ circles.

Students should show another way to model 9. Accept any reasonable answer.

(1 point)
6. This picture uses addition to show 13. Draw another addition picture that shows 13.

◉ ◉ ◉ ◉ ◉ ◉ ◉ ◉ + ◉ ◉ ◉ ◉ + ◉

Sample drawing:

● ● ● ● ● ● + ● ● ● ● ● ● + ●

(1 point)
7. This picture uses addition to show 10. Draw a subtraction picture that shows 10.

○ ○ ○ ○ ○ + ○ ○ ○ ○ ○

Sample drawing:

○ ○ ○ ○ ○ ○ ○ ○ ○ ○ ○ ⊗

Name _____ Date _____

Read each problem and follow the directions.
(1 point)
8. This picture shows 15. Which other picture also shows 15?

★ ★ ★ ★ ★ ★ ★ ★ ★ ★ + ★ ★ ★ ★ ★

A. ★ + ★ ★ ★ ★ ★   B. ★ ★ ★ ★ ★ ★ ★ ★ ★ + ★ ★ ★ ★

Ⓒ ★ ★ ★ ★ + ★ ★ ★ ★ / ★ ★ ★ ★ + ★ ★ ★   D. ★ ★ ★ ★ / ★ ★ ★ + ★ ★ ★ ★ / ★ ★ ★

(1 point)
9. This picture shows 12. Which other picture also shows 12?

● ● ● ● ● ● ● + ● ● ● ● ● ●

A. ● ● ● ● ● + ● ● ● / ● ● ●   B. ● ● ● ● + ● ● + ● ● ● / ● ● ●

C. ● + ● ●   Ⓓ ● ● ● + ● ● ● + ● ● ● / ● ● ●

(1 point)
10. Which picture shows the same number as the picture?

▢ ▢ ▢ ▢ ▢ ▢ ▢ ▢

A. ▢ ▢ ▢ ▢ – ▢   Ⓑ ▢ ▢ ▢ ▢ ▢ – ▢ ▢ / ▢ ▢ ▢ ▢ ▢

C. ▢ ▢ ▢ ▢ / ▢ ▢ ▢ ▢ – ▢ ▢ ▢ / ▢ ▢ ▢ ▢   D. ▢ ▢ ▢ ▢ ▢ – ▢ / ▢ ▢ ▢ ▢ ▢ – ▢ ▢

Name _____ Date _____

(1 point)
11. Which picture shows the same number as the picture?

▢ ▢ ▢ ▢

A. ▢ ▢ ▢ ▢ ▢ ▢ – ▢   B. ▢ ▢ ▢ ▢ ▢ – ▢ ▢ / ▢ ▢ ▢ ▢ ▢ – ▢ ▢ ▢

Ⓒ ▢ ▢ ▢ ▢ / ▢ ▢ ▢ ▢ – ▢ ▢ ▢ / ▢ ▢ ▢ – ▢ ▢ ▢   D. ▢ ▢ ▢ ▢ ▢ – ▢ ▢ / ▢ ▢ ▢ ▢ ▢ – ▢ ▢

Circle the missing number.

(1 point)	*(1 point)*
12. $4 = 8 - \square$	**13.** $\square = 2 - 1$
Ⓐ 4 B. 8 C. 12	Ⓐ 1 B. 2 C. 3
14. $10 - \square = 7$	**15.** $10 - 2 = \square$
A. 10 B. 7 Ⓒ 3	Ⓐ 8 B. 10 C. 2

Write the missing number.

(1 point)	*(1 point)*
16. $2 = 7 - \boxed{5}$	**17.** $4 = 11 - \boxed{7}$
18. $6 - \boxed{1} = 5$	**19.** $8 - \boxed{5} = 3$

Money and Measurement

▶ Unit Objectives

- Identify coins by name, given a picture of the coin (quarter, dime, nickel, and penny).
- State the value of coins (quarter, dime, nickel, and penny).
- Show different combinations of coins that equal the same value.
- Use direct comparison of objects to describe how the lengths of two or more objects compare (for example, the ruler is longer than the pencil).
- Describe the length of objects by using nonstandard units (for example, length of a page = 10 paper clips; width of a desk = 3 pencils).
- Use a nonstandard unit to describe how the lengths of two or more objects compare.

- Compare objects by weight (heavier and lighter).
- Use a nonstandard unit to describe the weight of an object and compare the weights of two or more objects (for example, the pencil is as heavy as 12 paper clips, and the marker is as heavy as 19 paper clips).
- Compare the capacities of objects (for example, the pail holds more water than the cup).
- Use a nonstandard unit to compare the volumes of two or more objects.

▶ Big Ideas

- Quantities can be compared, added, or subtracted if they have been measured by the same unit.
- A quantity can be measured by identifying a unit of measure and iterating (repeating) that unit over the quantity.

▶ Unit Introduction

Students will learn the characteristics, names, and values of pennies, nickels, dimes, and quarters. They will identify how many of a certain coin are in a group and learn to find the value of a group of one type of coin. Finally they will identify groups of coins that have the same value. Although the coin names are shown in online and offline activities, students are not required to read them.

Students will also learn to measure with nonstandard units and to compare length, weight, capacity, and volume.

Coins

Lesson Overview

Skills Update	5 minutes	ONLINE
LEARN Identify Coins and Their Values	20 minutes	ONLINE
LEARN Which Coin?	20 minutes	OFFLINE
TRY IT Practice Coins	15 minutes	OFFLINE

▶ Lesson Objectives

- Identify coins by name, given a picture of the coin (quarter, dime, nickel, and penny).
- State the value of coins (quarter, dime, nickel, and penny).

▶ Content Background

Students will identify coins and their values.

In lessons using coins, the traditional coins of the U.S. Mint will be pictured. Students should be aware that other designs of some U.S. coins, such as nickels, quarters, and $1 coins, may end up in their pockets.

The U.S. Mint has recently issued new state quarters that celebrate each of the 50 states with a design honoring its unique history, traditions, and symbols. The Westward Journey Nickel Series® includes five nickels that celebrate the Louisiana Purchase and the westward journey of Lewis and Clark.

A new series of $1 coins are being released to circulate alongside the Golden Dollar (a coin that features Sacagawea, the Shoshone guide who aided in the Lewis and Clark Expedition). Newer coins honor all the past U.S. presidents who have been deceased at least two years. The front of the coin features the president's portrait, name, and the years that the president's term began and ended. An image of the Statue of Liberty appears on the back of each coin.

Materials to Gather

SUPPLIED

Practice Coins activity page

ALSO NEEDED

play money – 6 each of pennies, nickels, dimes, and quarters

Keywords	**value** – an assigned or calculated quantity; often used with place value or monetary value; for example, the 2 in 23 has a value of 20. $2.50 has a value of 2 dollars and 50 cents.

LEARN Identify Coins and Their Values

ONLINE 20min

Students will learn about pennies, nickels, dimes, and quarters. They will learn the name and value of each coin.

1. As students look at the coins, ask questions such as the following:
   - What is on the heads side of the coin?
   - What is on the tails side of the coin?
   - What color is the coin?
   - Is the coin larger or smaller than a penny? nickel? dime? quarter?

2. Students may confuse the value of a coin with the number of coins in a group. Explain that the value of each coin is always the same, but the number of coins in a group can vary.

Objectives

- Identify coins by name, given a picture of the coin (quarter, dime, nickel, and penny).
- State the value of coins (quarter, dime, nickel, and penny).

Tips

If you wish, make a chart that shows the coins with the names and values for students to use as a reference.

If you wish, review the U.S. presidents with students to help them identify the president shown on each coin in the American presidents series.

LEARN Which Coin?

OFFLINE 20min

Students will identify and state the value of the penny, nickel, dime, and quarter. They will also count the number of coins in a group.
Gather the coins. Display one of each type of coin.

1. Show coins to students. For each coin, mention what is on the heads side and the tails side, how the edge feels, the value, the relative size, and the color (a copper-brown color for the penny and a silver color for the nickel, dime, and quarter). Have students hold and examine each coin.

2. Note that students might associate the size of a coin with its value. They may think that the larger the coin, the greater the value. Tell students that the smallest coin, the dime, has a greater value than the penny or the nickel.

3. Have students look at all the coins.

   Ask: Which is the largest coin?
   ANSWER: quarter

   Ask: Which is the smallest coin?
   ANSWER: dime

   Ask: Which coins have a bumpy edge?
   ANSWER: dime and quarter

   Ask: Which coin is a different color from the others?
   ANSWER: penny

4. Display one of each coin heads side up. Point to each coin and ask students to name it. If students have difficulty, ask a guiding question, such as, "What color is this coin?"

5. Turn over the coins so they are tails side up. Point to each coin and ask students to name it.

Objectives

- Identify coins by name, given a picture of the coin (quarter, dime, nickel, and penny).
- State the value of coins (quarter, dime, nickel, and penny).

Tips

If you wish, use real money instead of play money.

6. Ask students to point to the coin that has a value of 1 cent. Repeat for values of 10 cents, 5 cents, and 25 cents.

7. Repeat Steps 4–6 as necessary for students to become comfortable with the names and values.

8. Display a group of 5 quarters and 4 pennies in a random arrangement. Some coins should show heads, and others should show tails.

   Ask: What two types of coins are in this group?
   ANSWER: quarters and pennies

   Ask: How many quarters are there?
   ANSWER: 5

9. Repeat Step 8 with the following two groups:
   • 6 dimes and 2 pennies
   • 3 nickels and 5 pennies.

OFFLINE
15min

TRY IT Practice Coins

Objectives

Students will practice identifying the names and values of coins. Give students the Practice Coins activity page from their Activity Book and read the directions with them.

• Identify coins by name, given a picture of the coin (quarter, dime, nickel, and penny).

• State the value of coins (quarter, dime, nickel, and penny).

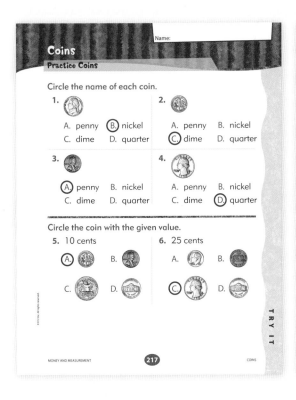

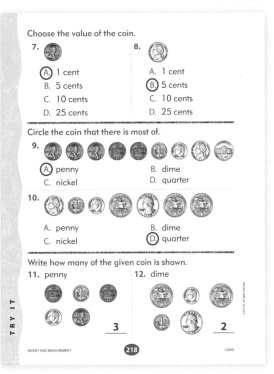

Identify Coins

Lesson Overview

Skills Update	5 minutes	**ONLINE**
LEARN Penny, Nickel, Dime, Quarter	15 minutes	**ONLINE**
LEARN What Coin Is It?	15 minutes	**OFFLINE**
TRY IT Coins and Values	15 minutes	**OFFLINE**
CHECKPOINT	10 minutes	**OFFLINE**

▶ Lesson Objectives

- Identify coins by name, given a picture of the coin (quarter, dime, nickel, and penny).
- State the value of coins (quarter, dime, nickel, and penny).

▶ Content Background

Students will continue to identify coins and their values.

Materials to Gather

SUPPLIED

Coins and Values activity page

Checkpoint (printout)

ALSO NEEDED

play money – 5 each of pennies, nickels, dimes, and quarters

LEARN Penny, Nickel, Dime, Quarter

ONLINE 15min

Students will identify coins based on sets of clues. Then they will play a game in which they answer questions about coin values and the number of coins in a group.

- The second activity, Tic-Tac-Go, calls for two players. You may act as the second player.
- Students might confuse the silver coins. Explain that of the three, the dime is the smallest and the quarter is the largest. Explain that the nickel has a smooth edge.
- Students are not expected to read coin names. Read the names to students, if necessary.

Objectives

- Identify coins by name, given a picture of the coin (quarter, dime, nickel, and penny).
- State the value of coins (quarter, dime, nickel, and penny).

Tips

If you wish, make a chart that shows the coins with their names and values for students to use as a reference.

If you wish, review the U.S. presidents with students to help them identify the president shown on each coin in the American presidents series.

LEARN What Coin Is It?

Student will identify, describe, and state the value of coins. They will also count the number of a particular coin in a mixed group, as well as tell which coin has a given value.

Gather the coins. Display one of each type of coin.

1. Ask students to identify the penny.

2. **Say:** Tell me what you know about the penny.

   Students may share the following: It has a copper-brown color. Its value is 1 cent. Its edge is smooth. Abraham Lincoln's head is on the front. The Lincoln Memorial is on the back.

3. Fill in any details that students miss in their descriptions.

4. Repeat Steps 1–3 with the nickel, dime, and quarter.

   - Nickel: It has a silver color. Its value is 5 cents. Its edge is smooth. It is smaller than the quarter and larger than the dime. Thomas Jefferson's head is on the front. Jefferson's Monticello is on the back.

   - Dime: It has a silver color. Its value is 10 cents. Its edge is rough. It is the smallest coin. Franklin Delano Roosevelt's head is on the front. A symbol with a torch is on the back.

   - Quarter: It has a silver color. Its value is 25 cents. Its edge is rough. It is larger than the penny, nickel, and dime. George Washington's head is on the front. An eagle is on the back.

5. Hold up the dime.

   Ask: What coin is this, and what is its value?
   ANSWER: dime; 10 cents

   If students answer incorrectly, give them a hint or ask a question.

6. Repeat Step 5 with the quarter, penny, and nickel.

7. Display a group of 8 coins, including 3 dimes.

   Ask students to point to each dime in the group.

   Ask: How many dimes are there?
   ANSWER: 3

8. Repeat Step 7, having students identify and count the quarters, nickels, and dimes in groups of coins. Do not put more than 8 coins in a group.

9. Display one of each type of coin.

   Ask: Which coin has a value of 5 cents?
   ANSWER: nickel

10. Repeat Step 9 for 25 cents, 1 cent, and 10 cents.

Objectives

- Identify coins by name, given a picture of the coin (quarter, dime, nickel, and penny).

- State the value of coins (quarter, dime, nickel, and penny).

Tips

Although it is tempting to say that the quarter is the "largest" coin, it is only larger than the penny, nickel, or dime. It is not the largest coin. The quarter is smaller than the half-dollar coin and smaller than some dollar coins.

If students have difficulty counting a given coin in a group of coins, have them pick up and move each coin from the group as they count it.

If you wish, use real money instead of play money.

TRY IT Coins and Values

OFFLINE 15 min

Students will practice identifying the names and values of coins. Give students the Coins and Values activity page from their Activity Book and read the directions with them.

Objectives

- Identify coins by name, given a picture of the coin (quarter, dime, nickel, and penny).
- State the value of coins (quarter, dime, nickel, and penny).

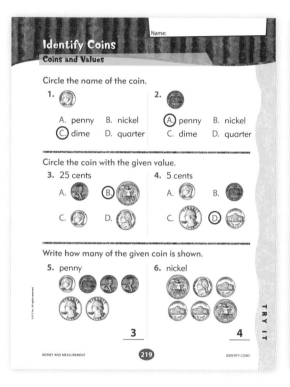

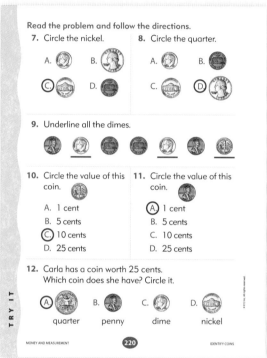

CHECKPOINT

Print the Checkpoint and have students complete it on their own. Read the directions, problems, and answer choices to students if necessary. Use the answer key to score the Checkpoint, and then enter the results online.

Objectives

- Identify coins by name, given a picture of the coin (quarter, dime, nickel, and penny).
- State the value of coins (quarter, dime, nickel, and penny).

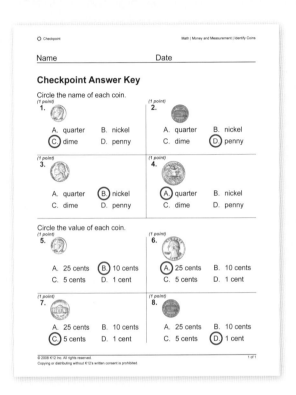

Equal Money Amounts

Lesson Overview

Skills Update	5 minutes	ONLINE
GET READY Tell About Coins	5 minutes	ONLINE
LEARN Count Coins	15 minutes	ONLINE
LEARN Equal Coin Values	15 minutes	ONLINE
TRY IT Same Value Coin Groups	10 minutes	OFFLINE
CHECKPOINT	10 minutes	OFFLINE

▶ Lesson Objectives

Show different combinations of coins that equal the same value.

▶ Prerequisite Skills

- Identify coins by name, given a picture of the coin (quarter, dime, nickel, and penny).
- State the value of coins (quarter, dime, nickel, and penny).

▶ Content Background

Students will learn how to find the value of groups of coins. They will then learn how to identify groups of coins with the same value.

Materials to Gather

SUPPLIED

Same Value Coin Groups activity page

Checkpoint (printout)

ALSO NEEDED

play money – 10 pennies, 6 nickels, 3 dimes, and 1 quarter

GET READY Tell About Coins

ONLINE 5min

Students will answer Yes or No questions about pennies, nickels, dimes, and quarters. If students answer any of the questions incorrectly, have them click Replay at the end of the activity to repeat it.

Objectives

- Identify coins by name, given a picture of the coin (quarter, dime, nickel, and penny).
- State the value of coins (quarter, dime, nickel, and penny).

LEARN Count Coins

ONLINE 15min

Students will learn to find the value of groups of all pennies, all nickels, or all dimes using the Money: Coins Learning Tool. To find the value, they will count by 1s, 5s, or 10s. The total value of the coins will not exceed 30 cents.

Note: You will see the ¢ symbol on-screen, but students are not expected to learn this symbol yet. Read the symbol to students as "cent" or "cents."

Objectives

- Show different combinations of coins that equal the same value.

DIRECTIONS FOR USING THE MONEY: COINS LEARNING TOOL

1. Click Problem Type 4.
2. Point to the penny, nickel, dime, and quarter on the screen, one at a time, and review the coin's name and value.
3. Point to the penny.

   Say: A penny is worth 1 cent. To find the value of a group of pennies, count by ones. Count by ones with me to find the value of these pennies.

   Drag 4 pennies into the box, counting aloud as you place each penny: 1 cent, 2 cents, 3 cents, 4 cents.
4. Click Show Value.

   Say: These 4 pennies are worth 4 cents altogether.
5. **Ask:** What do you notice about the value of the pennies and the number of pennies?
   ANSWER: The value and number are the same.
6. Click Next Problem to clear the screen. Repeat Steps 3 and 4 with 2 dimes, counting by 10s to find the value.
7. Clear the screen. Drag 3 dimes into the box, counting aloud by 10s.

   Ask: What is the value of 3 dimes altogether?
   ANSWER: 30 cents

   Click Show Value to show 30 cents.
8. **Say:** There are 3 dimes, but the value is 30 cents altogether. The number of dimes does not equal the total value of the dimes.
9. Clear the screen. Repeat Steps 3 and 4 with 3 nickels, counting by 5s to find the value.
10. Clear the screen. Drag 6 nickels into the box, counting aloud by 5s.

    Ask: What is the value of 6 nickels altogether?
    ANSWER: 30 cents

    Click Show Value to show 30 cents.
11. **Say:** There are 6 nickels, but their value is 30 cents altogether. The number of nickels is not equal to the total value of the nickels.

ONLINE

15 min

LEARN Equal Coin Values

Objectives

- Show different combinations of coins that equal the same value.

Students will identify groups of coins that have the same value using the Money: Coins Learning Tool.

Note: You will see the ¢ symbol on-screen, but students are not expected to learn this symbol yet. Read the symbol to students as "cent" or "cents."

DIRECTIONS FOR USING THE MONEY: COINS LEARNING TOOL

1. Click Problem Type 4.
2. Drag a nickel into the box.

   Ask: What is the value of the nickel?
   ANSWER: 5 cents

   Click Show Value to show the answer. Then clear the screen.

3. **Say:** There is another way to show 5 cents. We can use pennies to make 5 cents.

   Have students drag 5 pennies into the box. Then click Show Value to show 5 cents. Count the pennies aloud with students: 1 cent, 2 cents, 3 cents, 4 cents, 5 cents.

4. Clear the screen. Repeat Steps 2 and 3. First show 10 cents with a dime. Then have students show 10 cents with 10 pennies.

5. **Say:** You can show 10 cents with 1 dime or with 10 pennies. There are other ways to show 10 cents.

   Allow students to experiment with the learning tool to find another way to make 10 cents. If they have difficulty, guide them to drag 2 nickels into the box, counting aloud as they place each nickel: 5 cents, 10 cents.

   Also show students how to make 10 cents using 1 nickel and 5 pennies.

6. Clear the screen. Repeat Steps 2 and 3. First show 25 cents with a quarter. Then have students show 25 cents with 25 pennies.

7. **Say:** You can show 25 cents with 1 quarter or with 25 pennies. There are other ways to show 25 cents.

   Allow students to experiment with the learning tool to find another way to make 25 cents. If they have difficulty, guide them to drag 5 nickels into the box, counting aloud as they place each nickel: 5 cents, 10 cents, 15 cents, 20 cents, 25 cents.

   Also show students how to make 25 cents using 2 dimes and 1 nickel, and using 1 dime and 3 nickels.

8. Create a few problems for students to practice reviewing what they have learned. You may ask them to use the coins to show 5 cents, 10 cents, or 25 cents. You may also show combinations of coins that equal 5 cents, 10 cents, or 25 cents and ask students to tell you the value of the coins altogether. If students appear ready for a challenge, click Menu to locate additional problems.

TRY IT Same Value Coin Groups

Objectives

- Show different combinations of coins that equal the same value.

Students will practice finding values of groups of coins and determining groups with equal values. Give students the coins and Same Value Coin Groups activity page from their Activity Book. Read the directions with them.

Students may use the coins to help them throughout the activity. For Problem 10, they will need to show groups of coins for a given value.

Tips

If you wish, use real money instead of play money.

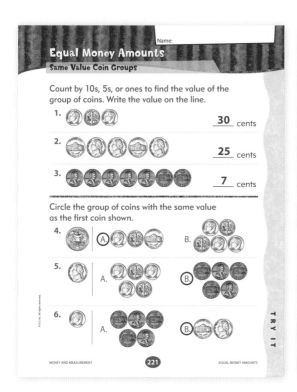

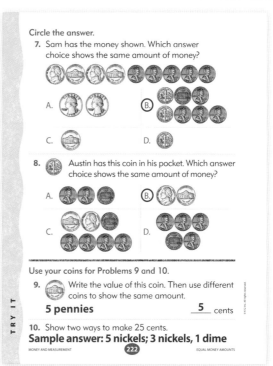

CHECKPOINT

Objectives

- Show different combinations of coins that equal the same value.

Print the Checkpoint and have students complete it on their own. Read the directions, problems, and answer choices to students, if necessary. Use the answer key to score the Checkpoint, and then enter the results online.

Gather the coins. Students may use the coins to help them throughout the activity. For Problems 3 and 4, students will need to show groups of coins for a given value.

Tips

If you wish, use real money instead of play money.

Name _____   Date _____

Checkpoint Answer Key

Circle the answer.

(1 point)
1. Jasmine keeps the money shown in her coin purse. Which answer choice shows the same amount of money?

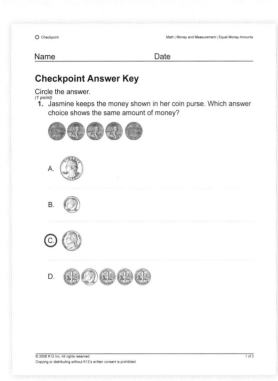

Name _____   Date _____

(1 point)
2. These coins are in Jeremy's piggy bank. Which answer choice shows the same amount of money?

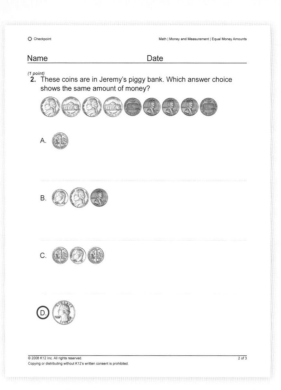

Name _____   Date _____

Use your coins for Problems 3 and 4.

3. Write the value of this coin. Then use different coins to show the same amount.

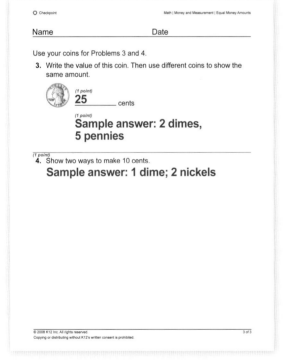

(1 point)
25 _____ cents

(1 point)
Sample answer: 2 dimes, 5 pennies

(1 point)
4. Show two ways to make 10 cents.

Sample answer: 1 dime; 2 nickels

Measure and Compare Length

Skills Update	5 minutes	ONLINE
GET READY Compare Objects	5 minutes	ONLINE
LEARN Nonstandard Units	15 minutes	OFFLINE
LEARN Compare and Measure Length	15 minutes	OFFLINE
TRY IT Measurement Practice	10 minutes	OFFLINE
CHECKPOINT	10 minutes	OFFLINE

▶ Lesson Objectives

- Use direct comparison of objects to describe how the lengths of two or more objects compare (for example, the ruler is longer than the pencil).
- Describe the length of objects by using nonstandard units (for example, length of a page = 10 paper clips; width of a desk = 3 pencils).
- Use a nonstandard unit to describe how the lengths of two or more objects compare.

▶ Prerequisite Skills

- Compare objects by length (for example, note which object is shorter, longer, or taller).
- Measure the length of objects by using nonstandard units.
- Use direct comparison of objects to describe how the lengths of two or more objects compare (for example, the ruler is longer than the pencil).

▶ Advance Preparation

Highlight one long edge of each index card blue. Highlight one short edge of each index card yellow. Save cards for use in future lessons.

For household objects, choose at least one pair that is equal in length, such as a red marker and a blue marker.

▶ Safety

Supervise students as they work with toothpicks, paper clips, and other pointy household items.

▶ Content Background

Students will measure length using nonstandard units. They will also compare the length of objects, telling if one object is longer or shorter, or if the objects are the same length.

All measurement involves a number of a certain unit, such as 14 inches. Units can be standard or nonstandard. Standard units are ones that everyone knows

Materials to Gather

SUPPLIED

blocks – O (all colors)

Measurement Practice activity page

Checkpoint (printout)

ALSO NEEDED

craft stick

toothpicks – 20

index cards – 25

paper clips –10 large, 20 small

household objects – 2 each of several types (crayons, books, straws, and so on)

highlighters – 1 blue, 1 yellow

crayon

and agrees are specific sizes, such as inches, centimeters, quarts, liters, pounds, and kilograms.

Nonstandard units also must each be the same size, but can be anything people choose to use. For example, some people will use their index finger to measure the length of an object at a store when they don't have a ruler. Other nonstandard units for length might be a set of small paper clips, toothpicks, or craft sticks. Using nonstandard units in early measurement activities with students helps them realize that the number of units will differ depending on the size of the nonstandard unit. They can then transfer this idea to standard units of measure.

Keywords

compare – to find the similarities or differences among sizes, values, or amounts

length – the distance between two points

longer – having a greater time or distance than another

measure (verb) – to use standard units to find a distance, area, volume, capacity, temperature, or interval of time

nonstandard units – any unit chosen to be used repeatedly to measure, such as a paper clip or triangular tile

shorter – having a lesser time or distance than another

GET READY Compare Objects

ONLINE
5 min

Students will compare the length and height of objects to determine which object is longer or shorter, or whether the objects are the same length.

Throughout the activity, have students describe the comparisons. For example, if the red crayon is longer than the blue crayon, students should say, "The red crayon is longer than the blue crayon." They should also say, "The blue crayon is shorter than the red crayon."

Objectives

- Compare objects by length (for example, note which object is shorter, longer, or taller).

Tips

Point out that it's easier to compare length when the objects are lined up at one end.

LEARN Nonstandard Units

OFFLINE
15 min

Students will measure length using nonstandard units.

Gather the toothpicks, craft stick, paper clips, and index cards you prepared.

1. Explain to students that they can use toothpicks to measure length. Point out that all the toothpicks are the same length.

2. Lay a pencil on a sheet of paper. Help students position the toothpicks end to end to measure the pencil's length. Make sure the ends of the toothpicks are touching but not overlapping.

3. Have students mark the end of each toothpick on the paper. Then have them count the marks.

   Ask: About how many toothpicks long is the pencil?
   SAMPLE ANSWER: The pencil is about 3 toothpicks long.

Objectives

- Use direct comparison of objects to describe how the lengths of two or more objects compare (for example, the ruler is longer than the pencil).

- Describe the length of objects by using nonstandard units (for example, length of a page = 10 paper clips; width of a desk = 3 pencils).

- Use a nonstandard unit to describe how the lengths of two or more objects compare.

4. Have students repeat Steps 2 and 3 to measure the craft stick using toothpicks.

5. Explain to students that now they'll measure with a different unit, index cards. Help students position the blue side of the index cards end to end to measure the length of the workspace.

6. Have students count the index cards.

   Ask: About how many blue index cards long is the workspace?
   SAMPLE ANSWER: The workspace is about 12 blue index cards long.

7. Repeat Steps 5 and 6 to measure the workspace using the yellow side of the index cards.

8. **Ask:** Did it take more blue index cards or yellow index cards to measure the workspace?
   ANSWER: yellow index cards

   Explain that it takes more smaller units than larger units to measure the length of the same object.

9. Repeat Steps 5–8, having students measure the same object with a larger unit and a smaller unit. For example, students may measure a book using large paper clips and then small paper clips.

LEARN Compare and Measure Length

Objectives

- Use direct comparison of objects to describe how the lengths of two or more objects compare (for example, the ruler is longer than the pencil).

- Describe the length of objects by using nonstandard units (for example, length of a page = 10 paper clips; width of a desk = 3 pencils).

- Use a nonstandard unit to describe how the lengths of two or more objects compare.

Students will measure and compare length using nonstandard units. Gather the cubes and household objects.

1. **Say:** Let's compare the length of two objects. Comparing length means telling if one object is longer or shorter, or if the objects are the same length.

2. Vertically align two household objects of different lengths, such as a short pencil and a long pencil, along the left edges.

   Say: To compare length, the objects must be lined up at one end.

3. Point to the longer pencil.

   Say: The tip of this pencil is farther right than the tip of the other pencil. So this pencil is longer.

4. **Say:** Let's measure with cubes to check that this pencil is longer.

   Have students use the cubes to measure each pencil. Students should snap the cubes together to form a train about the length of each pencil. Confirm with students that the pencil that extends farther to the right is more cubes long than the other pencil.

5. Line up the cube trains along the left edges.

   Ask: How many cubes longer is the longer cube train?

   Help students count the cubes that extend beyond the shorter cube train. Explain that the longer pencil is that many cubes longer than the shorter pencil.

6. Have students compare each pair of household objects. First have students tell which object is longer or shorter, or if the objects are the same length, without measuring. Then have students check their answer by measuring each object with cube trains. Finally have students tell how many cubes longer the longer object is than the shorter object.

If it is not possible to measure students' workspace, have students measure any table, desk, or similarly sized object.

Objectives

Students will practice measuring and comparing length. Give students the small paper clips, craft stick, crayon, and Measurement Practice activity page from their Activity Book. Read the directions with them.

- Use direct comparison of objects to describe how the lengths of two or more objects compare (for example, the ruler is longer than the pencil).

- Describe the length of objects by using nonstandard units (for example, length of a page = 10 paper clips; width of a desk = 3 pencils).

- Use a nonstandard unit to describe how the lengths of two or more objects compare.

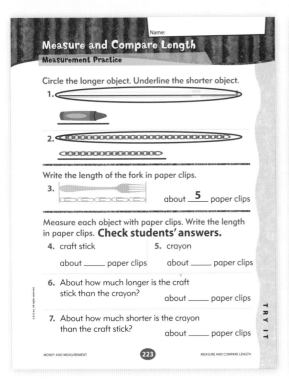

Name: _____

Measure and Compare Length
Measurement Practice

Circle the longer object. Underline the shorter object.

1.

2.

Write the length of the fork in paper clips.

3. about __5__ paper clips

Measure each object with paper clips. Write the length in paper clips. **Check students' answers.**

4. craft stick
   about _____ paper clips

5. crayon
   about _____ paper clips

6. About how much longer is the craft stick than the crayon?
   about _____ paper clips

7. About how much shorter is the crayon than the craft stick?
   about _____ paper clips

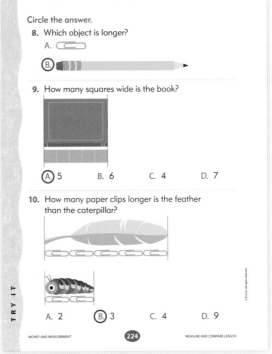

Circle the answer.

8. Which object is longer?
   A. (clip)
   B. (pencil)

9. How many squares wide is the book?

   A. 5 B. 6 C. 4 D. 7

10. How many paper clips longer is the feather than the caterpillar?

   A. 2 **B.** 3 C. 4 D. 9

OFFLINE
10 min

Print the Checkpoint. In Part 1, students will take a performance-based assessment. In Part 2, students will complete the problems on their own. Read the directions, problems, and answer choices to students, if necessary. Use the answer key to score the Checkpoint, and then enter the results online.

Gather the cubes, small paper clips, crayon, and one index card.

- Use direct comparison of objects to describe how the lengths of two or more objects compare (for example, the ruler is longer than the pencil).

- Describe the length of objects by using nonstandard units (for example, length of a page = 10 paper clips; width of a desk = 3 pencils).

- Use a nonstandard unit to describe how the lengths of two or more objects compare.

⚙ Checkpoint   Math | Money and Measurement | Measure and Compare Length

Name _____   Date _____

Checkpoint Answer Key

Part 1
Follow the instructions for each problem. Choose the response that best describes how the student performs on the task. When you have finished, enter the results online.
(1 point)
1. Say, "Use the cubes to measure how long the paper is."

   Did the student measure the paper correctly?

   A. Yes   B. No

---

2. Use paper clips to measure the length of the pencil and the crayon.

   About how many paper clips long is the pencil?

   About how many paper clips long is the crayon?

   How much longer is the pencil than the crayon in paper clips?
(1 point)
   Did the student measure the pencil correctly?

   A. Yes   B. No
(1 point)
   Did the student measure the crayon correctly?

   A. Yes   B. No
(1 point)
   Did the student correctly state how much longer the pencil is than the crayon?

   A. Yes   B. No

⚙ Checkpoint   Math | Money and Measurement | Measure and Compare Length

Name _____   Date _____

3. Use paper clips to measure the length of the paper and the index card.

   About how many paper clips long is the paper?

   About how many paper clips long is the index card?

   How much shorter is the index card than the paper in paper clips?
(1 point)
   Did the student measure the paper correctly?

   A. Yes   B. No
(1 point)
   Did the student measure the index card correctly?

   A. Yes   B. No
(1 point)
   Did the student correctly state how much shorter the index card is than the paper?

   A. Yes   B. No

Give students Part 2 of the Checkpoint.

⚙ Checkpoint   Math | Money and Measurement | Measure and Compare Length

Name _____   Date _____

Part 2
Circle the answer.
(1 point)
4. Which object is shorter?

   A. ⬥

   (B.) ⬥

(1 point)
5. Which word goes in the blank?

   An airplane is _____ than a feather.

   (A.) longer   B. shorter

(1 point)
6. How many paper clips long is the feather?

   A. 3   (B.) 4   C. 7   D. 9

(1 point)
7. How many cubes shorter is the crayon than the ruler?

   A. 12   B. 10   (C.) 8   D. 6

Weight

Lesson Overview

Skills Update	5 minutes	ONLINE
GET READY Compare Objects	5 minutes	OFFLINE
LEARN Use a Balance	20 minutes	OFFLINE
LEARN Weigh It	15 minutes	ONLINE
TRY IT Which Is Heavier?	10 minutes	OFFLINE
CHECKPOINT	5 minutes	OFFLINE

▶ Lesson Objectives

- Compare objects by weight (heavier and lighter).
- Use a nonstandard unit to describe the weight of an object and compare the weights of two or more objects (for example, the pencil is as heavy as 12 paper clips, and the marker is as heavy as 19 paper clips).

▶ Prerequisite Skills

Compare objects by weight (for example, note which object is heavier).

▶ Advance Preparation

Create a hanging balance. Gather a wire cutter, wire hanger, 2 paper cups, small hole punch, string, and masking or electrical tape.

1. Use the wire cutter to cut the middle section out of the bottom of the hanger.
2. Carefully bend each end up slightly.
3. Use the tape to cover the sharp ends.
4. Cut two 8-inch pieces of string.
5. Punch 2 holes in each cup $\frac{1}{2}$–1 inch below the rim and on opposite sides.
6. For each cup, thread one piece of string through both holes. Tie the ends of the string above the cup so that the string looks like a pail handle. Keep the string length of the two cups as identical as possible.
7. Hang each cup on one end of the hanger.

Gather a variety of household objects that vary in weight and can be held in one hand by students. Also gather objects that can be weighed on a balance. Include some fruit, such as strawberries and grapes.

Divide a sheet of paper into 4 sections by folding or drawing lines.

Materials to Gather

SUPPLIED

blocks – B (40 of any color)

blocks – O (20 of any color)

Which Is Heavier? activity page

Checkpoint (printout)

ALSO NEEDED

household objects – 6–8 that can be held and compared (metal fork, pencil, book, crayon, stuffed animal, shoe, spoon, piece of fruit)

paper clips – 20 large

household objects – about 10 that can be weighed on a balance (pencil, crayon, marker, spoon, small toy, small rock)

balance supplies – wire cutter, wire hanger, 2 paper cups, small hole punch, string, and masking or electrical tape

ruler – 12 inch

▶ Content Background

Students will use a balance to tell which of two objects is heavier or lighter. They will then use the balance and nonstandard units to find weights of objects and to compare objects by their weights.

Keywords	
	balance – an instrument used to compare two weights or capacities
	heavier – having a greater weight than another
	lighter – having a lesser weight than another
	weight – the measure of the heaviness of an object

GET READY Compare Objects

OFFLINE 5 min

Students will compare objects by weight.

Gather several household objects that students can hold in one hand.

1. Give students two objects. Have them hold one in each hand. Have students tell which object is heavier and which is lighter.

2. Repeat with several pairs of objects.

Objectives

- Compare objects by weight (for example, note which object is heavier).

LEARN Use a Balance

OFFLINE 20 min

Students will use a balance to compare the weight of objects. Then they will weigh objects using nonstandard units. They will record data about the weight of the objects.

Gather the household objects for weighing, paper clips, cubes, circle blocks, ruler, paper folded into 4 sections, and balance you made. Tape the ruler to a table so that one end extends beyond the table. Hang the balance on the ruler.

1. Explain how to use the balance to compare the weight of two objects. To compare weight, place an object in each cup. If one object is heavier, its cup will hang lower. If the objects have the same weight, the cups will hang at the same level.

2. Help students select and place two objects in the balance, one in each cup. Ask students which object is heavier.

3. Repeat Step 2 with several pairs of objects.

4. Explain how to use the balance to weigh an object using nonstandard units. To weigh an object, place it in one of the cups. Place units, such as cubes, in the other cup until the cups hang at the same level. Then count the units to find the weight.

5. Help students select and place an object in one cup of the balance. Give students a pile of cubes. Have students place cubes in the empty cup, counting aloud as they place each cube, until the cups are level.

Objectives

- Compare objects by weight (heavier and lighter).

- Use a nonstandard unit to describe the weight of an object and compare the weights of two or more objects (for example, the pencil is as heavy as 12 paper clips, and the marker is as heavy as 19 paper clips).

Tips

Label the four sections of the paper 1 through 4 to make it easier for students to identify in which section they should sketch the next object.

6. Have students sketch the object in one section of the paper. Below the sketch, have them write its weight in cubes.

7. Repeat Steps 5 and 6 with at least three more objects. Experiment with different nonstandard units, such as circle blocks and paper clips.

LEARN Weigh It

ONLINE
15 min

Students will compare weight using an online balance. Then they'll use the balance to weigh objects with a nonstandard unit.

ACTIVITY 1

1. Have students choose one object from the left group and one object from the right group.

2. Ask students to predict which object will be heavier and which will be lighter.

3. Have students drag the objects onto the balance.

4. Have students say which object is heavier and which is lighter. Have them explain how they know.

5. Repeat Steps 1–4 with three more pairs of objects.

ACTIVITY 2

6. Have students drag an object from the right group onto the balance.

7. Ask students how they would weigh the object using strawberries. (Place strawberries on the other side of the balance until the balance is level.)

8. Have students weigh each object using strawberries.

9. **Ask:** Which is heavier, the hermit crab or the pencil?
   ANSWER: hermit crab

   Ask: How do you know?
   ANSWER: The hermit crab weighs 9 strawberries. The pencil only weighs 1 strawberry.

10. Explain that another way to compare weight is to weigh each object using the same nonstandard unit and compare the objects' weights.

Objectives

- Compare objects by weight (heavier and lighter).

- Use a nonstandard unit to describe the weight of an object and compare the weights of two or more objects (for example, the pencil is as heavy as 12 paper clips, and the marker is as heavy as 19 paper clips).

Objectives

- Compare objects by weight (heavier and lighter).
- Use a nonstandard unit to describe the weight of an object and compare the weights of two or more objects (for example, the pencil is as heavy as 12 paper clips, and the marker is as heavy as 19 paper clips).

This Try It activity has two parts.

PART 1

Students will practice using a balance to compare objects' weights. Gather the balance and four household objects.

1. Give students two objects, and ask them to use the balance to compare the objects' weights.

2. Ask students to tell you which object is heavier and which object is lighter. Have them explain how they know.

3. Repeat Steps 1 and 2 with the other two objects.

PART 2

Students will practice comparing objects' weights. Give students the balance, a circle block, pencil, piece of fruit, crayon, paper clip, spoon, shoe, and Which Is Heavier? activity page from their Activity Book. Read the directions with them.

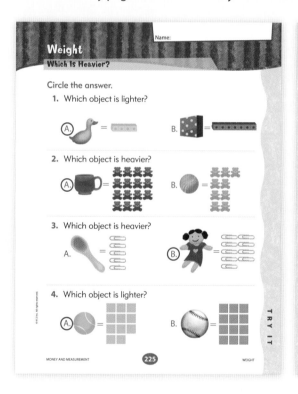

Use the balance to compare the weights of the two objects. For the orange, you may use a fruit of similar weight. Circle the answer.

5. Which is heavier?
   A. circle block
   B. pencil

6. Which is lighter?
   A. orange
   B. crayon

Hold one object in each hand to compare their weights. Circle the answer.

7. Which object is lighter?
   A. paper clip
   B. spoon

8. Which object is heavier?
   A. circle block
   B. shoe

Print the Checkpoint. Students will take a performance-based assessment. Read the directions and problems to students. Use the answer key to score the Checkpoint, and then enter the results online.

Gather the balance, circle blocks, paper clip, book, pencil, spoon, and crayon.

- Compare objects by weight (heavier and lighter).

- Use a nonstandard unit to describe the weight of an object and compare the weights of two or more objects (for example, the pencil is as heavy as 12 paper clips, and the marker is as heavy as 19 paper clips).

Checkpoint   Math | Money and Measurement | Weight

Name   Date

Checkpoint Answer Key

Follow the instructions for each item. Choose the response that best describes how the student performs on the task. When you have finished, enter the results online.

1. Give students the paper clip and the book. Tell them they will answer this question without using the balance. Ask, "Which is heavier?"
   (1 point) Did the student identify the book as the heavier object?
   A. Yes   B. No

2. Say, "Use the balance to compare the weights of the spoon and the pencil. Which is lighter?"
   (1 point) Did the student identify the lighter object?
   A. Yes   B. No

3. Say, "A box of crayons is as heavy as 20 cubes. A pencil is as heavy as 5 cubes. Which is heavier?"
   (1 point) Did the student answer that the box of crayons is heavier?
   A. Yes   B. No

4. Say, "Weigh the pencil and the crayon using the balance and circle blocks. Write the weight of each object on a sheet of paper."
   (1 point) Did the student write how many circles each object weighs?
   A. Yes   B. No
   (1 point) Did the student say which object is heavier?
   A. Yes   B. No

1 of 1

Capacity and Volume

Skills Update	5 minutes	ONLINE
LEARN Capacity	20 minutes	OFFLINE
LEARN Volume	15 minutes	OFFLINE
TRY IT Holds More, Holds Less	10 minutes	OFFLINE
CHECKPOINT	10 minutes	OFFLINE

▶ Lesson Objectives

- Compare the capacities of objects (for example, the pail holds more water than the cup).
- Use a nonstandard unit to compare the volumes of two or more objects.

▶ Advance Preparation

Gather the following containers for liquid measurement:

- 5 small containers of various sizes, such as paper cups, mugs, soda caps, and measuring spoons, with two the same size
- 5 large containers of various sizes, such as large drinking cups, empty water bottles, half-gallon pitchers, soup bowls, and cooking pots
- Basin or bucket to catch spills during pouring

Gather the following boxes for dry measurement:

- 5 small to medium-sized empty boxes of various sizes, such as small shoe boxes, tissue boxes, jewelry gift boxes, and index card holders, with two the same size

▶ Safety

Be sure all containers are cleaned thoroughly before use. Avoid using glass containers.

▶ Content Background

Students will compare the capacity and the volume of different containers. To measure capacity, they will use nonstandard units, such as paper cups of water. To measure volume, they will use different nonstandard units, such as snap cubes.

Materials to Gather

SUPPLIED

base-10 blocks – ones cubes

blocks – O (all colors)

Holds More, Holds Less activity page

Checkpoint (printout)

ALSO NEEDED

household objects – 1 basin or bucket, 5 boxes

containers – 5 large, 5 small

paper, drawing – 4 sheets

pencils, coloring

sticky notes – 3

Keywords

capacity – a measure indicating an amount a container can hold

volume – the amount of space anything takes up, or the amount of space inside a container

LEARN Capacity

Students will compare and measure the capacities of different containers.
   Gather the small and large containers, basin, coloring pencils, and 2 sheets of drawing paper.

- Compare the capacities of objects (for example, the pail holds more water than the cup).

Tips

In this activity, have students pour water from one container to another. Have them work outside or over a sink, tub, or dishpan to catch spills.
   Use a sink or a large container filled with water as a water source.

COMPARE CAPACITY

1. Choose one large container and one small container, such as a mixing bowl and plastic cup.
2. Write Experiment 1 on the drawing paper. Help students sketch the bowl and cup on the paper.
3. Have students predict which can hold more water, the bowl or the cup.
4. Working over the basin, fill the cup with water. Help students pour the water into the bowl.

   Say: There is still space for more water in the bowl. So the bowl holds more water than the cup.

5. Have students circle the bowl on the drawing paper.
6. Repeat Steps 1–3 with two other containers, one large and one small.
7. After students predict which container can hold more water, fill the larger container with water. Help students pour the water into the smaller container. Let the water overflow into the basin.

   Say: There is not enough space in the smaller container. So it holds less than the larger container.

8. Have students circle the larger container on the drawing paper.
9. Repeat Steps 1–3 with two containers that are the same size.
10. After students make a prediction, fill one container with water. Help students pour the water from one container into the other.

   Say: The second container is filled to the top with water. There is no space for more water, but the water does not overflow. The containers hold the same amount.

11. Have students write "Equal" under the sketches.

MEASURE CAPACITY

12. Choose one large container and one small container, such as a mixing bowl and plastic cup.
13. Write Experiment 4 on the drawing paper. Help students sketch the bowl and cup on the paper. Write "The bowl holds _____ cups of water."
14. Explain that the cup is the unit. Have students predict how many cups of water the bowl will hold.
15. Working over the basin, fill the cup with water. Help students pour the water into the bowl.

   Say: There is still space for more water in the bowl. So pour another cup into the bowl.

16. Have students continue pouring cups of water into the bowl until it is full, counting each cup as they pour it. If the last cup of water overflows, help students decide if they should count it. (If most of the water fit into the bowl, count it. If most overflowed, do not count it.)

17. Have students complete the sentence you wrote on the drawing paper.

18. Repeat Steps 12–17 with two other sets of containers.

OFFLINE
15 min

LEARN Volume

Students will compare and measure the volume of different containers.

Gather the boxes, snap cubes, ones cubes, and sticky notes. Display one large box and one small box.

COMPARE VOLUME WITH LIKE UNITS

1. Say: To find how much a box can hold, we can measure its volume. Volume is measured with cubes.

2. Have students fill each box with snap cubes, counting each cube as they put in the box. Have students write the number of snap cubes on a sticky note and stick it to the box.

3. Ask students which box holds more cubes. Explain that larger boxes will hold more cubes.

4. Display a box that is the same size as one of the other boxes. Have students move the cubes from the same-sized box to the new box. Ask students what they notice about the number of cubes in the two boxes. (The number of cubes is equal.) Have students move the sticky note to the new box.

Tips

Explain to students that you could measure a big box, such as a toy box, with a small nonstandard unit, such as as snap cubes. However, it would take so many snap cubes that you would probably run out.

COMPARE VOLUME WITH DIFFERENT UNITS

5. Have students fill the empty same-sized box with ones cubes, counting each cube as they put it in the box. Have students write the number of ones cubes on a sticky note and stick it to the box.

6. Ask: We know that these boxes have equal volumes. But there are more ones cubes in this box than snap cubes in that box. Why?
ANSWER: The snap cubes are larger than the ones cubes, so it takes more ones cubes to fill the box.

7. Explain that when the unit of volume is smaller, it takes more of that unit to fill the box.

OFFLINE
10 min

TRY IT Holds More, Holds Less

PART 1

Students will measure and compare capacity and volume.

Gather the basin, 2 large containers, 1 small container, 2 boxes, snap cubes, coloring pencils, and 1 sheet of drawing paper.

1. Show students the large containers. Have students sketch the containers on the drawing paper.

2. Ask them to predict which container will hold more water.

3. Using the small container as the unit, have them measure the amount of water each large container holds.

4. Have students circle the container that holds more and underline the container that holds less.

5. Now show students the boxes. Have students sketch the boxes on the drawing paper.

6. Ask them to predict which box will hold more cubes.

7. Have students use the cubes to measure the volume of each box.

8. Have students circle the box that holds more cubes and underline the box that holds fewer cubes.

PART 2

Students will practice comparing capacity and volume without measuring. Give students the Holds More, Holds Less activity page from their Activity Book and read the directions with them.

OFFLINE
10 min

CHECKPOINT

Print the Checkpoint. Students will take a performance-based assessment. Read the directions and problems to students. Use the answer key to score the Checkpoint, and then enter the results online.

Gather the basin, 1 small container, 2 different-sized large containers, 2 different-sized small boxes, snap cubes, 1 sheet of drawing paper, and coloring pencils.

Objectives

- Compare the capacities of objects (for example, the pail holds more water than the cup).

- Use a nonstandard unit to compare the volumes of two or more objects.

Name _____ Date _____

Checkpoint Answer Key

Part 1

Follow the instructions for each item. Choose the response that best describes how the student performs on the task. When you have finished, enter the results online.

1. Have students use the small container as a nonstandard unit to find how much water each of the 2 large containers holds. Then have them compare the capacity of the 2 large containers. Say, "Sketch your 2 large containers and write how many units each container holds. Underline the container that holds less. Circle the container that holds more."

   (1 point)
   Did the student sketch each container and write how many nonstandard units each holds?

   A. Yes   B. No

   (1 point)
   Did the student underline the container that holds less and circle the container that holds more?

   A. Yes   B. No

Name _____ Date _____

2. Have students use the snap cubes as a nonstandard unit to find the volume of each box. Then have them compare the volume of the 2 boxes. Say, "Sketch your 2 boxes and write how many units each one holds. Underline the box that holds less. Circle the box that holds more."

   (1 point)
   Did the student sketch the two boxes and write how many snap cubes each holds?

   A. Yes   B. No

   (1 point)
   Did the student underline the box that holds less and circle the box that holds more?

   A. Yes   B. No

Give students Part 2 of the assessment.

Name _____ Date _____

Part 2

(1 point)
3. Circle the mug that holds less.

A.   B.

(1 point)
4. Circle the bucket that holds more.

A.   B.

Unit Review

UNIT REVIEW Look Back	20 minutes	ONLINE
UNIT REVIEW Checkpoint Practice	20 minutes	OFFLINE
➥ **UNIT REVIEW** Prepare for the Checkpoint		

▶ Unit Objectives

This lesson reviews the following objectives:

- Identify coins by name, given a picture of the coin (quarter, dime, nickel, and penny).
- State the value of coins (quarter, dime, nickel, and penny).
- Show different combinations of coins that equal the same value.
- Use direct comparison of objects to describe how the lengths of two or more objects compare (for example, the ruler is longer than the pencil).
- Describe the length of objects by using nonstandard units (for example, length of a page = 10 paper clips; width of a desk = 3 pencils).
- Use a nonstandard unit to describe how the lengths of two or more objects compare.
- Compare objects by weight (heavier and lighter).
- Use a nonstandard unit to describe the weight of an object and compare the weights of two or more objects (for example, the pencil is as heavy as 12 paper clips, and the marker is as heavy as 19 paper clips).
- Compare the capacities of objects (for example, the pail holds more water than the cup).
- Use a nonstandard unit to compare the volumes of two or more objects.

▶ Advance Preparation

In this lesson, students will have an opportunity to review previous activities in the Money and Measurement unit. Look at the suggested activities in Unit Review: Prepare for the Checkpoint online and gather any needed materials.

Gather the hanging balance you created for the Weight lesson. If you do not have the balance, refer to the Weight lesson in the Lesson Guide for instructions on how to create it.

Gather a small household object that will fit in the balance, such as an eraser.

Materials to Gather

SUPPLIED

blocks – B (all colors)

Checkpoint Practice activity page

ALSO NEEDED

straw

paper clips – 10

balance from Weight lesson

household objects – 1 small (eraser)

Keywords	balance	measure (verb)
	capacity	nonstandard units
	compare	shorter
	heavier	weight
	length	value
	lighter	volume
	longer	

UNIT REVIEW Look Back

Objectives

• Review unit objectives.

In this unit, students have learned the characteristics, names, and values of pennies, nickels, dimes, and quarters. They identified how many of a certain coin are in a group and learned to find the value of a group of one type of coin. Finally they identified groups of coins that have the same value.

Students also learned to measure with nonstandard units and to compare length, weight, capacity, and volume. Students will review these concepts to prepare for the Unit Checkpoint.

UNIT REVIEW Checkpoint Practice

Objectives

• Review unit objectives.

Students will complete a Checkpoint Practice activity page to prepare for the Unit Checkpoint. If necessary, read the directions, problems, and answer choices to students. Have students answer the problems on their own. Carefully review the answers with students.

For Problem 1, give students the paper clips and straw. For Problem 2, give students the balance, circle blocks, and eraser or other small household object.

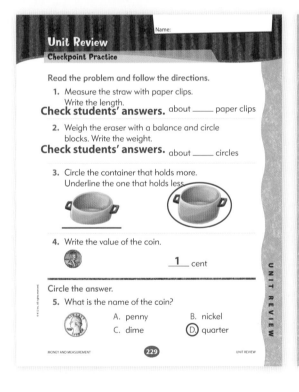

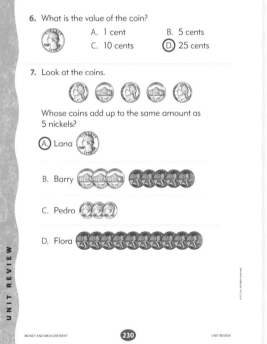

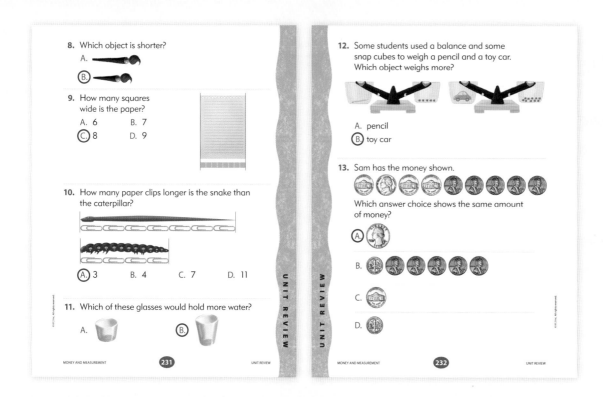

8. Which object is shorter?

A. ━━●

B. ━━● *(circled)*

9. How many squares wide is the paper?

A. 6   B. 7

C. 8 *(circled)*   D. 9

10. How many paper clips longer is the snake than the caterpillar?

A. 3 *(circled)*   B. 4   C. 7   D. 11

11. Which of these glasses would hold more water?

A.   B. *(circled)*

12. Some students used a balance and some snap cubes to weigh a pencil and a toy car. Which object weighs more?

A. pencil

B. toy car *(circled)*

13. Sam has the money shown.

Which answer choice shows the same amount of money?

A. *(circled)*

B.

C.

D.

⭲ UNIT REVIEW Prepare for the Checkpoint

What you do next depends on how students performed in the previous activity, Unit Review: Checkpoint Practice. If students had difficulty with any of the problems, complete the appropriate review activity listed in the table online.

Unit Checkpoint

UNIT CHECKPOINT Online	25 minutes	ONLINE
UNIT CHECKPOINT Offline	35 minutes	OFFLINE

▶ Unit Objectives

This lesson assesses the following objectives:

- Identify coins by name, given a picture of the coin (quarter, dime, nickel, and penny).
- State the value of coins (quarter, dime, nickel, and penny)
- Describe the length of objects by using nonstandard units (for example, length of a page = 10 paper clips; width of a desk = 3 pencils).
- Use a nonstandard unit to describe how the lengths of two or more objects compare.
- Compare objects by weight (heavier and lighter).
- Use a nonstandard unit to describe the weight of an object and compare the weights of two or more objects (for example, the pencil is as heavy as 12 paper clips, and the marker is as heavy as 19 paper clips).
- Compare the capacities of objects (for example, the pail holds more water than the cup).
- Use a nonstandard unit to compare the volumes of two or more objects.

▶ Advance Preparation

Gather the hanging balance you created for the Weight lesson. If you do not have the balance, refer to the Weight lesson in the Lesson Guide for instructions on how to create it.

Gather the following containers for liquid measurement:

- 1 small container, such as a paper cup, mug, soda cap, or measuring spoon
- 2 large containers of different sizes, such as large drinking cups, empty water bottles, half-gallon pitchers, soup bowls, and cooking pots
- Basin or bucket to catch spills during pouring

Gather the following boxes for dry measurement:

- 2 small to medium empty boxes of different sizes, such as small shoe boxes, tissue boxes, jewelry gift boxes, and index card holders

Materials to Gather

SUPPLIED

blocks – B (all colors)
blocks – O (all colors)
Unit Checkpoint (printout)

ALSO NEEDED

paper, drawing – 1 sheet
balance from Weight lesson
crayon
containers – 1 small, 2 large
household objects – 1 shoe, 1 sock, 1 basin or bucket, 2 boxes

---

UNIT CHECKPOINT Online

ONLINE 25min

Objectives

- Assess unit objectives.

Students will complete this part of the Unit Checkpoint online. Read the directions, problems, and answer choices to students. If necessary, help students with keyboard or mouse operations.

UNIT CHECKPOINT Offline

Objectives

• Assess unit objectives.

Students will complete this part of the Unit Checkpoint offline. Print the Unit Checkpoint. Students will take a performance-based assessment. Read the directions and problems to students. Use the answer key to score the Unit Checkpoint, and then enter the results online.

Gather the drawing paper, cubes, circle blocks, crayon, shoe, balance, sock, basin, containers, and boxes.

Name _____ Date _____

Unit Checkpoint Answer Key

Part 1

Follow the instructions for each problem. Choose the response that best describes how the student performs on the task. When you have finished, enter the results online.

1. Say, "Measure the length of the shoe and the crayon with cubes. Write how many cubes long each is on a sheet of paper."
   (1 point)

   Did the student write the length in cubes of the shoe and the crayon?

   A. Yes   B. No

   Ask, "How many cubes longer is the shoe than the crayon?"
   (1 point)

   Did the student say how many cubes longer the shoe is than the crayon?

   A. Yes   B. No

2. Say, "Use the balance to compare the weights of the sock and the crayon. Which is heavier?"
   (1 point)

   Did the student identify the heavier object?

   A. Yes   B. No

Name _____ Date _____

3. Say, "Weigh the sock and the crayon using the balance and circle blocks. Write the weight of each object on a sheet of paper."
   (1 point)

   Did the student write how many circle blocks the sock weighs and how many circle blocks the crayon weighs?

   A. Yes   B. No

---

4. Have the student use the small container as a nonstandard unit to find how much water each of the two large containers holds.

   Say, "Sketch your two large containers. Write how many units each container holds."
   (1 point)

   Did the student sketch the two containers and write how many nonstandard units each one holds?

   A. Yes   B. No

   Say, "Underline the container that holds less. Circle the container that holds more."
   (1 point)

   Did the student underline the container that holds less and circle the container that holds more?

   A. Yes   B. No

Name _____ Date _____

5. Have the student use the cubes as a nonstandard unit to find the volume of each box.

   Say, "Sketch your two boxes. Write how many units each box holds."
   (1 point)

   Did the student sketch the two boxes and write how many nonstandard units each one holds?

   A. Yes   B. No

   Say, "Underline the box that holds less. Circle the box that holds more."
   (1 point)

   Did the student underline the box that holds less and circle the box that holds more?

   A. Yes   B. No

Place Value, Addition, and Subtraction

▶ Unit Objectives

- Count and group objects in ones and tens, such as 4 groups of 10 objects with 2 more objects = 40 + 2 = 42.

- Estimate quantities and numbers of objects.

- Demonstrate understanding of place value by recording the number represented by groupings of tens and ones (for example, given 5 tens rods and 2 ones cubes or hearing "5 tens and 2 ones," record 52).

- Demonstrate understanding of place value by grouping given numbers into sets of tens and ones, such as 64 = 6 tens and 4 ones.

- Use concrete objects to model two-digit numbers in multiple ways (for example, 27 = 27 ones, or 1 ten and 17 ones, or 2 tens and 7 ones).

- Use concrete objects or sketches to model and solve addition or subtraction computation problems involving sums and minuends up through 100.

- Solve addition problems with a one- and a two-digit number with sums through 100 by using regrouping.

- Identify and explain the approach for addition or subtraction computation problems with sums or minuends up through 100.

- Solve subtraction problems with a two-digit minuend and a one-digit subtrahend by using regrouping.

▶ Big Ideas

- Numbers can represent basic counting results.
- Estimation is a useful tool in problem solving.
- Place-value notation makes it easier to write and operate on large numbers.
- Models and mathematical symbols can represent addition and subtraction.

▶ Unit Introduction

In this unit, students will learn about place value through 100. They will learn how to count and group objects as tens and ones, estimate a number of objects, and use base-10 blocks to model and write two-digit numbers as tens and ones. Students will model two-digit numbers different ways as an introduction to regrouping tens as ones and ones as tens. Students will then regroup to add and subtract with sums and minuends through 100. They will also learn several addition and subtraction strategies to help them find sums and differences of two-digit numbers.

Tens, Ones, and Estimation

Lesson Overview

Skills Update	5 minutes	ONLINE
LEARN Estimate	10 minutes	ONLINE
LEARN Model Tens and Ones	15 minutes	OFFLINE
LEARN Group and Count Tens and Ones	10 minutes	OFFLINE
TRY IT Count the Objects	10 minutes	OFFLINE
CHECKPOINT Online	5 minutes	ONLINE
CHECKPOINT Offline	5 minutes	OFFLINE

▶ Lesson Objectives

- Count and group objects in ones and tens, such as 4 groups of 10 objects with 2 more objects = 40 + 2 = 42.
- Estimate quantities and numbers of objects.

▶ Prerequisite Skills

Use concrete objects or sketches to represent a quantity up through 30.

▶ Common Errors and Misconceptions

Students might not think of numbers as groups of tens, hundreds, and so forth. For example, students might think of 24 only as 24 single units, not 2 tens and 4 ones.

▶ Advance Preparation

Prepare groups of items, as follows:

- 34 craft sticks (group tens with rubber bands)
- 58 craft sticks (group tens with rubber bands)
- 19 paper clips (group tens by attaching clips in chain)
- 25 paper clips (group tens by attaching paper clips in chain)
- 61 cubes (group tens by snapping them together)

▶ Content Background

Students will learn how to group objects as tens and ones and then count by 10s and 1s to find the total number of objects. Students will use this skill to estimate to the nearest 10.

When students are asked to express 34 as "3 tens and 4 ones," they begin to understand that the 3 in 34 represents 30 and the 4 represents 4 ones. When students realize that 34 can also be expressed as 2 tens and 14 ones, they are ready to understand *regrouping* in addition and subtraction problems. The mathematical term *regrouping* has now replaced both *carrying* and *borrowing*. *Regrouping* is a more descriptive term that applies to both addition and subtraction.

Materials to Gather

SUPPLIED

blocks – O (all colors)

Group and Count Tens and Ones activity page

Count the Objects activity page

Checkpoint (printout)

ALSO NEEDED

craft sticks – 92

paper clips – 44

rubber bands – 8

timer

LEARN Estimate ONLINE **10**min

Objectives

Students will estimate the number of objects to the nearest ten.

As students progress through the activity, have them ask themselves questions such as the following:

- How many objects are in the last group?
- Are there more or fewer than 5 objects?
- Do I count the last group as a ten?
- About how many tens are there altogether?

- Estimate quantities and numbers of objects.

LEARN Model Tens and Ones OFFLINE **15**min

Objectives

Students will count objects grouped as tens and ones to build estimation skills. Gather the groups of items you prepared.

1. Give students the 34 craft sticks. Have them count the craft sticks by first counting the tens (10, 20, 30) and then counting on the ones (31, 32, 33, 34). Students should move aside each bundle and single stick as they count it. Have students put the single sticks in one group.

2. Ask how many tens there are. (3) Ask how many ones are left over. (4)

   Say: There are 3 groups of tens and 4 ones left over. So there are 3 tens and 4 ones.

3. Ask what number is the same as 3 tens and 4 ones. (34)

4. Repeat Steps 1–3 with the following grouped items: 58 craft sticks, 19 paper clips, 25 paper clips, and 61 cubes.

- Count and group objects in ones and tens, such as 4 groups of 10 objects with 2 more objects $= 40 + 2 = 42$.

LEARN Group and Count Tens and Ones OFFLINE **10**min

Objectives

Students will group objects by tens and ones to count them. Gather the timer. Give students the Group and Count Tens and Ones activity page from their Activity Book and read the directions with them.

For each problem, have students tell you the number of tens and ones by saying, for example, "5 tens 8 ones." For Problem 6, you will need to time students.

- Count and group objects in ones and tens, such as 4 groups of 10 objects with 2 more objects $= 40 + 2 = 42$.

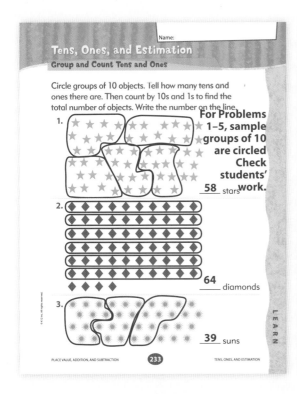

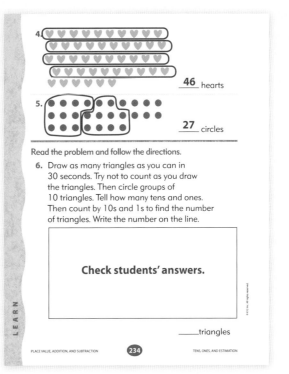

TRY IT Count the Objects

OFFLINE 10 min

Students will practice estimating and counting by 10s and 1s. Give students 39 cubes and the Count the Objects activity page from their Activity Book. Read the directions with them.

Objectives

- Count and group objects in ones and tens, such as 4 groups of 10 objects with 2 more objects $= 40 + 2 = 42$.

- Estimate quantities and numbers of objects.

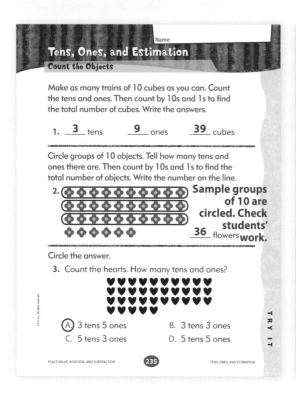

Tens, Ones, and Estimation
Count the Objects

Make as many trains of 10 cubes as you can. Count the tens and ones. Then count by 10s and 1s to find the total number of cubes. Write the answers.

1. __3__ tens   __9__ ones   __39__ cubes

Circle groups of 10 objects. Tell how many tens and ones there are. Then count by 10s and 1s to find the total number of objects. Write the number on the line.

2. **Sample groups of 10 are circled. Check students' work.**

__36__ flowers

Circle the answer.

3. Count the hearts. How many tens and ones?

(A.) 3 tens 5 ones   B. 3 tens 3 ones
C. 5 tens 3 ones   D. 5 tens 5 ones

TRY IT

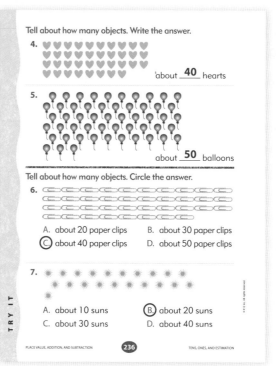

Tell about how many objects. Write the answer.

4.
about __40__ hearts

5.
about __50__ balloons

Tell about how many objects. Circle the answer.

6.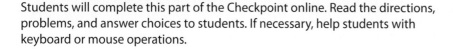

A. about 20 paper clips   B. about 30 paper clips
(C.) about 40 paper clips   D. about 50 paper clips

7.

A. about 10 suns   (B.) about 20 suns
C. about 30 suns   D. about 40 suns

TRY IT

CHECKPOINT Online

ONLINE 5 min

Students will complete this part of the Checkpoint online. Read the directions, problems, and answer choices to students. If necessary, help students with keyboard or mouse operations.

Objectives

- Count and group objects in ones and tens, such as 4 groups of 10 objects with 2 more objects = 40 + 2 = 42.
- Estimate quantities and numbers of objects.

OFFLINE
5min

Students will complete this part of the Checkpoint offline. Print the Checkpoint. Students will take a performance-based assessment. Read the directions and problems to students. Use the answer key to score the Checkpoint, and then enter the results online.

Gather 36 cubes to use for Problem 1.

- Count and group objects in ones and tens, such as 4 groups of 10 objects with 2 more objects = 40 + 2 = 42.

- Estimate quantities and numbers of objects.

☼ Checkpoint   Math | Place Value, Addition, and Subtraction | Tens, Ones, and Estimation

Name _____ Date _____

Checkpoint Answer Key

Follow the instructions for each problem. Choose the response that best describes how the student performs on the task. When you have finished, enter the results online. Place 36 cubes in front of the student.

1. Say, "Put these cubes into groups of 10. How many groups of 10 do you have?"
    (1 point)
    Did the student say 3 groups of 10?

    A. Yes   B. No

    Ask, "How many single cubes do you have left?"
    (1 point)
    Did the student say 6 cubes?

    A. Yes   B. No

    Ask, "If you have 3 groups of 10 cubes and 6 single cubes, how many cubes do you have?"
    (1 point)
    Did the student say 36 cubes?

    A. Yes   B. No

1 of 1

Place Value

Skills Update	5 minutes	ONLINE
GET READY Count Tens and Ones	5 minutes	ONLINE
LEARN Group Tens and Ones	15 minutes	ONLINE
LEARN Write Numbers as Tens and Ones	20 minutes	OFFLINE
TRY IT Numbers with Tens and Ones	15 minutes	OFFLINE

▶ Lesson Objectives

Demonstrate understanding of place value by recording the number represented by groupings of tens and ones (for example, given 5 tens rods and 2 ones cubes or hearing "5 tens and 2 ones," record 52).

▶ Prerequisite Skills

Count and group objects in ones and tens, such as 4 groups of 10 objects with 2 more objects = 40 + 2 = 42.

▶ Content Background

Students will learn how to model two-digit numbers with base-10 blocks to show place value.

Base-10 blocks are special blocks used to model numbers and show place value. The smallest base-10 block, a ones cube, represents 1. Ten ones cubes are "glued" together to make a tens rod, which represents 10. A tens rod equals 10 ones cubes.

Materials to Gather

SUPPLIED

Write Numbers as Tens and Ones activity page

Numbers with Tens and Ones activity page

Keywords

base-10 blocks – a set of blocks used to model the place values of numbers; blocks include ones cubes, tens rods, hundreds flats, and thousands cubes

hundreds flat – a block in the base-10 block set, showing 100 units and representing the hundreds place; equivalent to the combination of 100 ones cubes or 10 tens rods

model (verb) – to use physical objects, diagrams, or pictures to represent an amount, an expression, an equation, or a problem situation

ones cube – a block in the base-10 block set, showing one unit and representing the ones place

place value – the value of a digit, given its position in a number; for example, 23 means 2 tens and 3 ones

tens rod – a block in the base-10 block set, showing 10 units and representing the tens place

thousands cube – a block in the base-10 block set, showing 10 hundreds flats and representing the thousands place; equivalent to the combination of 1,000 ones cubes or 100 tens rods

GET READY Count Tens and Ones

Students will count objects grouped as tens and ones to prepare to learn about place value.

Objectives

- Count and group objects in ones and tens, such as 4 groups of 10 objects with 2 more objects $= 40 + 2 = 42$.

Tips

If students have difficulty, model the problems offline with craft sticks and tiles (E blocks). Have students take apart a bundle of craft sticks to see that there are 10.

LEARN Group Tens and Ones

Students will learn how to use base-10 blocks to model two-digit numbers.

Objectives

- Demonstrate understanding of place value by recording the number represented by groupings of tens and ones (for example, given 5 tens rods and 2 ones cubes or hearing "5 tens and 2 ones," record 52).

Tips

Allow students to use their base-10 blocks to model the numbers while they explore place value online.

LEARN Write Numbers as Tens and Ones

Students will write the number that a base-10 block model shows. Give students the Write Numbers as Tens and Ones activity page from their Activity Book and read the directions with them.

As students work through the problems, ask the following questions:

- How many tens are shown?
- How many ones are shown?
- What number has that many tens and ones?

Objectives

- Demonstrate understanding of place value by recording the number represented by groupings of tens and ones (for example, given 5 tens rods and 2 ones cubes or hearing "5 tens and 2 ones," record 52).

Tips

Allow students to use their base-10 blocks to model the problems on the activity page.

Name: _____

Place Value
Write Numbers as Tens and Ones

Look at the base-10 blocks. Count the tens rods. Count the ones cubes. Write the number of tens and ones. Say the number shown by the blocks. Then write the number.

1. Students should say "thirty-four."

   __3__ tens __4__ ones = __34__

2. Students should say "twenty-five."

   __2__ tens __5__ ones = __25__

3. Students should say "sixty-one."

   __6__ tens __1__ ones = __61__

4. Students should say "fifty-eight."

   __5__ tens __8__ ones = __58__

Complete the table.
Example

Base-10 Blocks	Tens	Ones	Number
	5 tens	2 ones	52
	8 tens	7 ones	87

Base-10 Blocks	Tens	Ones	Number
5.	9 tens	0 ones	90
6.	3 tens	8 ones	38
7.	1 tens	4 ones	14

TRY IT **Numbers with Tens and Ones**

Students will practice writing the number that a base-10 block model shows. Give students the Numbers with Tens and Ones activity page from their Activity Book and read the directions with them.

Tips

Allow students to use their base-10 blocks to model the problems on the activity page.

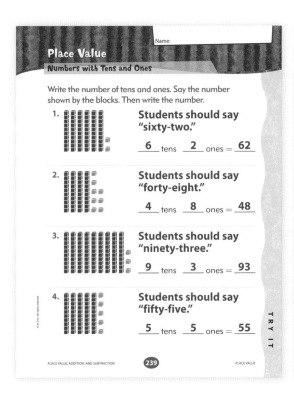

Place Value

Numbers with Tens and Ones

Write the number of tens and ones. Say the number shown by the blocks. Then write the number.

1. **Students should say "sixty-two."**

   __6__ tens __2__ ones = __62__

2. **Students should say "forty-eight."**

   __4__ tens __8__ ones = __48__

3. **Students should say "ninety-three."**

   __9__ tens __3__ ones = __93__

4. **Students should say "fifty-five."**

   __5__ tens __5__ ones = __55__

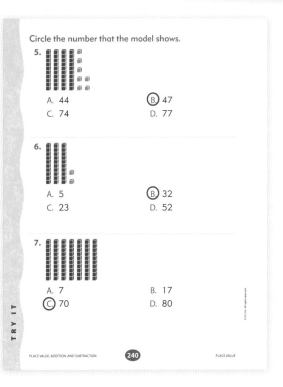

Circle the number that the model shows.

5.
   A. 44   B. 47
   C. 74   D. 77

6.
   A. 5   B. 32
   C. 23   D. 52

7.
   A. 7   B. 17
   C. 70   D. 80

Represent Numbers

Lesson Overview		
Skills Update	5 minutes	ONLINE
GET READY Build Numbers	10 minutes	ONLINE
LEARN Collect Tens	20 minutes	ONLINE
LEARN Place Value and Face Value	15 minutes	ONLINE
TRY IT Draw Tens and Ones	10 minutes	OFFLINE

▶ Lesson Objectives

Demonstrate understanding of place value by grouping given numbers into sets of tens and ones, such as 64 = 6 tens and 4 ones.

▶ Prerequisite Skills

Use concrete objects or sketches to represent a quantity up through 30.

▶ Common Errors and Misconceptions

- Students might not think of numbers as groups of tens, hundreds, and so forth. For example, students might think of 24 only as 24 single units, not 2 tens and 4 ones.
- Students might not realize that a digit's place-value position determines its value. For example, students might think the digits in 14 have values of 1 and 4, not 10 and 4.
- Students might not differentiate between a digit's face value and its place value. For example, they might think the digit 3 in 35 represents 3 ones instead of 3 tens.

▶ Content Background

Students will represent numbers with place-value models.

Materials to Gather

SUPPLIED

Draw Tens and Ones activity page

Keywords

place-value chart – a chart or arrangement that shows the value of each digit in a number

ten-frame – a grid that consists of ten squares, arranged in a two by five array; students use ten-frames to organize objects or sketches into groups of ten

GET READY Build Numbers

Students will represent numbers through 30 using objects. They will display these objects in ten-frames.

DIRECTIONS FOR USING THE COUNTING LEARNING TOOL

1. Click Problem Mode I.
   - Choose an object.
   - Click Yes to use ten-frames.
   - Click Start.
2. Have students drag objects into the ten-frames to represent the given number. Explain that students must fill an entire ten-frame before the computer will allow them to drag objects into a new ten-frame.
3. Have students continue answering problems as time allows.

Objectives

- Use concrete objects or sketches to represent a quantity up through 30.

LEARN Collect Tens

Students will display numbers as tens and ones in the place-value chart and practice regrouping 10 ones as 1 ten. They will go to a party with Rosa and pop balloons filled with confetti. Then they will put groups of 10 pieces of confetti into tubes. They will place the tubes in the Tens column of the place-value chart, and they will place the remaining pieces of confetti in the Ones column. Have students pop each balloon.

Objectives

- Demonstrate understanding of place value by grouping given numbers into sets of tens and ones, such as 64 = 6 tens and 4 ones.

LEARN Place Value and Face Value

Students will display numbers as tens and ones in the place-value chart and practice regrouping 10 ones as 1 ten. They will go to a party with Rosa and break piñatas filled with chips. Then they will put groups of 10 chips into tubes. They will place the tubes in the Tens column of the place-value chart, and they will place the remaining chips in the Ones column. Have students break each piñata.

Objectives

- Demonstrate understanding of place value by grouping given numbers into sets of tens and ones, such as 64 = 6 tens and 4 ones.

TRY IT Draw Tens and Ones

OFFLINE
10 min

Students will practice drawing place-value models for numbers. Give students the Draw Tens and Ones activity page from their Activity Book and read the directions with them. Use the answer key to check students' answers, and then enter the results online.

Objectives

- Demonstrate understanding of place value by grouping given numbers into sets of tens and ones, such as 64 = 6 tens and 4 ones.

Tips

Allow students to model the numbers using their circle blocks and place-value mat.

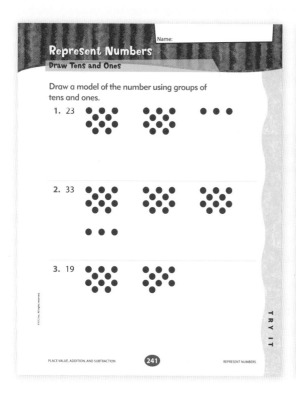

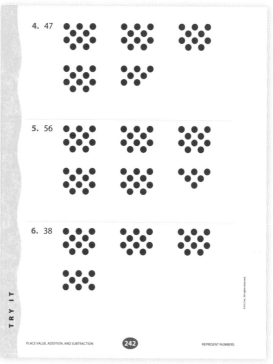

392 PLACE VALUE, ADDITION, AND SUBTRACTION

Place Value for Numbers

Skills Update	5 minutes	ONLINE
GET READY Use a Place-Value Chart	5 minutes	ONLINE
LEARN Build Numbers	20 minutes	OFFLINE
TRY IT What's the Number?	20 minutes	OFFLINE
CHECKPOINT	10 minutes	OFFLINE

▶ Lesson Objectives

- Demonstrate understanding of place value by recording the number represented by groupings of tens and ones (for example, given 5 tens rods and 2 ones cubes or hearing "5 tens and 2 ones," record 52).
- Demonstrate understanding of place value by grouping given numbers into sets of tens and ones, such as 64 = 6 tens and 4 ones.

▶ Prerequisite Skills

- Count and group objects in ones and tens, such as 4 groups of 10 objects with 2 more objects = 40 + 2 = 42.
- Use concrete objects or sketches to represent a quantity up through 30.

▶ Common Errors and Misconceptions

- Students might not think of numbers as groups of tens, hundreds, and so forth. For example, students might think of 24 only as 24 single units, not 2 tens and 4 ones.
- Students might not realize that a digit's place-value position determines its value. For example, students might think the digits in 14 have values of 1 and 4, not 10 and 4.
- Students might not differentiate between a digit's face value and its place value. For example, they might think the digit 3 in 35 represents 3 ones instead of 3 tens.

▶ Content Background

Students will create and interpret place-value models. They will use this knowledge to tell how many tens and ones are in numbers—without using models.

Keywords	**place-value mat** – a grid with columns labeled with place values (ones, tens . . .), used with corresponding base-10 blocks to illustrate place value

Materials to Gather

SUPPLIED

place-value mat

base-10 blocks

What's the Number? activity page

Checkpoint (printout)

GET READY Use a Place-Value Chart

Students will use ten-frames to help them represent a number in a place-value chart.

- Count and group objects in ones and tens, such as 4 groups of 10 objects with 2 more objects $= 40 + 2 = 42$.
- Use concrete objects or sketches to represent a quantity up through 30.

LEARN Build Numbers

Students will interpret and create place-value models.
  Gather the base-10 blocks and place-value mat.

1. Explain to students that you will show numbers with base-10 blocks.

2. Make the following models with blocks on the place-value mat. Have students tell you the number each model shows.
   - 1 tens rod, 4 ones cubes (14)
   - 3 tens rods, 6 ones cubes (36)
   - 5 tens rods, 3 ones cubes (53)
   - 6 tens rods, 2 ones cubes (62)
   - 4 tens rods, 7 ones cubes (47)

3. Place 19 ones cubes in the ones column of the place-value mat.

   Say: The ones digit of a two-digit number must be 0, 1, 2, 3, 4, 5, 6, 7, 8, or 9. But there are more than 9 ones in the ones column.

   Ask: How can we fix this?
   ANSWER: Move groups of 10 ones to the tens column.

4. **Say:** Make as many groups of 10 ones cubes as you can. Move each group to the tens column. Trade each group of 10 ones cubes for a tens rod.

   Students should move 10 ones cubes to the tens column and trade this group of ones cubes for a tens rod. The mat should show 1 tens rod and 9 ones cubes.

5. Have students model the following numbers on the place-value mat. Remind them to regroup if they have more than 10 ones in the ones columns.
   - 26 (2 tens rods, 6 ones cubes)
   - 43 (4 tens rods, 3 ones cubes)
   - 69 (6 tens rods, 9 ones cubes)
   - 45 (4 tens rods, 5 ones cubes)

- Demonstrate understanding of place value by recording the number represented by groupings of tens and ones (for example, given 5 tens rods and 2 ones cubes or hearing "5 tens and 2 ones," record 52).
- Demonstrate understanding of place value by grouping given numbers into sets of tens and ones, such as $64 = 6$ tens and 4 ones.

TRY IT What's the Number?

Objectives

Students will practice interpreting and creating place-value models. Give students the base-10 blocks and What's the Number? activity page from their Activity Book. Read the directions with them. Use the answer key to check students' answers, and then enter the results online.

- Demonstrate understanding of place value by recording the number represented by groupings of tens and ones (for example, given 5 tens rods and 2 ones cubes or hearing "5 tens and 2 ones," record 52).

- Demonstrate understanding of place value by grouping given numbers into sets of tens and ones, such as 64 = 6 tens and 4 ones.

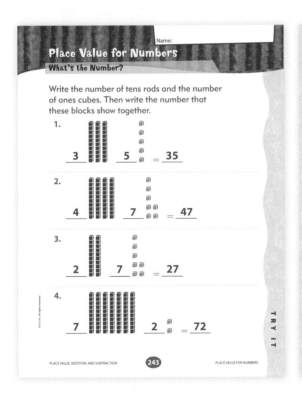

Name:

Place Value for Numbers

What's the Number?

Write the number of tens rods and the number of ones cubes. Then write the number that these blocks show together.

1. **3** **5** = **35**

2. **4** **7** = **47**

3. **2** **7** = **27**

4. **7** **2** = **72**

T R Y   I T

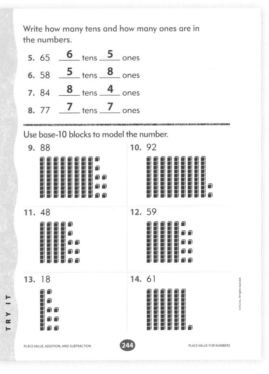

Write how many tens and how many ones are in the numbers.

5. 65 **6** tens **5** ones

6. 58 **5** tens **8** ones

7. 84 **8** tens **4** ones

8. 77 **7** tens **7** ones

Use base-10 blocks to model the number.

9. 88

10. 92

11. 48

12. 59

13. 18

14. 61

T R Y   I T

OFFLINE
10 min

Print the Checkpoint. In Part 1, students will take a performance-based assessment. In Part 2, students will complete the problems on their own. Read the directions, problems, and answer choices to students, if necessary. Use the answer key to score the Checkpoint, and then enter the results online.

Gather the base-10 blocks and place-value mat. For Problem 1, give students the blocks and mat. Students may use the mat if they choose, but they do not have to.

- Demonstrate understanding of place value by recording the number represented by groupings of tens and ones (for example, given 5 tens rods and 2 ones cubes or hearing "5 tens and 2 ones," record 52).

- Demonstrate understanding of place value by grouping given numbers into sets of tens and ones, such as 64 = 6 tens and 4 ones.

⚙ Checkpoint   Math | Place Value, Addition, and Subtraction | Place Value for Numbers

Name _____ Date _____

Checkpoint Answer Key

Part 1
Follow the instructions for each problem. Choose the response that best describes how the student performs on the task. When you have finished, enter the results online.

1. Place the base-10 blocks in a pile in front of the student. If needed, the student may also use the place-value mat.
   Say, "Show the number 73 using tens rods and ones cubes."

   The student needs to show 7 tens and 3 ones.

   Did the student show the number 73 using the base-10 blocks?
   (1 point)
   A. Yes   B. No

Give students Part 2 of the assessment.

⚙ Checkpoint   Math | Place Value, Addition, and Subtraction | Place Value for Numbers

Name _____ Date _____

Part 2
Circle the answer.
(1 point)
2. Which shows the number 94?

   A.

   (B.)

   C.

   D.

(1 point)
3. How many tens are in the number shown?

   A. 10   B. 7   (C.) 6   D. 4

(1 point)
4. How many tens and how many ones are in the number 49?
   A. 13 ones   B. 9 tens 4 ones
   C. 4 tens 0 ones   (D.) 4 tens 9 ones

⚙ Checkpoint   Math | Place Value, Addition, and Subtraction | Place Value for Numbers

Name _____ Date _____

(1 point)
5. What number do the blocks show?

   A. 27   B. 70   (C.) 72   D. 90

(1 point)
6. If I have 8 tens and 2 ones, what number do I have?
   A. 10   B. 28   C. 80   (D.) 82

Write the answer.
(1 point)
7. How many tens and how many ones are in the number 16?

   __**1**__ ten __**6**__ ones

(1 point)
8. You have a number with 5 tens and 6 ones. What is your number?

   __**56**__

Model Numbers Different Ways

Skills Update	5 minutes	ONLINE
GET READY Understand Place Value	5 minutes	ONLINE
LEARN Different Models, Same Number	30 minutes	ONLINE
TRY IT Model 2-Digit Numbers	10 minutes	OFFLINE
CHECKPOINT	10 minutes	OFFLINE

▶ Lesson Objectives

Use concrete objects to model two-digit numbers in multiple ways (for example, 27 = 27 ones, or 1 ten and 17 ones, or 2 tens and 7 ones).

▶ Prerequisite Skills

Demonstrate understanding of place value by grouping given numbers into sets of tens and ones, such as 64 = 6 tens and 4 ones.

▶ Content Background

Students will learn how to model the same number using different combinations of tens rods and ones cubes in order to build regrouping skills. They will need to understand this concept when they have to regroup to add and subtract.

Keywords	**regroup; regrouping** – to use place-value concepts to rename numbers, such as one ten and 3 ones = 13 ones; often used in addition and subtraction

Materials to Gather

SUPPLIED

base-10 blocks

Model 2-Digit Numbers activity page

Checkpoint (printout)

GET READY Understand Place Value

ONLINE 5min

Students will use the Place Value Learning Tool to show numbers as groups of tens and ones.

DIRECTIONS FOR USING THE PLACE VALUE LEARNING TOOL

1. Click Begin Setup and choose the following:
   - Work with NUMBERS up to: 99
   - Use regrouping: NO
   - Teacher or Parent Makes Questions
2. Use the following numbers: 35, 63, and 50.
3. For each problem, have students say how many tens and how many ones are in the number before they show the number on the place-value mat.

Objectives

- Demonstrate understanding of place value by grouping given numbers into sets of tens and ones, such as 64 = 6 tens and 4 ones.

LEARN Different Models, Same Number

Students will learn how to regroup to show numbers different ways by watching animations using base-10 blocks.

As students progress through the activity, ask questions such as the following:

- How many ones equal 1 ten?
- What does it mean to regroup 10 ones as 1 ten?
- How can two different models show the same number?

Objectives

- Use concrete objects to model two-digit numbers in multiple ways (for example, 27 = 27 ones, or 1 ten and 17 ones, or 2 tens and 7 ones).

Tips

Allow students to use their base-10 blocks to model the numbers shown online.

TRY IT Model 2-Digit Numbers

Students will practice modeling numbers different ways by regrouping tens and ones. Give students the base-10 blocks and Model 2-Digit Numbers activity page from their Activity Book. Read the directions with them.

Objectives

- Use concrete objects to model two-digit numbers in multiple ways (for example, 27 = 27 ones, or 1 ten and 17 ones, or 2 tens and 7 ones).

Name:

Model Numbers Different Ways
Model 2-Digit Numbers

Use base-10 blocks to make the model.
Then answer the problem.

1. Show 28 ones. What is another way to show 28? **1 ten 18 ones or** __2__ tens __8__ ones

2. Show 4 tens 1 one. What is another way to show 41? __3__ tens __11__ ones
2 tens 21 ones ,1 ten 31 ones, or 41 ones

Use base-10 blocks to model the number three different ways. Write the number of tens and ones in each model.

3. 67   **See below.** ____ tens ____ ones

____ tens ____ ones   ____ tens ____ ones

4. 30 **Possible answers: 3 tens 0 ones,
2 tens 10 ones,**   ____ tens ____ ones
1 ten 20 ones, 30 ones
____ tens ____ ones   ____ tens ____ ones

5. 79   **See below.** ____ tens ____ ones

____ tens ____ ones   ____ tens ____ ones

PLACE VALUE, ADDITION, AND SUBTRACTION   245   MODEL NUMBERS DIFFERENT WAYS

TRY IT

Circle the model that shows the same number as the given model.

6. A.   B.   C.   D.

7. A.   B.   C.   D.

8. A.   B.   C.   D.

PLACE VALUE, ADDITION, AND SUBTRACTION   246   MODEL NUMBERS DIFFERENT WAYS

TRY IT

Additional Answers

3. **Possible answers:** 6 tens 7 ones, 5 tens 17 ones, 4 tens 27 ones, 3 tens 37 ones, 2 tens 47 ones, 1 ten 57 ones, 67 ones

5. **Possible answers:** 7 tens 9 ones, 6 tens 19 ones, 5 tens 29 ones, 4 tens 39 ones, 3 tens 49 ones, 2 tens 59 ones, 1 ten 69 ones, 79 ones

CHECKPOINT

Objectives

Print the Checkpoint. Students will take a performance-based assessment. Read the directions and problems to students. Use the answer key to score the Checkpoint, and then enter the results online.

Gather the base-10 blocks.

- Use concrete objects to model two-digit numbers in multiple ways (for example, 27 = 27 ones, or 1 ten and 17 ones, or 2 tens and 7 ones).

Name _____ Date _____

Checkpoint Answer Key

Follow the instructions for each problem. Choose the response that best describes how the student performs on the task. When you have finished, enter the results online.

1. Display 3 tens rods and 2 ones cubes.
   Say, "The number 32 is shown here. Use base-10 blocks to show another way to make 32."

   Possible answers: 2 tens rods and 12 ones cubes, 1 tens rod and 22 ones cubes, or 0 tens rods and 32 ones cubes.
   (1 point)
   Did the student use base-10 blocks to show another way to make 32?

   A. Yes   B. No

---

2. Display 5 tens rods and 16 ones cubes.
   Say, "The number 66 is shown here. Use base-10 blocks to show another way to make 66."

   Possible answers: 66 ones cubes, 6 tens rods and 6 ones cubes, 4 tens rods and 26 ones cubes, or 3 tens rods and 36 ones cubes.
   (1 point)
   Did the student use base-10 blocks to show another way to make 66?

   A. Yes   B. No

Name _____ Date _____

3. Display the base-10 blocks.
   Say, "Use base-10 blocks to model the number 54 in two different ways."

   Possible answers: 54 ones cubes, 5 tens rods and 4 ones cubes, 4 tens rods and 14 ones cubes, or 3 tens rods and 24 ones cubes.
   (1 point)
   Did the student use base-10 blocks to model the number 54 one way?

   A. Yes   B. No

   (1 point)
   Did the student use base-10 blocks to model the number 54 another (different) way?

   A. Yes   B. No

---

4. Display the base-10 blocks.
   Say, "Use base-10 blocks to model the number 43 in two different ways."

   Possible answers: 43 ones cubes, 4 tens rods and 3 ones cubes, 3 tens rods and 13 ones cubes, or 2 tens rods and 23 ones cubes.
   (1 point)
   Did the student use base-10 blocks to model the number 43 one way?

   A. Yes   B. No

   (1 point)
   Did the student use base-10 blocks to model the number 43 another (different) way?

   A. Yes   B. No

Use Objects to Add

Skills Update	5 minutes	ONLINE
GET READY Add with Bears	10 minutes	ONLINE
LEARN Make Groups of Ten to Add	15 minutes	OFFLINE
LEARN Use Base-10 Blocks to Add	20 minutes	OFFLINE
TRY IT Addition with Objects	10 minutes	OFFLINE

▶ Lesson Objectives

Use concrete objects or sketches to model and solve addition or subtraction computation problems involving sums and minuends up through 100.

▶ Prerequisite Skills

Use concrete objects or sketches to model and solve addition or subtraction problems with sums and minuends up through 30.

▶ Common Errors and Misconceptions

Students might say more than one number for each object when counting objects in a group. Or they might skip objects. To avoid such problems, draw a line down the center of a sheet of paper. Have students move objects from one side of the paper to the other as they count.

▶ Content Background

Students will learn to add greater numbers more easily by using groups of 10. They will then use the tens rods and ones cubes from the base-10 blocks to add.

Keywords	**add** – to combine, or put together, groups of objects or numbers
	sum – the solution to an addition problem

Materials to Gather

SUPPLIED

blocks – B (all colors)

base-10 blocks

place-value mat

Addition with Objects activity page

ALSO NEEDED

paper, construction – 3 sheets

paper plates – 10

GET READY Add with Bears

ONLINE
10min

Students will add using countable bears online. They will watch as two groups of bears, representing two addends, combine to form one group. Then they will find the sum.

 If students have difficulty, encourage them to count the bears in the combined group. Or encourage students to start with the greater addend and count on the bears representing the lesser addend. For example, in the group of 9 black bears and 5 brown bears, students may start at 9 and count on the 5 brown bears: 10, 11, 12, 13, 14.

Objectives

• Use concrete objects or sketches to model and solve addition or subtraction problems with sums and minuends up through 30.

LEARN Make Groups of Ten to Add

Objectives

- Use concrete objects or sketches to model and solve addition or subtraction computation problems involving sums and minuends up through 100.

Students will learn to make groups of 10 to add two numbers.
Gather the circle blocks, construction paper, and paper plates.

1. Have students place 14 circles on one sheet of paper and 20 on another sheet.

    Say: To add 14 and 20, move all the circles to the last sheet of paper and count them.

2. **Ask:** What is 14 plus 20?
    ANSWER: 34

3. Repeat Steps 1 and 2 with $23 + 34 = 57$.

4. Point out that counting 57 circles takes a long time and that students must be careful not to make an error while counting. Even counting on 23 from 34 is difficult. Explain that putting the objects into groups of 10 will make them easier to count.

5. Have students sort the 57 circles into groups of 10 using the paper plates. Students should place 10 circles on each of 5 plates. They should place the remaining 7 circles on a sixth plate.

6. **Say:** There are 10 circles on each plate, so you can count each plate as 1 ten

    Point to the sixth plate.

    Say: Then you can count the circles on this plate by ones to find the total.

7. Have students point to the plates as they count by 10s. Have them point to the circles on the sixth plate as they count on by ones. (10, 20, 30, 40, 50, 51, 52, 53, 54, 55, 56, 57)

    Ask: What is the total?
    ANSWER: 57

8. For the following problems, have students first make a group of circles for each addend. Then have them combine the groups. To find the total, have them make and count groups of 10 and a group of the remaining ones, as described in Steps 5–7.

    - $41 + 18 = 59$
    - $25 + 21 = 46$
    - $11 + 24 = 35$

LEARN Use Base-10 Blocks to Add

Students will use base-10 blocks to add two numbers.

Gather the circle blocks, paper plates, base-10 blocks, and place-value mat.

1. Have students add 31 and 23 by first making a group of circles for each addend. Then have them combine the groups to represent the total (54). Have students sort the 54 circles into groups of 10 using the paper plates. Students should place 10 circles on each of 5 plates. They should place the remaining 4 circles on a sixth plate. Have them count by 10s and ones to find the total: 10, 20, 30, 40, 50, 51, 52, 53, 54.

2. Hold up a tens rod.

   Say: This tens rod represents 10 ones. We can use base-10 blocks instead of circles to add greater numbers. Each plate stands for 1 ten, so we can replace each plate with a tens rod. We can replace the single circles with ones cubes.

3. Display the place-value mat, and explain that it can help students organize the base-10 blocks when they add.

4. Point to the columns.

   Say: This is the tens column. You place tens rods here. This is the ones column. You place ones cubes here.

5. Have students replace each group of 10 circles with a tens rod. Have them replace each of the single circles with a ones cube. Have them move the tens rods and ones cubes to the appropriate columns on the place-value mat.

6. Ask students how many tens rods and ones cubes are on the mat. (5 tens rods and 4 ones cubes)

   Say: There are 5 tens rods and 4 ones cubes, or 5 tens and 4 ones. Count by 10s and then by ones to find the total: 10, 20, 30, 40, 50, 51, 52, 53, 54. So 5 tens and 4 ones equals 54.

7. Set aside the circles and plates. Tell students they will add 54 and 23 using base-10 blocks and the place-value mat.

8. Have students use base-10 blocks to show the first addend, 54.

9. Below the blocks for 54, have students show the second addend, 23.

Hundreds	Tens	Ones
	▮▮▮▮▮ + ▮▮	▫ ▫ ▫ ▫ + ▫ ▫ ▫

10. Have students count by 10s and ones to find the total number of blocks, which is the sum. Have them tell you the sum. (77)

11. Repeat Steps 8–10 with $15 + 53 = 68$ and $24 + 71 = 95$.

Tips

If you wish, have students occasionally count the number of ones cubes that are "glued" together to make the tens rod to remind themselves why it represents 10.

Use concrete objects or sketches to model and solve addition or subtraction computation problems involving sums and minuends up through 100.

OFFLINE
10min

Objectives

Students will practice modeling and solving addition problems using base-10 blocks. Give students the base-10 blocks, place-value mat, and Addition with Objects activity page from their Activity Book. Read the directions with them.

- Use concrete objects or sketches to model and solve addition or subtraction computation problems involving sums and minuends up through 100.

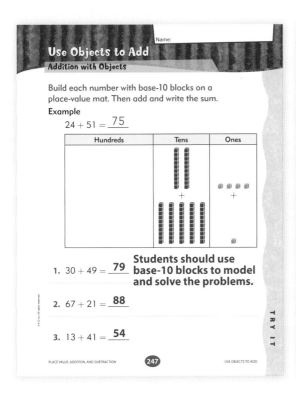

Use Objects to Add
Addition with Objects

Build each number with base-10 blocks on a place-value mat. Then add and write the sum.

Example
24 + 51 = _75_

Hundreds	Tens	Ones

1. 30 + 49 = _79_ Students should use base-10 blocks to model and solve the problems.

2. 67 + 21 = _88_

3. 13 + 41 = _54_

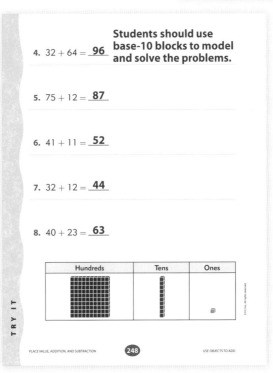

4. 32 + 64 = _96_ Students should use base-10 blocks to model and solve the problems.

5. 75 + 12 = _87_

6. 41 + 11 = _52_

7. 32 + 12 = _44_

8. 40 + 23 = _63_

Hundreds	Tens	Ones

Use Sketches to Add

Skills Update	5 minutes	ONLINE
GET READY Use Drawings to Add	10 minutes	OFFLINE
LEARN Sketch Groups of 10 to Add	15 minutes	OFFLINE
LEARN Sketch Base-10 Blocks to Add	20 minutes	OFFLINE
TRY IT Sketch to Add	10 minutes	OFFLINE

▶ Lesson Objectives

Use concrete objects or sketches to model and solve addition or subtraction computation problems involving sums and minuends up through 100.

▶ Prerequisite Skills

Use concrete objects or sketches to model and solve addition or subtraction problems with sums and minuends up through 30.

▶ Common Errors and Misconceptions

Students might say more than one number for each object when counting objects in a group. Or they might skip objects. To avoid such problems, draw a line down the center of a sheet of paper. Have students move objects from one side of the paper to the other as they count.

▶ Content Background

Students will use sketches to add greater numbers. They will learn to group their sketches as tens and ones, and then to sketch base-10 blocks to represent tens and ones.

Materials to Gather

SUPPLIED
base-10 blocks
Sketch to Add activity page

ALSO NEEDED
crayons
paper, drawing – 5 sheets

GET READY Use Drawings to Add

OFFLINE 10 min

Students will use a sketch to model and solve an addition problem.
Gather the crayons and one sheet of drawing paper.

1. Tell students to listen carefully as you read a story problem aloud.

   Say: There are 6 gray bunnies and 8 brown bunnies. How many bunnies are there altogether?

2. Have students make a sketch to model the problem. Remind students to use simple shapes, such as circles, to represent the bunnies. For example, students may draw 6 gray dots and 8 brown dots.

3. Have students count the items they sketched and tell you how many bunnies there are altogether. (14)

4. Have students write the number sentence that their sketch shows. ($6 + 8 = 14$)

Objectives

- Use concrete objects or sketches to model and solve addition or subtraction problems with sums and minuends up through 30.

LEARN Sketch Groups of 10 to Add

Students will learn to draw objects in groups of 10 when sketching to add. Gather the crayons and two sheets of drawing paper.

1. Have students draw 15 red triangles and 23 blue triangles. Then have students count all the triangles to find how many in all.

    Ask: What is 15 plus 23?
    ANSWER: 38

2. Repeat Step 1 with $32 + 17 = 49$.

3. Point out that as students add greater and greater numbers, counting objects can take a long time. Students must also be careful not to make an error while counting. Explain that circling groups of 10 objects will make students' sketches easier to use.

4. **Say:** Let's find the sum of $32 + 17$ again, but this time we'll use groups of 10. Look at the picture you drew for $32 + 17$. Draw a circle around as many groups of 10 triangles as you can.

    Students should circle 4 groups of 10. They should have 9 triangles that are not circled.

5. **Ask:** How many groups of 10 did you circle?
    ANSWER: 4

    Ask: How many triangles were left over?
    ANSWER: 9

6. **Say:** There are 10 triangles in each circled group, so you can count each group as 1 ten. Then you can count on the leftover triangles by ones.

7. Have students point to the circled groups as they count by 10s. Have them point to the leftover triangles as they count by ones. (10, 20, 30, 40, 41, 42, 43, 44, 45, 46, 47, 48, 49)

8. **Ask:** Was it easier to add with groups of 10? Why or why not?
    ANSWER: Yes, I could count by 10s and count on the ones.

9. Have students follow the process described in Steps 4–7 to solve the following problems. Guide students as needed.

    - $32 + 13 = 45$
    - $21 + 36 = 57$
    - $25 + 11 = 36$

Tips

Remind students to use simple shapes for sketches. Suggest that they use 2 by 5 arrays (as shown below) to show each group of 10.

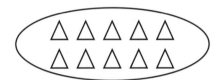

LEARN Sketch Base-10 Blocks to Add

Students will learn how to sketch base-10 blocks to add.
Gather the base-10 blocks, crayons, and two sheets of drawing paper.

1. Have students sketch groups of 10 to add 27 and 11. They should draw a group of 27 objects and a group of 11 objects. Then they should circle 3 groups of 10. They should count the objects in all: 10, 20, 30, 31, 32, 33, 34, 35, 36, 37, 38.

   Ask: What is 27 plus 11?
   ANSWER: 38

- Use concrete objects or sketches to model and solve addition or subtraction computation problems involving sums and minuends up through 100.

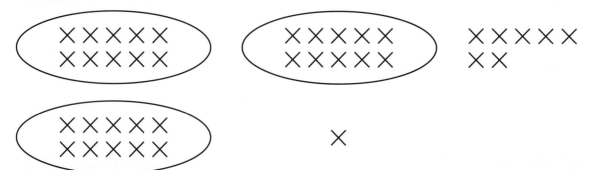

2. Repeat Step 1 with $32 + 25 = 57$.

3. Hold up a tens rod.

   Say: This tens rod represents 10 ones. Even if you don't have base-10 blocks, you can use sketches of them to help you add greater numbers. To sketch the blocks quickly, draw a line or skinny rectangle to stand for a tens rod. Draw a dot or small square to stand for a ones cube.

4. Point to the sketch students made to solve $32 + 25 = 57$.

   Say: Let's sketch base-10 blocks to add $32 + 25$. We can replace each circled group with a sketch of a tens rod. We can replace each leftover object with a sketch of a ones cube.

5. Using their previous sketch for reference, have students draw a line to represent each ten. Have students draw a dot to represent each of the ones.

6. Ask students how many tens rods they sketched. (5)

   Ask them how many ones cubes they sketched. (7)

   Say: You sketched 5 tens rods and 7 ones cubes, so the total is 5 tens and 7 ones, or 57.

7. Have students sketch base-10 blocks to solve the following problems. They should sketch blocks to show the first addend, sketch blocks to show the second addend, and then count the tens rods and ones cubes in all to find the sum. Guide students as needed.

   - $12 + 55 = 67$
   - $55 + 21 = 76$
   - $35 + 54 = 89$

Tips

Note that students can draw base-10 blocks however they wish, as long as the blocks are countable and students can tell the difference between the tens rod and the ones cube.

TRY IT Sketch to Add

OFFLINE 10 min

Students will practice sketching and using sketches to add greater numbers. Give students the Sketch to Add activity page from their Activity Book and read the directions with them.

Objectives

- Use concrete objects or sketches to model and solve addition or subtraction computation problems involving sums and minuends up through 100.

Name:

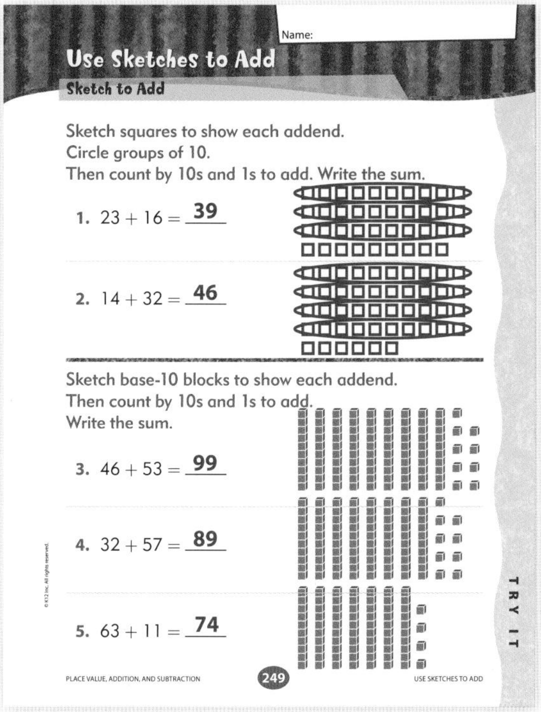

Use Sketches to Add

Sketch to Add

Sketch squares to show each addend.
Circle groups of 10.
Then count by 10s and 1s to add. Write the sum.

1. 23 + 16 = **39**

2. 14 + 32 = **46**

Sketch base-10 blocks to show each addend.
Then count by 10s and 1s to add.
Write the sum.

3. 46 + 53 = **99**

4. 32 + 57 = **89**

5. 63 + 11 = **74**

TRY IT

PLACE VALUE, ADDITION, AND SUBTRACTION 249 USE SKETCHES TO ADD

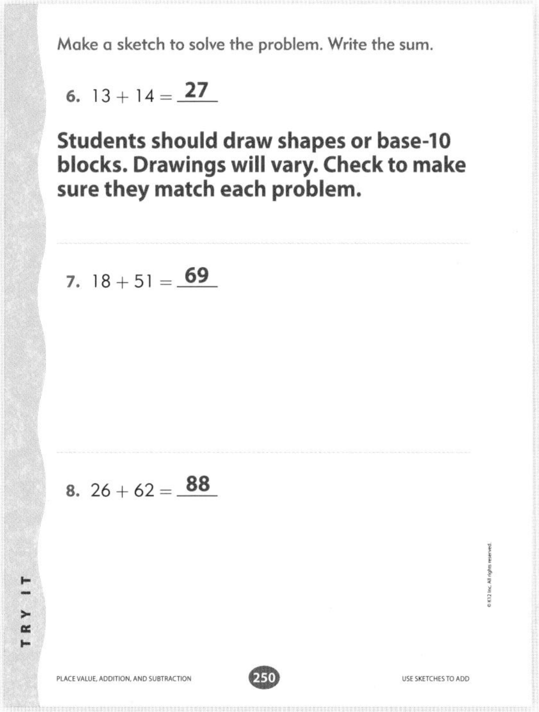

Make a sketch to solve the problem. Write the sum.

6. 13 + 14 = **27**

Students should draw shapes or base-10 blocks. Drawings will vary. Check to make sure they match each problem.

7. 18 + 51 = **69**

8. 26 + 62 = **88**

TRY IT

PLACE VALUE, ADDITION, AND SUBTRACTION 250 USE SKETCHES TO ADD

Addition with Sums Through 100

Lesson Overview

Skills Update	5 minutes	ONLINE
GET READY Basic Addition Facts	10 minutes	ONLINE
LEARN Add 2-Digit and 1-Digit Numbers	30 minutes	ONLINE
TRY IT Sums Through 100	10 minutes	OFFLINE
CHECKPOINT	5 minutes	OFFLINE

▶ Lesson Objectives

Solve addition problems with a one- and a two-digit number with sums through 100 by using regrouping.

▶ Prerequisite Skills

- Use concrete objects or sketches to model and solve addition or subtraction problems with sums and minuends up through 30.
- Demonstrate automatic recall of addition facts with sums through 20.
- Demonstrate understanding of the rule for adding zero.

▶ Content Background

Students will learn how to add a one-digit number to a two-digit number. They will learn how to regroup ones as tens in order to add. They will also learn how to regroup 10 tens as 1 hundred in order to find a sum of 100.

Materials to Gather

SUPPLIED
base-10 blocks
place-value mat
Sums Through 100 activity page
Checkpoint (printout)

GET READY   Basic Addition Facts

ONLINE
10 min

Objectives

Students will use flash cards to review basic addition facts. Guide students to say the sum aloud before they flip the card. Have students work through each of the three decks.

Encourage students to use base-10 blocks, counters, or drawings to help them find the sum if they cannot recall the fact automatically.

- Use concrete objects or sketches to model and solve addition or subtraction problems with sums and minuends up through 30.
- Demonstrate automatic recall of addition facts with sums through 20.
- Demonstrate understanding of the rule for adding zero.

LEARN Add 2-Digit and 1-Digit Numbers

Objectives

- Solve addition problems with a one- and a two-digit number with sums through 100 by using regrouping.

Students will learn how to regroup ones as tens in order to add two-digit and one-digit numbers for which the sum of the ones is greater than 9. They will also learn how to regroup 10 tens as 1 hundred in order to find a sum of 100. To learn this concept, students will be introduced to the hundreds flat, the base-10 block that represents 100.

DIRECTIONS FOR USING THE PLACE VALUE ADDITION LEARNING TOOL

1. Click Begin Setup and choose the following:
   - QUESTIONS set by: Learning Coach
     (The other fields will become disabled.)

2. Enter the following problems:
   - $38 + 6$
   - $92 + 8$
   - $53 + 9$
   - $68 + 2$
   - $95 + 5$

   Click Submit to begin the first problem.

3. Have students model the addends.

   Ask: What should we do first to add 38 and 6?
   ANSWER: Combine the ones.

4. Have students click $+$ to add the ones. Point out that there are 12 ones cubes in the Ones column.

   Say: We can only have up to 9 ones cubes in the Ones column. Regroup 10 ones cubes as 1 tens rod.

5. Have students click the arrow to trade 10 ones cube for 1 tens rod.

6. After students regroup, have them add the tens rods.

   Say: Now we have 4 tens rods and 4 ones cubes. So 38 plus 6 equals 44.

7. Have students model the addends in the second problem.

   Ask: What should we do first to add 92 and 8?
   ANSWER: Combine the ones.

8. Have students add the ones. They should then trade the 10 ones cubes for 1 tens rods. Prompt them to do so if they don't automatically make the trade.

   Ask: What should we do next?
   ANSWER: Combine the tens.

9. Have students add the tens. Point out that there cannot be more than 10 tens rods in the Tens column. Have them trade the 10 tens rods for a hundreds flat.

   Say: A hundreds flat is equal to 10 tens rods. 10 tens equal 1 hundred. The sum of 92 and 8 equals 100.

10. Have students complete the remaining problems. Assist them as needed using the process described in Steps 3–9.

11. If time remains, have students complete the following problems:

- $97 + 3$
- $44 + 8$
- $23 + 9$
- $49 + 5$
- $99 + 1$

TRY IT Sums Through 100

OFFLINE

10 min

Objectives

- Solve addition problems with a one- and a two-digit number with sums through 100 by using regrouping.

Students will practice adding two-digit and one-digit numbers with sums through 100, regrouping when necessary. Give students the base-10 blocks, place-value mat, and Sums Through 100 activity page from their Activity Book. Read the directions with them.

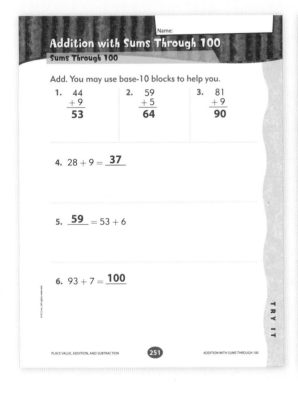

Name: _____

Addition with Sums Through 100

Sums Through 100

Add. You may use base-10 blocks to help you.

1. 44
       +9
       53

2. 59
       +5
       64

3. 81
       +9
       90

4. $28 + 9 =$ **37**

5. **59** $= 53 + 6$

6. $93 + 7 =$ **100**

TRY IT

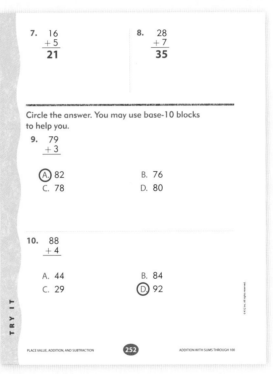

7. 16
       +5
       21

8. 28
       +7
       35

Circle the answer. You may use base-10 blocks to help you.

9. 79
       +3

A. 82   B. 76
C. 78   D. 80

10. 88
        +4

A. 44   B. 84
C. 29   D. 92

TRY IT

Print the Checkpoint and have students complete it on their own. Read the directions, problems, and answer choices to students, if necessary. Use the answer key to score the Checkpoint, and then enter the results online.

Allow students to use the base-10 blocks and place-value mat to solve the problems.

- Solve addition problems with a one- and a two-digit number with sums through 100 by using regrouping.

Checkpoint — Math | Place Value, Addition, and Subtraction | Addition with Sums Through 100

Name _____ Date _____

Checkpoint Answer Key

Add.

(1 point)

1. 73
   + 9
   82

(1 point)

2. 16
   + 8
   24

Circle the answer.

(1 point)

3. 56
   + 7

   A. 49   (B.) 63   C. 60   D. 57

(1 point)

4. 52
   + 9

   A. 59   B. 43   (C.) 61   D. 60

Different Ways to Add

Skills Update	5 minutes	ONLINE
GET READY Regroup to Add	10 minutes	ONLINE
LEARN Two Addition Strategies	15 minutes	ONLINE
LEARN Break Apart Numbers to Add	15 minutes	ONLINE
TRY IT Add Different Ways	15 minutes	OFFLINE

▶ Lesson Objectives

Identify and explain the approach for addition or subtraction computation problems with sums or minuends up through 100.

▶ Prerequisite Skills

Solve addition problems with a one- and a two-digit number with sums through 100 by using regrouping.

▶ Common Errors and Misconceptions

- Students might have difficulty seeing the connection between addition and subtraction situations.
- Students might be able to execute algorithms, but they might not be able to explain what they are doing. For example, when adding 19 and 23, students might "carry" a 1 to the tens column but not understand that they regrouped 10 ones as 1 ten.

▶ Advance Preparation

Print three copies of the Ten-Frames. Also print the Number Line 0–100. Cut out the number lines and tape them together to form one number line from 0 to 100.

▶ Content Background

Students will learn that they can use different strategies to solve addition problems. This lesson focuses on both new and previously learned strategies. Students may choose strategies that best meet their own needs in different situations.

Materials to Gather

SUPPLIED
base-10 blocks
blocks – B (all colors)
Ten-Frames (printout)
Number Line 0–100 (printout)
Add Different Ways activity page

SUPPLIED
scissors, adult
tape, clear

Keywords

count on – to add two groups by starting with the number of objects in one group and then counting up, in order, the number of objects in the other group
decompose – to break apart numbers, such as $34 = 30 + 4$ or $34 = 14 + 20$; often used to make calculations easier
number line – a line consisting of points equally spaced, each of which corresponds to a unique number

GET READY Regroup to Add

ONLINE
10 min

Objectives

- Solve addition problems with a one- and a two-digit number with sums through 100 by using regrouping.

Students will be guided through the process of regrouping to add two numbers with a sum less than 100.

Encourage students to ask themselves questions such as the following:

- How many ones are there altogether?
- Do I need to regroup? How do I know?
- How many tens are there altogether?

LEARN Two Addition Strategies

ONLINE
15 min

Objectives

- Identify and explain the approach for addition or subtraction computation problems with sums or minuends up through 100.

Students will learn that they can use different strategies to solve addition problems. They will see how the same problems can be solved by using either a number line or base-10 blocks.

Tips

Allow students to use base-10 blocks and the Number Line 0–100 to follow along with the problems shown online.

LEARN Break Apart Numbers to Add

ONLINE
15 min

Objectives

- Identify and explain the approach for addition or subtraction computation problems with sums or minuends up through 100.

Students will use ten-frames to help them decompose, or break apart, numbers. They will learn that by breaking apart numbers, they can make them easier to add.

There are several ways students can use ten-frames to decompose numbers before adding. When using ten-frames to add 48 + 6, students might choose to move 4 circles from 48 to complete the ten-frame with 6 circles, creating the expression 44 + 10. Or students might choose to move 2 circles from 6 to complete the ten-frame with 8 circles, creating the expression 50 + 4. Both expressions have the same sum, 54.

Tips

Allow students to use circle blocks and the Ten-Frames to follow along with the problems shown online.

TRY IT Add Different Ways

Objectives

Students will practice using different strategies to find sums through 100. Give students the base-10 blocks, circle blocks, Number Line 0–100, Ten-Frames, and Add Different Ways activity page from their Activity Book. Read the directions with them.

- Identify and explain the approach for addition or subtraction computation problems with sums or minuends up through 100.

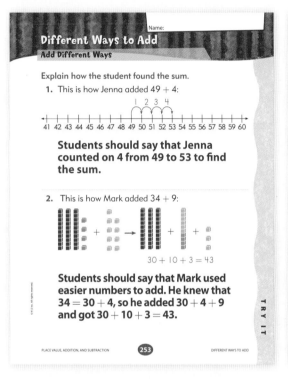

Name:

Different Ways to Add

Add Different Ways

Explain how the student found the sum.

1. This is how Jenna added 49 + 4:

Students should say that Jenna counted on 4 from 49 to 53 to find the sum.

2. This is how Mark added 34 + 9:

30 + 10 + 3 = 43

Students should say that Mark used easier numbers to add. He knew that 34 = 30 + 4, so he added 30 + 4 + 9 and got 30 + 10 + 3 = 43.

PLACE VALUE, ADDITION, AND SUBTRACTION   253   DIFFERENT WAYS TO ADD

TRY IT

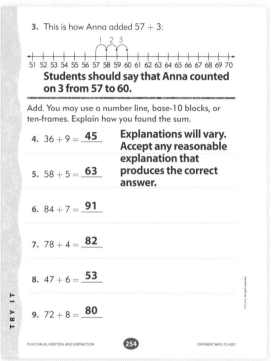

3. This is how Anna added 57 + 3:

Students should say that Anna counted on 3 from 57 to 60.

Add. You may use a number line, base-10 blocks, or ten-frames. Explain how you found the sum.

4. 36 + 9 = __45__

5. 58 + 5 = __63__

Explanations will vary. Accept any reasonable explanation that produces the correct answer.

6. 84 + 7 = __91__

7. 78 + 4 = __82__

8. 47 + 6 = __53__

9. 72 + 8 = __80__

TRY IT

PLACE VALUE, ADDITION, AND SUBTRACTION   254   DIFFERENT WAYS TO ADD

Use Objects to Subtract

Lesson Overview

Skills Update	5 minutes	ONLINE
GET READY Model Subtraction	10 minutes	OFFLINE
LEARN Make Groups of 10 to Subtract	15 minutes	OFFLINE
LEARN Use Base-10 Blocks to Subtract	20 minutes	OFFLINE
TRY IT Subtract with Objects	10 minutes	OFFLINE

▶ Lesson Objectives

Use concrete objects or sketches to model and solve addition or subtraction computation problems involving sums and minuends up through 100.

▶ Prerequisite Skills

Use concrete objects or sketches to model and solve addition or subtraction problems with sums and minuends up through 30.

▶ Common Errors and Misconceptions

Students might say more than one number for each object when counting objects in a group. Or they might skip objects. To avoid such problems, draw a line down the center of a sheet of paper. Have students move objects from one side of the paper to the other as they count.

▶ Content Background

Students will learn to subtract with greater numbers more easily by using groups of ten. They will then use the tens rods and ones cubes from the base-10 blocks to subtract.

Keywords	**difference** – the solution to a subtraction problem
	subtract – to take away objects from a group or to find a difference between two groups

Materials to Gather

SUPPLIED

blocks – B (all colors)

base-10 blocks

place-value mat

Subtract with Objects activity page

ALSO NEEDED

counting objects – 30

household objects – 9 plastic cups,
    1 paper plate

GET READY Model Subtraction

Students will use objects to solve subtraction problems with minuends through 30. Gather the counting objects (for example, dry macaroni) and paper plate.

- • Use concrete objects or sketches to model and solve addition or subtraction problems with sums and minuends up through 30.

1. Have students place 25 objects on the plate.

2. Ask students to take away 11 of the objects and count how many are left. (14) Suggest that students move each object from one side of the plate to the other as they count it.

3. Explain that the objects left on the plate represent the difference. Ask students what number sentence they showed. (25 − 11 = 14)

4. Repeat Steps 1–3 with the number sentence 29 − 12 = 17.

Tips

For counting objects, use small, durable household items (for example, dry macaroni, shells, or twists).

LEARN Make Groups of 10 to Subtract

Students will learn to make groups of 10 to subtract two numbers. Gather the circle blocks and plastic cups.

- • Use concrete objects or sketches to model and solve addition or subtraction computation problems involving sums and minuends up through 100.

1. Have students place 38 circles on a sheet of paper, take away 24 circles, and count the circles that remain.

   Ask: What is 38 minus 24?
   ANSWER: 14

2. Repeat Step 1 with 47 − 24 = 23.

3. Point out that counting 47 circles takes a long time and that students must be careful not to make an error while counting. Explain that putting objects into groups of 10 will make them easier to subtract.

4. Place 47 circles on the paper.

   Say: Let's subtract 47 − 24 again, but this time we'll use groups of 10. Make as many groups of 10 circles as you can with the 47 circles. Put each group of 10 in a cup. Put the circles that are left over next to the cups.

   Students should place 10 circles in each of 4 cups. They should place the remaining 7 circles next to the cups.

5. **Ask:** How many groups of 10 were you able to make?
   ANSWER: 4

   Ask: How many circles were left over?
   ANSWER: 7

6. Now explain how to subtract 24.

   Say: Each cup shows 1 ten. There are 2 tens in 24. To subtract 2 tens, take away 2 cups. There are 4 ones in 24. To subtract 4 ones, take away 4 of the leftover circles that are not in cups.

7. **Say:** To find the difference, count the remaining cups by 10s and remaining leftover circles by ones.

   Students should count 10, 20 for the cups and 21, 22, 23 for the circles not in the cups.

   Say: There are 2 tens and 3 ones left, so the difference is 23. 47 − 24 = 23

Tips

Watch that students do not count each circle in the cups. Remind them that they do not need to recount the circles because they already counted out 10 for each cup.

8. Have students follow the process described in Steps 4–7 to solve the following problems. Guide students as needed.

- $52 - 31 = 21$
- $45 - 14 = 31$
- $58 - 10 = 48$

LEARN Use Base-10 Blocks to Subtract

Objectives

- Use concrete objects or sketches to model and solve addition or subtraction computation problems involving sums and minuends up through 100.

Students will use base-10 blocks to represent tens and ones when subtracting two numbers.

Gather the base-10 blocks, place-value mat, circle blocks, and plastic cups.

1. Have students use the circles and cups to subtract $54 - 23 = 31$. They should place 10 circles in each of 5 cups and place the remaining 4 circles outside of the cups. Then they should take away 2 cups and 3 leftover circles. They should count the remaining cups and leftover circles: 10, 20, 30, 31.

2. Repeat Step 1 with $65 - 31 = 34$.

3. Hold up a tens rod.

Say: This tens rod represents 10 ones. We can use base-10 blocks instead of circles to subtract greater numbers. Each cup stands for 1 ten, so we can replace each cup with a tens rod. We can replace the single circles with ones cubes.

4. Display the place-value mat, and explain that it can help students organize the base-10 blocks when they subtract.

5. Point to the columns.

Say: This is the tens column. You place tens rods here. This is the ones column. You place ones cubes here.

6. Have students set up the cups again to show 65. Have them replace each cup with a tens rod. Have them replace each of the single circles with a ones cube. Have them move the tens rods and ones cubes to the appropriate columns on the place-value mat.

7. Say: Show $65 - 31$ again, this time using base-10 blocks. There are 3 tens and 1 one in 31. So to subtract 31, take away 3 tens rods and 1 ones cube.

8. Ask how many tens rods and ones cubes are left on the mat. (3 tens rods and 4 ones cubes)

Say: To find the difference, count by 10s and then by ones.

Students should count 10, 20, 30, 31, 32, 33, 34.

9. Set aside the circles and cubes. Have students use the base-10 blocks and place-value mat to solve the following problems:

- $96 - 42 = 54$
- $59 - 21 = 38$
- $78 - 35 = 43$

TRY IT Subtract with Objects

Objectives

Students will practice using objects to subtract. Give students the base-10 blocks, place-value mat, circle blocks, plastic cups, and Subtract with Objects activity page from their Activity Book. Read the directions with them.

- Use concrete objects or sketches to model and solve addition or subtraction computation problems involving sums and minuends up through 100.

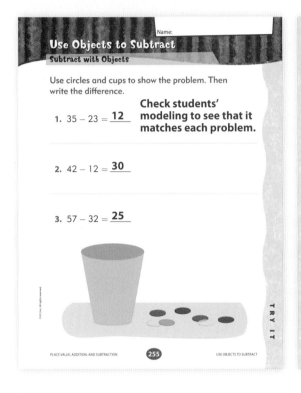

Name:

Use Objects to Subtract

Subtract with Objects

Use circles and cups to show the problem. Then write the difference.

Check students' modeling to see that it matches each problem.

1. 35 − 23 = __12__

2. 42 − 12 = __30__

3. 57 − 32 = __25__

TRY IT

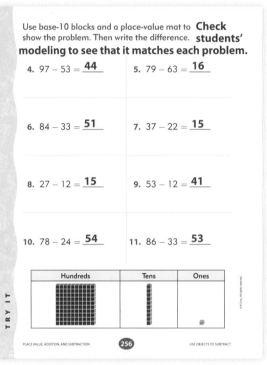

Use base-10 blocks and a place-value mat to **Check** show the problem. Then write the difference. **students'**
modeling to see that it matches each problem.

4. 97 − 53 = __44__   5. 79 − 63 = __16__

6. 84 − 33 = __51__   7. 37 − 22 = __15__

8. 27 − 12 = __15__   9. 53 − 12 = __41__

10. 78 − 24 = __54__   11. 86 − 33 = __53__

Hundreds	Tens	Ones

TRY IT

Use Sketches to Subtract

Lesson Overview

Skills Update	5 minutes	ONLINE
GET READY Use Drawings to Subtract	5 minutes	ONLINE
LEARN Sketch Groups of 10 to Subtract	15 minutes	OFFLINE
LEARN Sketch Base-10 Blocks to Subtract	15 minutes	OFFLINE
TRY IT Sketch to Subtract	10 minutes	OFFLINE
CHECKPOINT	10 minutes	OFFLINE

▶ Lesson Objectives

Use concrete objects or sketches to model and solve addition or subtraction computation problems involving sums and minuends up through 100.

▶ Prerequisite Skills

Use concrete objects or sketches to model and solve addition or subtraction problems with sums and minuends up through 30.

▶ Common Errors and Misconceptions

Students might say more than one number for each object when counting objects in a group. Or they might skip objects. To avoid such problems, draw a line down the center of a sheet of paper. Have students move objects from one side of the paper to the other as they count.

▶ Content Background

Students will use sketches to subtract with greater numbers. They will learn to group their sketches as tens and ones, and then to sketch base-10 blocks to represent tens and ones.

Keywords	
	minuend – in subtraction, the quantity or number from which another number is subtracted; 8 is the minuend in the problem $8 - 7 = ?$
	subtrahend – the number that is subtracted in a subtraction problem; 7 is the subtrahend in the problem $8 - 7 = ?$

Materials to Gather

SUPPLIED

base-10 blocks

Sketch to Subtract activity page

Checkpoint (printout)

ALSO NEEDED

paper, drawing – 4 sheets

GET READY Use Drawings to Subtract

Students will use sketches to solve subtraction problems. They will see a subtraction expression modeled by a sketch, and they will be asked to use the sketch to find the difference. For example, $7 - 3$ would be shown as a group of 7 sketches with Xs drawn through 3 of the sketches. To find the difference, students should count the sketches that are not crossed out.

- Use concrete objects or sketches to model and solve addition or subtraction problems with sums and minuends up through 30.

LEARN Sketch Groups of 10 to Subtract

Students will learn to draw objects in groups of 10 when sketching to subtract. Gather two sheets of drawing paper.

- Use concrete objects or sketches to model and solve addition or subtraction computation problems involving sums and minuends up through 100.

1. Have students draw 27 objects. Tell them to cross out 6 objects. Then have students count the objects that are not crossed out.

   Ask: What is 27 minus 6?
   ANSWER: 21

2. Repeat Step 1 with $56 - 24 = 32$.

3. Point out that as students subtract with greater and greater numbers, counting objects can take a long time. Students must also be careful not to make an error while counting. Explain that circling groups of 10 objects will make students' sketches easier to use.

4. **Say:** Let's subtract $56 - 24$ again, but this time we'll use groups of 10. Draw 56 objects. Draw circles around as many groups of 10 as you can.

   Students should circle 5 groups of 10. They should have 6 objects that are not circled.

5. **Ask:** How many groups of 10 did you circle?
   ANSWER: 5

   Ask: How many objects were left over?
   ANSWER: 6

6. Now explain how to subtract 24.

   Say: Each circled group shows 1 ten. There are 2 tens in 24. To subtract 24, cross out 2 circled groups. There are 4 ones in 24. To subtract 4 ones, cross out 4 of the leftover objects that are not in groups.

7. **Say:** To find the difference, count the remaining circled groups by 10s and remaining leftover objects by ones.

   Students should count 10, 20, 30 for the groups and 31, 32 for the objects not in groups.

   Say: There are 3 tens and 2 ones left, so the difference is 32.

8. **Ask:** Was it easier to subtract with groups of 10? Why or why not?
   ANSWER: Yes, it was easier. I could count by 10s and count on the ones.

9. Have students follow the process described in Steps 4–7 to solve the following problems. Guide students as needed.

   - $25 - 13 = 12$
   - $79 - 25 = 54$
   - $41 - 21 = 20$

Tips

Remind students to use simple shapes for sketches. Suggest that they use 2 by 5 arrays (as shown below) to show each group of 10.

LEARN Sketch Base-10 Blocks to Subtract

Students will learn how to sketch base-10 blocks to subtract. Gather the base-10 blocks and two sheets of drawing paper.

- Use concrete objects or sketches to model and solve addition or subtraction computation problems involving sums and minuends up through 100.

1. Have students sketch groups of 10 to subtract 47 − 21 = 26. They should draw 47 objects and circle 4 groups of 10. Then they should cross out 2 circled groups and 1 leftover object. They should count the remaining objects: 10, 20, 21, 22, 23, 24, 25, 26.

   Ask: What is 47 minus 21?
   ANSWER: 26

2. Repeat Step 1 with 53 − 12 = 41.

3. Hold up a tens rod.

   Say: This tens rod represents 10 ones. Even if you don't have base-10 blocks, you can use sketches of them to help you subtract greater numbers. To sketch the blocks quickly, draw a line or skinny rectangle to stand for a tens rod. Draw a dot or small square to stand for a ones cube.

4. Point to the sketch students made to solve 53 − 12 = 41.

   Say: Let's sketch base-10 blocks to subtract 53 − 12. We can replace each circled group with a sketch of a tens rod. We can replace each leftover object with a sketch of a ones cube.

5. Using their previous sketch for reference, have students draw a line to represent each ten in 53. Have students draw a dot to represent each of the ones.

6. **Say:** To subtract 12, cross out 1 tens rod and 2 ones cubes.

7. **Ask:** What is the difference?
   ANSWER: 41

   Ask: How do you know?
   ANSWER: There are 4 tens rods and 1 ones cube that are not crossed out.

8. Have students sketch base-10 blocks to solve the following problems. Guide students as needed.

   - 93 − 51 = 42
   - 78 − 22 = 56
   - 39 − 28 = 11

TRY IT Sketch to Subtract

Objectives

Students will practice sketching and using sketches to subtract greater numbers. Give students the Sketch to Subtract activity page from their Activity Book and read the directions with them.

- Use concrete objects or sketches to model and solve addition or subtraction computation problems involving sums and minuends up through 100.

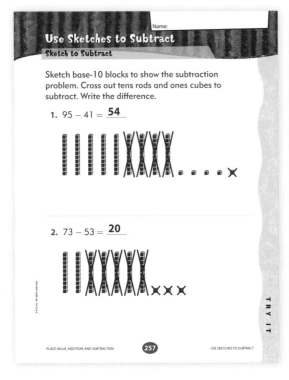

Name: _____

Use Sketches to Subtract

Sketch to Subtract

Sketch base-10 blocks to show the subtraction problem. Cross out tens rods and ones cubes to subtract. Write the difference.

1. $95 - 41 =$ **54**

2. $73 - 53 =$ **20**

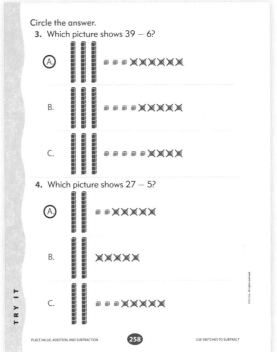

Circle the answer.

3. Which picture shows $39 - 6$?

A.

B.

C.

4. Which picture shows $27 - 5$?

A.

B.

C.

CHECKPOINT

OFFLINE 10 min

Print the Checkpoint and have students complete it on their own. Read the directions, problems, and answer choices to students, if necessary. Use the answer key to score the Checkpoint, and then enter the results online.

Objectives

- Use concrete objects or sketches to model and solve addition or subtraction computation problems involving sums and minuends up through 100.

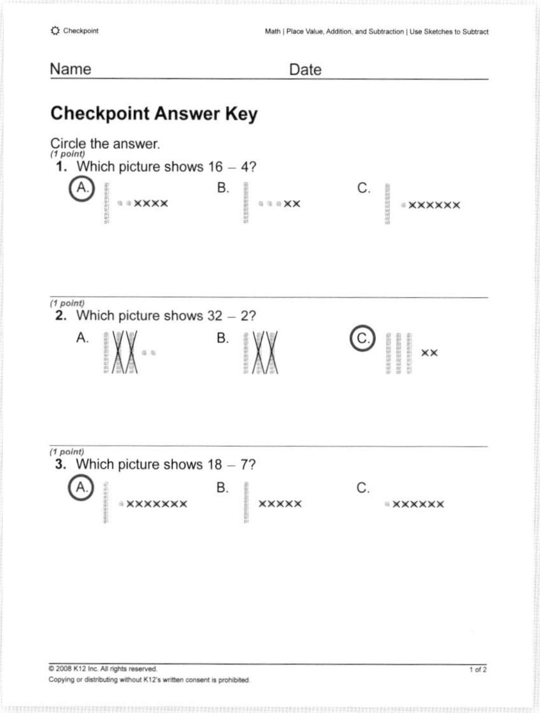
Checkpoint — Math | Place Value, Addition, and Subtraction | Use Sketches to Subtract

Name Date

Checkpoint Answer Key

Circle the answer.

(1 point)
1. Which picture shows 16 – 4? (A.) B. C.

(1 point)
2. Which picture shows 32 – 2? A. B. (C.)

(1 point)
3. Which picture shows 18 – 7? (A.) B. C.

© 2008 K12 Inc. All rights reserved. Copying or distributing without K12's written consent is prohibited. 1 of 2

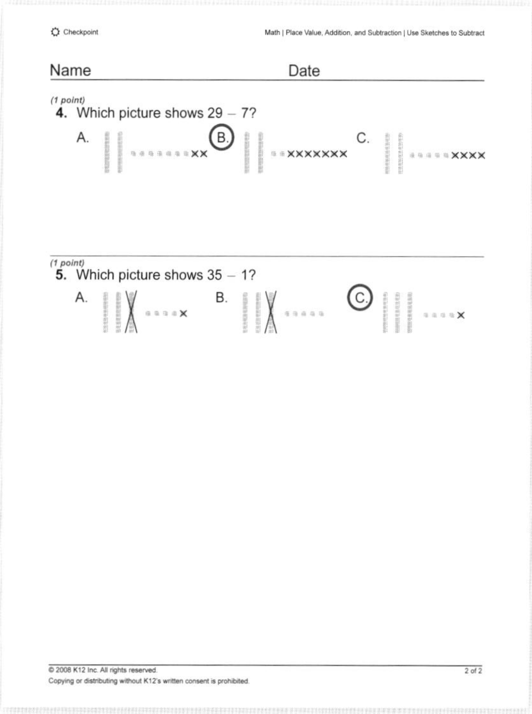
Checkpoint — Math | Place Value, Addition, and Subtraction | Use Sketches to Subtract

Name Date

(1 point)
4. Which picture shows 29 – 7? A. (B.) C.

(1 point)
5. Which picture shows 35 – 1? A. B. (C.)

© 2008 K12 Inc. All rights reserved. Copying or distributing without K12's written consent is prohibited. 2 of 2

Subtraction with Regrouping

Lesson Overview

Skills Update	5 minutes	ONLINE
GET READY Basic Subtraction Facts	5 minutes	ONLINE
LEARN Regroup to Subtract	10 minutes	OFFLINE
LEARN Subtraction	25 minutes	ONLINE
TRY IT Find the Difference	15 minutes	OFFLINE

▶ Lesson Objectives

Solve subtraction problems with a two-digit minuend and a one-digit subtrahend by using regrouping.

▶ Prerequisite Skills

- Use concrete objects or sketches to model and solve addition or subtraction problems with sums and minuends up through 30.
- Demonstrate automatic recall of subtraction facts with minuends through 20.
- Demonstrate understanding of the result of subtracting zero from a given quantity.

▶ Content Background

Students will learn how to find the difference when a one-digit number is subtracted from a two-digit number. They will regroup tens and ones in order to subtract.

Materials to Gather

SUPPLIED

base-10 blocks

place-value mat

Find the Difference activity page

GET READY Basic Subtraction Facts

ONLINE
5 min

Students will use flash cards to review basic subtraction facts. Guide students to say the difference aloud before they flip the card. Have students work through each of the three decks.

Encourage students to use base-10 blocks, counters, or sketches to help them find the difference if they cannot recall the fact automatically.

Objectives

- Use concrete objects or sketches to model and solve addition or subtraction problems with sums and minuends up through 30.
- Demonstrate automatic recall of subtraction facts with minuends through 20.
- Demonstrate understanding of the result of subtracting zero from a given quantity.

LEARN Regroup to Subtract

Students will regroup tens and ones in different ways to show numbers. It is essential that students understand this skill so that they can use it to successfully subtract with regrouping.

Gather the base-10 blocks and place-value mat.

1. Have students write 34 on a sheet of paper.

2. Have students use their blocks and mat to model the number 34. Tell students to use as many tens rods as they can.

   Ask: How many tens did you show? How many ones?
   ANSWER: 3 tens 4 ones

3. Have students write their answer on the paper.

4. Have students regroup one of the tens rods as 10 ones cubes. Have them write the new number of tens and ones on the paper below their first answer. (2 tens 14 ones)

5. Repeat Step 4 until students have regrouped all of the tens rods. The final model should show only ones cubes.

6. Point to students' answers.

   Say: Circle the group of tens and ones that shows the first time you regrouped 1 tens rod as 10 ones cubes.

   Students should circle "2 tens 14 ones."

   Say: This answer shows 1 ten regrouped as 10 ones. This is how you will regroup, if you need to, when subtracting.

7. Repeat Steps 1–6 with the following numbers: 28, 16, 45.

LEARN Subtraction

Students will learn how to regroup when subtracting a one-digit number from a two-digit number. Gather the base-10 blocks and place-value mat.

Follow the directions on each screen. When directed, have students use the blocks and place-value mat to solve the given subtraction problems. As students solve these problems, encourage them to ask themselves questions such as the following:

• How many ones are there all together?

• Are there enough ones to subtract?

• Do I need to regroup? How do I know?

• Where do I put the regrouped ones?

• How many tens are there altogether?

• What is the difference?

TRY IT Find the Difference

Objectives

Students will practice solving subtraction problems, some of which require regrouping. Give students the base-10 blocks, place-value mat, and Find the Difference activity page from their Activity Book. Read the directions with them.

- Solve subtraction problems with a two-digit minuend and a one-digit subtrahend by using regrouping.

Name:

Subtraction with Regrouping
Find the Difference

Find the difference. Use base-10 blocks and a place-value mat to model the problem. Regroup when necessary.

1. 26 − 7 **19**	2. 31 − 9 **22**	**Check students' models.**

3. 18 − 4 **14**	4. 23 − 6 **17**

5. 34 − 6 **28**	6. 32 − 8 **24**

7. 28 − 9 = **19**

8. **26** = 33 − 7

---

9. 21 − 4 **17**	10. 29 − 5 **24**

11. 33 − 4 **29**	12. 40 − 3 **37**

13. 22 − 9 **13**	14. 25 − 3 **22**

15. 28 − 9 **19**	16. 15 − 9 **6**

17. 21 − 2 **19**	18. 25 − 9 **16**

19. **33** = 39 − 6

20. 26 − 8 = **18**

More Subtraction with Regrouping

Skills Update	5 minutes	ONLINE
GET READY Basic Subtraction Review	10 minutes	OFFLINE
LEARN Subtract 1-Digit Numbers	15 minutes	ONLINE
LEARN Regroup to Solve	15 minutes	OFFLINE
TRY IT Practice Subtraction with Regrouping	10 minutes	OFFLINE
CHECKPOINT	5 minutes	OFFLINE

▶ Lesson Objectives

Solve subtraction problems with a two-digit minuend and a one-digit subtrahend by using regrouping.

▶ Prerequisite Skills

- Use concrete objects or sketches to model and solve addition or subtraction problems with sums and minuends up through 30.
- Demonstrate automatic recall of subtraction facts with minuends through 20.
- Demonstrate understanding of the result of subtracting zero from a given quantity.

▶ Advance Preparation

Use index cards to make flash cards for the following subtraction facts through 20. One side of the card should have the difference. The other side should have the subtraction expression.

10 − 10 = 0	14 − 10 = 4	18 − 6 = 12
11 − 10 = 1	15 − 6 = 9	18 − 11 = 7
12 − 9 = 3	15 − 12 = 3	19 − 4 = 15
12 − 11 = 1	16 − 3 = 13	19 − 16 = 3
13 − 4 = 9	16 − 14 = 2	20 − 3 = 17
13 − 11 = 2	17 − 7 = 10	20 − 15 = 5
14 − 7 = 7	17 − 12 = 5	

```
 _____        _____
|                |      |                |
|    16 − 16     |      |       0        |
|                |      |                |
 ‾‾‾‾‾‾‾‾‾‾‾‾‾‾‾‾        ‾‾‾‾‾‾‾‾‾‾‾‾‾‾‾‾
 Front of Flash Card     Back of Flash Card
```

Materials to Gather

SUPPLIED

base-10 blocks

place-value mat

Practice Subtraction with Regrouping activity page

Checkpoint (printout)

ALSO NEEDED

index cards – 20

▶ Content Background

In this lesson, students will learn how to subtract a one-digit number from a number through 99 by regrouping when necessary.

GET READY Basic Subtraction Review

OFFLINE 10 min

Students will use flash cards to review basic subtraction facts.
  Gather the flash cards you prepared.

1. **Say:** I am going to hold up a flash card with a subtraction fact. When you see the fact, say the difference.

2. Explain that you will make a pile of the facts that students know and another pile of the facts they still need to work on.

3. After they have gone through the deck of flash cards, give students the facts they missed. Have them use a strategy to help them find the differences to these facts. Strategies could include use objects to model, use a pattern, use a related addition fact, and count back.

Objectives

- Use concrete objects or sketches to model and solve addition or subtraction problems with sums and minuends up through 30.
- Demonstrate automatic recall of subtraction facts with minuends through 20.
- Demonstrate understanding of the result of subtracting zero from a given quantity.

LEARN Subtract 1-Digit Numbers

ONLINE 15 min

Students will learn how to regroup when subtracting a one-digit number from a two-digit number.

Objectives

- Solve subtraction problems with a two-digit minuend and a one-digit subtrahend by using regrouping.

Tips

Allow students to use the base-10 blocks and place-value mat to follow along with the problems shown online.

LEARN Regroup to Solve

Objectives

- Solve subtraction problems with a two-digit minuend and a one-digit subtrahend by using regrouping.

Students will learn how to regroup when subtracting a one-digit number from a two-digit number.

Gather the base-10 blocks and place-value mat. Have students use the base-10 blocks and place-value mat to model and solve the following problems:

- $53 - 8 = 45$
- $42 - 4 = 38$
- $83 - 5 = 78$
- $76 - 9 = 67$

As students solve the problems, encourage them to ask themselves questions such as the following:

- Do I need to regroup? How do I know?
- What happens to the tens when I regroup?
- What happens to the ones when I regroup?
- How do I know how many cubes to take away?

TRY IT Practice Subtraction with Regrouping

Objectives

- Solve subtraction problems with a two-digit minuend and a one-digit subtrahend by using regrouping.

Students will practice solving subtraction problems, some of which require regrouping. Give students the base-10 blocks, place-value mat, and Practice Subtraction with Regrouping activity page from their Activity Book. Read the directions with them.

Name:

More Subtraction with Regrouping
Practice Subtraction with Regrouping

Subtract. You may use base-10 blocks and a place-value mat to help you.

1. $\begin{array}{r} 54 \\ -\ 8 \\ \hline 46 \end{array}$
2. $\begin{array}{r} 81 \\ -\ 3 \\ \hline 78 \end{array}$
3. $\begin{array}{r} 47 \\ -\ 6 \\ \hline 41 \end{array}$

4. $\begin{array}{r} 75 \\ -\ 7 \\ \hline 68 \end{array}$
5. $\begin{array}{r} 94 \\ -\ 6 \\ \hline 88 \end{array}$
6. $\begin{array}{r} 67 \\ -\ 9 \\ \hline 58 \end{array}$

7. $\begin{array}{r} 58 \\ -\ 7 \\ \hline 51 \end{array}$
8. $\begin{array}{r} 82 \\ -\ 9 \\ \hline 73 \end{array}$
9. $\begin{array}{r} 72 \\ -\ 4 \\ \hline 68 \end{array}$

10. $\begin{array}{r} 60 \\ -\ 3 \\ \hline 57 \end{array}$
11. $\begin{array}{r} 93 \\ -\ 5 \\ \hline 88 \end{array}$
12. $\begin{array}{r} 44 \\ -\ 8 \\ \hline 36 \end{array}$

T R Y   I T

---

13. $66 - 4 = \underline{\textbf{62}}$
14. $\underline{\textbf{76}} = 83 - 7$

15. $\underline{\textbf{89}} = 92 - 3$
16. $56 - 9 = \underline{\textbf{47}}$

17. $71 - 9 = \underline{\textbf{62}}$
18. $\underline{\textbf{79}} = 81 - 2$

Circle the answer. You may use base-10 blocks and a place-value mat to help you.

19. $\begin{array}{r} 82 \\ -\ 4 \end{array}$

Ⓐ 78
B. 86
C. 84
D. 92

20. $\begin{array}{r} 92 \\ -\ 8 \end{array}$

A. 100
B. 96
C. 48
Ⓓ 84

T R Y   I T

CHECKPOINT

Objectives

Print the Checkpoint and have students complete it on their own. Read the directions, problems, and answer choices to students, if necessary. Use the answer key to score the Checkpoint, and then enter the results online

   Allow students to use the base-10 blocks and place-value mat to solve the problems.

- Solve subtraction problems with a two-digit minuend and a one-digit subtrahend by using regrouping.

⟳ Checkpoint   Math | Place Value, Addition, and Subtraction | More Subtraction with Regrouping

Name _____   Date _____

Checkpoint Answer Key

Subtract.
(1 point)
1.   47
       − 8
       39

(1 point)
2.   31
       − 5
       26

Circle the answer.
(1 point)
3.   43
       − 7

   (A.) 36
   B. 50
   C. 56
   D. 65

(1 point)
4.   22
       − 3

   A. 33
   (B.) 19
   C. 25
   D. 35

Different Ways to Subtract

Skills Update	5 minutes	ONLINE
GET READY Addition Strategies	10 minutes	ONLINE
LEARN Two Subtraction Strategies	20 minutes	ONLINE
LEARN Number Line Subtraction	15 minutes	ONLINE
TRY IT Subtract Different Ways	10 minutes	OFFLINE

▶ Lesson Objectives

Identify and explain the approach for addition or subtraction computation problems with sums or minuends up through 100.

▶ Prerequisite Skills

Solve addition problems with a one- and a two-digit number with sums through 100 by using regrouping.

▶ Common Errors and Misconceptions

- Students might have difficulty seeing the connection between addition and subtraction situations.
- Students might be able to execute algorithms, but they might not be able to explain what they are doing. For example, when adding 19 and 23, students might "carry" a 1 to the tens column but not understand that they regrouped 10 ones as 1 ten.

▶ Advance Preparation

Print the Number Line 0–100. Cut out the number lines and tape them together to form one number line from 0 to 100.

▶ Content Background

Students will learn that there are different ways to subtract. They will learn two subtraction strategies: counting back on a number line and breaking apart numbers into numbers that are easier to work with.

When students are introduced to numbers and operations, they will often create their own strategies for solving problems. They should test strategies on many problems to see if a strategy always works, and they should ask an adult to check to see if a strategy makes sense mathematically. Once strategies are proven to work, students should decide which strategies are most efficient for them. The algorithm many adults have been taught is often not as efficient as another strategy. Encourage students to use the strategy that they feel works best in a given situation.

The mathematical term *decomposition* describes the breaking apart of numbers into *friendly numbers* for easier computation. In dialogue with students, this lesson uses the phrase *breaking apart* in place of *decomposition*.

Materials to Gather

SUPPLIED

Number Line 0–100 (printout)

Subtract Different Ways activity page

ALSO NEEDED

scissors, adult

tape, clear

count back – to subtract by starting with the number of objects in one group and then counting back, in order, the number of objects in the other group

GET READY Addition Strategies

Students will review two different addition strategies—counting on a number line and decomposing numbers to make them easier to add.

Objectives

- Solve addition problems with a one- and a two-digit number with sums through 100 by using regrouping.

LEARN Two Subtraction Strategies

Students will learn that they can use different strategies to solve subtraction problems by watching Rosa subtract by using a number line and Serena subtract by breaking apart numbers into numbers that are easier to work with.

Objectives

- Identify and explain the approach for addition or subtraction computation problems with sums or minuends up through 100.

Tips

Allow students to use the Number Line 0–100 printout to follow along with the problems shown online.

LEARN Number Line Subtraction

Students will learn ways to be more efficient when they count back on a number line. Instead of counting back by ones, they will learn that they can jump back to the next 10, and then count back by ones from there. Then students will use the Number Line Learning Tool to practice these new strategies.

Objectives

- Identify and explain the approach for addition or subtraction computation problems with sums or minuends up through 100.

DIRECTIONS FOR USING THE NUMBER LINE LEARNING TOOL

1. Click — and choose the following:
   - Minuends through: 20

   Click OK.

   A subtraction number sentence will be shown, such as $17 - 2 = ?$.

2. Have students click the minuend (17) on the number line.

3. Have students use the number line to help them subtract the subtrahend (2). Encourage students to count aloud as they count back, pointing to the numbers on the number line with the mouse. Students may count back by ones or by other numbers, such as 2s, 5s, and 10s.

4. Have students click the answer on the number line.

5. Ask students to explain how they solved the problem.

6. Repeat Steps 2–5 with at least two more problems.

TRY IT   Subtract Different Ways

OFFLINE
10min

Objectives

Students will practice using different subtraction strategies. Give students the Number Line 0–100 printout and Subtract Different Ways activity page from their Activity Book. Read the directions with them.

- Identify and explain the approach for addition or subtraction computation problems with sums or minuends up through 100.

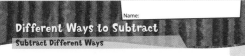

Name:

Different Ways to Subtract
Subtract Different Ways

Explain how the student found the difference.

1. This is how Bobby subtracted 66 − 8:

```
51 52 53 54 55 56 57 58 59 60 61 62 63 64 65 66 67 68 69 70
```

Students should say that Bobby knew that 8 = 6 + 2, so he made one hop of 6 back to 60, and then another hop of 2 to 58 to find that 66 − 8 = 58.

2. This is how Gina subtracted 54 − 7:

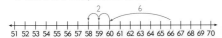

$(40 + 14) − 7$
$40 + (14 − 7)$
$40 + 7 = 47$
$54 − 7 = 47$

Students should say that Gina knew that 54 equals 40 + 14. After breaking apart 54 into 40 + 14, she subtracted 7 from 14 to get 7. Then she added 7 + 40 to get 47. So 54 − 7 = 47.

3. Lauren subtracted 94 − 5 using a number line. Explain how she could have used the number line to find the answer.
Sample answer: She started at 94 and counted back 5 to 89.

TRY IT

TRY IT

Subtract. You may use a number line. Explain how you found the difference.

4. $56 − 9 =$ **47**   5. $23 − 5 =$ **18**
Explanations will vary. Accept any reasonable explanation that produces the correct answer.

6. $91 − 4 =$ **87**   7. $33 − 7 =$ **26**

Circle the answer.

8. This is how Vani subtracted 71 − 7:

```
7 6 5 4 3 2 1
61 62 63 64 65 66 67 68 69 70 71 72 73 74 75 76 77 78 79 80
```

Which strategy did Vani use? Circle the answer.

(A) She counted back from the greater number.

B. She broke apart the greater number into numbers that were easier to work with.

C. She first subtracted the tens and then the ones.

Add and Subtract

Lesson Overview

Skills Update	5 minutes	ONLINE
GET READY Subtraction Strategies	5 minutes	ONLINE
LEARN So Many Strategies	25 minutes	OFFLINE
TRY IT Use Strategies	15 minutes	OFFLINE
CHECKPOINT	10 minutes	OFFLINE

▶ Lesson Objectives

Identify and explain the approach for addition or subtraction computation problems with sums or minuends up through 100.

▶ Prerequisite Skills

Solve addition problems with a one- and a two-digit number with sums through 100 by using regrouping.

▶ Common Errors and Misconceptions

- Students might have difficulty seeing the connection between addition and subtraction situations.
- Students might be able to execute algorithms, but they might not be able to explain what they are doing. For example, when adding 19 and 23, students might "carry" a 1 to the tens column but not understand that they regrouped 10 ones as 1 ten.

▶ Advance Preparation

Print the Number Line 0–100. Cut out the number lines and tape them together to form one number line from 0 to 100.

▶ Content Background

Students have learned several different addition and subtraction strategies. In this lesson, they will learn that even though many strategies may lead to the correct answer, certain strategies may be more efficient in particular situations.

When students are introduced to numbers and operations, they will often create their own strategies for solving problems. They should test strategies on many problems to see if a strategy always works, and they should ask an adult to check to see if a strategy makes sense mathematically. Once strategies are proven to work, students should decide which strategies are most efficient for them. The algorithm many adults have been taught is often not as efficient as another strategy. Encourage students to use the strategy that they feel works best in a given situation.

Materials to Gather

SUPPLIED

base-10 blocks
Number Line 0–100 (printout)
Use Strategies activity page
Checkpoint (printout)

ALSO NEEDED

scissors, adult
tape, clear

GET READY Subtraction Strategies

Students will solve the same subtraction problem using two different strategies. Then students will explain which strategy works better for them.

When students count back on the number line, they may count back by ones, jump back to the nearest 10 and then count back by ones, or count back a different way. Have students explain their method. Accept any use of the number line that produces the correct answer and that students can explain.

- Solve addition problems with a one- and a two-digit number with sums through 100 by using regrouping.

LEARN So Many Strategies

Students will solve the same addition and subtraction problems using different strategies. After solving each problem, students will discuss which strategy worked best for the problem. Then students will solve addition and subtraction problems using any strategies they choose.

Gather the base-10 blocks and Number Line 0–100 printout.

- Identify and explain the approach for addition or subtraction computation problems with sums or minuends up through 100.

1. **Say:** Let's use three different strategies to subtract $33 - 7$. First let's count on from 7 to 33.

   Give students the ones cubes. Have them count on from 7 to 33, moving aside a ones cube as they say each number. Then have them count the ones cubes they've moved aside.

   Ask students how many ones cubes they have. (26) Then have them write a subtraction sentence to show the problem. ($33 - 7 = 26$)

2. Now have students subtract $33 - 7$ by counting back. Give students 33 ones cubes. Have them count back from 33 to 7, moving aside a ones cube as they say each number. Then have them count the ones cubes they've moved aside.

   Have students write a subtraction sentence to show the problem. ($33 - 7 = 26$)

3. Next have students use the number line to subtract $33 - 7$.

   Say: Start on 33, and then count back 7. Or count back 3 to 30 and then count back 4 more. You can do this because $3 + 4 = 7$.

   Have students write a subtraction sentence to show the problem. ($33 - 7 = 26$ or $33 - 3 = 30$ and $30 - 4 = 26$)

4. **Say:** You solved $33 - 7$ three different ways: by counting on, counting back, and using a number line.

   Ask: Which strategy would you have used? Why?

   Accept any answer. Explain that when subtracting greater numbers, students might not want to count on to find the answer. It might take a longer time to count all the numbers than if they counted back or used a number line.

5. **Say:** Let's use three different strategies to subtract $74 - 9$. First let's use base-10 blocks.

   Have students model 74 with 7 tens rods and 4 ones cubes.

   Ask: How can you take away 9 ones cubes from 4 ones cubes?
   ANSWER: Regroup 1 tens rod as 10 ones cubes. Then subtract the ones.

Students should regroup, subtract the ones, and count the remaining blocks. Have students write a subtraction sentence to show the problem. ($74 - 9 = 65$)

6. Now have students subtract $74 - 9$ by breaking apart the numbers into numbers that are easier to work with.

   Say: Start at 74. Then take 4 away from 74 to get 70. Think of 9 as $4 + 5$. So take away 5 more from 70.

   Have students write a subtraction sentence to show the problem. ($74 - 9 = 65$)

7. Next have students use the number line to subtract $74 - 9$. Students may count back in any way they choose. Have students write a subtraction sentence to show the problem. ($74 - 9 = 65$)

8. **Say:** You solved 74 – 9 three different ways: by using base-10 blocks, breaking apart the numbers, and using a number line.

   Ask: Which strategy would you have used? Why?

   Accept any answer.

9. **Say:** Let's use two different strategies to add $85 + 8$. First let's break apart the numbers into numbers that are easier to work with. Start at 85. Then add 5 to get 90. Think of 8 as $5 + 3$. So add 3 more to 90.

   Have students write an addition sentence to show the problem. ($85 + 8 = 93$)

10. Now have students count on using their fingers to add $85 + 8$. Have them hold up a finger as they count on each number. Then have students write an addition sentence to show the problem. ($85 + 8 = 93$)

11. **Say:** You solved $85 + 8$ two different ways: by breaking apart the numbers and counting on.

    Ask: Which strategy would you have used? Why?

    Accept any answer.

12. Have students solve the problems $58 + 6$ (64) and $92 - 8$ (84). For each problem, have students tell you two strategies they could use. Then have students choose a strategy and solve the problem. Have them explain why they chose that strategy.

    When choosing a strategy, students should ask themselves the following questions:

    - How many numbers do I need to count on to use this strategy?
    - Which strategy will take me longer?
    - Which strategy would I rather use? Why do I think it is better?

TRY IT Use Strategies

OFFLINE

15 min

Objectives

Students will practice choosing the best strategy to solve addition and subtraction problems. Give students the base-10 blocks, Number Line 0–100 printout, and Use Strategies activity page from their Activity Book. Read the directions with them.

- Identify and explain the approach for addition or subtraction computation problems with sums or minuends up through 100.

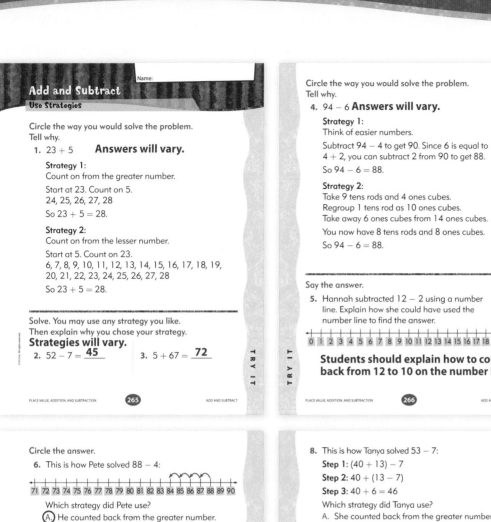

Add and Subtract

Use Strategies

Name: _____

Circle the way you would solve the problem.
Tell why.

1. $23 + 5$ **Answers will vary.**

   Strategy 1:
   Count on from the greater number.
   Start at 23. Count on 5.
   24, 25, 26, 27, 28
   So $23 + 5 = 28$.

   Strategy 2:
   Count on from the lesser number.
   Start at 5. Count on 23.
   6, 7, 8, 9, 10, 11, 12, 13, 14, 15, 16, 17, 18, 19,
   20, 21, 22, 23, 24, 25, 26, 27, 28
   So $23 + 5 = 28$.

Solve. You may use any strategy you like.
Then explain why you chose your strategy.
Strategies will vary.

2. $52 - 7 = $ __45__

3. $5 + 67 = $ __72__

Circle the way you would solve the problem.
Tell why.

4. $94 - 6$ **Answers will vary.**

   Strategy 1:
   Think of easier numbers.
   Subtract $94 - 4$ to get 90. Since 6 is equal to
   $4 + 2$, you can subtract 2 from 90 to get 88.
   So $94 - 6 = 88$.

   Strategy 2:
   Take 9 tens rods and 4 ones cubes.
   Regroup 1 tens rod as 10 ones cubes.
   Take away 6 ones cubes from 14 ones cubes.
   You now have 8 tens rods and 8 ones cubes.
   So $94 - 6 = 88$.

Say the answer.

5. Hannah subtracted $12 - 2$ using a number
   line. Explain how she could have used the
   number line to find the answer.

   0 1 2 3 4 5 6 7 8 9 10 11 12 13 14 15 16 17 18 19 20

   **Students should explain how to count
   back from 12 to 10 on the number line.**

Circle the answer.

6. This is how Pete solved $88 - 4$:

   71 72 73 74 75 76 77 78 79 80 81 82 83 84 85 86 87 88 89 90

   Which strategy did Pete use?
   (A.) He counted back from the greater number.
   B. He broke apart the greater number into
   numbers that were easier to work with.
   C. He first subtracted the tens and then the ones.

7. This is how Ana solved $39 + 7$:

   31 32 33 34 35 36 37 38 39 40 41 42 43 44 45 46 47 48 49 50

   Which strategy did Ana use?
   A. She first added the ones, then added the tens,
   and then added both numbers together.
   B. She took enough from the lesser number to
   increase the greater number to the next ten,
   and then added the remaining ones.
   (C.) She counted on from the greater number.

8. This is how Tanya solved $53 - 7$:

   Step 1: $(40 + 13) - 7$
   Step 2: $40 + (13 - 7)$
   Step 3: $40 + 6 = 46$

   Which strategy did Tanya use?
   A. She counted back from the greater number.
   (B.) She broke apart the greater number into
   numbers that were easier to work with.
   C. She first subtracted the tens and then the ones.

Say the answer.

9. This is how Callie solved $58 - 9$:

   Step 1: $(40 + 18) - 9$
   Step 2: $40 + (18 - 9)$
   Step 3: $40 + 9 = 49$

   Explain how she solved the problem.
   **Callie first broke apart 58 into $40 + 18$
   and then subtracted 9 from 18 to make
   9. Finally, she added what she had left
   over to get $40 + 9 = 49$.**

CHECKPOINT

Objectives

- Identify and explain the approach for addition or subtraction computation problems with sums or minuends up through 100.

Print the Checkpoint. In Part 1, students will take a performance-based assessment. In Part 2, students will complete the problems on their own. Read the directions, problems, and answer choices to students, if necessary. Use the answer key to score the Checkpoint, and then enter the results online.

Gather the base-10 blocks and Number Line 0–100 printout. Students may use these materials to solve Problem 1, if they wish.

Checkpoint   Math | Place Value, Addition, and Subtraction | Add and Subtract

Name _____ Date _____

Checkpoint Answer Key

Part 1

Follow the instructions. Choose the response that best describes how the student performs on the task. When you have finished, enter the results online.

1. Write this problem on a sheet of paper for the student to solve:

$$\begin{array}{r} 78 \\ +4 \\ \hline \end{array}$$

Say, "Explain how you solved the problem and why you chose to solve it that way."

(1 point)
Did the student answer 82 and explain how he or she solved the problem?

A. Yes   B. No

(1 point)
Did the student explain why he or she chose to solve it that way?

A. Yes   B. No

Give students Part 2 of the assessment.

Checkpoint   Math | Place Value, Addition, and Subtraction | Add and Subtract

Name _____ Date _____

Part 2

Circle the answer.

(1 point)
2. Which is **not** a strategy you could use to solve the following addition problem?

$46 + 7 = ?$

A. Add 4 to 46 to get 50, and then add 3.

B. Count on 7 from 46.

C. Add 4 to 6 to get 10, and then add 3. *(circled)*

D. Add 7 and 6 to get 13, and then add 13 to 40.

(1 point)
3. This is how Benita solved $7 + 12$:

Which strategy did Benita use?

A. She counted on from the lesser number.

B. She counted on from the greater number. *(circled)*

C. She added the ones and then added the tens.

Checkpoint   Math | Place Value, Addition, and Subtraction | Add and Subtract

Name _____ Date _____

(1 point)
4. This is how Tom solved $37 + 7$:

Step 1: $37 + 3 = 40$

Step 2: $40 + 4 = 44$

Which strategy did Tom use?

A. He first added the ones, then added the tens, and then added both numbers together.

B. He broke apart a number into numbers that were easier to work with. *(circled)*

C. He counted on from the greater number.

(1 point)
5. This is how Tali solved $71 - 7$:

Which strategy did Tali use?

A. She counted back from the greater number. *(circled)*

B. She broke apart the greater number into numbers that were easier to work with.

C. She first subtracted the tens and then the ones.

Unit Review

UNIT REVIEW Look Back	20 minutes	ONLINE
UNIT REVIEW Checkpoint Practice	20 minutes	OFFLINE
⤞ **UNIT REVIEW** Prepare for the Checkpoint		

▶ Unit Objectives

This lesson reviews the following objectives:

- Count and group objects in ones and tens, such as 4 groups of 10 objects with 2 more objects $= 40 + 2 = 42$.
- Estimate quantities and numbers of objects.
- Demonstrate understanding of place value by recording the number represented by groupings of tens and ones (for example, given 5 tens rods and 2 ones cubes or hearing "5 tens and 2 ones," record 52).
- Demonstrate understanding of place value by grouping given numbers into sets of tens and ones, such as $64 = 6$ tens and 4 ones.
- Use concrete objects to model two-digit numbers in multiple ways (for example, $27 = 27$ ones, or 1 ten and 17 ones, or 2 tens and 7 ones).
- Use concrete objects or sketches to model and solve addition or subtraction computation problems involving sums and minuends up through 100.
- Solve addition problems with a one- and a two-digit number with sums through 100 by using regrouping.
- Identify and explain the approach for addition or subtraction computation problems with sums or minuends up through 100.
- Solve subtraction problems with a two-digit minuend and a one-digit subtrahend by using regrouping.

Materials to Gather

SUPPLIED

base-10 blocks
place-value mat
Checkpoint Practice activity page

▶ Advance Preparation

In this lesson, students will have an opportunity to review previous activities in the Place Value, Addition, and Subtraction unit. Look at the suggested activities in Unit Review. Prepare for the Checkpoint online and gather any needed materials.

Keywords		
	add	**ones cube**
	base-10 blocks	**place value**
	count back	**place-value chart**
	count on	**place-value mat**
	decompose	**regroup; regrouping**
	difference	**subtract**
	estimate (verb)	**subtrahend**
	hundreds flat	**sum**
	minuend	**ten-frame**
	model (verb)	**tens rod**
	number line	**thousands cube**

UNIT REVIEW Look Back

* Review unit objectives.

In this unit, students learned about place value through 100. They learned how to count and group objects as tens and ones, estimate a number of objects, and use base-10 blocks to model and write two-digit numbers as tens and ones. Students modeled two-digit numbers different ways as an introduction to regrouping tens as ones and ones as tens. Students then regrouped to add and subtract with sums and minuends through 100. Students learned several addition and subtraction strategies to help them find sums and differences of two-digit numbers. Students will review these concepts to prepare for the Unit Checkpoint.

UNIT REVIEW Checkpoint Practice

* Review unit objectives.

Students will complete a Checkpoint Practice activity page to prepare for the Unit Checkpoint. If necessary, read the directions, problems, and answer choices to students. Have students answer the problems on their own. Review any missed problems with students.

Gather the base-10 blocks and the place-value mat.

Unit Review
Checkpoint Practice

Name: _____

Read the problem and follow the directions.

1. Grace subtracted 28 − 7 using a number line. Explain how she could have used the number line to find the answer.

11 12 13 14 15 16 17 18 19 20 21 22 23 24 25 26 27 28 29 30

Count back 7 from 28 to 21 on the number line.

2. Write the number of tens and ones.

_____5_____ tens _____9_____ ones

3. Use base-10 blocks to model the number three different ways. Write the number of tens and ones in each model.

53
See below.

_____ tens _____ ones

_____ tens _____ ones

_____ tens _____ ones

Add or subtract. You may use base-10 blocks, sketches, or another strategy.

4. $\begin{array}{r} 28 \\ +\ 9 \\ \hline \mathbf{37} \end{array}$

5. $\begin{array}{r} 52 \\ -\ 9 \\ \hline \mathbf{43} \end{array}$

6. **65** = 59 + 6

7. 95 − 6 = **89**

Make a sketch to solve the problem.

8. 28 − 17 = **11**

Sketches will vary. Sample answer:

Additional Answers

3. **Possible answers:** 5 tens 3 ones, 4 tens 13 ones, 3 tens 23 ones, 2 tens 33 ones, 1 tens 43 ones, 53 ones

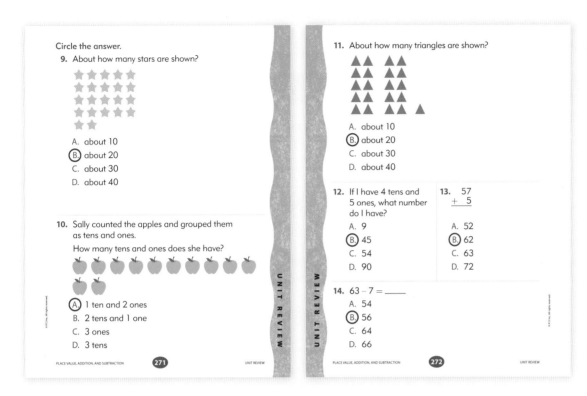

Circle the answer.

9. About how many stars are shown?

A. about 10
B. about 20
C. about 30
D. about 40

10. Sally counted the apples and grouped them as tens and ones.

How many tens and ones does she have?

A. 1 ten and 2 ones
B. 2 tens and 1 one
C. 3 ones
D. 3 tens

11. About how many triangles are shown?

A. about 10
B. about 20
C. about 30
D. about 40

12. If I have 4 tens and 5 ones, what number do I have?

A. 9
B. 45
C. 54
D. 90

13.
$$57$$
$$+ \ 5$$

A. 52
B. 62
C. 63
D. 72

14. $63 - 7 = $ _____

A. 54
B. 56
C. 64
D. 66

⊠ UNIT REVIEW Prepare for the Checkpoint

What you do next depends on how students performed in the previous activity, Unit Review: Checkpoint Practice. If students had difficulty with any of the problems, complete the appropriate review activity listed in the table online.

Unit Checkpoint

UNIT CHECKPOINT Offline   60 minutes   **OFFLINE**

▶ Unit Objectives

This lesson assesses the following objectives:

- Count and group objects in ones and tens, such as 4 groups of 10 objects with 2 more objects = $40 + 2 = 42$.

- Estimate quantities and numbers of objects.

- Demonstrate understanding of place value by recording the number represented by groupings of tens and ones (for example, given 5 tens rods and 2 ones cubes or hearing "5 tens and 2 ones," record 52).

- Demonstrate understanding of place value by grouping given numbers into sets of tens and ones, such as 64 = 6 tens and 4 ones.

- Use concrete objects to model two-digit numbers in multiple ways (for example, 27 = 27 ones, or 1 ten and 17 ones, or 2 tens and 7 ones).

- Use concrete objects or sketches to model and solve addition or subtraction computation problems involving sums and minuends up through 100.

- Solve addition problems with a one- and a two-digit number with sums through 100 by using regrouping.

- Identify and explain the approach for addition or subtraction computation problems with sums or minuends up through 100.

- Solve subtraction problems with a two-digit minuend and a one-digit subtrahend by using regrouping.

Materials to Gather

SUPPLIED

base-10 blocks

Unit Checkpoint (printout)

UNIT CHECKPOINT Offline

OFFLINE
60min

Objectives

- Assess unit objectives.

Students will complete the Unit Checkpoint offline. In Part 1, students will take a performance-based assessment. In Part 2, students will complete the problems on their own. Print the Unit Checkpoint. Read the directions, problems, and answer choices to students if necessary. Use the answer key to score the Checkpoint, and then enter the results online.

Gather the base-10 blocks.

Name _____   Date _____

Unit Checkpoint Answer Key

Part 1

Follow the instructions for each item. Choose the response that best describes how the student performed on the task.

1. Place 36 ones cubes in front of the student.
   Say, "How many groups of 10 are there?
   How many ones are left?
   How many cubes are there in all?"
   (1 point)
   Did the student say that there are 3 groups of 10 and 6 ones left over?

   A. Yes   B. No

   (1 point)
   Did the student say that there are 36 cubes in all?

   A. Yes   B. No

2. Say, "Use base-10 blocks and the place-value chart to model and solve this problem: $27 - 12 = ?$"
   (1 point)
   Did the student use base-10 blocks to model and solve the problem? For example, students could show 2 tens rods and 7 ones cubes and then take away 1 tens rod and 2 ones cubes.

   A. Yes   B. No

   (1 point)
   Did the student then see that they are left with 1 tens rod and 5 ones cubes, which is 15? The student should then say $27 - 12 = 15$.

   A. Yes   B. No

Name _____   Date _____

3. Say, "Make a sketch to solve the problem $20 + 13 = ?$
   What is the answer?"
   (1 point)
   Did the student draw a picture to solve the problem?
   Pictures will vary. One example picture may be 2 rectangles to represent 2 tens to show 20, 1 rectangle to represent 1 ten, and 3 squares to represent ones to show 13.

   A. Yes   B. No

   (1 point)
   Did the student then add the tens and ones to get 3 tens and 3 ones? The student should then say $20 + 13 = 33$.

   A. Yes   B. No

4. Place the base-10 blocks in front of the student.
   Say, "Model the number 54 in two different ways."
   (1 point)
   Did the student model the number 54 correctly?
   Possible models include, but are not limited to, the following:
   54 ones cubes
   5 tens rods and 4 ones cubes
   4 tens rods and 14 ones cubes
   3 tens rods and 24 ones cubes

   A. Yes   B. No

Name _____   Date _____

5. Say, "A number has 4 ones and 3 tens. What is the number?"
   (1 point)
   Did the student say 34?

   A. Yes   B. No

6. Show the student 4 tens rods and 6 ones cubes.
   Say, "What number is modeled with these base-10 blocks?"
   (1 point)
   Did the student say 46?

   A. Yes   B. No

7. Say, "Callie solved the subtraction problem $57 - 9$ in the following way.
   Step 1: $(40 + 17) - 9$
   Step 2: $40 + (17 - 9)$
   Step 3: $40 + 8 = 48$
   Explain how she solved the problem."
   (1 point)
   Did the student say Callie first broke apart 57 into $40 + 17$, then subtracted 9 from 17 to make 8, and finally added what she had left over to get $40 + 8 = 48$?

   A. Yes   B. No

Give students Part 2 of the assessment.

Name _____   Date _____

Part 2

Write the answer.
(1 point)
8. About how many peanuts are on the plate?   about **20** peanuts

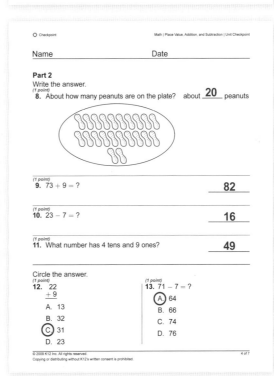

(1 point)
9. $73 + 9 = ?$ **82**

(1 point)
10. $23 - 7 = ?$ **16**

(1 point)
11. What number has 4 tens and 9 ones?   **49**

Circle the answer.

(1 point)
12. $\begin{array}{r} 22 \\ +\ 9 \\ \hline \end{array}$

   A. 13
   B. 32
   Ⓒ 31
   D. 23

(1 point)
13. $71 - 7 = ?$

   Ⓐ 64
   B. 66
   C. 74
   D. 76

Name _____ Date _____

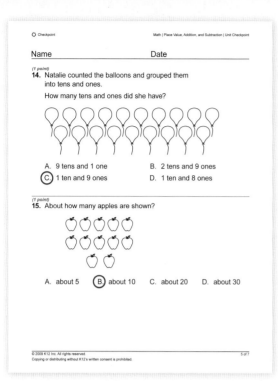

(1 point)
14. Natalie counted the balloons and grouped them into tens and ones.

How many tens and ones did she have?

A. 9 tens and 1 one   B. 2 tens and 9 ones
C. 1 ten and 9 ones   D. 1 ten and 8 ones

(1 point)
15. About how many apples are shown?

A. about 5   B. about 10   C. about 20   D. about 30

Name _____ Date _____

(1 point)
16. How many cubes are shown here?

A. 8 tens and 3 ones   B. 8 tens and 8 ones
C. 8 tens and 10 ones   D. 8 tens and 11 ones

(1 point)
17. One way to model the number 26 is shown.

Which shows another way to model the number 26?

A.   B.

C.   D.

Name _____ Date _____

(1 point)
18. Which model shows how to solve the following problem?

$38 - 5 = ?$

A.   B.   C.

(1 point)
19. Julie solved the problem $4 + 88$ by using the number line shown here.

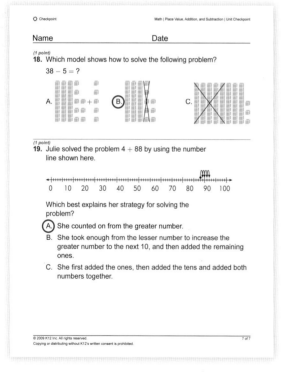

Which best explains her strategy for solving the problem?

A. She counted on from the greater number.

B. She took enough from the lesser number to increase the greater number to the next 10, and then added the remaining ones.

C. She first added the ones, then added the tens and added both numbers together.

Add or Subtract: Problem Solving

▶ Unit Objectives

- Use concrete objects or sketches to model and solve addition or subtraction computation problems involving sums and minuends up through 100.

- Recognize and solve word problems involving sums up through 100 in which two quantities are combined.

- Recognize and solve word problems involving sums or minuends up through 100 in which one quantity changes by addition or subtraction.

- Recognize and solve word problems involving numbers up to 100 in which two quantities are compared by the use of addition or subtraction.

▶ Big Ideas

- Models and mathematical symbols can represent addition and subtraction.

- The use of letters, numbers, and mathematical symbols makes possible the translation of complex situations or long word statements into concise mathematical sentences or expressions.

▶ Unit Introduction

In this unit, students will solve story problems about the number of stars on the U.S. flag. They will learn that, as we added states to our country, we added stars to the flag. Students will use base-10 blocks or sketches to solve addition story problems with sums to 100. They will also use base-10 blocks or sketches to solve subtraction story problems. Students will use models and sketches to solve addition and subtraction story problems and to describe and solve story problems. They will act out problems to decide if they have to subtract or add to solve them. Students will work with the concept of parts and total for combine story problems. They will learn how to recognize a problem in which amounts are combined. They will learn that they can use subtraction to solve a problem in which one part and the total are given and the other part is missing. Students will solve combine problems in which the total is missing as well as problems in which a part is missing.

Add and Subtract with Base-10 Models

Lesson Overview

Skills Update	5 minutes	ONLINE
GET READY Adding Stars to the Flag	10 minutes	ONLINE
LEARN Adding Greater Numbers	15 minutes	ONLINE
LEARN Subtracting Greater Numbers	15 minutes	ONLINE
TRY IT Base-10 Blocks and Sketches	15 minutes	OFFLINE

▶ Lesson Objectives

Use concrete objects or sketches to model and solve addition or subtraction computation problems involving sums and minuends up through 100.

▶ Prerequisite Skills

Use concrete objects or sketches to model and solve addition or subtraction computation problems with sums and minuends up through 30.

▶ Content Background

Students will use sketches and models to solve addition and subtraction problems with numbers up through 100.

Materials to Gather

SUPPLIED
base-10 blocks
Base-10 Blocks and Sketches activity page

GET READY Adding Stars to the Flag

ONLINE 10 min

Students will solve problems about the number of stars on the U.S. flag. They will learn that when a new state became part of the United States, a star was added to the flag. Students will use various versions of the flag as models to help them solve the problems.

Objectives

- Use concrete objects or sketches to model and solve addition or subtraction computation problems involving sums and minuends up through 30.

LEARN Adding Greater Numbers

ONLINE 15 min

Students will use base-10 blocks to model and solve addition problems with sums through 100. Then they will learn how to sketch base-10 blocks to model addition.

Objectives

- Use concrete objects or sketches to model and solve addition or subtraction computation problems involving sums and minuends up through 100.

DIRECTIONS FOR USING THE PLACE VALUE ADDITION LEARNING TOOL

1. Click Begin Setup and choose the following:
   - Present addition problems with SUMS up to: 99
   - Allow REGROUPING in problems: YES
   - Computer Makes Questions

2. Guide students through the first problem. Review how each addend is modeled with tens rods and ones cubes. For example, if the problem were 20 + 44, you could say "The first addend is 20, so we model it with 2 tens rods and 0 ones cubes. The second addend is 44, so we model it with 4 tens rods and 4 ones cubes. All the ones cubes go in the Ones column. All the tens rods go in the Tens column."

3. Have them add the ones by combining the ones cubes from both addends.

   Have students click + to combine the ones.

4. Explain to students that they can have only up to 9 ones cubes in the Ones column. If there are more than 9 ones cubes, then they need to regroup 10 ones cubes as 1 tens rod.

   Have students count the ones cubes and, if necessary, click the arrow to regroup (for 20 + 44, no regrouping is necessary).

5. Ask students how many ones cubes are now in the Ones column. The number of ones cubes will be the digit in the Ones column in the sum.

   Have them count the ones cubes and enter the ones digit.

6. Explain that students will now add the tens by combining the tens rods from both addends.

   Have students click + to combine the tens.

7. Have students count the tens rods. The number of tens rods will be the digit in the Tens column in the sum.

   Have students count the tens rods and enter the tens digit.

8. Have students solve two more problems. As necessary, guide students through the problems using the process described in Steps 2–7.

LEARN Subtracting Greater Numbers

ONLINE
15min

Students will use base-10 blocks to model and solve subtraction problems with starting numbers, or minuends, through 100. Then they will learn how to sketch base-10 blocks to model subtraction.

DIRECTIONS FOR USING THE PLACE VALUE SUBTRACTION LEARNING TOOL

1. Click Begin Setup and choose the following:
   - Present subtraction problems with MINUENDS up to: 99
   - Allow REGROUPING in problems: YES
   - Computer Makes Questions

2. Guide students through the first problem.

   Explain that for these problems, they will take away to subtract. So, they will only model the first number, and then they will take away ones and tens to subtract the lesser number.

3. **Ask:** How many ones are in the first number? How many ones do we need to take away? Do we have enough ones?

   Explain that if there are fewer ones in the first number, students need to trade 1 ten for 10 ones.

Objectives

- Use concrete objects or sketches to model and solve addition or subtraction computation problems involving sums and minuends up through 100.

4. After students have regrouped, if necessary, have them click ones cubes to take them away. When they click ones cubes, the cubes will move into the trash can to show subtraction. Then have students count the remaining ones and enter the ones digit.

5. Next, have students click on any tens they need to take away. Have them count the remaining tens and enter the tens digit.

6. Have students solve two more problems. As necessary, guide students through the problems using the process described in Steps 2–5.

TRY IT Base-10 Blocks and Sketches

OFFLINE
15 min

Students will use base-10 blocks and sketches of base-10 blocks to solve addition and subtraction problems. They should use lines to represent tens rods and dots to represent ones cubes. Give students the base-10 blocks and the Base-10 Blocks and Sketches activity page from their Activity Book. Read the directions with them. Use the answer key to check students' answers, and then enter the results online.

Objectives

- Use concrete objects or sketches to model and solve addition or subtraction computation problems involving sums and minuends up through 100.

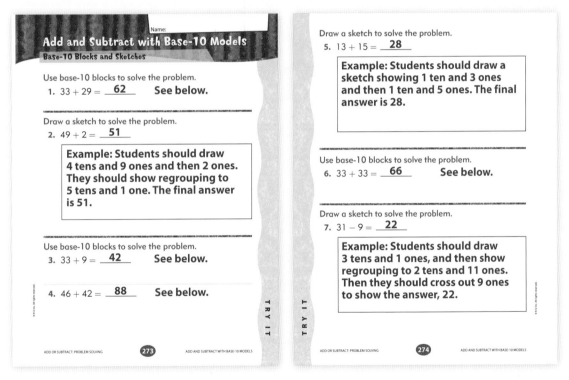

Name:

Add and Subtract with Base-10 Models
Base-10 Blocks and Sketches

Use base-10 blocks to solve the problem.
1. $33 + 29 =$ __62__   **See below.**

Draw a sketch to solve the problem.
2. $49 + 2 =$ __51__

> **Example: Students should draw 4 tens and 9 ones and then 2 ones. They should show regrouping to 5 tens and 1 one. The final answer is 51.**

Use base-10 blocks to solve the problem.
3. $33 + 9 =$ __42__   **See below.**

4. $46 + 42 =$ __88__   **See below.**

TRY IT

ADD OR SUBTRACT: PROBLEM SOLVING   273   ADD AND SUBTRACT WITH BASE-10 MODELS

Draw a sketch to solve the problem.
5. $13 + 15 =$ __28__

> **Example: Students should draw a sketch showing 1 ten and 3 ones and then 1 ten and 5 ones. The final answer is 28.**

Use base-10 blocks to solve the problem.
6. $33 + 33 =$ __66__   **See below.**

Draw a sketch to solve the problem.
7. $31 - 9 =$ __22__

> **Example: Students should draw 3 tens and 1 ones, and then show regrouping to 2 tens and 11 ones. Then they should cross out 9 ones to show the answer, 22.**

TRY IT

ADD OR SUBTRACT: PROBLEM SOLVING   274   ADD AND SUBTRACT WITH BASE-10 MODELS

Additional Answers

1. **Example:** Students should show 3 tens rods and 3 ones cubes plus 2 tens rods and 9 ones cubes. Then they should trade 10 ones cubes for a tens rod. The final answer is 62.

3. **Example:** Students should show 3 tens rods and 3 ones cubes, plus 9 ones cubes. They should trade 10 ones cubes for a tens rod. The final answer is 42.

4. **Example:** Students should show 4 tens rods and 6 ones cubes, plus 4 tens rods and 2 ones cubes. The final answer is 88.

6. **Example:** Students should show 3 tens rods and 3 ones cubes, plus 3 tens rods and 3 ones cubes. The final answer is 66.

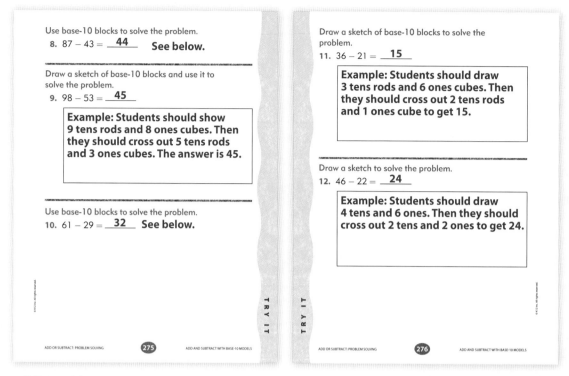

Use base-10 blocks to solve the problem.

8. $87 - 43 =$ __44__   **See below.**

Draw a sketch of base-10 blocks and use it to solve the problem.

9. $98 - 53 =$ __45__

> **Example: Students should show 9 tens rods and 8 ones cubes. Then they should cross out 5 tens rods and 3 ones cubes. The answer is 45.**

Use base-10 blocks to solve the problem.

10. $61 - 29 =$ __32__   **See below.**

Draw a sketch of base-10 blocks to solve the problem.

11. $36 - 21 =$ __15__

> **Example: Students should draw 3 tens rods and 6 ones cubes. Then they should cross out 2 tens rods and 1 ones cube to get 15.**

Draw a sketch to solve the problem.

12. $46 - 22 =$ __24__

> **Example: Students should draw 4 tens and 6 ones. Then they should cross out 2 tens and 2 ones to get 24.**

TRY IT

Additional Answers

8. **Example:** Students should show 8 tens rods and 7 ones cubes. They should remove 4 tens rods and 3 ones cubes. The final answer is 44.

10. **Example:** First students should show 6 tens rods and 1 ones cube. Then they should show regrouping to 5 tens rods and 11 ones cubes. They should remove 2 tens rods and 9 ones cubes. The answer is 32.

Solve Compare and Change Problems

Lesson Overview

Skills Update	5 minutes	ONLINE
LEARN Compare to Find the Difference	20 minutes	ONLINE
LEARN Take Away to Find What's Left	20 minutes	ONLINE
TRY IT Solving with Sketches and Models	15 minutes	OFFLINE

▶ Lesson Objectives

Use concrete objects or sketches to model and solve addition or subtraction computation problems involving sums and minuends up through 100.

▶ Prerequisite Skills

Use concrete objects or sketches to model and solve addition or subtraction computation problems with sums and minuends up through 30.

▶ Content Background

In this lesson, students will learn how to use comparison models to solve subtraction problems with numbers up through 100. They will also review how to use take-away and addition models to solve problems.

Materials to Gather

SUPPLIED

base-10 blocks

Solving with Sketches and Models activity page

LEARN Compare to Find the Difference

ONLINE 20min

Students will use base-10 blocks and sketches of base-10 blocks to help them compare two numbers in order to find the difference. When they compare two amounts, they will model both amounts.

Have students ask themselves questions similar to the following:

- What are the two numbers?
- Which number is greater?
- How many tens and ones do not have a match?
- What is the difference between the two numbers?

Objectives

- Use concrete objects or sketches to model and solve addition or subtraction computation problems involving sums and minuends up through 100.

LEARN Take Away to Find What's Left

ONLINE 20min

Students will use base-10 blocks and sketches of base-10 blocks to help them subtract by taking away. When they subtract by taking away an amount, they will model only the starting amount.

Have students ask themselves questions similar to the following:

- What are the two numbers?
- Which number is greater?
- How many tens and ones should I take away?
- What is left after I take some away?

Objectives

- Use concrete objects or sketches to model and solve addition or subtraction computation problems involving sums and minuends up through 100.

TRY IT Solving with Sketches and Models

Students will use sketches and base-10 blocks to compare two numbers to find the difference or take an amount away to find what's left. Give students the base-10 blocks and the Solving with Sketches and Models activity page from their Activity Book. Read the directions with them. Use the answer key to check students' answers, and then enter the results online.

- Use concrete objects or sketches to model and solve addition or subtraction computation problems involving sums and minuends up through 100.

Name:

Solve Compare and Change Problems
Solving with Sketches and Models

Draw a sketch to help solve the problem.

1. $45 - 43 = $ __2__

   **Sketches may vary.
   See below.**

2. $85 - 43 = $ __42__

   **Sketches may vary.
   See below.**

3. __31__ $= 96 - 65$

   **Sketches may vary.
   See below.**

4. $83 - 21 = $ __62__

   **Sketches may vary.
   See below.**

5. __45__ $= 65 - 20$

   **Sketches may vary.
   See below.**

Use base-10 blocks to help solve the problem.

6. $27 - 9 = $ __18__

7. __66__ $= 45 + 21$

8. $79 - 35 = $ __44__

TRY IT

ADD OR SUBTRACT: PROBLEM SOLVING 277 SOLVE COMPARE AND CHANGE PROBLEMS

ADD OR SUBTRACT: PROBLEM SOLVING 278 SOLVE COMPARE AND CHANGE PROBLEMS

Additional Answers

1. **Example:**

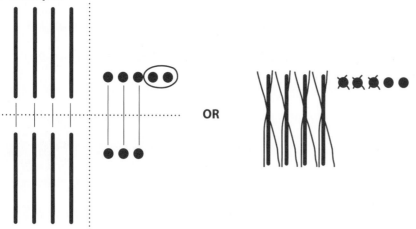

OR

2–5. Students should sketch base-10 blocks to correctly model the subtraction. Use the sample sketches shown for Problem 1 as a guide for checking their sketches.

Story Problems: More Exploration

Lesson Overview

Skills Update	5 minutes	ONLINE
REVIEW Extend Your Understanding	40 minutes	ONLINE
CHECKPOINT	15 minutes	ONLINE

▶ Lesson Objectives
Use concrete objects or sketches to model and solve addition or subtraction computation problems involving sums and minuends up through 100.

▶ Prerequisite Skills
Use concrete objects or sketches to model and solve addition or subtraction computation problems with sums and minuends up through 30.

▶ Content Background
Students will have an opportunity for continued review. Then they will take a Checkpoint. If you wish, you may have students begin the next lesson after they complete the Checkpoint.

Materials to Gather

SUPPLIED
base-10 blocks

REVIEW Extend Your Understanding
ONLINE 40min

To prepare for the Checkpoint, students will have a chance to practice skills they've learned in previous lessons.

Objectives
- Use concrete objects or sketches to model and solve addition or subtraction computation problems involving sums and minuends up through 100.

CHECKPOINT
ONLINE 15min

Students will complete an online Checkpoint. Read the directions, problems, and answer choices to students. If necessary, help students with keyboard or mouse operations.
   Give students the base-10 blocks.

Objectives
- Use concrete objects or sketches to model and solve addition or subtraction computation problems involving sums and minuends up through 100.

Part-Part-Total Problems

Skills Update	5 minutes	ONLINE
GET READY Recipe Math	5 minutes	ONLINE
LEARN Use Part-Part-Total for Problems	15 minutes	ONLINE
LEARN More Uses of Part-Part-Total	20 minutes	OFFLINE
TRY IT Combine Story Problems	15 minutes	OFFLINE

▶ Lesson Objectives

Recognize and solve word problems involving sums up through 100 in which two quantities are combined.

▶ Prerequisite Skills

Use concrete objects or sketches to represent a quantity up through 30.

▶ Advance Preparation

Print six copies of the Part-Part-Total Sheet.

▶ Content Background

Students will work with the concept of parts and total to solve combine story problems. They will learn that the amounts being combined are the parts and that the amount in all is the total. For example, in the problem "Jill has 12 marbles. 3 of the marbles are red, and the rest are white. How many of the marbles are white?" 3 and the missing value 9 are the parts and 12 is the total.

Materials to Gather

SUPPLIED

blocks – B (all colors)

base-10 blocks

Part-Part-Total Sheet (printout)

More Uses of Part-Part-Total activity page

Combine Story Problems activity page

GET READY Recipe Math

ONLINE 5 min

Students will solve story problems by combining two parts to find the total.

Objectives

- Solve addition problems with a one- and a two-digit number with sums through 100 by using regrouping.

LEARN Use Part-Part-Total for Problems

ONLINE 15 min

Students will learn how to identify the parts and totals in addition story problems. First they will learn how to model the parts with objects and how to combine the objects to find the total. Next students will learn how to use numbers to represent each part. They will add the numbers to find the total. At the end of the activity, students will be asked to write a number sentence without using the part-part-total chart.

Objectives

- Recognize and solve word problems involving sums up through 100 in which two quantities are combined.

As students work through the activity, have them ask themselves questions similar to the following:

- What are the parts given in the problem? Is the total given?
- How do I show the parts on the part-part-total chart?
- How many circles do I use?
- How do I find the total?

LEARN More Uses of Part-Part-Total

OFFLINE
20min

Students will use a part-part-total chart to solve problems in which a part and the total are given and the other part is missing. Then they will learn how to count on with circle blocks or base-10 blocks to find the answer.

Gather the circle blocks, base-10 blocks, Part-Part-Total Sheets, and More Uses of Part-Part-Total activity page.

MODEL WITH CIRCLES

1. Read aloud Problem 1 on the activity page. Point to the numbers in the number sentence $9 + \underline{\quad} = 16$. The problem says there is a total of 16 coins. The problem also says that the total is made up of two parts, pennies and nickels. One of the parts is given, 9 nickels. Students have to find the other part.

2. Have students put 9 red circles in one Part section of the Part-Part-Total Sheet to model the known part. Have them write the number 9 in that section as well.

3. Have students sketch 16 circles in the Total section to model the total. Each sketch should be about the size of a circle block. Have students write the number 16 in the Total section.

4. Guide the student to move the part they know, 9, into the Total section. Then they can use the 9 circles to cover 9 of the sketches.

   Assist students in moving the 9 circles into the Total section. Place exactly 1 circle over each sketch.

5. Explain that the sketches without circle blocks represent the missing part. Guide students to place blue circles on these sketches, counting as the circles are placed. The number of blue circles is the missing part.

   Place a blue circle on each of the remaining sketches. Have students count with you as your place the circles: 1, 2, 3, 4, 5, 6, 7.

6. Point to the number sentence in Problem 1. Explain that the number 7 completes this number sentence. It's the missing part in this problem. There are 7 pennies in the jar.

   Have students fill in the missing part.

7. Repeat Steps 1–6 with Problem 2.

MODEL WITH BASE-10 BLOCKS

8. Point out that students needed to use a lot of circles to model Problem 2. Explain that when problems involve greater numbers, students can model them with base-10 blocks.

9. Read aloud Problem 3. Have students show 15 with base-10 blocks in one Part section to represent the 15 square stickers. Students should place 1 tens rod and 5 ones cubes in one of the Part sections. Have them write the number 15 in that section.

10. Have students sketch base-10 blocks in the Total section to represent 28. Students should sketch 2 lines and 8 dots. Make sure students' sketches are about the same size as the actual base-10 blocks. Have them write the number 28 in that section.

11. Help students move the part they know into the Total section. Students should place the tens rods on one of the lines they sketched. They should place each ones cubes each on a dot, covering 5 dots.

12. Explain that the sketches that are not covered represent the missing part. Help students place tens rods and ones cubes over the remaining sketches. As students place the blocks, have them count aloud, beginning with the tens rod and counting on the ones cubes: 10, 11, 12, 13.

Have students write the missing part to Problem 3.

13. Repeat Steps 9–12 with Problem 4.

14. Read aloud Problem 5. Explain that in this problem students need to decide which number is the part, which number is the total, and which number is missing.

Have students identify the known part and total. Have them write these numbers in the number sentence. Have them write a question mark for the missing part. Help them only as necessary.

15. Have students follow the process described in Steps 9–12 to use base-10 blocks to find the missing part.

16. Have students complete Problem 6 on their own. Assist them as necessary.

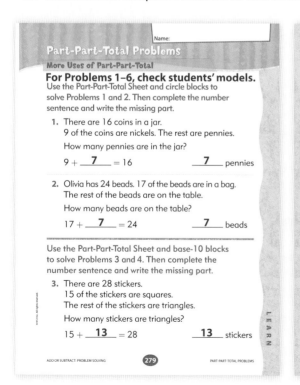

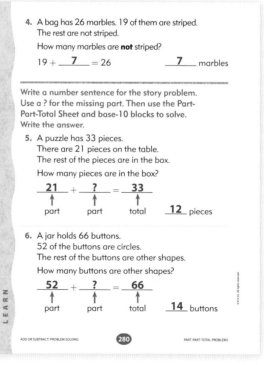

TRY IT Combine Story Problems

Students will practice solving combine story problems. Give students the base-10 blocks and Combine Story Problems activity page from their Activity Book. Read the directions with them. Use the answer key to check students' answers, and then enter the results online.

Objectives

- Recognize and solve word problems involving sums up through 100 in which two quantities are combined.

Name:

Part-Part-Total Problems
Combine Story Problems

Use base-10 blocks or a part-part-total chart to solve the problem, if needed.

1. Evan's hens laid 10 eggs.
   4 of the eggs were brown and
   the rest were white.
   How many eggs were white?   __6__

2. Heidi's garden has 14 trees.
   6 of the trees have red leaves.
   How many trees do **not** have red leaves?   __8__

3. Annie bought 19 notecards.
   11 of the notecards had flowers
   on them and the rest had hearts.
   How many notecards had hearts?   __8__

4. Claire rode her bike for 12 miles and
   Yael rode her bike for 19 miles.
   How many miles did they ride altogether?   __31__

---

5. Heidi's garden has 11 trees.
   6 trees have red leaves.
   The rest have green leaves.
   How many trees have green leaves?   __5__

6. Kyle had 13 red trucks.
   Vince had 19 red trucks.
   How many red trucks did the boys have
   altogether?   __32__

7. Grant planted 29 sunflower seeds and
   Daphne planted 8.
   How many sunflower seeds did they
   plant in all?   __37__

8. Izzie has 32 pennies and Mellie has
   6 pennies.
   How many pennies do they have in all?   __38__

9. Sally washed 22 cars and Janie washed
   27 cars.
   How many cars did they wash in all?   __49__

TRY IT

Problems with Parts and Total

Lesson Overview

Skills Update	5 minutes	ONLINE
GET READY Missing Numbers	5 minutes	ONLINE
LEARN Subtract for Missing Numbers	15 minutes	ONLINE
LEARN Related Problems	15 minutes	ONLINE
LEARN Choose Combine Problems	10 minutes	ONLINE
TRY IT Missing Parts in Combined Stories	10 minutes	OFFLINE

▶ Lesson Objectives

Recognize and solve word problems involving sums up through 100 in which two quantities are combined.

▶ Prerequisite Skills

Use concrete objects or sketches to represent a quantity up through 30.

▶ Content Background

Students will learn how to recognize and solve combine story problems. In some combine problems, students must put together two or more groups to find the sum. In other combine problems, they will be given the sum and will need to find one of the addends. They will learn that they can subtract to find the missing addend when solving this type of combine problem.

Materials to Gather

SUPPLIED

Missing Parts in Combined Stories activity page

GET READY Missing Numbers

ONLINE

5min

Objectives

- Use concrete objects or sketches to represent a quantity up through 30.

Students will complete number sentences in which there is a missing addend. As they work through the activity, encourage them to ask themselves questions similar to the following:

- What part do I know?
- What is the total?
- How many do I count on, if I count from the part I'm given to the total?

LEARN Subtract for Missing Numbers

ONLINE **15**min

Objectives

- Recognize and solve word problems involving sums up through 100 in which two quantities are combined.

Students will model and solve combine problems in which one of the parts is missing. They will learn that it's not always easy to count on to solve these kinds of problems. They will be encouraged to solve these problems by subtracting the known part from the total to get the other part.

LEARN Related Problems

ONLINE **15**min

Objectives

- Recognize and solve word problems involving sums up through 100 in which two quantities are combined.

Students will continue to solve combine problems. They will work with Alexander and Serena to solve pairs of problems that use the same numbers but ask different questions. Through solving these problems, students will explore the relationship between addition and subtraction.

   As students work through the activity, encourage them to ask themselves questions similar to the following:

- Which is missing: a part or the total?
- Should I add or subtract to find the missing number?
- How are the two related problems alike? How are the problems different?

LEARN Choose Combine Problems

ONLINE **10**min

Objectives

- Recognize and solve word problems involving sums up through 100 in which two quantities are combined.

Students will learn to recognize when the two amounts in a problem are being combined. Then they will practice solving combine problems. Remind them that when amounts are combined, they are put together. Use the part-part-total concept to remind students that in some combine problems, one part may be missing.

OFFLINE 10 min

TRY IT Missing Parts in Combined Stories

Give students the Missing Parts in Combined Stories activity page from their Activity Book and read the directions with them. Use the answer key to score the assessment, and then go to the next screen to enter the results.

Objectives

- Recognize and solve word problems involving sums up through 100 in which two quantities are combined.

Name:

Problems with Parts and Total

Missing Parts in Combined Stories

Circle the answer.

1. Which of the following shows two amounts being combined?
   A. Tanya scored 15 goals in the soccer game. Helen scored 20 goals. How many more goals did Helen score than Tanya?
   (B.) Jake made 18 cheese pizzas and 13 mushroom pizzas for his restaurant. How many pizzas did he make in all?
   C. Kate flew her kite for 20 minutes. Tom flew his kite for 27 minutes. How much longer did Tom fly his kite than Kate did?

Solve.

2. Jesse was on vacation for 21 days. He went to the beach on 13 of the days. How many days did Jesse **not** go to the beach? __8__
3. Becky picked 14 peaches. Three of them were not ripe. The rest were ripe. How many of the peaches were ripe? __11__

TRY IT

4. Hal baked 15 apples. He added sugar to 3 of them and cinnamon to the rest. How many apples had cinnamon? __12__
5. Tessie read 15 books. Two of the books were mystery books and the rest were comedies. How many books were comedies? __13__
6. Nina baked 44 lemon bars for the bake sale. She put 23 of them in a box. How many lemon bars were **not** in a box? __21__
7. Judy baked 24 cupcakes. Five of the cupcakes were chocolate and the rest were vanilla. How many cupcakes were vanilla? __19__
8. Toby has 34 trains. Ten of them are black and the rest are red. How many trains are red? __24__

TRY IT

Combine Problems: More Exploration

▶ Lesson Objectives

Recognize and solve word problems involving sums up through 100 in which two quantities are combined.

▶ Prerequisite Skills

Use concrete objects or sketches to represent a quantity up through 30.

▶ Content Background

Students will have an opportunity for continued review. Then they will take a Checkpoint. If you wish, you may have students begin the next lesson after they complete the Checkpoint.

Materials to Gather

There are no materials to gather for this lesson.

REVIEW Extend Your Understanding

ONLINE **40min**

To prepare for the Checkpoint, students will have a chance to practice skills they've learned in previous lessons.

Objectives

- Recognize and solve word problems involving sums up through 100 in which two quantities are combined.

CHECKPOINT

ONLINE **15min**

Students will complete an online Checkpoint. Read the directions, problems, and answer choices to students. If necessary, help students with keyboard or mouse operations.

Objectives

- Recognize and solve word problems involving sums up through 100 in which two quantities are combined.

Change Problems

Skills Update	5 minutes	ONLINE
GET READY Addition Story Problems	10 minutes	ONLINE
LEARN Model Story Problems	15 minutes	ONLINE
LEARN Problems That Change	10 minutes	ONLINE
LEARN What's the Change?	10 minutes	ONLINE
TRY IT Solve with Start-Change-Result	10 minutes	OFFLINE

▶ Lesson Objectives

Recognize and solve word problems involving sums or minuends up through 100 in which one quantity changes by addition or subtraction.

▶ Prerequisite Skills

Recognize and solve word problems involving sums or minuends up through 20 in which one quantity changes through addition or subtraction.

▶ Advance Preparation

Print two copies of the Start-Change-Result Chart.

▶ Content Background

Students will solve change story problems. In change problems, they must add to or take away from a group—the number of objects in the group changes. First students will count on to find the answer to addition change problems. Then they will use the start-change-result model to solve change problems.

The start-change-result model is very similar to the part-part-total model, which students may have used. Although these models can be used interchangeably to represent addition and subtraction story problems involving an amount that changes, the start-change-result model suggests the action of a change problem more clearly. Therefore, this model helps students more easily recognize a problem involving change versus one in which two parts are simply combined.

Materials to Gather

SUPPLIED

base-10 blocks

Start-Change-Result Chart (printout)

Solve with Start-Change-Result activity page

GET READY Addition Story Problems

ONLINE 10 min

Students will solve addition story problems involving combining and changing numbers and also identify when a problem involves a change in an amount. As students work through the activity, encourage them to ask themselves questions similar to the following:

- What is happening in the problem?
- Is the starting number changing during the action of the problem?
- Are objects being put together or taken away?
- Do I need to add or subtract?
- What is the answer to the problem?

Objectives

- Recognize and solve word problems involving sums or minuends up through 20 in which one quantity changes through addition or subtraction.

LEARN Model Story Problems

ONLINE 15 min

Students will learn how to solve story problems involving a change of the starting amount. Johnny will show them how to count on using base-10 blocks to solve the problems. Give students the base-10 blocks.

Objectives

- Recognize and solve word problems involving sums or minuends up through 100 in which one quantity changes by addition or subtraction.

Tips

Remind students to count by 10s for tens rods and ones for ones cubes.

LEARN Problems That Change

ONLINE 10 min

Students will use a start-change-result chart to solve problems in which amounts change by addition or subtraction.

The goal is to use the chart to learn how to set up the problem and then move away from using the chart to use only numbers.

Objectives

- Recognize and solve word problems involving sums or minuends up through 100 in which one quantity changes by addition or subtraction.

Tips

Allow students to use base-10 blocks to model the addition and subtraction, but encourage them to try the problems without the blocks.

LEARN What's the Change?

Students will use a start-change-result chart to solve problems in which amounts change by addition or subtraction. The problem will give the starting value and the result, and students will find the amount by which the starting value changes.

The goal is to use the chart to learn how to set up the problem and then move away from using the chart to use only numbers.

Objectives

- Recognize and solve word problems involving sums or minuends up through 100 in which one quantity changes by addition or subtraction.

Tips

Allow students to use base-10 blocks to model the addition and subtraction, but encourage them to try the problems without the blocks.

TRY IT Solve with Start-Change-Result

Students will practice using a start-change-result chart to solve change problems. Give students the Start-Change-Result Charts and Solve with Start-Change-Result activity page from their Activity Book. Read the directions with them. Use the answer key to check students' answers, and then enter the results online.

Objectives

- Recognize and solve word problems involving sums or minuends up through 100 in which one quantity changes by addition or subtraction.

Name: _____

Change Problems
Solve with Start-Change-Result

Use the Start-Change-Result Chart to solve.

1. Patrick had 53 stamps.
   Susan gave him 21 more stamps.

   How many stamps does Patrick have now?   __74__

2. Patrick had 53 stamps.
   He gave Susan 21 of his stamps.

   How many stamps does Patrick have now?   __32__

3. Patrick had 53 stamps.
   Susan gave him some more stamps.
   Patrick now has 67 stamps.

   How many stamps did Susan give Patrick?   __14__

4. Patrick had 53 stamps.
   He gave some stamps to Susan.
   Patrick now has 31 stamps.

   How many stamps did Patrick give to Susan?   __22__

ADD OR SUBTRACT: PROBLEM SOLVING   **285**   CHANGE PROBLEMS

TRY IT

5. Franca had 62 books.
   His friends gave him more books for his birthday.
   He now has 73 books.

   How many books did Franca get for his birthday?   __11__

6. Sherri had 36 ribbons.
   She bought 9 more.

   How many ribbons does Sherri have now?   __45__

7. Blake had 87 nails.
   He used 25 of them.

   How many nails does Blake have left?   __62__

8. The pancake house made 65 pancakes.
   The children ate some of these pancakes.
   There were 13 pancakes left.

   How many pancakes did the children eat?   __52__

ADD OR SUBTRACT: PROBLEM SOLVING   **286**   CHANGE PROBLEMS

TRY IT

Missing Numbers in Story Problems

Lesson Overview

Skills Update	5 minutes	ONLINE
GET READY Use a Place-Value Chart	10 minutes	ONLINE
LEARN What's the Missing Start Number?	15 minutes	ONLINE
LEARN What's Missing: Start, Change, Result	15 minutes	OFFLINE
TRY IT Start, Change, and Result	15 minutes	OFFLINE

▶ Lesson Objectives

Recognize and solve word problems involving sums or minuends up through 100 in which one quantity changes by addition or subtraction.

▶ Prerequisite Skills

Use concrete objects or sketches to represent a quantity up through 30.

▶ Advance Preparation

Print two copies of the Start-Change-Result Chart.

▶ Content Background

Students will continue to solve change story problems. In change problems, students must add to or take away from a group—the number of objects in the group changes. In this lesson, students will need to find the original number of objects in the group. For example, "Emma had some stickers. She got 5 more. Now she has 11. How many stickers did Emma have at the beginning?"

The start-change-result model is very similar to the part-part-total model, which students may have used. Although these models can be used inter-changeably to represent addition and subtraction story problems involving an amount that changes, the start-change-result model suggests the action of a change problem more clearly. Therefore, this model helps students more easily recognize a problem involving change versus one in which two parts are simply combined.

> **Materials to Gather**
>
> **SUPPLIED**
>
> Start-Change-Result Chart (printout)
>
> What's Missing: Start, Change, Result activity page
>
> Start, Change, and Result activity page

GET READY Use a Place-Value Chart ONLINE 10min

Students will review how to use a place-value chart.

Objectives

- Use concrete objects or sketches to represent a quantity up through 30.

LEARN What's the Missing Start Number?

Objectives

Students will use models and a start-change-result chart to solve story problems in which the starting amount changes. The problem will give the amount of change and the result, and students will find the starting number.

Have students ask themselves questions such as the following:

- What do I know—the value of the start? the value of the change? the value of the result?
- What value is missing?
- Should I add or should I subtract to find the missing value?
- What is the answer to the problem?

- Recognize and solve word problems involving sums or minuends up through 100 in which one quantity changes by addition or subtraction.

LEARN What's Missing: Start, Change, Result

Objectives

Students will use a start-change-result chart as a tool to determine what information is missing in the problem: the starting number, the amount of change taking place, or the result.

Students should build a greater understanding of the positioning of each number in a story problem to determine how they will solve the problem. To facilitate this understanding, have students ask themselves questions similar to the following:

- What do I know?
- What do I need to find?
- Where do I place each number on the chart?
- How will I solve this problem?
- What is the answer to the problem?

Give students the What's Missing: Start, Change, or Result activity page from their Activity Book. Read the directions with them.

- Recognize and solve word problems involving sums or minuends up through 100 in which one quantity changes by addition or subtraction.

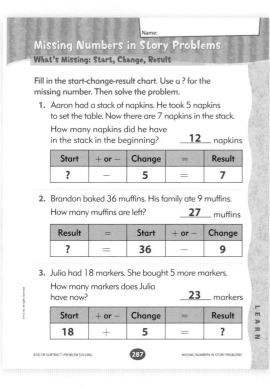

Missing Numbers in Story Problems
What's Missing: Start, Change, Result

Fill in the start-change-result chart. Use a ? for the missing number. Then solve the problem.

1. Aaron had a stack of napkins. He took 5 napkins to set the table. Now there are 7 napkins in the stack.

   How many napkins did he have in the stack in the beginning? __12__ napkins

Start	+ or −	Change	=	Result
?	−	5	=	7

2. Brandon baked 36 muffins. His family ate 9 muffins. How many muffins are left? __27__ muffins

Result	=	Start	+ or −	Change
?	=	36	−	9

3. Julia had 18 markers. She bought 5 more markers.

   How many markers does Julia have now? __23__ markers

Start	+ or −	Change	=	Result
18	+	5	=	?

L E A R N

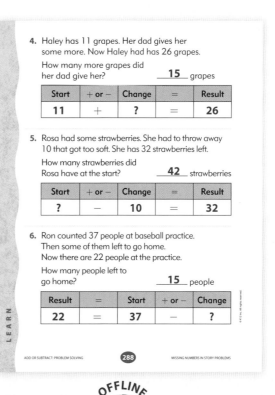

4. Haley has 11 grapes. Her dad gives her some more. Now Haley had has 26 grapes.

   How many more grapes did her dad give her? __15__ grapes

Start	+ or −	Change	=	Result
11	+	?	=	26

5. Rosa had some strawberries. She had to throw away 10 that got too soft. She has 32 strawberries left.

   How many strawberries did Rosa have at the start? __42__ strawberries

Start	+ or −	Change	=	Result
?	−	10	=	32

6. Ron counted 37 people at baseball practice. Then some of them left to go home. Now there are 22 people at the practice.

   How many people left to go home? __15__ people

Result	=	Start	+ or −	Change
22	=	37	−	?

L E A R N

TRY IT Start, Change, and Result

OFFLINE 15 min

Objectives

Students will practice solving story problems where one amount changes using addition or subtraction. Give students the Start-Change-Result Charts and the Start, Change, and Result activity page from their Activity Book. Read the directions with them. Use the answer key to check students' answers, and then enter the results online.

- Recognize and solve word problems involving sums or minuends up through 100 in which one quantity changes by addition or subtraction.

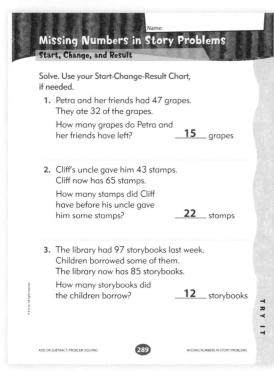

Missing Numbers in Story Problems
Start, Change, and Result

Solve. Use your Start-Change-Result Chart, if needed.

1. Petra and her friends had 47 grapes. They ate 32 of the grapes.

   How many grapes do Petra and her friends have left? __15__ grapes

2. Cliff's uncle gave him 43 stamps. Cliff now has 65 stamps.

   How many stamps did Cliff have before his uncle gave him some stamps? __22__ stamps

3. The library had 97 storybooks last week. Children borrowed some of them. The library now has 85 storybooks.

   How many storybooks did the children borrow? __12__ storybooks

T R Y I T

4. Kamilah had 68 coins in his collection. He was given 21 more coins.

   How many coins does Kamilah have now? __89__ coins

5. Monica had 25 markers. She found some more. Now she has 34 markers.

   How many markers did Monica find? __9__ markers

6. After lunch, there were 13 carrot sticks left on the plate. The family had eaten 36 carrot sticks for lunch.

   How many carrot sticks were on the plate before lunch? __49__ carrot sticks

T R Y I T

Change Problems: More Exploration

Lesson Overview

Skills Update	5 minutes	ONLINE
REVIEW Extend Your Understanding	40 minutes	ONLINE
CHECKPOINT	15 minutes	ONLINE

▶ Lesson Objectives

Recognize and solve word problems involving sums or minuends up through 100 in which one quantity changes by addition or subtraction.

▶ Prerequisite Skills

Use concrete objects or sketches to represent a quantity up through 30.

▶ Content Background

Students will have an opportunity for continued review. Then they will take a Checkpoint. If you wish, you may have students begin the next lesson after they complete the Checkpoint.

Materials to Gather

There are no materials to gather for this lesson.

REVIEW Extend Your Understanding

ONLINE 40 min

To prepare for the Checkpoint, students will have a chance to practice skills they've learned in previous lessons.

Objectives

- Recognize and solve word problems involving sums or minuends up through 100 in which one quantity changes by addition or subtraction.

CHECKPOINT

ONLINE 15 min

Students will complete an online Checkpoint. Read the directions, problems, and answer choices to students. If necessary, help students with keyboard or mouse operations.

Objectives

- Recognize and solve word problems involving sums or minuends up through 100 in which one quantity changes by addition or subtraction.

Comparison Story Problems

Skills Update	5 minutes	ONLINE
GET READY Compare Problems	5 minutes	ONLINE
LEARN Match to Compare	15 minutes	ONLINE
LEARN Subtract to Compare	10 minutes	ONLINE
LEARN Greater Numbers	10 minutes	ONLINE
TRY IT Compare Story Problems	15 minutes	OFFLINE

▶ Lesson Objectives

Recognize and solve word problems involving numbers up to 100 in which two quantities are compared by the use of addition or subtraction.

▶ Prerequisite Skills

Recognize and solve word problems involving numbers up to 10 in which two quantities are compared by the use of addition or subtraction.

▶ Content Background

Students will learn to recognize and solve story problems in which two amounts are compared. In *compare problems*, students must compare two groups to determine how many more or fewer objects are in one group. They will first compare groups using models that are aligned so that the objects in the two groups match one-to-one. To find how many more or fewer, students will count the unmatched objects. When comparing greater numbers, counting isn't practical. Students will learn that they can subtract, rather than count, to solve compare problems. They will also learn that they can use the same subtraction sentence to compare whether they are finding how many more or how many fewer.

Materials to Gather

SUPPLIED

Compare Story Problems activity page

GET READY Compare Problems

ONLINE 5 min

Students will use models to solve story problems in which two quantities are compared. They will add or subtract to solve these problems.

Objectives

- Recognize and solve word problems involving numbers up to 10 in which two quantities are compared by the use of addition or subtraction.

LEARN Match to Compare

Students will use a variety of methods to solve story problems in which two amounts are compared. As students work through the activity, encourage them to ask themselves questions similar to the following:

- What numbers are in the story problem?
- Which is the greater number?
- Which is the lesser number?
- What is the difference between the two numbers?

Objectives

- Recognize and solve word problems involving numbers up to 100 in which two quantities are compared by the use of addition or subtraction.

LEARN Subtract to Compare

ONLINE 10min

Students will solve comparison subtraction problems. They will begin by learning how to use base-10 blocks as models as well as subtraction number sentences. As the activity progresses, students will be asked to solve the subtraction sentences without models. If they have difficulty solving the problems without models, they may see base-10 block hints until they understand the connection between the models and the number sentences.

Objectives

- Recognize and solve word problems involving numbers up to 100 in which two quantities are compared by the use of addition or subtraction.

Tips

Reinforce with students that when they subtract to compare, the greater number comes first in the number sentence.

LEARN Greater Numbers

ONLINE 10min

Students will use number sentences to solve story problems in which two amounts are compared. They will learn that it can be easier to solve problems involving greater numbers with subtraction rather than models.

As students work through the activity, encourage them to ask themselves questions similar to the following:

- What numbers are being compared?
- Which is the greater number?
- Which is the lesser number?
- How do I write the subtraction problem?
- Do I need to regroup?
- What is my answer?

Objectives

- Recognize and solve word problems involving numbers up to 100 in which two quantities are compared by the use of addition or subtraction.

TRY IT Compare Story Problems

Objectives

Students will practice solving story problems in which they must compare two amounts. Give students the Compare Story Problems activity page from their Activity Book and read the directions with them. Use the answer key to check students' answers, and then enter the results online.

- Recognize and solve word problems involving numbers up to 100 in which two quantities are compared by the use of addition or subtraction.

Name: _____

Comparison Story Problems
Compare Story Problems

Solve.

1. Mark has gone bowling 57 times.
   Pamela has gone bowling 34 times.

   How many more times has Mark
   gone bowling than Pamela?   **23** more

2. Jennifer has 43 comic books.
   Anne has 55 comic books.

   How many fewer comic books
   does Jennifer have than Anne?   **12** fewer

3. Julian has visited the zoo 28 times.
   Artie has visited the zoo 22 times.

   How many fewer times has Artie
   visited the zoo than Julian?   **6** fewer

4. Archie has flown on a plane 13 times.
   Elaine has flown on a plane 25 times.

   How many more times has Elaine
   flown on a plane than Archie?   **12** more

ADD OR SUBTRACT: PROBLEM SOLVING   **291**   COMPARISON STORY PROBLEMS

TRY IT

---

5. Antoine has 46 books.
   Karl has 25 books.

   How many more books does
   Antoine have than Karl?   **21** more

6. The flower shop has 23 tulips
   and 59 daffodils.

   How many fewer tulips does it
   have than daffodils?   **36** fewer

7. Diane has 89 crayons.
   Sarah has 36 crayons.

   How many fewer crayons
   does Sarah have than Diane?   **53** fewer

8. Theresa painted 15 pictures.
   Carol painted 67 pictures.

   How many more pictures did Carol
   paint than Theresa?   **52** more

TRY IT

ADD OR SUBTRACT: PROBLEM SOLVING   **292**   COMPARISON STORY PROBLEMS

Story Problems That Compare

Lesson Overview

Skills Update	5 minutes	ONLINE
LEARN Compare with Models	15 minutes	ONLINE
LEARN Compare and Add	15 minutes	ONLINE
LEARN Are You Comparing?	15 minutes	ONLINE
TRY IT Let's Compare	10 minutes	OFFLINE

▶ Lesson Objectives

Recognize and solve word problems involving numbers up to 100 in which two quantities are compared by the use of addition or subtraction.

▶ Prerequisite Skills

Recognize and solve word problems involving sums or minuends up through 100 in which one quantity changes by addition or subtraction.

▶ Content Background

Students will solve compare story problems. In *compare problems*, students must compare two groups to determine how many more or fewer objects are in one group. First they will use models to find the answers. Then they will learn that they can add to solve some compare problems.

Materials to Gather

SUPPLIED

base-10 blocks

Let's Compare activity page

LEARN Compare with Models

ONLINE 15min

Students will solve story problems in which two amounts are compared and modeled with base-10 blocks. They will solve problems in which the missing amount is a given amount that is more than another amount.

1. Help students understand what the problem is asking.

2. Be sure they can connect the wording in the problem to the model that represents the problem.

3. Have students tell you how they found the answer to each problem.

Objectives

- Recognize and solve word problems involving numbers up to 100 in which two quantities are compared by the use of addition or subtraction.

LEARN Compare and Add

ONLINE 15min

Students will solve story problems in which two amounts are compared and modeled with circle blocks or base-10 blocks. They will solve problems in which the missing number of objects is a given number fewer than another.

1. Help students understand what the problem is asking.

2. Be sure they can connect the wording in the problem to the model that represents the problem.

3. Have students tell you how they found the answer to each problem.

Objectives

- Recognize and solve word problems involving numbers up to 100 in which two quantities are compared by the use of addition or subtraction.

LEARN Are You Comparing?

ONLINE 15min

Students will decide if a story problem involves comparing two amounts and choose the number sentence that would solve the problem.

As students complete the activity, encourage them to ask themselves questions such as the following:

- What numbers are in the story problem?
- Are the numbers being compared?
- Do I add or subtract to find the answer?

Objectives

- Recognize and solve word problems involving numbers up to 100 in which two quantities are compared by the use of addition or subtraction.

TRY IT Let's Compare

OFFLINE 10min

Students will practice solving compare story problems. Give students the base-10 blocks and Let's Compare activity page from their Activity Book. Read the directions with them. Use the answer key to check students' answers, and then enter the results online.

Objectives

- Recognize and solve word problems involving numbers up to 100 in which two quantities are compared by the use of addition or subtraction.

Story Problems That Compare

Let's Compare

Solve by adding or subtracting. You may use base-10 blocks to help you.

1. Jacquie has 47 books.
Shirley has 98 books.

How many more books does
Shirley have than Jacquie? ___**51**___ books

2. Jamil has 21 trading cards.
Frank has 36 more cards than Jamil.

How many cards does Frank have? ___**57**___ cards

3. Rob's team scored 45 points in
the basketball game.
Sam's team scored 34 points.

How many fewer points did
Sam's team score than Rob's
team? ___**11**___ points

TRY IT

4. Joan has 82 stickers.
Megan has 6 fewer stickers than Joan.

How many stickers does
Megan have? ___**76**___ stickers

5. Margo has 23 finger puppets.
Rhea has 9 more finger puppets than
Margo.

How many finger puppets
does Rhea have? ___**32**___ puppets

6. Geoff has 78 pennies.
Devon has 32 fewer pennies
than Geoff.

How many pennies does
Devon have? ___**46**___ pennies

7. Ryan ran 6 laps around the
field last week.
Peter ran 24 laps around the
field last week.

How many fewer laps did
Ryan run than Peter? ___**18**___ laps

TRY IT

8. The deli sold 59 turkey sandwiches.
The deli also sold 35 tuna sandwiches.

How many more turkey
sandwiches did the deli sell
than tuna sandwiches? ___**24**___ sandwiches

Determine if the problem compares amounts.
Then circle the number sentence.

9. The snack stand sold 22 nacho snacks and
8 candy bars.

How many fewer candy bars did it sell than
nacho snacks?

Does this problem involve comparing two
amounts?

(A) Yes   B. No

Which number sentence would solve this
problem?

A. 22 + 8 = ?   (B.) 22 − 8 = ?

TRY IT

10. Children bought 11 tickets. Adults bought
4 more tickets than children.

How many tickets did adults buy?

Does this problem involve comparing
two amounts?

(A) Yes   B. No

Which number sentence would solve this
problem?

(A) 11 + 4 = ?   B. 11 − 4 = ?

Compare Problems: More Exploration

Skills Update	5 minutes	ONLINE
REVIEW Extend Your Understanding	40 minutes	ONLINE
CHECKPOINT	15 minutes	OFFLINE

▶ Lesson Objectives

Recognize and solve word problems involving numbers up to 100 in which two quantities are compared by the use of addition or subtraction.

▶ Content Background

Students will have an opportunity for continued review. Then they will take a Checkpoint. If you wish, you may have students begin the next lesson after they complete the Checkpoint.

Materials to Gather

SUPPLIED

base-10 blocks

Checkpoint (printout)

REVIEW Extend Your Understanding

ONLINE 40min

To prepare for the Checkpoint, students will have a chance to practice skills they've learned in previous lessons.

Objectives

- Recognize and solve word problems involving numbers up to 100 in which two quantities are compared by the use of addition or subtraction.

CHECKPOINT

Objectives

Print the Checkpoint and have students complete it on their own. Read the directions, problems, and answer choices to students, if necessary. Use the answer key to score the Checkpoint, and then enter the results online.

Give students the base-10 blocks. Students may use them if they wish.

- Recognize and solve word problems involving numbers up to 100 in which two quantities are compared by the use of addition or subtraction.

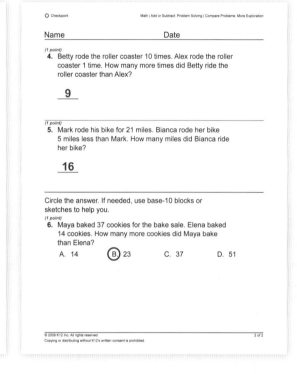

Checkpoint   Math | Add or Subtract: Problem Solving | Compare Problems: More Exploration

Name   Date

Checkpoint Answer Key

Solve. If needed, use base-10 blocks or sketches to help you.
(1 point)
1. Phillip counted 13 red cars on his trip to the city. His brother Drew counted 8 red cars on the same trip. How many fewer red cars did Drew count than Phillip?

    5

(1 point)
2. Joel has 3 baseball bats. Frank has 2 more baseball bats than Joel. How many baseball bats does Frank have?

    5

(1 point)
3. Sam ran six laps around the track. Mikey ran two more laps than Sam. How many laps did Mikey run?

    8

Checkpoint   Math | Add or Subtract: Problem Solving | Compare Problems: More Exploration

Name   Date

(1 point)
4. Betty rode the roller coaster 10 times. Alex rode the roller coaster 1 time. How many more times did Betty ride the roller coaster than Alex?

    9

(1 point)
5. Mark rode his bike for 21 miles. Bianca rode her bike 5 miles less than Mark. How many miles did Bianca ride her bike?

    16

Circle the answer. If needed, use base-10 blocks or sketches to help you.
(1 point)
6. Maya baked 37 cookies for the bake sale. Elena baked 14 cookies. How many more cookies did Maya bake than Elena?

    A. 14   **B.** 23   C. 37   D. 51

Unit Review

UNIT REVIEW Look Back	10 minutes	**ONLINE**
UNIT REVIEW Checkpoint Practice	50 minutes	**OFFLINE**
⏩ **UNIT REVIEW** Prepare for the Checkpoint		

▶ Unit Objectives

This lesson reviews the following objectives:

- Use concrete objects or sketches to model and solve addition or subtraction computation problems involving sums and minuends up through 100.
- Recognize and solve word problems involving sums up through 100 in which two quantities are combined.
- Recognize and solve word problems involving sums or minuends up through 100 in which one quantity changes by addition or subtraction.
- Recognize and solve word problems involving numbers up to 100 in which two quantities are compared by the use of addition or subtraction.

▶ Advance Preparation

In this lesson, students will have an opportunity to review previous activities in the Add or Subtract: Problem Solving unit. Look at the suggested activities in Unit Review: Prepare for the Checkpoint online and gather any needed materials.

Print one copy each of the Part-Part-Total Chart and Start-Change-Result Chart.

Materials to Gather

SUPPLIED

base-10 blocks

Part-Part-Total Chart (printout)

Start-Change-Result Chart (printout)

Checkpoint Practice activity page

UNIT REVIEW Look Back

ONLINE
10 min

Objectives

- Review unit objectives.

Students began the unit by solving addition and subtraction problems using place-value models, such as base-10 blocks and sketches of base-10 blocks. Then students applied their knowledge of addition and subtraction to solving story problems.

They focused on two types of story problems: combine problems and change problems. For some combine problems, students had to put together two or more groups to find the sum. For other combine problems, however, they were given the sum and needed to find one of the addends. They learned how to use a part-part-total chart to help them solve combine problems. For the change problems, students had to add to or take away from a group—the number of objects in the group changed. They learned how to use a start-change-result chart to solve change problems.

Students will review these concepts to prepare for the Unit Checkpoint.

Objectives

- Review unit objectives.

Students will complete a Checkpoint Practice activity page to prepare for the Unit Checkpoint. If necessary, read the directions, problems, and answer choices to students. Have students answer the problems on their own. Review any missed problems with students.

Gather the base-10 blocks, Part-Part-Total Chart, and Start-Change-Result Chart.

Unit Review
Checkpoint Practice

Name:

Circle Add or Subtract to tell how you would solve the problem. Then use base-10 blocks or sketches to solve. **Check students' models or sketches.**

1. Sierra had 26 dolls in her collection.
She got 15 more dolls.

How many dolls does Sierra have now? _____**41**_____ dolls

(A.) Add   B. Subtract

2. Tony had 36 golf balls.
He gave 16 golf balls to his sister.

How many golf balls does Tony have left? _____**20**_____ golf balls

A. Add   (B.) Subtract

Solve the problem. If needed, use base-10 blocks and a part-part-total chart to help you.

3. Max has 15 blue cups and 21 red cups.

How many cups does he have in all? _____**36**_____ cups

---

4. Sari has 36 photos. 14 of the photos are of her friends.
The rest are of her family.

How many of Sari's photos are of her family? _____**22**_____ photos

5. The Rose Café had 54 chairs outside.
They added some more. Now the café has 87 chairs outside.

How many chairs did the café add? _____**33**_____ chairs

Solve the problem. If needed, use a start-change-result chart to help you.

6. In the morning, there were 47 boxes of cereal on the shelf at the store.
At the end of the day, there were 20 boxes of cereal on the shelf.

How many boxes of cereal did people buy during the day? _____**27**_____ boxes

7. Jeff picked 23 red tomatoes.
Then he bought 12 more tomatoes.

How many tomatoes does Jeff have in all? _____**35**_____ tomatoes

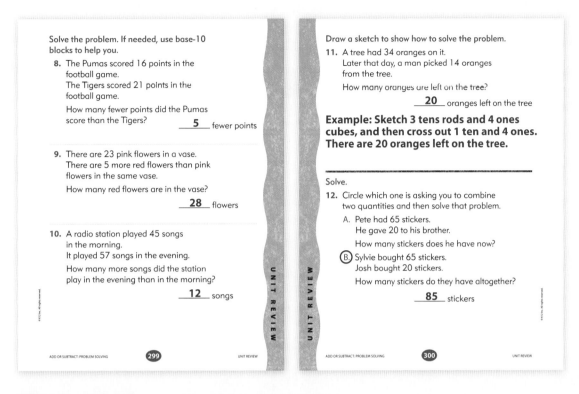

Solve the problem. If needed, use base-10 blocks to help you.

8. The Pumas scored 16 points in the football game.
The Tigers scored 21 points in the football game.

How many fewer points did the Pumas score than the Tigers?   ___5___ fewer points

9. There are 23 pink flowers in a vase.
There are 5 more red flowers than pink flowers in the same vase.

How many red flowers are in the vase?   ___28___ flowers

10. A radio station played 45 songs in the morning.
It played 57 songs in the evening.

How many more songs did the station play in the evening than in the morning?   ___12___ songs

UNIT REVIEW

Draw a sketch to show how to solve the problem.

11. A tree had 34 oranges on it.
Later that day, a man picked 14 oranges from the tree.

How many oranges are left on the tree?
   ___20___ oranges left on the tree

Example: Sketch 3 tens rods and 4 ones cubes, and then cross out 1 ten and 4 ones. There are 20 oranges left on the tree.

Solve.

12. Circle which one is asking you to combine two quantities and then solve that problem.

   A. Pete had 65 stickers.
   He gave 20 to his brother.

   How many stickers does he have now?

   (B.) Sylvie bought 65 stickers.
   Josh bought 20 stickers.

   How many stickers do they have altogether?

   ___85___ stickers

UNIT REVIEW

➡ UNIT REVIEW Prepare for the Checkpoint

What you do next depends on how students performed in the previous activity, Unit Review: Checkpoint Practice. If students had difficulty with any of the problems, complete the appropriate review activity listed in the table online.

Unit Checkpoint

UNIT CHECKPOINT Offline	60 minutes	**OFFLINE**

▶ Unit Objectives

This lesson assesses the following objectives:

- Use concrete objects or sketches to model and solve addition or subtraction computation problems involving sums and minuends up through 100.
- Recognize and solve word problems involving sums up through 100 in which two quantities are combined.
- Recognize and solve word problems involving sums or minuends up through 100 in which one quantity changes by addition or subtraction.
- Recognize and solve word problems involving numbers up to 100 in which two quantities are compared by the use of addition or subtraction.

Materials to Gather

SUPPLIED

base-10 blocks (optional)

Unit Checkpoint (printout)

OFFLINE
60 min

UNIT CHECKPOINT Offline

Objectives

- Assess unit objectives.

Students will complete the Unit Checkpoint offline. Print the Checkpoint and have students complete it on their own. Read the directions, problems, and answer choices to students, if necessary. Use the answer key to score the Checkpoint, and then enter the results online.

Give students the base-10 blocks to use with Problems 2–14, if needed.

○ Checkpoint   Math | Add or Subtract: Problem Solving | Unit Checkpoint

Name _____ Date _____

Unit Checkpoint Answer Key

Draw a sketch to solve this problem.
(2 points)
1. Mark had 59 balloons.
   37 of the balloons popped.

   How many balloons does Mark have left? __**22**__ balloons

   Students should make a sketch to solve the problem. An example of a correct sketch would be 5 tens rods and 9 ones cubes with 3 tens and 7 ones crossed out. There are 22 balloons left.

Solve. If needed, use base-10 blocks or sketches to help you.
(2 points)
2. Miguel has gone to 32 baseball games this year.
   Javier has gone to 12 more baseball games than Miguel.

   How many baseball games has Javier gone to? __**44**__ baseball games

(1 point)
3. Sandy had 10 flowers.
   Later that day she added 11 more flowers to her collection.

   Which picture shows how many flowers she has now?

   Ⓐ 🌸🌸🌸🌸🌸🌸🌸🌸🌸🌸🌸
       🌸🌸🌸🌸🌸🌸🌸🌸🌸🌸🌸

   B. 🌸🌸🌸🌸🌸🌸🌸🌸🌸🌸

   C. 🌸🌸🌸🌸🌸🌸🌸🌸🌸🌸🌸

1 of 3

○ Checkpoint   Math | Add or Subtract: Problem Solving | Unit Checkpoint

Name _____ Date _____

Circle the answer. If needed, use base-10 blocks or sketches to help you.
(1 point)
4. The bookstore had 56 car magazines.
   Over the weekend it sold 22 of them.

   How many car magazines did the bookstore have left?

   A. 22   Ⓑ 34   C. 56   D. 78

(1 point)
5. Samantha saved 56 pennies.
   Her brother gave her some more.
   Now she has 99 pennies.

   How many pennies did Samantha's brother give her?

   A. 155   B. 99   C. 56   Ⓓ 43

(1 point)
6. Andy read 26 books over the summer break.
   Michelle read 8 books over the summer break.

   How many fewer books did Michelle read than Andy?

   A. 8   Ⓑ 18   C. 26   D. 34

(1 point)
7. Molly roasted 12 marshmallows and Amanda roasted 8.

   How many marshmallows did they roast altogether?

   A. 12   B. 18   Ⓒ 20   D. 22

(1 point)
8. Daisy picked 64 flowers altogether.
   She picked 21 pink flowers and the rest were yellow.

   How many flowers were yellow?

   A. 21   Ⓑ 43   C. 64   D. 85

2 of 3

Name _____ Date _____

Solve. If needed, use base-10 blocks or sketches to help you.

(1 point)
9. There were 89 stickers in Janice's album.
She bought 7 more stickers.

How many stickers does she have now?   **96** stickers

(1 point)
10. Penny had some beads.
She gave 22 beads to Joyce.
Now Penny has 66 beads.

How many beads did Penny have to start with?   **88** beads

(1 point)
11. Corrine scored 29 points on her new video game.
Marilyn scored 22 points on the video game.

How many more points did Corrine score
than Marilyn?   **7** points

(1 point)
12. The Panthers soccer team scored 8 goals.
They scored 2 fewer goals than the Eagles.

How many goals did the Eagles score?   **10** goals

(1 point)
13. Fawn walked for 23 minutes and then rode her bike
for 15 minutes.

How many minutes did Fawn exercise altogether? **38** minutes

(1 point)
14. Sally did 28 math problems.
13 of them were subtraction and the rest
were addition.

How many problems were addition?   **15** problems

Add or Subtract: More Problem Solving

▶ Unit Objectives

- Recognize and solve word problems involving numbers up to 100 in which one quantity must be changed to equal another quantity.

- Write and solve addition or subtraction number sentences for problem-solving situations with sums and minuends up through 100.

- Check the accuracy of calculations from the context of the problem.

- Justify the procedures selected for addition or subtraction problem-solving situations with sums or minuends up through 100.

- Given a problem and solution, solve a similar problem by identifying connections between the two problems.

- Given a number sentence involving addition, subtraction, or both addition and subtraction, create a problem represented by the number sentence.

▶ Big Ideas

The use of letters, numbers, and mathematical symbols makes possible the translation of complex situations or long word statements into concise mathematical sentences or expressions.

▶ Unit Introduction

In this unit, students will learn to recognize and solve story problems in which one quantity must be changed to equal another quantity, and they will also write number sentences for all types of story problems. Students will learn to check the accuracy of an answer to a story problem, compare two story problems to see how they are similar, and create story problems that represent number sentences. They will also learn how to justify their procedures when solving story problems.

Equalize Story Problems

Lesson Overview

Skills Update	5 minutes	ONLINE
GET READY Balance Numbers	5 minutes	ONLINE
LEARN Balance Story Problems	20 minutes	ONLINE
LEARN Hop to Solve	20 minutes	ONLINE
TRY IT Make the Numbers Equal	10 minutes	OFFLINE

▶ Lesson Objectives

Recognize and solve word problems involving numbers up to 100 in which one quantity must be changed to equal another quantity.

▶ Prerequisite Skills

Use concrete objects or sketches to represent a quantity up through 30.

▶ Advance Preparation

Print the Number Line 0–100. Cut out the number lines and tape them together to form one number line from 0 to 100.

▶ Content Background

Students will solve story problems in which they add or subtract to make one amount equal to another. For example, "Ralph read for 27 minutes yesterday. Today, he's read for 15 minutes. How many more minutes must Ralph read today in order to read for the same amount of time he read yesterday?"

Materials to Gather

SUPPLIED
Number Line 0–100 (printout)
Make the Numbers Equal activity page

ALSO NEEDED
scissors, adult
tape, clear

GET READY Balance Numbers

ONLINE 5 min

Objectives

- Use concrete objects or sketches to represent a quantity up through 30.

A number sentence is like a balance—just as the objects on each side of a level balance have the same mass, the expressions on each side of the equals symbol have the same value. By placing blocks on the "lighter" side of a balance, students will make two equal numbers by adding. By removing blocks from the "heavier" side of a balance, students will make two equal numbers by subtracting. They will see that by adding or subtracting blocks, the balance becomes level and the expressions become equal.

Remind students that when one side of the balance is higher than the other, the higher side has fewer blocks. Likewise, when one side of the balance is lower than the other, the lower side has more blocks. When the sides are level, each side has the same number of blocks.

LEARN Balance Story Problems

ONLINE 20min

Students will solve problems using a balance.

- Students should understand that a level balance represents a situation in which the same number of cubes is on each side, given that all cubes are identical.

- Students also need to understand that to make the balance level, they need to either add blocks to the side that is positioned higher or take away blocks from the side that is positioned lower.

- Be sure students connect the adding and taking away of the cubes to the addition and subtraction expressions they are trying to make equal.

- Also, be sure students understand why the correct number sentence best describes the action taking place in the problem.

Objectives

- Recognize and solve word problems involving numbers up to 100 in which one quantity must be changed to equal another quantity.

LEARN Hop to Solve

ONLINE 20min

Students will use number lines to solve problems in which they have to make one amount equal to another. After they use the number lines, they will then complete a number sentence. As students work through the activity, have them ask themselves questions similar to the following:

- Do I need to count on or count back?

- How many 10s should I count?

- How many ones should I count?

- How many do I need to count on or count back so that both kangaroos are at the same place on the number line?

- How does the number sentence show the action of the problem?

- What is the answer to the problem?

Objectives

- Recognize and solve word problems involving numbers up to 100 in which one quantity must be changed to equal another quantity.

Tips

Remind students to count by 10s for the long hops and then switch to counting by ones for the short hops.

TRY IT Make the Numbers Equal

OFFLINE 10min

Students will practice solving story problems in which they have to make one number equal to another. Give students the Number Line 0–100 printout and Make the Numbers Equal activity page from their Activity Book. Read the directions with them.

They will use number lines for the first set of problems. For the second set of problems, students may use the printout if they need help. Use the answer key to check students' answers, and then enter the results online.

Objectives

- Recognize and solve word problems involving numbers up to 100 in which one quantity must be changed to equal another quantity.

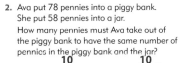

Equalize Story Problems
Make the Numbers Equal

Draw jumps on the number line from one number to the other to model the story problem. First make jumps of 10 if you can. Then make jumps of 1. Then solve the story problem by counting the lengths of the jumps you made.

1. The bakery has already sold 57 cookies today. Yesterday the bakery sold 69 cookies.

   How many more cookies must the bakery sell today to sell the same number of cookies as it sold yesterday?

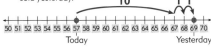

   $57 + \underline{\textbf{12}} = 69$

   $\underline{\textbf{12}}$ cookies

2. Ava put 78 pennies into a piggy bank. She put 58 pennies into a jar.

   How many pennies must Ava take out of the piggy bank to have the same number of pennies in the piggy bank and the jar?

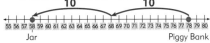

   $78 - 58 = \underline{\textbf{20}}$

   $\underline{\textbf{20}}$ pennies

3. Ryan read 34 pages. Luke read 21 pages.

   How many more pages must Luke read to have read the same number of pages as Ryan?

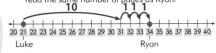

   $21 + \underline{\textbf{13}} = 34$

   $\underline{\textbf{13}}$ pages

Solve the story problem. You may use a number line to help you.

4. Troy bought 88 stickers. Jonathan bought 53 stickers.

   How many more stickers does Jonathan need to buy to have as many stickers as Troy?

   $\underline{\textbf{35}}$ stickers

5. Eduardo has 17 books. Ron has 12 books.

   How many books does Ron have to buy to have as many books as Eduardo?

   $\underline{\textbf{5}}$ books

6. Susan collected 24 shells. Laura collected 77 shells.

   How many more shells does Susan have to collect to have the same number of shells as Laura?

   $\underline{\textbf{53}}$ shells

7. Claire has 6 peanuts. Susan has 2 peanuts.

   How many peanuts does Claire have to eat to have as many peanuts as Susan?

   $\underline{\textbf{4}}$ peanuts

8. Marie's necklace has 64 beads. Edna's necklace has 42 beads.

   How many beads must Marie take off her necklace to have the same number of beads as Edna?

   $\underline{\textbf{22}}$ beads

9. Ira has 15 plants. Helen has 39 plants.

   How many plants does Helen need to give away to have the same number of plants as Ira?

   $\underline{\textbf{24}}$ plants

Make Them Equal

Lesson Overview

Skills Update	5 minutes	ONLINE
LEARN Make Numbers Equal	20 minutes	ONLINE
LEARN Use a Balance	20 minutes	ONLINE
TRY IT Equal Amounts	15 minutes	OFFLINE

▶ Lesson Objectives

Recognize and solve word problems involving numbers up to 100 in which one quantity must be changed to equal another quantity.

▶ Prerequisite Skills

Use concrete objects or sketches to represent a quantity up through 30.

▶ Content Background

Students will continue to solve story problems that involve equal amounts. In this lesson, they'll find various missing numbers in these problems. For example, "Dave read for 27 minutes yesterday. If he reads for 12 more minutes today, he'll have read for the same amount of time as he did yesterday. How many minutes has Dave already read today?"

> **Materials to Gather**
>
> **SUPPLIED**
> base-10 blocks
> Equal Amounts activity page

LEARN Make Numbers Equal

ONLINE 20min

Students will solve story problems in which they have to add or take away an amount to make the amounts equal. As students work through the activity, have them ask themselves questions similar to the following:

- Do I need to add to make the groups equal?
- Do I need to subtract to make the groups equal?
- How many are there after I add more?
- How many are there after I take away some?
- What is the number sentence I would use?
- What is the answer to the problem?

Objectives

- Recognize and solve word problems involving numbers up to 100 in which one quantity must be changed to equal another quantity.

LEARN Use a Balance

ONLINE 20 min

Students will solve story problems in which they have to add or take away to make two amounts equal. They will use an online balance and base-10 blocks.

1. To solve each problem, have students add or take away base-10 blocks from one side of the balance until the balance is level.

2. Have students ask themselves questions such as the following:

   - For this problem, do I need to add more to make the balance level? How many more?

   - For this problem, do I need to take away some to make the balance level? How many should I take away?

   - How much is on each side?

   - What is the answer to the problem?

3. Help students make the connections among the problem, the action on the balance, and their final answer.

Objectives

- Recognize and solve word problems involving numbers up to 100 in which one quantity must be changed to equal another quantity.

Tips

Remind students that when the balance is level, the balance has the same amount on both sides. A level balance shows that the amounts are equal.

TRY IT Equal Amounts

OFFLINE 15 min

Students will practice solving story problems in which they must make one amount equal to the other. Give students the base-10 blocks and Equal Amounts activity page from their Activity Book. Read the directions with them. Use the answer key to check students' answers, and then enter the results online.

Objectives

- Recognize and solve word problems involving numbers up to 100 in which one quantity must be changed to equal another quantity.

Tips

Remind students of the models they have used, such as number lines and the balance, to solve these problems.

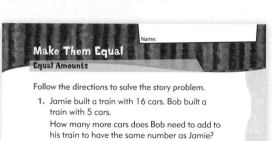

Make Them Equal
Equal Amounts

Follow the directions to solve the story problem.

1. Jamie built a train with 16 cars. Bob built a train with 5 cars.

   How many more cars does Bob need to add to his train to have the same number as Jamie?

   Use a number line to mark the number of cars Jamie used and the number Bob used. Mark the line with a "J" for Jamie and a "B" for Bob.

```
    5        10      1
   ┌──────────────┐ ⌐
 ──┼──┼─●─┼──┼──┼──┼──●──┼──┼──┼──→
     B (5)          J (16)
```

   To find out how many more Bob needs, jump by 10s then ones to move from 5 to 16. Then answer the question "How many more cars does Bob need to add to his train to have the same number of cars as Jamie?"

   11 cars

TRY IT

Circle the number sentence you could use to solve the problem.

2. Tom has 30 pencils.
   If Tom gives away 10 pencils, he will have the same number of pencils as Frank.

   How many pencils does Frank have?

   (A) $30 - 10 = 20$
   B. $30 + 10 = 40$
   C. $10 + 30 = 40$

Solve. You may use a number line to help you.

3. Kelly has 44 comic books and Fran has 10 comic books.

   How many more comic books does Fran need to have the same number of comic books as Kelly?

   34 comic books

4. Joe has 45 hens and Pete has 12 hens.

   How many hens does Joe need to give away to have the same number of hens as Pete?

   33 hens

TRY IT

---

5. Melinda has 54 marbles.
   If Melinda buys 25 more marbles, she will have the same number of marbles as Linda.

   How many marbles does Linda have?

   79 marbles

6. Daryl scored 5 goals.
   If Daryl scores 3 more goals, he will have scored the same number of goals as Brandon.

   How many goals did Brandon score?

   8 goals

7. Ron rode his bike 15 miles on Saturday.
   If Ron had ridden 22 more miles, he would have ridden the same number of miles as John.

   How many miles has John ridden?

   37 miles

TRY IT

---

8. Beth baked 12 muffins.
   If Beth gives away 5 muffins, she will have the same number of muffins as Jim.

   How many muffins does Jim have?

   7 muffins

9. Barbara picked 54 apples.
   If Barbara gives 23 apples away, she will have the same number of apples as Cathy.

   How many apples does Cathy have?

   31 apples

10. Rich has 76 comic books.
    If Rich gives away 24 comic books, he will have the same number of comic books as Chris.

    How many comic books does Chris have?

    52 comic books

TRY IT

More Story Problems

Skills Update	5 minutes	ONLINE
LEARN Making Equal Amounts or Not?	10 minutes	ONLINE
LEARN Make Groups Equal	15 minutes	OFFLINE
TRY IT Practice Equalize Problems	15 minutes	OFFLINE
CHECKPOINT	15 minutes	OFFLINE

▶ Lesson Objectives

Recognize and solve word problems involving numbers up to 100 in which one quantity must be changed to equal another quantity.

▶ Prerequisite Skills

Use concrete objects or sketches to represent a quantity up through 30.

▶ Advance Preparation

Print the Number Line 0–100. Cut out the number lines and tape them together to form one number line from 0 to 100.

▶ Content Background

Students will continue to recognize and solve story problems that involve equal amounts. In this lesson, they'll have to decide when to add or subtract to solve each problem.

Materials to Gather

SUPPLIED

base-10 blocks

Number Line 0–100 (printout)

Make Groups Equal activity page

Practice Equalize Problems activity page

Checkpoint (printout)

ALSO NEEDED

paper plates – 2

scissors, adult

tape, clear

LEARN Making Equal Amounts or Not?

ONLINE
10 min

Students will decide if a story problem involves making amounts equal and choose the number sentence that would solve the problem.

As students complete the activity, encourage them to ask themselves questions such as the following:

- What numbers are in the story problem?
- Is the problem asking me to make two amounts equal by adding or subtracting?
- What number sentence would solve this problem?

Objectives

- Recognize and solve word problems involving numbers up to 100 in which one quantity must be changed to equal another quantity.

OFFLINE
15min

Students will solve problems in which they need to make amounts equal. They will use base-10 blocks and paper plates to model the problems. Gather the Make Groups Equal activity page, base-10 blocks, Number Line 0–100 printout, and paper plates.

Work with students to help them model and solve the problems. Be sure students understand the relationship between the problems and the models they are using to solve the problems.

For Problems 1–4, provide base-10 blocks for the students and set 2 paper plates side-by-side. For Problems 5–8, provide the Number Line 0–100 printout.

- Recognize and solve word problems involving numbers up to 100 in which one quantity must be changed to equal another quantity.

1. For Problems 1–4, have students use their base-10 blocks to build the first amount mentioned in the problem on their left plate and the second amount mentioned in the problem on their right plate.

2. Remind students that the goal is to end up with the same amount on each plate.

3. **Ask:** To answer the question, do you need to add blocks to the plate with the lesser number or take away blocks from the plate with the greater number?

   - If students are adding blocks to a plate, have them put those blocks in a separate part of the plate than the ones already there so they can easily see how many blocks they have added.

   - If students are subtracting blocks from a plate, have them put those blocks in a specific place to the side so they can easily see how many blocks they took away.

4. After the students have added or taken away the proper amount, ask them how many blocks are on each plate now. The amounts should be equal based on the "target number" in the problem.

5. Ask students what is the answer to the problem. Notice that the answer is how many blocks they added or took away, not how many are left on the plates.

6. Have students write their answers on their Activity Book page for Problems 1–4.

7. Have students use the number lines for Problems 5–8.

8. Tell them to write the 2 numbers some distance apart on the number line.

9. Ask students if they need to move forward to add to the lesser number or move backward to take away from the greater number to answer the question.

10. Instruct students to start at the proper number and jump first by 10s and then ones to the other number. Have them draw arcs and place the length of each jump (10 or 1) above each arc.

11. After the students have added or taken away the proper amount, ask them how far did they jump on the number line.

12. Ask students what is the answer to the problem. The answer will be the distance they jumped.

13. Have students write their answers on their Activity Book page for Problems 5–8.

More Story Problems

Make Groups Equal

Check students' models.

Use base-10 blocks and paper plates to solve.

1. A pet store has 93 guppies.
   If it sells 42 guppies, it will have the same number of guppies as angelfish.

   How many angelfish does the pet store have?

   __51__ angelfish

2. The Cardinals brought 23 basketballs for their warm up.
   If the other team had 11 more basketballs, it would have same number of basketballs as the Cardinals.

   How many basketballs does the other team have?

   __12__ basketballs

3. Mr. Lee has 44 hot dogs to sell.
   If he gets 14 more hot dogs, he will have the same number of hot dogs as hot dog buns.

   How many hot dog buns does Mr. Lee have?

   __58__ buns

L E A R N

4. One apartment building has 64 floors.
   Another apartment building being built has 33 floors so far.

   How many more floors need to be built so that both buildings have the same number of floors?

   __31__ floors

Use a number line to solve.

5. Hannah has 12 marbles.
   Jacob has 18 marbles.

   How many more marbles does Hannah need buy to have as many marbles as Jacob has?

   __6__ marbles

6. The grocery store has 55 apples.
   It also has 35 oranges.

   How many apples does the grocery store need to sell to have the same number of apples as oranges?

   __20__ apples

L E A R N

7. The gardener planted 75 bushes in one area of the park.
   She also planted 52 trees in another area of the park.

   How many more trees does she need to plant to have the same number of trees as bushes?

   __23__ trees

8. The animal shelter has 28 dogs ready to be adopted.
   It also has 15 cats.

   How many dogs will have to be adopted so that the shelter has the same number of dogs as cats?

   __13__ dogs

L E A R N

TRY IT Practice Equalize Problems

Objectives

Students will practice solving story problems that involve equal amounts. They will need to decide how to approach each problem before solving it. Give students the base-10 blocks, Number Line 0–100 printout, and Practice Equalize Problems activity page from their Activity Book. Read the directions with them. Students may use the base-10 blocks and printout if they wish. Use the answer key to check students' answers, and then enter the results online.

- Recognize and solve word problems involving numbers up to 100 in which one quantity must be changed to equal another quantity.

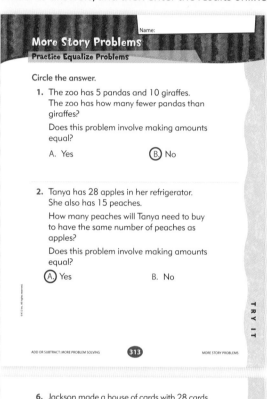

Name: _____

More Story Problems

Practice Equalize Problems

Circle the answer.

1. The zoo has 5 pandas and 10 giraffes. The zoo has how many fewer pandas than giraffes?

   Does this problem involve making amounts equal?

   A. Yes   (B.) No

2. Tanya has 28 apples in her refrigerator. She also has 15 peaches.

   How many peaches will Tanya need to buy to have the same number of peaches as apples?

   Does this problem involve making amounts equal?

   (A.) Yes   B. No

3. Edward drew 11 pictures and Pete drew 7 pictures. How many pictures did they draw altogether?

   Does this problem involve making amounts equal?

   A. Yes   (B.) No

4. The zoo has 28 snakes. The zoo also has 39 frogs.

   How many more snakes does the zoo need to get to have the same number of snakes as frogs?

   Does this problem involve making amounts equal?

   (A.) Yes   B. No

Solve.

5. Ken biked 17 miles. Jim biked 10 miles. How many more miles does Jim need to bike to travel the same distance as Ken?

   _____7_____ miles

6. Jackson made a house of cards with 28 cards. Makena made a house of cards with 20 cards.

   How many cards should Jackson remove from his house to have the same number of cards as Makena?

   _____8_____ cards

7. Wendy picked 54 plums. If she gives 24 plums away, she will have the same number of plums as Ben.

   How many plums does Ben have?

   _____30_____ plums

8. Wade rode his bike 24 miles on Sunday. If he had ridden 23 more miles, he would have ridden the same number of miles as Brad.

   How many miles had Brad ridden?

   _____47_____ miles

CHECKPOINT

Objectives

- Recognize and solve word problems involving numbers up to 100 in which one quantity must be changed to equal another quantity.

Print the Checkpoint and have students complete it on their own. Read the directions, problems, and answer choices to students, if necessary. Use the answer key to score the Checkpoint, and then enter the results online.

   Students may use the Number Line 0–100 printout or base-10 blocks to help them.

Name _____ Date _____

Checkpoint Answer Key

Circle the answer. Use the number line or base-10 blocks if needed.

(1 point)
1. John has 27 baseball cards and Pete has 22 baseball cards. How many baseball cards do they have altogether?

Does this problem involve making amounts equal?

A. Yes   (B.) No

(1 point)
2. The park has 3 slides. The park also has 4 swings.

How many more slides does the park need to buy to have the same number of slides as swings?

Does this problem involve making amounts equal?

(A.) Yes   B. No

Circle the answer.

(1 point)
3. Maddie baked 25 cookies. Molly baked 15 cookies.

How many more cookies does Molly need to bake to have the same number of cookies as Maddie?

(A.) 10
B. 15
C. 25
D. 40

(1 point)
4. Lily picked 45 cherries. If Lily eats 5 cherries she will have the same number of cherries as Hayden.

How many cherries does Hayden have?

A. 50
B. 45
(C.) 40
D. 5

Name _____ Date _____

(1 point)
5. Cathy has 35 photos in her album. If she puts 14 more photos in her album she will have as many photos as Kelly.

How many photos does Kelly have?

A. 14
B. 21
C. 35
(D.) 49

Explore Number Sentences

Lesson Overview

Skills Update	5 minutes	ONLINE
GET READY Solve with Charts and Models	10 minutes	ONLINE
LEARN What's Missing?	15 minutes	ONLINE
LEARN Part-Part-Total Number Sentences	15 minutes	ONLINE
TRY IT Solve Problems with Number Sentences	15minutes	OFFLINE

▶ Lesson Objectives

Write and solve addition or subtraction number sentences for problem-solving situations with sums and minuends up through 100.

▶ Prerequisite Skills

- Solve addition problems with a one- and a two-digit number with sums through 100 by using regrouping.
- Solve subtraction problems with a two-digit minuend and a one-digit subtrahend by using regrouping.

▶ Content Background

Students have used models to solve several types of story problems. They have seen and completed some number sentences for these story problems, but their work with number sentences has been informal. In this lesson, students will transition from using models to writing number sentences to solve story problems.

Every addition and subtraction number sentence has a total and at least two parts. In addition, the sum is the total, and the numbers being added, or addends, are the parts. For example, in $5 = 4 + 1$, the total is 5, and the parts are 4 and 1. In a subtraction sentence, one part is subtracted from the total to get the other part. For example, in $5 - 4 = 1$, again the total is 5, and the parts are 4 and 1. This part-part-total relationship and the use of a part-part-total chart can help students understand the opposite or *inverse* relationship between addition and subtraction.

In problems where the starting amount changes using addition or subtraction, the problem still has two parts and a total. However, to emphasize that the starting amount is changing, a start-change-result chart is used in place of the part-part-total chart.

In *combine problems*, students must put together two or more groups to find the sum. Students may write an addition sentence, such as $3 + 4 = ?$, to solve a combine problem. In some combine problems, they will be given the sum and will need to find one of the addends. For these combine problems, they may still write an addition sentence, such as $3 + ? = 7$. To find the missing addend, students may subtract 3 from 7. Or they may ask themselves, "3 plus what number is the same as 7?"

In *compare problems*, students must compare two groups to determine how many more or fewer objects are in one group. They have learned to compare groups using models that are aligned so that the objects in the two groups

Materials to Gather

SUPPLIED

Solve Problems with Number Sentences activity page

match one-to-one. To find how many more or fewer, they have counted the unmatched objects or spaces. When comparing greater numbers, counting isn't practical. Students will learn that they can subtract, rather than count, to solve compare problems. For example, to find how many more 37 is than 25, they may solve the subtraction sentence $37 - 25 = ?$.

GET READY Solve with Charts and Models

ONLINE 10 min

Students will see how Ron thinks about solving story problems using charts to help him organize his thoughts. Then they will solve the problems, which involve addition and subtraction with regrouping.

Objectives

- Solve addition problems with a one- and a two-digit number with sums through 100 by using regrouping.
- Solve subtraction problems with a two-digit minuend and a one-digit subtrahend by using regrouping.

LEARN What's Missing?

ONLINE 15 min

Students will see how models can help them write number sentences for story problems in which two amounts are compared or where two amounts need to be made equal to one another. They must identify the missing part in the number sentence with a question mark (?). They do not need to solve the problems.

Check that students can correctly explain what is happening in each story.

Objectives

- Write and solve addition or subtraction number sentences for problem-solving situations with sums and minuends up through 100.

LEARN Part-Part-Total Number Sentences

ONLINE 15 min

Students will use an online part-part-total chart to organize the numbers in story problems. They will then use the chart to write number sentences for the problems. Students will not solve their number sentences.

Have students ask themselves questions such as the following:

- What is given in the problem?
- What is missing: a part or the total?
- Are the parts being added or subtracted?
- How do I show the information on the part-part-total chart?
- What numbers do I write?
- Do I write an addition or subtraction number sentence?

Objectives

- Write and solve addition or subtraction number sentences for problem-solving situations with sums and minuends up through 100.

TRY IT Solve Problems with Number Sentences **15**min

Objectives

Students will identify sentences to solve problems in which two amounts are compared or amounts are made equal. Give students the Solve Problems with Number Sentences activity page from their Activity Book and read the directions with them. Use the answer key to check students' answers, and then enter the results online.

- Write and solve addition or subtraction number sentences for problem-solving situations with sums and minuends up through 100.

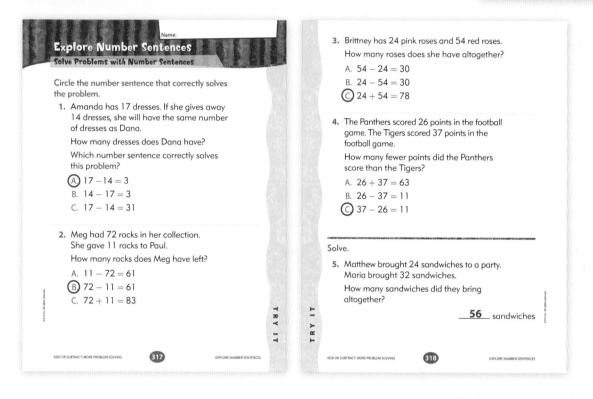

Explore Number Sentences

Solve Problems with Number Sentences

Circle the number sentence that correctly solves the problem.

1. Amanda has 17 dresses. If she gives away 14 dresses, she will have the same number of dresses as Dana.

   How many dresses does Dana have?

   Which number sentence correctly solves this problem?

   (A) $17 - 14 = 3$
   B. $14 - 17 = 3$
   C. $17 - 14 = 31$

2. Meg had 72 rocks in her collection. She gave 11 rocks to Paul.

   How many rocks does Meg have left?

   A. $11 - 72 = 61$
   (B) $72 - 11 = 61$
   C. $72 + 11 = 83$

3. Brittney has 24 pink roses and 54 red roses.

   How many roses does she have altogether?

   A. $54 - 24 = 30$
   B. $24 - 54 = 30$
   (C) $24 + 54 = 78$

4. The Panthers scored 26 points in the football game. The Tigers scored 37 points in the football game.

   How many fewer points did the Panthers score than the Tigers?

   A. $26 + 37 = 63$
   B. $26 - 37 = 11$
   (C) $37 - 26 = 11$

Solve.

5. Matthew brought 24 sandwiches to a party. Maria brought 32 sandwiches.

   How many sandwiches did they bring altogether?

   __56__ sandwiches

TRY IT

Number Sentences

Lesson Overview

Skills Update	5 minutes	ONLINE
GET READY Fact Family Triangles	5 minutes	ONLINE
LEARN Number Sentences: A Shortcut	10 minutes	ONLINE
LEARN What's the Number Sentence?	25 minutes	ONLINE
TRY IT Story Problems with Number Sentences	15 minutes	OFFLINE

▶ Lesson Objectives

Write and solve addition or subtraction number sentences for problem-solving situations with sums and minuends up through 100.

▶ Prerequisite Skills

- Solve addition problems with a one- and a two-digit number with sums through 100 by using regrouping.
- Solve subtraction problems with a two-digit minuend and a one-digit subtrahend by using regrouping.

▶ Content Background

Students will expand their understanding of how to write number sentences to solve story problems. They will write a number sentence for a story problem without first modeling the problem with something concrete, such as base-10 blocks, charts, or a number line. Students should begin to understand that writing a number sentence is a shortcut for solving story problems.

Every addition and subtraction number sentence has a total and at least two parts. In addition, the sum is the total, and the numbers being added, or addends, are the parts. For example, in $5 = 4 + 1$, the total is 5, and the parts are 4 and 1. In a subtraction sentence, one part is subtracted from the total to get the other part. For example, in $5 - 4 = 1$, again the total is 5, and the parts are 4 and 1. This part-part-total relationship and the use of a part-part-total chart can help students understand the opposite or *inverse* relationship between addition and subtraction.

In problems where the starting amount changes using addition or subtraction, the problem still has two parts and a total. However, to emphasize that the starting amount is changing, a start-change-result chart is used in place of the part-part-total chart.

In *combine problems*, students must put together two or more groups to find the sum. Students may write an addition sentence, such as $3 + 4 = ?$, to solve a combine problem. In some combine problems, they will be given the sum and will need to find one of the addends. For these combine problems, they may still write an addition sentence, such as $3 + ? = 7$. To find the missing addend, students may subtract 3 from 7. Or they may ask themselves, "3 plus what number is the same as 7?"

Materials to Gather

SUPPLIED

Story Problems with Number Sentences activity page

In *compare problems*, students must compare two groups to determine how many more or fewer objects are in one group. They have learned to compare groups using models that are aligned so that the objects in the two groups match one-to-one. To find how many more or fewer, they have counted the unmatched objects or spaces. When comparing greater numbers, counting isn't practical. Students will learn that they can subtract, rather than count, to solve compare problems. For example, to find how many more 37 is than 25, they may solve the subtraction sentence $37 - 25 = ?$.

In *equalize problems*, students must make one quantity equal to another quantity. Students may need to add or subtract in order to solve this type of problem. For example, to change 10 to make it equal to 7, students must solve the number sentence $10 - ? = 7$. To change 3 to make it equal to 5, they must solve the number sentence $3 + ? = 5$.

Keywords

change problem – a problem in which one quantity changes by having an amount added or taken away
combine problem – an addition problem in which two numbers are put together to find a sum
equalize problem – a problem in which one quantity is changed to equal another quantity

---

GET READY Fact Family Triangles   ONLINE 5min

Students will use fact family triangles to write number sentences with missing numbers.

Objectives

- Given concrete objects, show how two sets can be added together, and then reverse the operation to show how a number can be subtracted from the whole.

LEARN Number Sentences: A Shortcut   ONLINE 10min

Students will write number sentences for story problems in which the starting amount changes. The problem states the change and the result, but not the starting amount.

As students work through the problems, have them ask themselves questions such as the following:

- What is happening in the problem?
- What information is given?
- What type of information is missing?
- What numbers do I write?
- Do I write an addition or subtraction number sentence?

Objectives

- Write and solve addition or subtraction number sentences for problem-solving situations with sums and minuends up through 100.

Tips

If students have difficulty understanding what is happening in the problem, have them use a drawing or models. Encourage students to explain how their models or drawing helps them write a number sentence.

LEARN What's the Number Sentence?

In this activity, students will begin to learn how to write a number sentence from a story problem without using a model. They will write and solve addition or subtraction number sentences for problems in which they need to make two amounts equal.

Objectives

- Write and solve addition or subtraction number sentences for problem-solving situations with sums and minuends up through 100.

TRY IT Story Problems with Number Sentences

OFFLINE 15min

Students will practice solving story problems. They will need to decide how to approach each problem before solving it. Give students the Story Problems with Number Sentences activity page from their Activity Book and read the directions with them. Use the answer key to check students' answers, and then enter the results online.

Objectives

- Write and solve addition or subtraction number sentences for problem-solving situations with sums and minuends up through 100.

Number Sentences
Story Problems with Number Sentences

Name: _____

Circle the number sentence that solves the problem.

1. Jack has 23 comic books. If Jack gets 9 more comic books, then he will have the same number of comic books as Hannah. How many comic books does Hannah have?
   A. 23 − 9 = 14
   B. 23 + 9 = 32
   C. 32 + 9 = 41

2. George has 7 fewer toy trucks than Andrew. Andrew has 39 toy trucks. How many toy trucks does George have?
   A. 39 − 7 = 32
   B. 39 + 7 = 46
   C. 46 − 7 = 29

3. Some ducks are swimming in a pond. 14 ducks fly away. There are 25 ducks left in the pond. How many ducks were in the pond at the beginning?
   A. 25 + 14 = 39
   B. 14 + 11 = 25
   C. 25 − 14 = 11

ADD OR SUBTRACT: MORE PROBLEM SOLVING   319   NUMBER SENTENCES

Write a number sentence and solve the problem.

4. Carol has 9 stickers. If Carol gets 3 more stickers, she will have the same number of stickers as Ron. How many stickers does Ron have?
   9 (+) **3** = ?   **12** stickers

5. Roger picked 6 more apples than Andrew. Andrew picked 4 apples. How many apples did Roger pick?
   4 (+) **6** = ?   **10** apples

6. Some children were playing in the park. 8 children went home. There are now 13 children playing in the park. How many children were playing in the park at the beginning?
   ? (−) **8** = **13**   **21** children

Circle the number sentence that solves the problem.

7. Bobby has 22 grapes. If he gives away 12 grapes, he will have the same number of grapes as Carlos. How many grapes does Carlos have?
   A. 22 − 12 = 10
   B. 12 − 22 = 10
   C. 22 + 12 = 34

ADD OR SUBTRACT: MORE PROBLEM SOLVING   320   NUMBER SENTENCES

8. Ashley has 46 stickers. If she gives away 23 stickers, she will have the same number of stickers as her sister. How many stickers does her sister have?

A. $46 + 23 = 69$

B. $46 - 23 = 23$

C. $23 - 46 = 23$

9. Ricky sold 38 comics. Tim sold 49 comics. How many more comics must Ricky sell to have sold as many comics as Tim?

A. $38 - 49 = 11$

B. $38 + 49 = 87$

C. $49 - 38 = 11$

10. Sam ran 46 laps around the track. Miley ran 2 more laps than Sam. How many laps did Miley run around the track?

A. $46 - 2 = 44$

B. $2 - 46 = 44$

C. $46 + 2 = 48$

11. Tim had 38 cards. His dad gave him some more cards. Now Tim has 69 cards. How many cards did Tim's dad give him?

A. $38 + 69 = 107$

B. $69 - 38 = 31$

C. $69 - 38 = 21$

12. Polly had 55 dimes. Her mom gave her some more dimes. Now Polly has 67 dimes. How many dimes did Polly's mom give her?

A. $67 - 55 = 12$

B. $55 + 67 = 122$

C. $55 - 67 = 12$

Write and Solve Number Sentences

Lesson Overview

Skills Update	5 minutes	**ONLINE**
LEARN Answer Story Problems	15 minutes	**ONLINE**
LEARN Write and Solve Sentences	15 minutes	**OFFLINE**
TRY IT Solve Story Problems	15 minutes	**OFFLINE**
CHECKPOINT	10 minutes	**OFFLINE**

▶ Lesson Objectives

Write and solve addition or subtraction number sentences for problem-solving situations with sums and minuends up through 100.

▶ Prerequisite Skills

- Solve addition problems with a one- and a two-digit number with sums through 100 by using regrouping.
- Solve subtraction problems with a two-digit minuend and a one-digit subtrahend by using regrouping.

▶ Content Background

Students will solve the addition and subtraction number sentences they write for given story problems. They will also learn that it is important to know what the answer means in the context of the problem.

Every addition and subtraction number sentence has a total and at least two parts. In addition, the sum is the total, and the numbers being added, or addends, are the parts. For example, in $5 = 4 + 1$, the total is 5, and the parts are 4 and 1. In a subtraction sentence, one part is subtracted from the total to get the other part. For example, in $5 - 4 = 1$, again the total is 5, and the parts are 4 and 1. This part-part-total relationship and the use of a part-part-total chart can help students understand the opposite or *inverse* relationship between addition and subtraction.

In problems where the starting amount changes using addition or subtraction, the problem still has two parts and a total. However, to emphasize that the starting amount is changing, a start-change-result chart is used in place of the part-part-total chart.

Writing a number sentence is a short way for students to show the process they will use to solve a story problem. They may think of the number sentence as the code that leads to the answer. Remind students that there is more than one way to solve a story problem. They can write a related subtraction number sentence for every addition number sentence. They can also write a related addition number sentence for every subtraction number sentence.

When students solve story problems, much of their thinking goes into visualizing the problem and deciding what operation or number sentence to use. A key last step in problem solving is to develop the habit of checking whether the final answer seems reasonable by reading the original problem again and asking, "Does my answer make sense?"

Materials to Gather

SUPPLIED

Write and Solve Sentences activity page

Solve Story Problems activity page

Checkpoint (printout)

LEARN Answer Story Problems

Students have learned how to write number sentences for story problems. In this activity, they will continue to write numbers sentences and learn how to solve number sentences to answer questions about a story. They will also explain what the answer means in the context of the problem.

As students work through the activity, have them ask themselves questions similar to the following:

- What information is given in the problem?
- What do I have to find?
- Should I write an addition or subtraction number sentence?
- Should I use a fact family to help me solve for the missing value?
- What is the sum or difference?
- What does the answer mean?

- Write and solve addition or subtraction number sentences for problem-solving situations with sums and minuends up through 100.

LEARN Write and Solve Sentences

Students will write and solve number sentences to find the answer to story problems. Give students the Write and Solve Sentences activity page from their Activity Book and read the directions with them.

1. Read aloud Problem 1. Ask students to think about what's happening in the problem. Then have them explain what's happening.

2. **Ask:** What information is given? What information do you need to find?
   ANSWER: I know that Trent has 56 books in all. I know he has 14 books in the box. I need to find how many books Trent has on the bookshelves.

3. Have students first write the number sentence that shows what is happening in the problem. Note that students may write the number sentence in one of two ways with respect to the equals symbol, such as $14 + ? = 56$ or $56 = ? + 14$. Also, with addition, they may write the numbers in either order, such as $14 + ? = 56$ or $? + 14 = 56$. (This will be true for all addition number sentences.)

4. Now have students discuss the number sentence they will use to solve the problem.
   Ask: Can you solve the original number sentence easily? Would using a fact family triangle help you?

5. Once students determine the number sentence they will use, have them find the missing value.

6. **Ask:** What does the answer mean?
   ANSWER: Trent has 42 books on the bookshelves.

7. Guide students carefully through the rest of the problems. For each problem, ask students what the answer means.

- Write and solve addition or subtraction number sentences for problem-solving situations with sums and minuends up through 100.

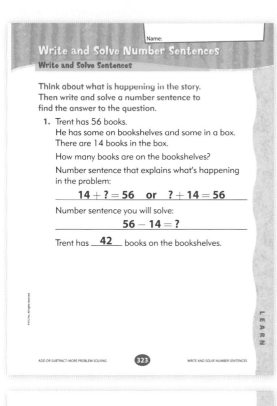

Name: _____

Write and Solve Number Sentences

Write and Solve Sentences

Think about what is happening in the story. Then write and solve a number sentence to find the answer to the question.

1. Trent has 56 books.
   He has some on bookshelves and some in a box.
   There are 14 books in the box.

   How many books are on the bookshelves?

   Number sentence that explains what's happening in the problem:

   $$14 + ? = 56 \quad \text{or} \quad ? + 14 = 56$$

   Number sentence you will solve:

   $$56 - 14 = ?$$

   Trent has __42__ books on the bookshelves.

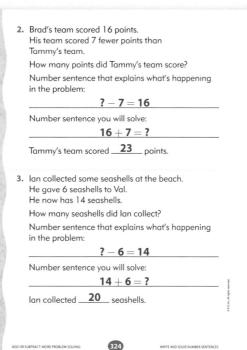

2. Brad's team scored 16 points.
   His team scored 7 fewer points than Tammy's team.

   How many points did Tammy's team score?

   Number sentence that explains what's happening in the problem:

   $$? - 7 = 16$$

   Number sentence you will solve:

   $$16 + 7 = ?$$

   Tammy's team scored __23__ points.

3. Ian collected some seashells at the beach.
   He gave 6 seashells to Val.
   He now has 14 seashells.

   How many seashells did Ian collect?

   Number sentence that explains what's happening in the problem:

   $$? - 6 = 14$$

   Number sentence you will solve:

   $$14 + 6 = ?$$

   Ian collected __20__ seashells.

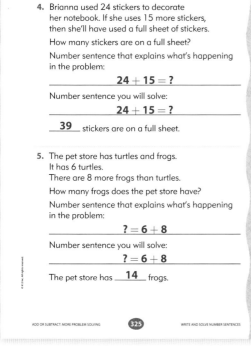

4. Brianna used 24 stickers to decorate her notebook. If she uses 15 more stickers, then she'll have used a full sheet of stickers.

   How many stickers are on a full sheet?

   Number sentence that explains what's happening in the problem:

   $$24 + 15 = ?$$

   Number sentence you will solve:

   $$24 + 15 = ?$$

   __39__ stickers are on a full sheet.

5. The pet store has turtles and frogs.
   It has 6 turtles.
   There are 8 more frogs than turtles.

   How many frogs does the pet store have?

   Number sentence that explains what's happening in the problem:

   $$? = 6 + 8$$

   Number sentence you will solve:

   $$? = 6 + 8$$

   The pet store has __14__ frogs.

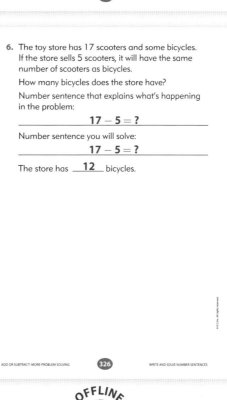

6. The toy store has 17 scooters and some bicycles. If the store sells 5 scooters, it will have the same number of scooters as bicycles.

   How many bicycles does the store have?

   Number sentence that explains what's happening in the problem:

   $$17 - 5 = ?$$

   Number sentence you will solve:

   $$17 - 5 = ?$$

   The store has __12__ bicycles.

OFFLINE 15 min

TRY IT Solve Story Problems

Students will write and solve number sentences to find the answer to story problems. Give students the Solve Story Problems activity page from their Activity Book and read the directions with them. Use the answer key to check students' answers, and then enter the results online.

Objectives

- Write and solve addition or subtraction number sentences for problem-solving situations with sums and minuends up through 100.

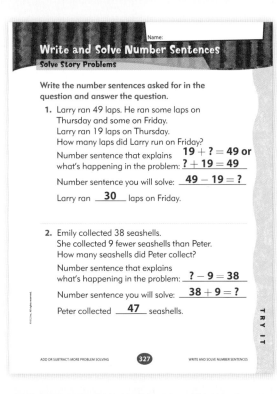

Write and Solve Number Sentences
Solve Story Problems

Write the number sentences asked for in the question and answer the question.

1. Larry ran 49 laps. He ran some laps on Thursday and some on Friday.
Larry ran 19 laps on Thursday.
How many laps did Larry run on Friday?

   Number sentence that explains what's happening in the problem: **$19 + ? = 49$ or $? + 19 = 49$**

   Number sentence you will solve: **$49 - 19 = ?$**

   Larry ran **30** laps on Friday.

2. Emily collected 38 seashells.
She collected 9 fewer seashells than Peter.
How many seashells did Peter collect?

   Number sentence that explains what's happening in the problem: **$? - 9 = 38$**

   Number sentence you will solve: **$38 + 9 = ?$**

   Peter collected **47** seashells.

ADD OR SUBTRACT: MORE PROBLEM SOLVING   (327)   WRITE AND SOLVE NUMBER SENTENCES

T R Y   I T

3. Mark gave 4 of his coins away. Mark now has 21 coins. How many coins did he have at the start?

   Number sentence that explains what's happening in the problem: **$? - 4 = 21$**

   Number sentence you will solve: **$21 + 4 = ?$**

   Mark had **25** coins at the start.

4. The fruit stand has 59 red apples and some green apples. If the stand sells 14 red apples, it will have the same number of red apples as green apples. How many green apples does the stand have?

   Number sentence that explains what's happening in the problem: **$59 - 14 = ?$**

   Number sentence you will solve: **$59 - 14 = ?$**

   The stand has **45** green apples.

Circle the number sentence that shows how to solve the problem.

5. Tom ate 26 carrot sticks last week and 12 carrot sticks this week. How many carrot sticks did Tom eat altogether?

   A. $26 - 12 = 14$
   B. $12 - 26 = 14$
   C. $26 + 12 = 38$ ⟲

6. There were 14 gophers on the grass. 9 gophers went into a hole. How many gophers are left on the grass?

   A. $14 + 9 = 23$
   B. $14 - 9 = 5$ ⟲
   C. $9 - 14 = 5$

T R Y   I T

ADD OR SUBTRACT: MORE PROBLEM SOLVING   (328)   WRITE AND SOLVE NUMBER SENTENCES

CHECKPOINT

OFFLINE
10 min

Print the Checkpoint and have students complete it on their own. Read the directions, problems, and answer choices to students, if necessary. Use the answer key to score the Checkpoint, and then enter the results online.

Objectives

- Write and solve addition or subtraction number sentences for problem-solving situations with sums and minuends up through 100.

○ Checkpoint   Math | Add or Subtract: More Problem Solving | Write and Solve Number Sentences

Name   Date

Checkpoint Answer Key

Write a number sentence. Then answer the question.

(1 point)
1. Stephen has 62 crayons in one box and 24 crayons in another box.

   How many crayons does Stephen have altogether?

   Complete this number sentence to solve the problem.

   62 (+) **24** = **86**

(1 point)
2. Carla has 57 grapes.
If Carla gives away 32 grapes, she will have the same number of grapes as Amelia.

   How many grapes does Amelia have?

   Complete this number sentence to solve the problem.

   57 − **32** = **25**

Circle the number sentence that solves the problem.
(1 point)
3. Cole had a box of 25 crayons. He then bought a box of 12 crayons.

   How many crayons does Cole have now?

   A. $12 - 25 = 13$
   B. $25 - 12 = 13$
   C. $25 + 12 = 37$ ⟲

(1 point)
4. There were 24 ducks on the grass.
9 ducks jumped into the lake.

   How many ducks are left on the grass?

   A. $24 + 9 = 33$
   B. $24 - 9 = 15$ ⟲
   C. $9 - 24 = 15$

1 of 1

Check Your Answers

Lesson Overview

Skills Update	5 minutes	**ONLINE**
LEARN Check for Errors	15 minutes	**ONLINE**
LEARN Check Answers to Story Problems	15 minutes	**ONLINE**
TRY IT Answer Check	15 minutes	**OFFLINE**
CHECKPOINT	10 minutes	**OFFLINE**

▶ Lesson Objectives

Check the accuracy of calculations from the context of the problem.

▶ Prerequisite Skills

Write and solve addition or subtraction number sentences for problem-solving situations with sums and minuends up through 100.

▶ Content Background

Students will learn how to check answers to story problems. They will learn to decide if the answer makes sense for the problem.

Materials to Gather

SUPPLIED
Answer Check activity page
Checkpoint (printout)

LEARN Check for Errors

ONLINE 15min

Students will check to see if the solution for a problem is reasonable within the context of the problem. First students will hear Rosa discuss some mistakes that she made and how to check those errors. As they work through the activity, guide students to ask themselves questions such as the following:

- What question is the problem asking?
- Does the work show the answer to that question?
- Is the work done correctly? Was there a mistake in regrouping? Was there a simple addition or subtraction mistake?

Objectives

- Check the accuracy of calculations from the context of the problem.

LEARN Check Answers to Story Problems

ONLINE 15min

Students will decide if an answer is reasonable within the context of a story problem. Then they will check the accuracy of answers of story problems using opposite operations with fact families.

Objectives

- Check the accuracy of calculations from the context of the problem.

TRY IT Answer Check

Students will practice checking if an answer is accurate by thinking about the context of the problem. Give students the Answer Check activity page from their Activity Book and read the directions with them.

Objectives

- Check the accuracy of calculations from the context of the problem.

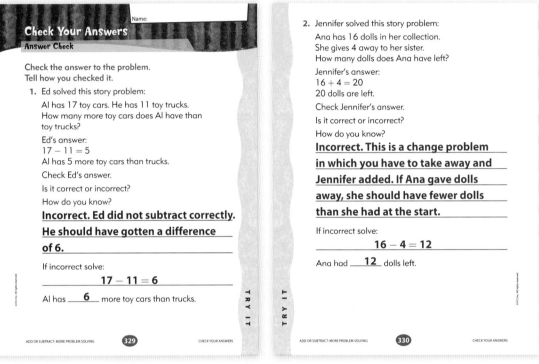

Name: _____

Check Your Answers
Answer Check

Check the answer to the problem.
Tell how you checked it.

1. Ed solved this story problem:

Al has 17 toy cars. He has 11 toy trucks. How many more toy cars does Al have than toy trucks?

Ed's answer:
$17 - 11 = 5$
Al has 5 more toy cars than trucks.

Check Ed's answer.

Is it correct or incorrect?

How do you know?

Incorrect. Ed did not subtract correctly. He should have gotten a difference of 6.

If incorrect solve:

$17 - 11 = 6$

Al has ____**6**____ more toy cars than trucks.

2. Jennifer solved this story problem:

Ana has 16 dolls in her collection. She gives 4 away to her sister. How many dolls does Ana have left?

Jennifer's answer:
$16 + 4 = 20$
20 dolls are left.

Check Jennifer's answer.

Is it correct or incorrect?

How do you know?

Incorrect. This is a change problem in which you have to take away and Jennifer added. If Ana gave dolls away, she should have fewer dolls than she had at the start.

If incorrect solve:

$16 - 4 = 12$

Ana had ____**12**____ dolls left.

3. Pete solved this story problem:

Eric wants to run 45 laps at the track. He has run 23 laps already. How many laps does Eric have left to run?

Pete's answer:
$45 - 23 = 22$
Eric has 22 laps left to run.

Check Pete's answer.

Is it correct or incorrect?

How do you know?

Correct. Pete subtracted to find the number of laps left. His math was correct. $45 - 23 = 22$

If incorrect solve: **Ed's answer is correct; the student does not need to solve the problem.**

Eric has _____ more laps to run.

Solve the problem and then check the solution using another method you have learned.

4. Bill had 23 blocks in the box. He gave 12 blocks to Amy. How many blocks does Bill have left?

Example answer: Solve this way: $23 - 12 = 11$.

Check this way: $11 + 12 = 23$.

Circle the answer to the problem.

5. Sam solved this story problem:

Dee saved 12 pennies. Paul saved 29 pennies. How many pennies did they save in all?

Sam's answer: $12 + 29 = 41$ pennies

Which number sentence could you use to check Sam's work?

A. $12 + 41 = 52$
B. $41 - 12 = 29$
C. $41 + 29 = 70$

6. Which problem is solved correctly?

A. Maria has 26 stickers. She bought 9 more. How many stickers does Maria have altogether?
   Answer: 36 stickers

B. Michael has 14 games. He has 27 books. How many more books than games does Michael have?
   Answer: 41 more books

C. Joe had 35 baseball cards. He gave 23 to his brother. How many baseball cards does Joe have now?
   Answer: 12 baseball cards

CHECKPOINT

Objectives

Print the Checkpoint and have students complete it on their own. Read the directions, problems, and answer choices to students, if necessary. Use the answer key to score the Checkpoint, and then enter the results online.

- Check the accuracy of calculations from the context of the problem.

Name _____ Date _____

Checkpoint Answer Key

Circle the correct answer to each problem.

(1 point)
1. Sam solved this story problem:

Ashley made 23 bracelets.
Rebecca made 17 bracelets.
How many bracelets did they make in all?

Sam's answer: $23 + 17 = 40$ bracelets

Which number sentence could be used to check
Sam's work?

A. $40 + 23 = 73$

B. $23 - 17 = 6$

Ⓒ $40 - 23 = 17$

(1 point)
2. Which story problem gives a correct answer?

A. Jillian had 56 stickers. She gave 10 stickers to her sister.
How many stickers does Jillian have now?

Answer: 66 stickers

B. Nolan has 14 comics and 22 books. How many more
books than comics does Nolan have?

Answer: 36 more books

Ⓒ John had 35 baseball cards. He gave 10 cards to his
brother. How many baseball cards does John have now?

Answer: 25 baseball cards

Name _____ Date _____

Check each problem. Tell how you checked it.

3. Jimmy solved this story problem:

Jenny saved $17 one summer. Her sister saved $28.
How much more money did Jenny's sister save than
Jenny saved?

Jimmy's answer: $17 + 28 = 45$

Check Jimmy's answer.
(1 point)
Is it correct or incorrect?
(1 point)
How do you know?

**Incorrect. Example answer: Jimmy
has added the two numbers, but the
problem requires you to subtract the
two numbers to find out how much
more money Jenny's sister saved
than Jenny.**

Name _____ Date _____

4. Christian solved this story problem:

Blake has 21 balloons.
He has 11 blue balloons.
How many balloons does Blake have that are not blue?

Christian's answer: $21 - 11 = 10$

There are 10 balloons that are not blue.

Check Christian's answer.
(1 point)
Is it correct or incorrect?
(1 point)
How do you know?

**Correct. Example answer: Students
should explain how they checked
the problem and determined it was
correct. Christian correctly subtracted
the number of blue balloons from the
total number of balloons to find out
how many balloons were not blue.**

Explain Solution Strategies

Skills Update	5 minutes	ONLINE
LEARN Tree House Math	15 minutes	ONLINE
LEARN Identify Kinds of Problems	15 minutes	ONLINE
LEARN Model or Sketch to Solve	15 minutes	OFFLINE
TRY IT Explain How to Solve	10 minutes	OFFLINE

▶ Lesson Objectives

Justify the procedures selected for addition or subtraction problem-solving situations with sums or minuends up through 100.

▶ Prerequisite Skills

Write and solve addition or subtraction number sentences for problem-solving situations with sums and minuends up through 100.

▶ Content Background

Students will solve story problems and justify the solutions.

One of the most important skills that students need to learn is how to justify their actions, both in math and in everyday life. Math is one way to help students verbalize and write their reasons for making the choices they have made. Mathematical justification is at the heart of proof.

Materials to Gather

SUPPLIED

base-10 blocks

Model or Sketch to Solve activity page

Explain How to Solve activity page

ALSO NEEDED

paper, drawing – 1 sheet

Keywords

justify – to explain why something is true; for example, to justify a procedure or answer to a math problem

LEARN Tree House Math

ONLINE
15min

Students will learn how to explain why addition or subtraction was chosen as the operation to solve a story problem. As they work through the activity, have them explain why amounts were added or subtracted. Have students point out how the question in the problem can help them decide which operation to use.

Objectives

- Justify the procedures selected for addition or subtraction problem-solving situations with sums or minuends up through 100.

LEARN Identify Kinds of Problems

ONLINE 15min

Objectives

- Justify the procedures selected for addition or subtraction problem-solving situations with sums or minuends up through 100.

Students will identify whether they would use addition or subtraction to solve a story problem and explain that choice. As students explain how they decided whether to use addition or subtraction, listen for explanations such as the following:

- When groups are combined, I add.

- When an amount is made greater, I add.

- When two amounts are compared to find how many more or fewer, I subtract.

- When I need to find how many more to make equal groups, I subtract to find the missing addend.

LEARN Model or Sketch to Solve

OFFLINE 15min

Objectives

- Justify the procedures selected for addition or subtraction problem-solving situations with sums or minuends up through 100.

Students will solve story problems by using sketches or models. Using visuals will help students decide how to solve a problem and can also help them justify why they solved the problem the way they did.

Give students the Model or Sketch to Solve activity page from their Activity Book and read the directions with them. Gather the drawing paper and base-10 blocks. Read each problem to students. Guide students to either use base-10 blocks or make the type of sketch that is suggested for each problem. Have students find each answer and explain their solution. Accept any reasonable explanation.

Name: _____

Explain Solution Strategies
Model or Sketch to Solve

Use sketches or base-10 blocks to solve.

1. There were 73 flags in a park.
   The veterans place 22 more flags.
   How many flags are in the park now?

   95 flags
   See right.

2. The jar had 38 peanuts and 26 almonds.
   How many more peanuts were in the jar than almonds?

   12 more peanuts
   See right.

3. Mr. Mead's class read 29 books.
   Ms. Little's class read 16 books.
   How many more books does Ms. Little's class need to read to have read as many books as Mr. Mead's class?

   13 more books
   See right.

ADD OR SUBTRACT: MORE PROBLEM SOLVING **333** EXPLAIN SOLUTION STRATEGIES

L E A R N

Additional Answers

1. **Possible model with base-10 blocks:** 7 tens rods and 3 ones cubes in one group and 2 tens rods and 2 ones in another group that are combined to show the total. When students combine the blocks, they should get 9 tens rods and 5 ones cubes. They solve $73 + 22 = ?$ to get their answer of 95 flags in the park now.

2. **Possible sketch with base-10 blocks:** Sketch of 3 tens rods and 8 ones cubes in a row and underneath, with tens rods lined up and ones cubes lined up, 2 tens rods and 6 ones cubes. Students will see how many blocks do not have matches. They can then solve $38 - 26 = ?$ to get their answer of 12 more peanuts than almonds in the jar.

3. **Possible sketch:** Sketch of a fact family triangle:

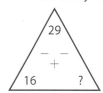

Students will see that they can solve the number sentence $29 = 16 + ?$ by subtracting 16 from 29. They will find that Ms. Little's class needs to read 13 more books to have read as many books as Mr. Mead's class.

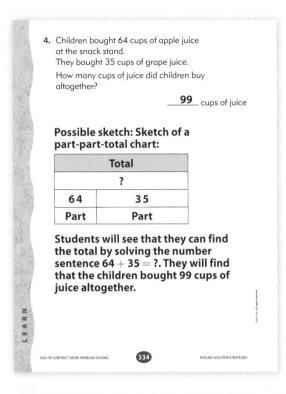

4. Children bought 64 cups of apple juice at the snack stand.
   They bought 35 cups of grape juice.
   How many cups of juice did children buy altogether?

   99 cups of juice

   Possible sketch: Sketch of a part-part-total chart:

Total	
?	
6 4	3 5
Part	Part

   Students will see that they can find the total by solving the number sentence 64 + 35 = ?. They will find that the children bought 99 cups of juice altogether.

OFFLINE
10min

TRY IT Explain How to Solve

Students will determine if the number sentences are correct for the problem-solving situations and justify their solutions. Give students the base-10 blocks and Explain How to Solve activity page from their Activity Book. Read the directions with them. Use the answer key to check students' answers, and then enter the results online.

Objectives

- Justify the procedures selected for addition or subtraction problem-solving situations with sums or minuends up through 100.

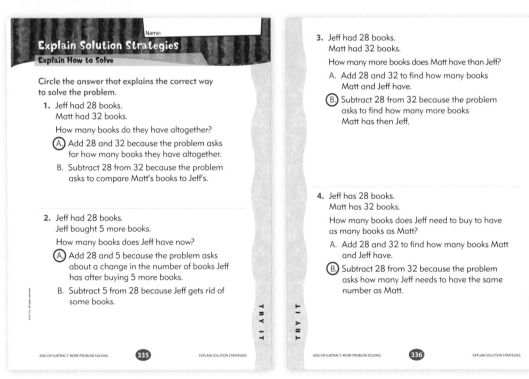

Name:

Explain Solution Strategies
Explain How to Solve

Circle the answer that explains the correct way to solve the problem.

1. Jeff had 28 books.
   Matt had 32 books.
   How many books do they have altogether?

   (A) Add 28 and 32 because the problem asks for how many books they have altogether.

   B. Subtract 28 from 32 because the problem asks to compare Matt's books to Jeff's.

2. Jeff had 28 books.
   Jeff bought 5 more books.
   How many books does Jeff have now?

   (A) Add 28 and 5 because the problem asks about a change in the number of books Jeff has after buying 5 more books.

   B. Subtract 5 from 28 because Jeff gets rid of some books.

3. Jeff had 28 books.
   Matt had 32 books.
   How many more books does Matt have than Jeff?

   A. Add 28 and 32 to find how many books Matt and Jeff have.

   (B) Subtract 28 from 32 because the problem asks to find how many more books Matt has then Jeff.

4. Jeff has 28 books.
   Matt has 32 books.
   How many books does Jeff need to buy to have as many books as Matt?

   A. Add 28 and 32 to find how many books Matt and Jeff have.

   (B) Subtract 28 from 32 because the problem asks how many Jeff needs to have the same number as Matt.

Circle the answer. You may use base-10 blocks to help you.

5. Carl threw 51 pitches in the baseball game. Tony threw 31 pitches.

   How many pitches did they throw altogether?

   To solve this problem, Joey used this number sentence: $51 + 31 = 82$.

   Did Joey correctly solve this problem?

   A. No, because you have to use subtraction to find the difference between the two numbers of pitches.

   B. Yes, because you need to add the two numbers together to find out the total number of pitches.

   C. Yes, because you need to add the two numbers together to find the difference between the two numbers of pitches.

6. Which best explains how to correctly solve this problem?

   Cash just got 8 new pond snails for his fish tank. He already had 25 pond snails.

   How many pond snails does Cash have now?

   A. $25 + 8$, because Cash has 8 more snails than when he started.

   B. $25 - 8$, because Cash has 8 fewer snails than when he started.

   C. $25 + 8$, because Cash has 8 fewer snails than when he started.

7. Which best explains how to correctly solve this problem?

   Jasmine has 11 cookies.
   If Jasmine gives away 7 cookies, she will have the same number of cookies as Casey.
   How many cookies does Casey have?

   A. Add 11 and 7 to find out how many cookies there are altogether.

   B. Subtract 7 from 11 to find out how many cookies Casey has.

   C. Add 11 and 7 to find out how many cookies Casey has.

8. Which best explains how to correctly solve this problem?

   Callie painted 34 tiles.
   Alice painted 28 tiles.
   How many fewer tiles did Alice paint than Callie?

   A. $34 + 28$, because Alice and Callie painted 62 tiles altogether.

   B. $28 - 34$, because Alice painted fewer tiles than Callie.

   C. $34 - 28$, because Alice painted fewer tiles than Callie.

9. Which best explains how to correctly solve this problem?

   Simon picked 17 apples and Anna picked 12 apples.
   How many more apples did Simon pick than Anna?

   A. $12 - 17$, because Anna picked more apples than Simon.

   B. $17 - 12$, because Simon picked more apples than Anna.

   C. $17 + 12$, because Simon picked more apples than Anna.

TRY IT

Justify Selected Procedures

Lesson Overview

Skills Update	5 minutes	ONLINE
LEARN Math Ice Cream	20 minutes	ONLINE
LEARN Different Explanations	20 minutes	ONLINE
TRY IT Use a Number Sentence to Solve	15 minutes	OFFLINE

▶ Lesson Objectives

Justify the procedures selected for addition or subtraction problem-solving situations with sums or minuends up through 100.

▶ Prerequisite Skills

Write and solve addition or subtraction number sentences for problem-solving situations with sums and minuends up through 100.

▶ Content Background

Students will learn to solve addition and subtraction story problems and to justify their solutions.

One of the most important skills that students need to learn is how to justify their actions, both in math and in everyday life. Math is one way to help students verbalize and write their reasons for making the choices they have made. Mathematical justification is at the heart of proof.

Materials to Gather

SUPPLIED

Use a Number Sentence to Solve activity page

LEARN Math Ice Cream

ONLINE
20min

Students will decide whether to add or subtract to solve story problems. They will learn how to justify their choice. As students work through the activity, they should ask themselves questions similar to the following:

- What is the question in the problem?
- Do I add or subtract the amounts in the problem?
- How do I know whether I should add or subtract?

Objectives

- Justify the procedures selected for addition or subtraction problem-solving situations with sums or minuends up through 100.

LEARN Different Explanations

Students will learn that some story problems can be solved in more than one way. Have them answer the questions and justify their solutions along with Rosa and Alexander.

Objectives

- Justify the procedures selected for addition or subtraction problem-solving situations with sums or minuends up through 100.

TRY IT Use a Number Sentence to Solve

Students will determine if the number sentences are correct for the problem-solving situations and justify their solutions. Give students the Use a Number Sentence to Solve activity page from their Activity Book and read the directions with them. Use the answer key to check students' answers, and then enter the results online.

Objectives

- Justify the procedures selected for addition or subtraction problem-solving situations with sums or minuends up through 100.

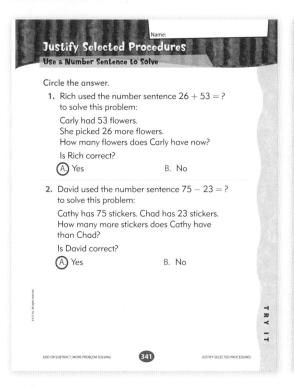

Justify Selected Procedures
Use a Number Sentence to Solve

Circle the answer.

1. Rich used the number sentence $26 + 53 = ?$ to solve this problem:

   Carly had 53 flowers.
   She picked 26 more flowers.
   How many flowers does Carly have now?

   Is Rich correct?
   (A.) Yes   B. No

2. David used the number sentence $75 - 23 = ?$ to solve this problem:

   Cathy has 75 stickers. Chad has 23 stickers.
   How many more stickers does Cathy have than Chad?

   Is David correct?
   (A.) Yes   B. No

Decide if the number sentence will solve the problem, and tell why or why not.

3. Lisa used the number sentence $45 + 21 = ?$ to solve this problem:

   The bakery made 45 muffins.
   21 are apple and the rest are blueberry.
   How many muffins are blueberry?

   Is Lisa correct? Explain your answer.
   See below.

4. Raul used the number sentence $25 - 62 = ?$ to solve this problem:

   Rhonda has 25 books.
   Lucy has 62 books.
   How many fewer books does Rhonda have than Lucy?

   Is Raul correct? Explain your answer.
   See below.

5. Jonathan used the number sentence $41 - 9 = ?$ to solve this problem:

   Becky had 41 toy cars.
   She gave 9 to her sister.
   How many toy cars does Becky have now?

   Is Jonathan correct? Explain your answer.
   See below.

ADD OR SUBTRACT: MORE PROBLEM SOLVING   341   JUSTIFY SELECTED PROCEDURES

ADD OR SUBTRACT: MORE PROBLEM SOLVING   342   JUSTIFY SELECTED PROCEDURES

Additional Answers

3. No, Lisa is not correct. **Sample explanation:** She should have subtracted and used the number sentence $45 - 21 = ?$ because the problem is asking for the part of the muffins that are blueberry.

4. No, Raul is not correct. **Sample explanation:** Raul should have used $62 - 25 = ?$ because the lesser number should be subtracted from the greater number.

5. Yes, Jonathan is correct. **Sample explanation:** Jonathan used $41 - 9 = ?$ because Becky will have fewer cars after she gave some away.

Justify Different Solutions

Skills Update	5 minutes	ONLINE
LEARN What's a Different Way?	15 minutes	ONLINE
LEARN Explain the Solution	15 minutes	OFFLINE
TRY IT Justify Solutions	15 minutes	OFFLINE
CHECKPOINT	10 minutes	OFFLINE

▶ Lesson Objectives

Justify the procedures selected for addition or subtraction problem-solving situations with sums or minuends up through 100.

▶ Prerequisite Skills

Write and solve addition or subtraction number sentences for problem-solving situations with sums and minuends up through 100.

▶ Advance Preparation

Cut out each of the strips that show a problem and its explanation from the Explain the Solution activity page. Fold each strip so that the problem is on the front (top) and the explanation is on the back (bottom).

▶ Content Background

Students will continue to solve addition and subtraction story problems and to justify their solutions.

One of the most important skills that students need to learn is how to justify their actions, both in math and in everyday life. Math is one way to help students verbalize and write their reasons for making the choices they have made. Mathematical justification is at the heart of proof.

Materials to Gather

SUPPLIED
Explain the Solution activity page
Justify Solutions activity page
Checkpoint (printout)

ALSO NEEDED
scissors, adult

LEARN What's a Different Way?

ONLINE 15 min

Students will see four different story problems with two different ways of solving each problem. Once they finish each problem, and before they move ahead, have students explain which solution they think is better and why.

Objectives

- Justify the procedures selected for addition or subtraction problem-solving situations with sums or minuends up through 100.

LEARN Explain the Solution

Students will practice deciding how to solve a story problem and justifying their decision. Gather the cut-out problems with their accompanying explanations from the Explain the Solution activity page.

1. Read each problem to students.

2. Ask students to explain how they would solve the problem and why, including the number sentence they would use.

3. After students have given their explanation, read the explanation on the back of the problem strip. Students should listen to verify that their explanation was correct or hear another viable explanation. Students' explanations don't need to match the strip exactly—there are many correct ways to solve each problem.

Objectives

- Justify the procedures selected for addition or subtraction problem-solving situations with sums or minuends up through 100.

Name:

Justify Different Solutions

Explain the Solution

Cut out the strips and fold them in half.
Explain how you would solve each problem and
explain why. Then check your answer.

1. On Monday, the ice show sold 67 tickets online. So far today, the show has sold 43 tickets online. How many more tickets does the show need to sell online today to equal the number of tickets sold on Monday?	I'm trying to make two amounts equal. I know that 67 is the number I need to reach. I can think of this as, "43 + a missing number is 67." $43 + ? = 67$ I can find the missing number by solving the fact family number sentence $67 - 43 = ?$
2. At the start of the show, 18 boys skated onto the ice. Then 9 girls join them. How many skaters are on the ice now?	I know that there are 18 boys at the start and that amount changes when 9 girls join them. Since there are more skaters now, I will add. $18 + 9 = ?$
3. The usher had some programs. She got 63 more to hand out and now she has 95. How many programs did she have at the beginning?	I don't know how many programs the usher had at the start, but when she got more, she had 95. Since she got 63 more, I need to add 63 to a missing amount to make 95. $? + 63 = 95$ I can find the missing number by solving the fact family number sentence $95 - 63 = ?$
4. Luke ate 32 raisins during the show. Marcy ate 44 raisins. How many fewer raisins did Luke eat than Marcy?	In this problem, I need to compare Luke's amount to Marcy's to see how many fewer raisins Luke ate. I need to find the difference, so I will subtract. $44 - 32 = ?$
5. During one act, 45 skaters were on the ice. Then 23 skated off. How many skaters were left on the ice?	In this problem, 45 skaters were on the ice. The 23 that skated off would be taken away from the 45, so I'll subtract. $45 - 23 = ?$

LEARN

TRY IT Justify Solutions

Objectives

Students will practice deciding how to solve a story problem and justifying their decision. Give students the Justify Solutions activity page from their Activity Book and read the directions with them. Use the answer key to check students' answers, and then enter the results online.

- Justify the procedures selected for addition or subtraction problem-solving situations with sums or minuends up through 100.

Name:

Justify Different Solutions
Justify Solutions

Read the story problem. Circle Add or Subtract to show how you would solve the problem, and then tell why you would add or subtract.

1. Mike took 85 photos.
Jake took 32 photos.

How many more photos did Mike take than Jake?

A. Add   (B.) Subtract

Sample explanation: Students should say they would subtract because they are comparing 85 and 32 to find the difference.

2. The circus sold 98 tickets on Saturday. On Sunday morning, it sold 61 tickets.

How many more tickets does the circus need to sell on Sunday to equal the number of tickets sold on Saturday?

A. Add   (B.) Subtract

Sample explanation: Students should say that they would subtract because they have a missing addend; they can use the related subtraction number sentence to solve $98 - 61 = ?$.

---

3. Sally had 75 programs.
She gave out 43 programs.
How many programs are left?

A. Add   (B.) Subtract

Sample explanation: Students should say that Sally gave out 43 programs, so they would subtract 43 from 75 to find how many are left.

4. The snack shack sold 56 lemon ice drinks. It sold 22 strawberry ice drinks.

How many ice drinks did the snack shack sell altogether?

(A) Add   B. Subtract

Sample explanation: Students should say that they would add to find the total amount.

Read the problem and follow the directions.

5. Heidi had 24 pencil erasers.
Her mom buys her 7 new erasers.
How many pencil erasers does Heidi have now?

What is a correct way to solve this problem?

Explain why you would solve it that way.

Example answer: Add 24 and 7.
Sample explanation: Heidi starts with some erasers. Then she gets more. She is adding her new erasers to the ones she already has, so you would add.

---

6. Olivia has 49 barrettes.
18 barrettes are rectangle shaped.
The rest of the barrettes are square.
How many square barrettes does Olivia have?

What is a correct way to solve this problem?

Explain why you would solve it that way.

Example answer: Subtract 18 from 49. Students may say that the number sentence in this problem would be $18 + ? = 49$, but they would use subtraction to find the missing addend.
Sample explanation: You know the total number of barrettes is 49, and part of this total is 18, so you subtract to find the other part.

7. Chase used 45 gallons of water to wash his truck. Annie used 33 gallons of water to wash her truck. How many fewer gallons of water did Annie use than Chase?

What is a correct way to solve this problem?

Explain why you would solve it that way.

Example answer: Subtract 33 from 45.
Sample explanation: You want to compare the two numbers. The difference between the two numbers tells how many fewer gallons Annie used.

Circle the answer.

8. Justine has 35 raisins.
Michelle has 31 raisins.
How many more raisins does Justine have than Michelle?

Which expression could be used to solve this problem?

Why is this expression used?

(A) $35 - 31$, because you subtract to find the difference in the number of raisins Justine and Michelle have.

B. $35 + 31$, because you add find how many raisins they have altogether.

C. $31 - 35$, because you subtract to find how many more raisins Justine has.

CHECKPOINT

Objectives

Print the Checkpoint and have students complete it on their own. Read the directions, problems, and answer choices to students, if necessary. Use the answer key to score the Checkpoint, and then enter the results online.

- Justify the procedures selected for addition or subtraction problem-solving situations with sums or minuends up through 100.

Name _____ Date _____

Checkpoint Answer Key

Circle the answer.

(1 point)
1. Which best explains how to correctly solve this problem?

There are 40 chairs in the café and 55 people.
How many people will not get a chair?

A. $40 + 55 = ?$
Add 40 and 55 to find out how many chairs there are in all.

(B.) $55 - 40 = ?$
Subtract 40 from 55 to find how many more people there are than chairs.

C. $40 - 55 = ?$
Subtract 55 from 40 to find how many more chairs there are than people.

Read the problem and follow the directions.

2. Jack used this number sentence $54 - 42 = 12$ to solve this problem:

Jorge saved 42 dollars. Suze saved 54 dollars.
How much money did they save altogether?

(1 point)
Is this number sentence correct to use when solving this problem? **No, the number sentence is not**
(1 point)
Explain your answer. **correct.**
Sample explanation: To find out how much money was saved altogether, you need to add $54 + 42$ to get 96.

Name _____ Date _____

3. Billy had 35 pieces of licorice.
He ate 6 pieces.
How many pieces of licorice does Billy have left?
(1 point)
Explain how to solve this problem.
(1 point)
Explain how you decided whether to add or subtract.

Sample explanation: I would subtract 6 from 35. I need to subtract to find the change in the number of pieces after Billy ate 6 pieces.

4. Carlie has 76 spoons in her spoon collection.
If she gives away 12 spoons, Carlie will have the same number of spoons as Bryce.
How many spoons does Bryce have?
(1 point)
Explain how to solve this problem.
(1 point)
Explain why you would solve it that way.

Sample explanation: I would subtract 12 from 76. If Carlie gives away 12 of her 76 spoons, she will have the same number of spoons as Bryce. So if you subtract 12 from 76 you will have Bryce's number of spoons.

Story Problems That Are Alike

Lesson Overview

Skills Update	5 minutes	ONLINE
GET READY Flower Story Problems	5 minutes	ONLINE
LEARN Explore Similar Problems	15 minutes	ONLINE
LEARN Identify Problem Similarities	15 minutes	ONLINE
TRY IT Problems That Are Alike	10 minutes	OFFLINE
CHECKPOINT	10 minutes	OFFLINE

▶ Lesson Objectives

Given a problem and solution, solve a similar problem by identifying connections between the two problems.

▶ Prerequisite Skills

Write and solve addition or subtraction number sentences for problem-solving situations with sums and minuends up through 100.

▶ Content Background

Students will learn to look for similarities in story problems. Then they can solve similar problems using the same approach.

Materials to Gather

SUPPLIED

Problems That Are Alike activity page

Checkpoint (printout)

GET READY Flower Story Problems

ONLINE 5 min

Students will choose the number sentence that solves a story problem. Then they will solve the problem.

Objectives

- Write and solve addition or subtraction number sentences for problem-solving situations with sums and minuends up through 100.

Tips

As you read each problem to students, help them focus on whether they should add or subtract to solve the problem.

LEARN Explore Similar Problems

ONLINE 15 min

Students will be given two story problems and will learn to recognize and explain how they are alike. Then they will read a story problem and the number sentence used to solve it. Students will use this worked-out problem to help them solve a similar problem. Finally they will write and solve their own story problem that is similar to a given problem.

Objectives

- Given a problem and solution, solve a similar problem by identifying connections between the two problems.

Tips

Allow students to use base-10 blocks to solve the problems.
   As students compare problems, focus their attention on whether they add or subtract to solve each problem

LEARN Identify Problem Similarities

ONLINE 15 min

Students will compare story problems and tell how they are alike. Then students will choose the two similar story problems in a group of three problems.

Objectives

- Given a problem and solution, solve a similar problem by identifying connections between the two problems.

Tips

As students compare problems, focus their attention on whether they add or subtract to solve each problem.

TRY IT Problems That Are Alike

OFFLINE 10 min

Students will practice identifying similar problems and solving similar problems using the same method. Give students the Problems That Are Alike activity page from their Activity Book and read the directions with them.

Objectives

- Given a problem and solution, solve a similar problem by identifying connections between the two problems.

Story Problems That Are Alike
Problems That Are Alike

Read the problem and follow the directions.

1. Read the story problems. Tell how you can use Problem 1 to help you solve Problem 2. Then solve Problem 2.

Problem 1

Heather has 59 stuffed animals.
Ellen has 8 stuffed animals.

How many fewer stuffed animals does Ellen have than Heather?

$59 - 8 = 51$

Problem 2

There are 39 apples.
There are 7 oranges.

How many more apples are there than oranges?

$39 - 7 = 32$

Both problems ask how many fewer or how many more, so both problems use subtraction to compare groups.

2. Write a number sentence and solution for Problem 1. Then use that number sentence and solution to help you solve Problem 2.

Problem 1

There are 36 boys at the park.
There are 8 girls at the park.

How many children are at the park altogether?

$36 + 8 = 44$ 44 children

Problem 2

There are 15 brown bears and 5 black bears at the zoo.
How many bears are there in all?

$15 + 5 = 20$
or $5 + 15 = 20$ 20 bears

What is alike about Problem 1 and Problem 2? Circle the answer.

Both are solved with subtraction.   (Both are solved with addition.)

3. Use the solution to Problem 1 to help you solve Problem 2.

Problem 1

There are 22 peanut butter and 5 turkey sandwiches.
How many sandwiches are there altogether?
$22 + 5 = 27$

Problem 2

There are 34 goldfish.
9 goldfish join them.
How many goldfish are there in all?

$34 + 9 = 43$ or $9 + 34 = 43$

What is alike about Problem 1 and Problem 2? Circle the answer.

Both are solved with subtraction.   (Both are solved with addition.)

4. Use the solution to Problem 1 to help you solve Problem 2.

Problem 1

Ted had 17 seashells.
He gave 5 seashells to his brother.
How many seashells does Ted have now?
$17 - 5 = 12$

Problem 2

Anne's book has 79 pages.
She read 9 pages.
How many pages does Anne have left to read?

$79 - 9 = 70$

What is alike about Problem 1 and Problem 2? Circle the answer.

(Both are solved with subtraction.)   Both are solved with addition.

TRY IT

CHECKPOINT

Print the Checkpoint and have students complete it on their own. Read the directions, problems, and answer choices to students, if necessary. Use the answer key to score the Checkpoint, and then enter the results online.

- Given a problem and solution, solve a similar problem by identifying connections between the two problems.

Name   Date

Checkpoint Answer Key

Write and solve a number sentence to solve the story problem. Use Problem 1 to help you solve Problem 2.

(1 point)
1. Tina ran 27 laps around the track.
Becky ran 9 laps around the track.

How many more laps did Tina run than Becky?

$$27 - 9 = 18$$

(1 point)
2. There are 75 cows on the farm.
There are 4 goats on the farm.

How many more cows than goats are there?

$$75 - 4 = 71$$

(1 point)
3. What is alike about Problem 1 and Problem 2?
Circle the answer.

(Subtraction was used to solve both problems.) | Addition was used to solve both problems. |

Name   Date

Write and solve a number sentence to solve the story problem. Use Problem 4 to help you solve Problem 5.

(1 point)
4. Jeff had 99 baseball cards.
He gave away 7 baseball cards.

How many baseball cards does Jeff have left?

$$99 - 7 = 92$$

(1 point)
5. Carol had 45 raisins.
She ate 3 raisins.
How many raisins does she have left?

$$45 - 3 = 42$$

(1 point)
6. What is alike about Problem 4 and Problem 5?
Circle the answer.

(Both are solved with subtraction.) | Both are solved with addition. |

Name   Date

Write and solve a number sentence to solve the story problem. Use Problem 7 to help you solve Problem 8.

(1 point)
7. Peter had 73 bugs in his collection.
He found 6 more bugs at the park.

How many bugs does he have altogether?

$$73 + 6 = 79$$

(1 point)
8. John read 21 books last week.
He read 7 more this week.

How many books did John read in all?

$$21 + 7 = 28 \text{ or } 7 + 21 = 28$$

(1 point)
9. What is alike about Problem 7 and Problem 8?
Circle the answer.

| Both are solved with subtraction. | (Both are solved with addition.)

Name   Date

Write and solve a number sentence to solve the story problem. Use Problem 10 to help you solve Problem 11.

(1 point)
10. Kevin has 29 toy cars.
Paul has 6 toy cars.

How many more toy cars does Kevin have than Paul?

$$29 - 6 = 23$$

(1 point)
11. Mary did 16 push-ups.
Kate did 5 push-ups.

How many fewer push-ups did Kate do than Mary?

$$16 - 5 = 11$$

(1 point)
12. What is alike about Problem 10 and Problem 11?
Circle the answer.

(Both are solved with subtraction.) | Both are solved with addition. |

STORY PROBLEMS THAT ARE ALIKE   **523**

Write Story Problems

Lesson Overview

Skills Update	5 minutes	ONLINE
GET READY Represent Addition	5 minutes	OFFLINE
LEARN Tell Story Problems	15 minutes	OFFLINE
LEARN Create Story Problems	15 minutes	OFFLINE
TRY IT Matching Story Problems	10 minutes	OFFLINE
CHECKPOINT	10 minutes	OFFLINE

▶ Lesson Objectives

Given a number sentence involving addition, subtraction, or both addition and subtraction, create a problem represented by the number sentence.

▶ Prerequisite Skills

Use models and math symbols to represent addition.

▶ Content Background

Students will create story problems that can be solved using given number sentences. They will need to consider the operation(s) in the number sentence and the magnitude of the numbers when thinking of an appropriate everyday situation.

Materials to Gather

SUPPLIED
blocks – O (yellow, red)
Create Story Problems activity page
Matching Story Problems activity page
Checkpoint (printout)

GET READY Represent Addition

OFFLINE 5 min

Objectives

- Use models and math symbols to represent addition.

Students will first model an addition expression, find the sum, and then write the completed number sentence. Then they will write their own addition expression, model it, find the sum, and write the completed number sentence.

Gather the cubes.

1. Display a train of 7 red cubes and 6 yellow cubes.

   Ask: What addition problem is shown?
   ANSWER: 7 plus 6

   Ask: What is the sum?
   ANSWER: 13

2. Have students write the number sentence for the problem. ($7 + 6 = 13$)

3. Write $9 + 5 = \underline{\ ?\ }$ on paper.

4. Have students use cubes to model $9 + 5$. (9 red cubes and 5 yellow cubes)

5. Have students use their model to help them complete the number sentence. ($9 + 5 = 14$)

6. Repeat Steps 3–5 with $7 + 18 = 25$ and $9 + 12 = 21$.

7. Have students make up two addition expressions of their own. Students should model the expressions with cubes, find the sum, and finally complete the number sentence.

LEARN Tell Story Problems

OFFLINE
15 min

Objectives

- Given a number sentence involving addition, subtraction, or both addition and subtraction, create a problem represented by the number sentence.

Students will create story problems to match addition and subtraction number sentences.

There are no materials to gather for this activity.

1. Write $9 + 1 = 10$ on paper. Read the number sentence to students.

2. **Say:** I'm going to tell you a story problem that matches this number sentence.

- Ron had 9 fish. He bought 1 more fish. How many fish does Ron have now?

3. **Say:** Now it's your turn to think of a story problem that could be solved using this number sentence. Make sure that in your problem, you have to add 9 and 1 to get the answer.

Check that students create a problem in which 1 is added to a group of 9.

4. Repeat Steps 1–3 with the following number sentences and story problems:

- $7 - 2 = 5$; Rosa had 7 necklaces. She gave 2 to Serena. How many necklaces does Rosa have left?

- $15 - 10 = 5$; Emma has 15 pretzels. She gives 10 to a friend. How many pretzels does she have left?

- $11 + 14 = 25$; Luke has 11 baseball cards. Mark has 14 baseball cards. How many baseball cards do they have altogether?

5. Write the following number sentences on the paper, one at a time. After writing each number sentence, have students create at least two story problems that match the number sentence.

- $12 - 6 = 6$
- $8 + 3 = 11$
- $13 + 16 = ?$
- $19 - 17 = ?$

LEARN Create Story Problems

OFFLINE
15min

Students will create story problems that can be solved by using a given number sentence. Give students the Create Story Problems activity page from their Activity Book and read the directions with them.

Have students choose at least two problems to write themselves. For the rest of the problems, you may write them as students say the problems aloud.

Objectives

- Given a number sentence involving addition, subtraction, or both addition and subtraction, create a problem represented by the number sentence.

Tips

If students need help writing story problems, you may wish to suggest story contexts. For example, tell them they may use apples or other fruits, toys, plants, flowers, birds, or anything else that they enjoy.

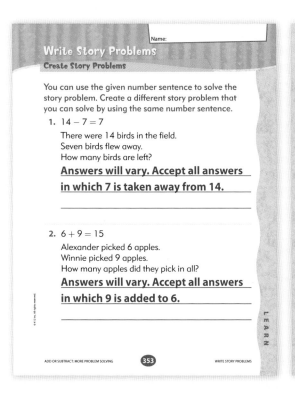

Name: _____

Write Story Problems

Create Story Problems

You can use the given number sentence to solve the story problem. Create a different story problem that you can solve by using the same number sentence.

1. $14 - 7 = 7$

There were 14 birds in the field.
Seven birds flew away.
How many birds are left?
Answers will vary. Accept all answers in which 7 is taken away from 14.

2. $6 + 9 = 15$

Alexander picked 6 apples.
Winnie picked 9 apples.
How many apples did they pick in all?
Answers will vary. Accept all answers in which 9 is added to 6.

ADD OR SUBTRACT: MORE PROBLEM SOLVING   353   WRITE STORY PROBLEMS

3. $12 - 8 = 4$

Serena had 12 books. She gave 8 books to the library. How many books does Serena have now?
Answers will vary. Accept all answers in which 8 is taken away from 12.

4. $3 + 5 - 4 = ?$

John made 3 cookies and Rosa made 5 cookies. They put the cookies together and gave 4 to Winnie. How many cookies do John and Rosa have now?
Answers will vary. Accept all answers in which 3 and 5 are added together and then 4 is taken away.

Create two story problems that can be solved by using the number sentence.

5. $3 + 4 = ?$
Answers will vary. Accept all answers in which 3 and 4 are added together.

6. $18 - 4 = ?$
Answers will vary. Accept all answers in which 4 is taken away from 18.

ADD OR SUBTRACT: MORE PROBLEM SOLVING   354   WRITE STORY PROBLEMS

Objectives

Students will practice creating story problems that can be solved by using a given number sentence. Give students the Matching Story Problems activity page from their Activity Book and read the directions with them.

Have students choose at least two problems to write themselves. For the rest of the problems, you may write them as students say the problems aloud.

- Given a number sentence involving addition, subtraction, or both addition and subtraction, create a problem represented by the number sentence.

Name:

Write Story Problems
Matching Story Problems

You can use the given number sentence to solve the story problem. Create a different story problem that you can solve by using the same number sentence.

1. $20 - 1 = 19$

There were 20 muffins in the box.
Kim took 1 muffin.

How many muffins are left in the box?

Answers will vary. Accept all answers in which 1 is taken away from 20.

2. $11 + 15 = 26$

There are 11 boys and 15 girls in the class.

How many students are in the class?

Answers will vary. Accept all answers in which 11 and 15 are added together.

---

3. $8 - 5 + 2 = ?$

Lynn had 8 stickers. She gave 5 stickers to Betsy. Then Mandy gave Lynn 2 more stickers.

How many stickers does Lynn have now?

Answers will vary. Accept all answers in which 5 is taken away from 8 and then 2 is added to the difference.

Create a story problem that can be solved by using the number sentence.

4. $8 + 4 = ?$

Answers will vary. Accept all answers in which 8 and 4 are added together.

---

5. $10 - 5 = ?$

Answers will vary. Accept all answers in which 5 is taken away from 10.

Create two story problems that can be solved by using the number sentence.

6. $2 + 9 = ?$

Answers will vary. Accept all answers in which 2 and 9 are added together.

Circle the number sentence you could use to solve the problem.

7. Anne had 6 toy cars.
She lost 3 toy cars.

How many cars does she have now?

A. $6 - 3 = ?$
B. $6 + 3 = ?$
C. $6 + 1 = ?$

8. Sasha had 7 doll dresses.
Then she gave 2 doll dresses to her friend.

How many doll dresses does Sasha have left?

A. $7 + 2 = ?$
B. $2 + 7 = ?$
C. $7 - 2 = ?$

OFFLINE
10min

Objectives

- Given a number sentence involving addition, subtraction, or both addition and subtraction, create a problem represented by the number sentence.

Print the Checkpoint and have students complete it on their own. Read the directions, problems, and answer choices to students, if necessary. Use the answer key to score the Checkpoint, and then enter the results online.

Students may either write or dictate the story problems.

◇ Checkpoint   Math | Add or Subtract: More Problem Solving | Write Story Problems

Name _____ Date _____

Checkpoint Answer Key

Create a story problem that can be solved by using the number sentence.

(1 point)
1. $5 - 2 = ?$

Sample answer: _____

Rick had 5 apples. He gave 2 apples to his friend.

How many apples does he have left?

_____

(1 point)
2. $6 + 4 = ?$

Sample answer: _____

Adam had 6 toys. He bought 4 more toys.

How many toys does Adam have in all?

_____

(1 point)
3. $12 - 6 = ?$

Sample answer: _____

I had 12 pencils. I gave 6 pencils to my friend.

How many pencils do I have left?

◇ Checkpoint   Math | Add or Subtract: More Problem Solving | Write Story Problems

Name _____ Date _____

Which number sentence can you use to solve this problem? Circle the answer.

(1 point)
4. Zoey had 6 cars.
     She lost 3 cars, but her friend gave her 1 more car.
     How many cars does Zoey have now?

   A. $6 - 3 - 1 = ?$ B. $6 + 3 + 1 = ?$ Ⓒ $6 - 3 + 1 = ?$

Unit Review

UNIT REVIEW Look Back	10 minutes	**ONLINE**
UNIT REVIEW Checkpoint Practice	50 minutes	**OFFLINE**
⤵ **UNIT REVIEW** Prepare for the Checkpoint		

▶ Unit Objectives

This lesson reviews the following objectives:

- Recognize and solve word problems involving numbers up to 100 in which one quantity must be changed to equal another quantity.
- Write and solve addition or subtraction number sentences for problem-solving situations with sums and minuends up through 100.
- Check the accuracy of calculations from the context of the problem.
- Justify the procedures selected for addition or subtraction problem-solving situations with sums or minuends up through 100.
- Given a problem and solution, solve a similar problem by identifying connections between the two problems.
- Given a number sentence involving addition, subtraction, or both addition and subtraction, create a problem represented by the number sentence.

▶ Advance Preparation

In this lesson, students will have an opportunity to review previous activities in the Add or Subtract: More Problem Solving unit. Look at the suggested activities in Unit Review: Prepare for the Checkpoint online and gather any needed materials.

Materials to Gather

SUPPLIED
Checkpoint Practice activity page

| **Keywords** | change problem | equalize problem |
| | combine problem | justify |

ONLINE
10min

UNIT REVIEW Look Back

In this unit, students have learned to check the accuracy of an answer to a story problem, compare two story problems to see how they are similar, and create story problems that represent number sentences. They have also learned how to justify their procedures when solving story problems. Students will review these concepts to prepare for the Unit Checkpoint.

Objectives

- Review unit objectives.

OFFLINE
50 min

Objectives

• Review unit objectives.

Students will complete a Checkpoint Practice activity page to prepare for the Unit Checkpoint. If necessary, read the directions, problems, and answer choices to students. Have students answer the problems on their own. Carefully review the answers with students.

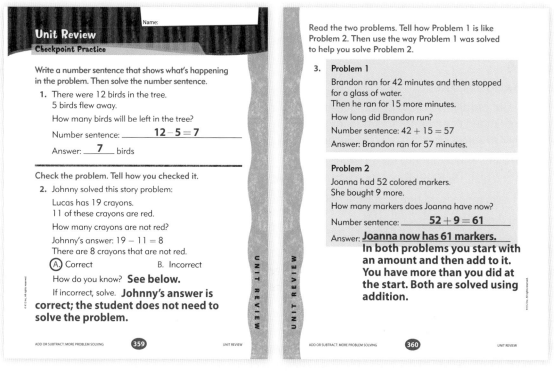

Name:

Unit Review
Checkpoint Practice

Write a number sentence that shows what's happening in the problem. Then solve the number sentence.

1. There were 12 birds in the tree.
   5 birds flew away.

   How many birds will be left in the tree?

   Number sentence: __**12 − 5 = 7**__

   Answer: __**7**__ birds

Check the problem. Tell how you checked it.

2. Johnny solved this story problem:

   Lucas has 19 crayons.
   11 of these crayons are red.

   How many crayons are not red?

   Johnny's answer: 19 − 11 = 8
   There are 8 crayons that are not red.

   (A) Correct   B. Incorrect

   How do you know? **See below.**

   If incorrect, solve. **Johnny's answer is correct; the student does not need to solve the problem.**

ADD OR SUBTRACT: MORE PROBLEM SOLVING   359   UNIT REVIEW

Read the two problems. Tell how Problem 1 is like Problem 2. Then use the way Problem 1 was solved to help you solve Problem 2.

3. **Problem 1**

   Brandon ran for 42 minutes and then stopped for a glass of water.
   Then he ran for 15 more minutes.

   How long did Brandon run?

   Number sentence: 42 + 15 = 57

   Answer: Brandon ran for 57 minutes.

   Problem 2

   Joanna had 52 colored markers.
   She bought 9 more.

   How many markers does Joanna have now?

   Number sentence: __**52 + 9 = 61**__

   Answer: **Joanna now has 61 markers.**
   In both problems you start with an amount and then add to it. You have more than you did at the start. Both are solved using addition.

ADD OR SUBTRACT: MORE PROBLEM SOLVING   360   UNIT REVIEW

Additional Answers

2. Answers will vary. Students should explain how they checked the problem and determined it was correct. Johnny correctly subtracted the number of red crayons from the total number of crayons to find out how many crayons were not red.

Circle the answer.

4. Max has 8 dogs.
   Ruby has 2 more dogs than Max.

   How many dogs does Ruby have?

   Which of the following best explains how to correctly solve this problem?

   (A) 8 + 2, because Ruby has 2 more dogs than Max.

   B. 2 − 8, because Ruby has 8 fewer dogs than Max.

   C. 8 − 2, because Ruby has 2 more dogs than Max.

5. Which story problem can be solved using the number sentence 21 + 15 = ?

   (A) Martha has 21 stickers. Blake has 15 more stickers than Martha. How many stickers does Blake have?

   B. Jacob has 21 rocks. Aaron has 15 rocks. How many more rocks does Jacob have than Aaron?

   C. Danica has 21 seashells. Helio has 15 seashells. How many more seashells does Helio have to find to have as many as Danica?

6. Sandro washed 26 cars.
   Toby washed 8 cars.

   How many more cars does Toby need to wash to have washed the same number as Sandro?

   A. 34   B. 26

   (C) 18   D. 8

→ UNIT REVIEW Prepare for the Checkpoint

What you do next depends on how students performed in the previous activity, Unit Review: Checkpoint Practice. If students had difficulty with any of the problems, complete the appropriate review activity listed in the table online.

Unit Checkpoint

UNIT CHECKPOINT Offline   60 minutes **OFFLINE**

▶ Unit Objectives

This lesson assesses the following objectives:

- Recognize and solve word problems involving numbers up to 100 in which one quantity must be changed to equal another quantity.

- Write and solve addition or subtraction number sentences for problem-solving situations with sums and minuends up through 100.

- Check the accuracy of calculations from the context of the problem.

- Justify the procedures selected for addition or subtraction problem-solving situations with sums or minuends up through 100.

- Given a problem and solution, solve a similar problem by identifying connections between the two problems.

- Given a number sentence involving addition, subtraction, or both addition and subtraction, create a problem represented by the number sentence.

Materials to Gather

SUPPLIED

Unit Checkpoint (printout)

UNIT CHECKPOINT Offline   OFFLINE **60**min

Objectives

- Assess unit objectives.

Students will complete the Unit Checkpoint offline. Print the Checkpoint and have students complete it on their own. Read the directions, problems, and answer choices to students, if necessary. Use the answer key to score the Checkpoint, and then enter the results online.

☼ Checkpoint   Math | Add or Subtract: More Problem Solving | Unit Checkpoint

Name _____ Date _____

Unit Checkpoint Answer Key

Read the problem and follow the directions.
(1 point)
1. Wendy picked 54 plums.
   If she gives 24 plums away,
   she will have the same number as Ben.

   How many plums does Ben have? __**30**__ plums

(1 point)
2. The zoo had some baby geckos.
   The zoo gave 22 baby geckos to the wild animal park.
   Now the zoo has 41 baby geckos.
   How many baby geckos did the zoo have in the beginning?

   Complete this number sentence to solve the problem.

   41 (+) **22** = **63**

(1 point)
3. Fireman Jake's team spent 6 hours cleaning the firehouse.
   If the team cleans for 2 more hours, it will have cleaned
   as long as Fireman Trevor's team.

   How many hours did Fireman Trevor's team clean? __**8**__ hours

(1 point)
4. Lisa had 39 apples. Holly had 22 apples.
   How many apples must Lisa eat to have the
   same number of apples as Holly? __**17**__ apples

1 of 5

☼ Checkpoint   Math | Add or Subtract: More Problem Solving | Unit Checkpoint

Name _____ Date _____

Circle the answer.
(1 point)
5. Anne solved this story problem:

   Steven collected 16 rocks. Jennifer collected 13 rocks.
   How many more rocks did Steven collect than Jennifer?

   Anne's answer: 16 − 13 = 3 rocks
   Which number sentence could you use to check Anne's work?

   A. 16 + 10 = 26   (B) 13 + 3 = 16
   C. 13 + 16 = 29   D. 16 + 3 = 19

(1 point)
6. Which story problem can be solved using the number
   sentence 15 + 8 = ?

   A. Jason had 15 apples. He ate 8 apples.
       How many apples does Jason have left?

   (B) Roberto had 15 apples. He bought 8 more apples.
       How many apples does Roberto have now?

   C. Melinda has 15 apples. Claire has 8 apples. How
       many more apples does Melinda have than Claire?

(1 point)
7. Jillian had 16 crackers. She ate 6 crackers.
   How many crackers does she have now?
   Which best explains how to correctly solve this problem?

   A. 16 + 6, because Jillian has more crackers now
       than when she started.

   (B) 16 − 6, because Jillian has fewer crackers now
       than when she started.

   C. 16 + 6, because Jillian has fewer crackers now
       than when she started.

2 of 5

Name _____ Date _____

(1 point)
8. Dan has 34 muffins. Sheri has 3 fewer muffins than Dan. How many muffins does Sheri have?

Which best explains how to solve this problem?

  A. $34 + 3$, because Sheri has more muffins than Dan.

  (B.) $34 - 3$, because Sheri has 3 fewer muffins than Dan.

  C. $3 - 34$, because Sheri has 34 fewer muffins than Dan.

(1 point)
9. Geoff had 63 mice. He bought 8 more mice. How many mice does Geoff have now?
Geoff now has 71 mice.

Which problem is solved using the same strategy and has the correct answer?

  A. Scott had 37 mice. He sold 9 of them. How many mice does he have left? He has 26 mice left.

  B. Scott has 37 white mice and 9 black mice. Scott has how many more white mice than black mice? He has 46 more white mice than black mice.

  (C.) Scott had 37 mice. He got 9 mice for his birthday. How many mice does he have now? He has 46 mice now.

(1 point)
10. Tim had 38 cards. His dad gave him some more cards. Now Tim has 69 cards. How many cards did Tim's dad give him?

  A. $38 + 69 = 107$

  (B.) $69 - 38 = 31$

  C. $69 - 38 = 21$

Name _____ Date _____

Write a story problem that can be solved using this number sentence.
(1 point)
11. $8 - 2 = ?$
Students should create a problem that can be solved by using the given number sentence.
Sample answer:
Ricki had 8 apples.
She gave 2 apples to her friend.
How many apples does Ricki have left?

Read the problem, and then tell a correct way to solve it. Explain why you would solve it that way.
(1 point)
12. Sophie swam 27 laps. If she swims 13 more laps, she will have swum the same number of laps as Candy. How many laps did Candy swim? **See below.**

Read these two story problems. Then describe how they can both be solved the same way.
(1 point)
13. Mary had 35 flowers. She gave 21 flowers to her mother. How many flowers does Mary have left?

    Steve had 47 postcards. He mailed 15 of them. How many postcards does he have left? **See below.**

Additional Answers

12. Students should explain how they would solve the problem and explain why they would solve it this way. Answers will vary.
Sample answer: I would add 27 and 13 because I need to find out the total number of laps that Sophie would swim. This is the same number of laps as Candy swam.

13. Students should describe how both problems can be solved in the same way. Possible answers are that in both problems you start with an amount, give part of it away, and are asked to find how much you have left, or that both problems can be solved using subtraction.

14. In both problems, two amounts are combined. Both are solved using addition.
$15 + 32 = 47$
47 bananas were eaten.

Name _____ Date _____

(1 point)
14. Tell how Problem 1 is like Problem 2.
(1 point)
Then use the solution to Problem 1 to help you solve Problem 2.

Problem 1:
There are 34 grapes on one plate and 32 grapes on the other plate.

How many grapes are there altogether?

$34 + 32 = 66$

There are 66 grapes altogether.

Problem 2:
The monkey ate 15 bananas. The elephant ate 32 bananas.

How many bananas were eaten altogether?
See right.

Geometric Figures, Data, and Attributes

▶ Unit Objectives

- Identify, describe, and compare plane figures, such as rectangle, square, triangle, circle, oval, including those on the faces of solid figures.

- Use concrete objects to show how two or more shapes can be put together or taken apart to create a different shape.

- Explain which attributes, such as color, position, shape, size, roundness, or number of corners, are being used for classification of familiar plane and solid figures.

- Sort objects and data by common attributes, such as geometric figures, tall or short, numbers less than 50 or numbers 50 and above, striped or solid or polka-dotted.

- Describe the categories that were used to sort objects and data by common attributes.

- Identify the next element in simple repeating patterns and explain how the element was found (for example, rhythmic, numeric, color, and shape patterns).

- Use tally charts to represent data.

- Use tally charts and bar graphs to compare data (for example, find largest, smallest, most often, least often).

- Use pictures and picture graphs to represent data.

- Use pictures and picture graphs to compare data (for example, find largest, smallest, most often, least often).

▶ Big Ideas

- Geometric figures can be described and classified by the shapes of their faces and by how many faces, sides, edges, or vertices they have.

- Shapes can be constructed from other shapes.

- Graphs and charts are useful ways to represent and compare numerical data.

▶ Unit Introduction

Students will learn how to identify, describe, and compare plane figures. They will explore the composition of plane figures by putting them together and taking them apart to create other shapes. Students will sort shapes and other objects by common attributes and describe how the objects are sorted.

Students will also learn about patterns and data displays. They will identify and continue repeating patterns. Then students will explore different ways to display data, including tally charts, bar graphs, and picture graphs. They will answer questions about data displayed in each of these ways.

Plane Figures

Lesson Overview

Skills Update	5 minutes	ONLINE
GET READY Identify Plane Figures	5 minutes	ONLINE
LEARN Pipe Cleaner Shapes	15 minutes	OFFLINE
LEARN Compare Shapes	15 minutes	OFFLINE
TRY IT Plane Shapes	10 minutes	OFFLINE
CHECKPOINT	10 minutes	OFFLINE

▶ Lesson Objectives

Identify, describe, and compare plane figures, such as rectangle, square, triangle, circle, oval, including those on the faces of solid figures.

▶ Prerequisite Skills

Identify common plane figures, such as circle, triangle, square, and rectangle.

▶ Common Errors and Misconceptions

- Students might have heard some geometric vocabulary words, but their definitions of these words might be incorrect.
- Students might not recognize that a shape might be positioned different ways. For example, students might not recognize that the second shape is a square.

- Students might inappropriately use *converse reasoning* when classifying shapes. For example, they might say, "All square have 4 sides. This shape has 4 sides, so it must be a square."

▶ Advance Preparation

Twist 2 pipe cleaners together to make a longer pipe cleaner. Do this four times to make 4 longer pipe cleaners.

Make 2-D flash cards for plane figures. Label 4 index cards as follows: **circle**, **square**, **rectangle**, and **triangle**. Draw the corresponding shape on the other side of each index card.

▶ Safety

Supervise students when they are working with the geometric solid blocks. These blocks have sharp corners.

▶ Content Background

The number of sides of a figure refers to the number of straight sides. Therefore, a curved figure, such as a circle or oval, is said to have no sides.

A vertex is a corner. A vertex can be a square corner or not. Square corners are corners with right angles such as those found in squares and rectangles. *Veritices* is the plural form of *vertex*.

A square is mathematically defined as a special type of rectangle. In this lesson, students are asked to differentiate between the more traditional rectangle that has two longer sides and two shorter sides and a square that has all sides equal. Therefore, the square is given its own category for sorting.

The term *diamond*, often used by young children for a square rotated onto one of its corners, is not a standard geometric term and will not be used in this course. Students should understand that a square rotated in any direction is still a square.

Keywords

circle – a plane figure with no straight sides or corners; the edge of a circle is a curve with all points the same distance from the center

cone – a geometric solid with a circular base and a curved surface that comes to a point, or vertex

corner – the point where two segments, lines, surfaces, or edges meet

cube – a geometric solid with 6 equal-sized square faces

curved figure – a 2-dimensional geometric figure with a rounded side, such as a circle

cylinder – a geometric solid with a curved surface and parallel circular base

face of a solid figure – a flat surface on a solid figure, such as a square face on a cube

oval – a plane figure resembling the outline of an egg, but often more symmetrical

rectangle – a plane figure with 4 sides and 4 square corners with opposite sides of equal length

rectangular prism – a geometric solid with 3 pairs of parallel rectangular faces, where each pair of faces is identical; a box is an example

side – a segment that forms the edge of a shape

square – a plane figure with 4 sides of equal length and 4 square corners

triangle – a plane figure with 3 sides and 3 corners

ONLINE
5 min

GET READY Identify Plane Figures

Objectives

- Identify common plane figures, such as circle, triangle, square, and rectangle.

Students will practice identifying plane figures.
   Guide students by asking questions such as the following:

- How many sides does the figure have?
- How many corners does it have?
- Is the figure curved?
- Are the sides straight?
- Are the sides the same length or different lengths?

LEARN Pipe Cleaner Shapes

Objectives

- Identify, describe, and compare plane figures, such as rectangle, square, triangle, circle, oval, including those on the faces of solid figures.

Students will describe, identify, and compare shapes.
Gather the pipe cleaners and the geometric solid blocks.

1. Tell students that they will use pipe cleaners to make different shapes. Demonstrate how to bend a pipe cleaner to make a triangle. Point out the sides and the corners of the shape. Explain that a corner is where 2 sides meet.

2. Guide to make each of these shapes: 2 squares, 2 different-sized rectangles, 1 oval, 2 circles, and 3 different-sized triangles. For each shape, have students tell you if the shape is rounded. If it is not rounded, have them tell you how many corners and sides the shape has. For the square, make sure that the sides are as equal as possible.

3. Compare two shapes at a time. For each pair, ask questions such as the following:
   - Which has more sides?
   - Which is a curved shape?
   - Which has 3 corners?
   - How are these shapes different? How are they the same?

4. Display the cube. Have students trace around a face of the cube. Then have them name the shape that they made.

5. Explain to students that the face is a square shape. Have students identify the pipe cleaner figure that most closely resembles their drawing.

6. Repeat Steps 4 and 5 with the following geometric solids:
   - Cone (circle)
   - Cylinder (circle)
   - Rectangular prism (rectangle)

Tips

If students have difficulty counting the sides of the cube, have them keep one finger on the first side or corner that they count, so they know where they started and do not count sides more than once.

LEARN Compare Shapes

Objectives

- Identify, describe, and compare plane figures, such as rectangle, square, triangle, circle, oval, including those on the faces of solid figures.

Students will describe, identify, and compare shapes.
Gather the 2-D flash cards and the geometric solid blocks.

1. Explain that students will play a game to compare shapes. Have students select a flash card without looking.

2. Show students the picture side of the card. Have them name the shape and describe it. For example, "This is a square. It has 4 sides that are all the same length. It has 4 corners." If students answer correctly, they may keep the card. If not, they should return the card to the deck.

3. Once students have collected all the cards, have them mix the cards and pull out two cards without looking.

4. Have students compare the shapes. If possible, they should tell at least one way that the shapes are the same, and one way that they are different. For example, "A square and a triangle both have straight sides, but one has 4 corners and one has 3 corners."

5. Continue until you have compared several shapes.

6. Display the geometric solid blocks. Hand students the circle flash card and ask them to find the geometric solid that has a face with the matching. (The cone or cylinder matches.)

7. Allow students to choose another flash card they want to match. Continue until students have matched the cone, sphere, and cube.

8. Have students select a geometric solid block and find an object in the room that has the same shape.

9. Have students match a 2-D flash card to the face of the object. For example, "A footstool is a cube. It has a face that is a square." Continue as time permits.

TRY IT Plane Shapes

OFFLINE **10** min

Students will practice identifying plane figures. Give students the Plane Shapes activity page from their Activity Book and read the directions with them.

Objectives

- Identify, describe, and compare plane figures, such as rectangle, square, triangle, circle, oval, including those on the faces of solid figures.

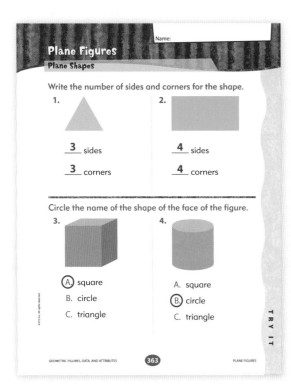

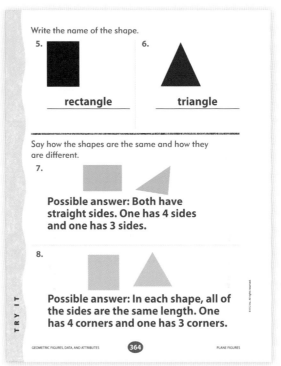

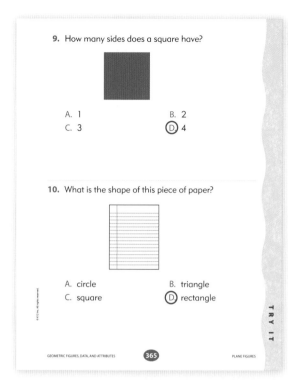

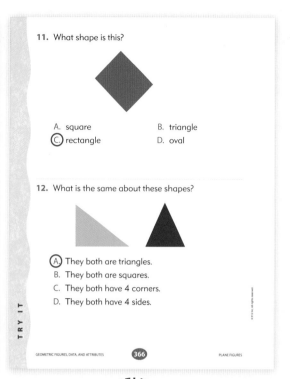

Put Together and Take Apart Shapes

Lesson Overview

Skills Update	5 minutes	ONLINE
GET READY Break Shapes Apart	5 minutes	ONLINE
LEARN Work with Shapes	15 minutes	ONLINE
LEARN Build and Take Apart Shapes	15 minutes	OFFLINE
TRY IT Practice Using Shapes	10 minutes	OFFLINE
CHECKPOINT	10 minutes	OFFLINE

▶ Lesson Objectives

Use concrete objects to show how two or more shapes can be put together or taken apart to create a different shape.

▶ Prerequisite Skills

Show how two or more plane figures can be taken apart to create different shapes (circles, triangles, rectangles, and squares only).

▶ Common Errors and Misconceptions

- Students might have heard some geometric vocabulary words, but their definitions of these words might be incorrect.
- Students might not recognize that a shape might be positioned different ways. For example, students might not recognize that the second shape is a square.

- Students might inappropriately use *converse reasoning* when classifying shapes. For example, they might say, "All square have 4 sides. This shape has 4 sides, so it must be a square."
- Students might fixate on specific properties of shapes, which can cause them to draw incorrect conclusions. For example, students might assume that all four-sided shapes are squares or that all quadrilaterals with the same perimeter will have the same area.

▶ Safety

Supervise students to make sure they use their scissors safely and stay seated.

▶ Content Background

Students will show how they can take apart and put together shapes to make other shapes.

Materials to Gather

SUPPLIED

blocks – E (red, yellow, green only), F, G, H, K, L, M, N

Practice Using Shapes activity page

Checkpoint (printout)

ALSO NEEDED

scissors, round-end safety

paper, drawing

ruler or straightedge

GET READY Break Shapes Apart

Students will explore cutting shapes apart to make other shapes. They will need to visualize how to cut apart a shape without actually doing so.

Help students visualize the larger shape by looking at the solid outside lines. Help them identify the smaller shapes by focusing on the dotted lines inside the larger shape. To help students name the smaller shapes, ask questions such as the following:

- How many sides does the shape have? How many corners?
- What shape has that number of sides and corners?

Objectives

- Show how two or more plane figures can be taken apart to create different shapes (circles, triangles, rectangles, and squares only).

Tips

If students have difficulty seeing the smaller shapes inside the larger shape, have them cover one part of the shape with their hand or an index card.

LEARN Work with Shapes

Students will determine what shapes they can make by taking apart and putting together shapes.

DIRECTIONS FOR USING THE ATTRIBUTE BLOCKS LEARNING TOOL

1. Click Practice Mode.
2. Drag two large squares into the work area. (Leave space between the squares.)
   Say: We can put these two squares together to make a new shape.
   Move the squares together to form a rectangle with long horizontal sides.

Objectives

- Use concrete objects to show how two or more shapes can be put together or taken apart to create a different shape.

3. Leave this shape on the screen and drag two more squares into the work area.
   Say: I can use the squares to show the rectangle a different way.
   Move the squares together to form a rectangle with long vertical sides.
   Say: Both of these rectangles are the same. They are just turned different ways.

4. Clear the work area. Drag two rectangles into the work area. Ask students to put together the two rectangles to form a larger rectangle. Then ask students to put together the two rectangles to form a different larger rectangle.

5. Drag a third rectangle into the work area. Show students how to place the third rectangle onto the shape to form an even longer rectangle.

6. Clear the work area. Drag a square and a triangle into the work area and put the shapes together to form a pentagon.

Ask: What shapes did I put together to make this new shape?
ANSWER: triangle and square

Have students take apart the pentagon to form a triangle and a square.

7. Repeat Step 6 with the following pairs of shapes:

- rectangle and circle
- 2 triangles
- square and circle

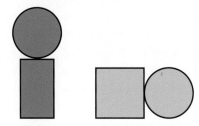

8. Say: You can take apart a shape to make more than 1 shape.

Drag 4 squares into the work area and put them together to form a large square.

Have students make as many different shapes as they can by taking pieces away from this shape.

Examples: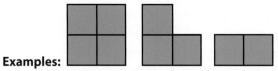

9. Allow students time to experiment with putting together and taking apart shapes. Watch for examples when students make the same shape but with a different orientation. Point out that the shapes are still the same but are just turned a different way.

LEARN Build and Take Apart Shapes

Objectives

- Use concrete objects to show how two or more shapes can be put together or taken apart to create a different shape.

Students will create geometric shapes by putting together their blocks, tracing them, and cutting them apart.

Gather the geometric solid blocks, drawing paper, ruler or straightedge, and scissors.

PUT SHAPES TOGETHER

1. Hold up each type of block and say its name. The only names students need to have memorized are *triangle* and *square*. (E is square, K is triangle, L is rhombus, M is trapezoid, and N is hexagon.)

2. Give students the blocks.

   Say: There are many ways to put together these shapes to make other shapes. Let's see how many you can find.

3. Hold up the blue rhombus.

   Say: Use triangles to make this shape.

4. Guide students to put together 2 triangles to make the rhombus. Students may lay the triangles on top of the rhombus to help them make the shape. After students form the rhombus, have them describe what they did: "I used two triangles to make the blue shape."

5. Repeat Steps 3 and 4 with the following shapes:
   - Use green triangles to make the yellow hexagon.
   - Use blue rhombuses to make the yellow hexagon.
   - Use green triangles to make the red trapezoid.
   - Use squares to make a rectangle.
   - Use squares to make a larger square.
   - Use green triangles to make a larger triangle.

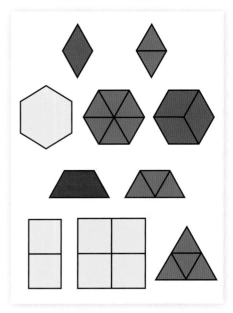

TAKE SHAPES APART

6. **Say:** We just put together shapes to make other shapes. We can also take apart shapes to make other shapes.

7. Have students trace the blue rhombus on their paper.

   Ask: What shapes from our blocks can you make if you were to take the rhombus apart by cutting it?
   ANSWER: 2 triangles

8. Have students draw a line with the ruler or straightedge to show how to cut the rhombus into 2 triangles and then have them cut along their line. After students form the triangles, have them describe what they did: "I cut apart one of the blue shapes to make two triangles."

9. Repeat Steps 7 and 8 with the following shapes. Students may stack the smaller blocks on top of the larger one to see how they might cut out the shapes.
   - Cut apart the hexagon into 2 trapezoids.
   - Cut apart the hexagon into 6 triangles.
   - Cut apart the trapezoid into 3 triangles.
   - Cut apart the square into 2 triangles. These triangles will be a different shape than the green triangle blocks.

TRY IT Practice Using Shapes

Objectives

Students will practice putting together and taking apart shapes. Give students the geometric solid blocks and the Practice Using Shapes activity page from their Activity Book. Read the directions with them.

- Use concrete objects to show how two or more shapes can be put together or taken apart to create a different shape.

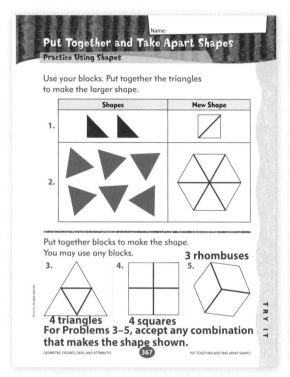

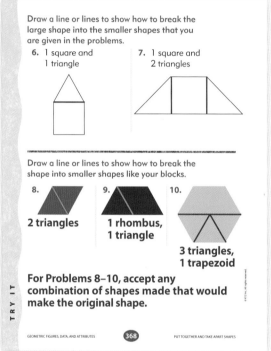

CHECKPOINT

Objectives

Print the Checkpoint. In Part 1, students will take a performance-based assessment. In Part 2, students will complete the problems on their own. Read the directions, problems, and answer choices to students, if necessary. Use the answer key to score the Checkpoint, and then enter the results online.

Gather the geometric solid blocks. For Problems 1–4, give students the blocks as directed by the problems. For Problems 5–6, allow students to use the blocks as needed.

- Use concrete objects to show how two or more shapes can be put together or taken apart to create a different shape.

Name _____ Date _____

Checkpoint Answer Key

Part 1

Follow the instructions for each item. Choose the response that describes how the student performs on the task.

(1 point)
1. Give students the following blocks: 2 right triangles (F).

   Say, "Put the small triangles together to make a larger triangle."

   Did the student put together 2 small triangles to make the larger triangle?

   A. Yes   B. No

(1 point)
2. Give students the following blocks: 3 small equilateral triangles (K), 1 trapezoid (M).

   Say, "Put the triangles together to make the larger shape."

   Did the student put together the small triangles to make the trapezoid?

   A. Yes   B. No

Name _____ Date _____

(1 point)
3. Give students the following blocks: 2 small equilateral triangles (K), 1 rhombus (L).

   Say, "Put the triangles together to make the larger shape."

   Did the student put together the small triangles to make the rhombus?

   A. Yes   B. No

(1 point)
4. Give students all the blocks for this Checkpoint. Separately show them the large right triangle (H).

   Say, "Put blocks together to make this shape."

   Example: **Answers will vary.**

   Did the student put together the smaller shapes to make the right triangle?

   A. Yes   B. No

Give students Part 2 of the assessment.

Name _____ Date _____

Part 2

Draw a line or lines to show how to break the shape that's pictured into the given shapes.

(1 point)
5. Draw 2 lines on this rectangle to make 1 square and 2 triangles. You may use your blocks to help you.

   Example: **Accept any combination of the shapes that would make the original shape.**

(1 point)
6. Draw 2 lines on this shape to make 1 triangle like your green triangle block and 2 shapes like your blue four-sided block.

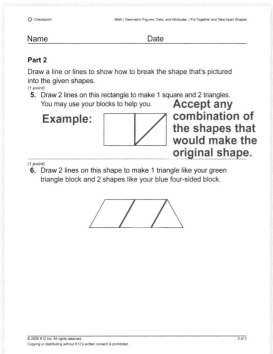

Group Shapes Different Ways

Skills Update	5 minutes	ONLINE
GET READY Compare Figures	5 minutes	ONLINE
LEARN Similar Shapes	15 minutes	OFFLINE
LEARN Group Shapes	15 minutes	ONLINE
TRY IT Practice Sorting Shapes	10 minutes	OFFLINE
CHECKPOINT	10 minutes	ONLINE

▶ Lesson Objectives

Explain which attributes, such as color, position, shape, size, roundness, or number of corners, are being used for classification of familiar plane and solid figures.

▶ Prerequisite Skills

- Compare plane figures by common attributes, such as number of sides and number of corners of triangles, rectangles, squares, pentagons, and circles.
- Compare common solid figures according to attributes, such as position, shape, size, roundness, or number of corners.

▶ Common Errors and Misconceptions

- Students might have heard some geometric vocabulary words, but their definitions of these words might be incorrect. For example, they may think that all triangles must have three *equal* sides. Actually, any shape with only three sides is a triangle.
- Students might not recognize that a shape might be positioned different ways. For example, students might not recognize that the second shape is a square.

  ◼ ◆

- Students might inappropriately use *converse reasoning* when classifying shapes. For example, they might say, "All squares have 4 sides. This shape has 4 sides, so it must be a square."
- Students might not recognize ways that a shape might be different. For example, they may think that a quadrilateral and a rectangle with the same perimeter must have the same area.

▶ Safety

Supervise students when they are working with the geometric solid blocks. These blocks have sharp corners.

Materials to Gather

SUPPLIED

blocks – AA, BB, CC, DD, EE, FF, GG, HH (all colors)

blocks – P, Q, R, T, U, V

Practice Sorting Shapes activity page

ALSO NEEDED

string – 1 piece, 20–24 inches long

▶ Content Background

Students will learn to identify a characteristic shared by all shapes in a given group.

Students should understand that color, position, shape, size, roundness, and number of corners are all attributes that may be used to classify geometric shapes.

Keywords   **attribute** – a characteristic, such as size, shape, or color

GET READY Compare Figures

ONLINE
5min

Students will compare plane and solid shapes.
Follow the directions on each screen.

1. Guide students' thinking as they compare the shapes. Sample questions include the following:
   • How many sides does each shape have?
   • How many corners does each shape have?
   • Are the shapes round? Are the sides straight?

2. Accept any reasonable answer for how the shapes are the same and how they are different.

Objectives

• Compare plane figures by common attributes, such as number of sides and number of corners of triangles, rectangles, squares, pentagons, and circles.

• Compare common solid figures according to attributes, such as position, shape, size, roundness, or number of corners.

Tips

Allow students to draw base-10 blocks however they wish, as long as the blocks are countable and students can tell the difference between the tens rod and the ones cube.

LEARN Similar Shapes

OFFLINE
15min

Students will identify an attribute that all objects in a group have in common. Then they will add to the group a shape with the same attribute.
Gather the string and the blocks (AA, BB, CC, DD, EE, FF, GG, and HH).

1. Use the piece of string to make a circle on the workspace. Put the following inside the string: circles, ovals, a cylinder, and a sphere. Put the shapes that are not curved outside the circle.

   Ask: What do the shapes inside the circle have in common?
   ANSWER: They are all round or have a round part.

Objectives

• Explain which attributes, such as color, position, shape, size, roundness, or number of corners, are being used for classification of familiar plane and solid figures.

2. Repeat Step 1 using the following attributes:
   - All one color
   - All having a shape with 4 sides
   - All big
   - All having a shape with 3 sides
   - All triangles that are pointing in the same direction.

3. Place a group of objects that share an attribute inside the circle. For example, put curved shapes inside the circle, but leave out the cone. Have students identify the common attribute. Then have them place another object in the group and explain why it belongs.

4. Have students place a group of objects inside the circle and then explain to you what attribute they used.

5. Have students place another group of objects inside the circle and ask you to guess what attribute they used.

LEARN Group Shapes

Students will use the Attribute Blocks Learning Tool to identify the common attribute in a group of objects.

Gather the geometric solid blocks.

DIRECTIONS FOR USING THE ATTRIBUTE BLOCKS LEARNING TOOL

1. Click Practice. Create a group of objects that have a common attribute. For example, make a group of all big shapes, blue shapes, or triangles.

2. Have students tell what the shapes have in common. Then have students add another shape that fits into the group and explain why they chose that shape.

3. Show students the geometric solid blocks. Have them identify any blocks that could be part of the group on-screen. They are not expected to know the names of all the solid shapes. They may simply point to the blocks that belong to the group.

4. Repeat Steps 1–3 with three more groups

5. Go back to the Attribute Blocks setup screen. Click Single Attribute Mode and choose the following:
   - Sort by: As time permits, have students sort by color, size and shape.
   - Shapes: 10
   - Containers: 2
   - Options: Visual Cues

Objectives

- Explain which attributes, such as color, position, shape, size, roundness, or number of corners, are being used for classification of familiar plane and solid figures.

TRY IT Practice Sorting Shapes

Students will practice identifying the attributes used to create groups of objects. Give students the Practice Sorting Shapes activity page from their Activity Book and read the directions with them.

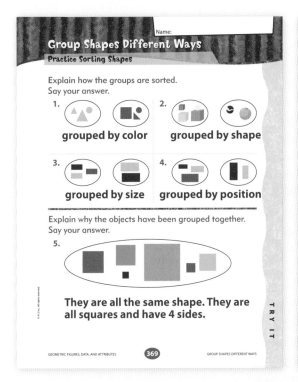

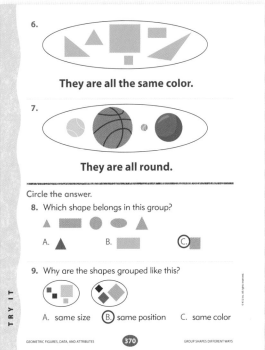

CHECKPOINT

Students will complete an online Checkpoint. Read the directions, problems, and answer choices to students. If necessary, help students with keyboard or mouse operations.

Classify Objects and Data

Skills Update	5 minutes	ONLINE
GET READY Sort Shapes	5 minutes	ONLINE
LEARN Sort and Identify Groups	15 minutes	ONLINE
LEARN Sort Numbers and Objects	15 minutes	OFFLINE
TRY IT Sort and Name	10 minutes	OFFLINE
CHECKPOINT Offline	5 minutes	OFFLINE
CHECKPOINT Online	5 minutes	ONLINE

▶ Lesson Objectives

- Sort objects and data by common attributes, such as geometric figures, tall or short, numbers less than 50 or numbers 50 and above, striped or solid or polka-dotted.
- Describe the categories that were used to sort objects and data by common attributes.

▶ Prerequisite Skills

Sort and classify objects by one attribute, such as color, shape, or size.

▶ Advance Preparation

Gather a variety of household objects for students to sort. Objects should vary in size, shape, and type. Examples include kitchen utensils, measuring cups, ladles, containers, lids, office desktop items, toys, and small cardboard boxes, such as those used for cereal and toothpaste.

Label 40 of the index cards with two- and three-digit numbers. Include at least five numbers in the 20s and five numbers in the 50s. Label the remaining 10 index cards with mathematical symbols (for example, $, +, =$) and nonmathematical symbols (for example, !, *, ?).

▶ Content Background

Students will identify how objects and numbers are sorted. They will sort objects and numbers according to given rules and according to rules they create.

Materials to Gather

SUPPLIED

blocks – B, O (red, blue)

blocks – AA, BB, CC, DD, EE, FF, GG, HH (all colors)

Sort and Name activity page

Checkpoint (printout)

ALSO NEEDED

crayons

index cards – 50 labeled

household objects – different sizes, types, and shapes (kitchen utensils, measuring cups, ladles, office desktop items, small boxes, containers, lids, toys, and so forth)

paper, construction – 2 sheets

GET READY Sort Shapes

Objectives

- Sort and classify objects by one attribute, such as color, shape, or size.

Students will identify how shapes were sorted.
To guide students, ask questions such as the following:

- Are all the figures the same shape?
- Are all the figures the same color?
- Are all the figures the same size?

LEARN Sort and Identify Groups

ONLINE 15 min

Objectives

- Sort objects and data by common attributes, such as geometric figures, tall or short, numbers less than 50 or numbers 50 and above, striped or solid or polka-dotted.
- Describe the categories that were used to sort objects and data by common attributes.

Students will identify how objects and numbers are sorted. Then they will sort objects and numbers according to given rules and, finally, according to rules they create.

1. As students work through the first activity, ask questions such as the following:
   - What do all the objects have in common?
   - Which objects match the label?
   - What other object belongs in this group?
2. Let students explore the second and third activities as time permits. You may wish to take turns with students in making groups and guessing the sorting rule.

LEARN Sort Numbers and Objects

OFFLINE 15 min

Objectives

- Sort objects and data by common attributes, such as geometric figures, tall or short, numbers less than 50 or numbers 50 and above, striped or solid or polka-dotted.
- Describe the categories that were used to sort objects and data by common attributes.

Students will identify how objects and numbers are sorted. Then they will sort objects and numbers according to given rules and, finally, according to rules they create.
Gather the household objects, number and symbol cards, and construction paper.

1. Sort some objects or cards into two groups based on a single attribute. Place one group on each sheet of paper. Sample categories include tall and short objects, round and not round objects, red and not red objects, objects with words and without words, deep and shallow objects, numbers in 20s and numbers in 50s, and two-digit numbers and three-digit numbers.
2. Have students tell how you sorted the objects. If needed, provide hint questions such as, "Are the objects all the same size? Same color? Same shape?"
3. Repeat Steps 1 and 2 twice with different rules. Move from easier sorting rules to harder sorting rules.
4. Repeat Steps 1 and 2 two more times with different rules. After students tell how you sorted, have them add an object or card to each group and explain why it belongs in the group. Students may come up with many creative reasons why an object belongs in a group. As long as they can justify their reasoning, accept their responses.
5. Tell students a sorting rule such as the following: "Make a group of curved objects and a group of objects that do not have curves." Students should sort according to the rule.
6. Repeat Step 5 with a different rule.

7. Have students create groups according to their own sorting rule. Try to guess the rule.

8. Then repeat two more times by having students add an object or number to each group, and then explain why an object or number belongs in each group.

9. Allow students to come up with many reasons that any object could fit in the group. As long as they can justify their reasoning, you should accept their responses.

10. Provide a sorting rule such as the following: "Make a group with curved objects and a group with objects that do not have curves."
Then have students make groups as directed. Do this twice.

11. To conclude the activity, have students create groups by using a sorting rule. Try to guess their rule.

TRY IT Sort and Name

OFFLINE
10min

Objectives

This Try It activity has two parts.

PART 1

Students will sort objects by a given rule.
    Gather the cubes and circle blocks. Lay out the blocks in a random arrangement. Have students sort the blocks by color.

PART 2

Students will practice sorting and identifying rules for sorted objects and numbers. Give students the crayons and Sort and Name activity page from their Activity Book. Read the directions with them. You may wish to write for them the words that they will use to describe the categories—for example, "solids" or "polka dots."

- Sort objects and data by common attributes, such as geometric figures, tall or short, numbers less than 50 or numbers 50 and above, striped or solid or polka-dotted.

- Describe the categories that were used to sort objects and data by common attributes.

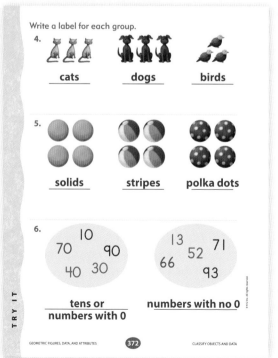

Read the problem and follow the directions.

7. Sort the triangles into 2 groups.
   Color one group green and the other group blue.

Students should color the polka-dotted triangles one color and the striped triangles the other color.

8. Circle the numbers that are less than 50.
   Cross out the numbers that are greater than 50.

9. Circle the numbers that are less than 20. Draw a line under the numbers that are greater than 20.

Circle the answer.

10. Why have these objects been grouped together?

   A. All are the same size.
   B. All are the same shape.
   C. All are in the same position.
   D. All are the same color.

11. Why have these numbers been grouped together?

   A. All have the same ones digit.
   B. All have the same tens digit.
   C. All have three digits.

12. Why are the tissue box and shoe box in one group and the orange and tennis ball in another group?

   A. Both are the same size.
   B. Both are the same shape.
   C. Both are the same color.
   D. Both are in the same position.

13. Why have these objects been grouped together?

   A. All are the same size.
   B. All are the same shape.
   C. All are in the same position.
   D. All are the same color.

14. Why have these objects been grouped together?

   A. All are the same size.
   B. All are the same shape.
   C. All are in the same position.
   D. All are the same color.

CHECKPOINT Offline

Objectives

- Sort objects and data by common attributes, such as geometric figures, tall or short, numbers less than 50 or numbers 50 and above, striped or solid or polka-dotted.

- Describe the categories that were used to sort objects and data by common attributes.

Students will complete this part of the Checkpoint offline. Print the Checkpoint. Students will take a performance-based assessment. Read the directions and problems to students. Use the answer key to score the Checkpoint, and then enter the results online.

Gather the blocks (AA, BB, CC, DD, EE, FF, GG, and HH). For Problem 1, lay out the blocks in a random arrangement.

⚙ Checkpoint   Math | Geometric Figures, Data, and Attributes | Classify Objects and Data

Name _____ Date _____

Checkpoint Answer Key

Follow the instructions for each problem. Choose the response that best describes how the student performs on the task. When you have finished, enter the results online.

(1 point)
1. Place the blocks on the table.
Say, "Sort the blocks into two groups by shape."

Did the student sort the blocks into two groups by shape?

A. Yes   B. No

(1 point)
2. Write the following numbers on a sheet of paper in random order:
1, 5, 13, 26, 33, 49, 52, 59, 64, 76, 85, 93
Say, "Circle the numbers that are less than 50. Draw a line under the numbers that are greater than 50."

Did the student circle 1, 5, 13, 26, 33, and 49, and underline 52, 59, 64, 76, 85, and 93?

A. Yes   B. No

CHECKPOINT Online

Objectives

- Sort objects and data by common attributes, such as geometric figures, tall or short, numbers less than 50 or numbers 50 and above, striped or solid or polka-dotted.

- Describe the categories that were used to sort objects and data by common attributes.

Students will complete this part of the Checkpoint online. Read the directions, problems, and answer choices to students. If necessary, help students with keyboard or mouse operations.

Patterns

Lesson Overview

Skills Update	5 minutes	ONLINE
GET READY Describe Patterns	5 minutes	OFFLINE
LEARN What Comes Next?	20 minutes	OFFLINE
LEARN Continue the Patterns	15 minutes	ONLINE
TRY IT Identify and Extend Patterns	10 minutes	OFFLINE
CHECKPOINT	5 minutes	OFFLINE

▶ Lesson Objectives

Identify the next element in simple repeating patterns and explain how the element was found (for example, rhythmic, numeric, color, and shape patterns).

▶ Prerequisite Skills

Identify and describe ABCC and ABC patterns of colors, shapes, or sizes.

▶ Advance Preparation

Dye pasta three different colors. Gather the pasta, rubbing alcohol, food coloring, tablespoon, resealable plastic bags, and paper towels. Make sure the pasta can easily be strung with yarn. Ziti and penne would work well.

1. Divide pasta into three sets of 20.
2. Place one set of pasta into each bag.
3. Pour 1 tablespoon of alcohol into each bag of pasta.
4. Pour several drops of food coloring into each bag. Use a different color for each bag.
5. Seal the bags, and shake them until the color covers all the pasta.
6. Pour pasta onto paper towels. Spread out, and leave to dry (about 10 minutes).

▶ Content Background

Students will learn about patterns. They will identify and name the pattern core, which is the part of the pattern that repeats. Then they will extend patterns. Identifying pattern cores will help students extend patterns. Pattern cores are often described with letters.

In an AB pattern, each object repeats once.

- AB pattern: triangle, square, triangle, square
  Pattern core: triangle, square
- AB pattern: TLTLTLTLTL
  Pattern core: TL

In an ABB pattern, the first object repeats once and the second object repeats twice.

- ABB pattern: moon, star, star, moon, star, star
  Pattern core: moon, star, star
- ABB pattern: 133133133133
  Pattern core: 133

Keywords

pattern – a sequence of objects and/or numbers with attributes that are repeated in a predictable way
pattern core – the repeating portion that defines a pattern; AB is the pattern core for the pattern ABABAB

GET READY Describe Patterns

OFFLINE 5min

Objectives

- Identify and describe ABCC and ABC patterns of colors, shapes, or sizes.

Students will describe patterns and identify pattern cores using words and letters.

Gather the blocks (AA, B, BB, CC, DD, EE, FF, GG, HH, and O).

1. Create the following pattern using the circle blocks (B): red, yellow, blue, red, yellow, blue, red, yellow, blue.

   Say: Use words to say the pattern.
   ANSWER: red, yellow, blue, red, yellow, blue, red, yellow, blue
2. Explain that the *pattern core* is the part of the pattern that repeats.

   Ask: What is the pattern core of this pattern?
   ANSWER: red, yellow, blue
3. Explain that students can use letters to describe pattern cores. The letter A stands for the first item in the pattern, B for the second, and C for the third. If an item repeats in the pattern core, its letter repeats. For example, the pattern core *heart*, *star*, *star* is described *ABB*.

   Say: Use letters to name the pattern core.
   ANSWER: ABC
4. Repeat Steps 1–3 with the following patterns:
   - Blocks of any color: square, triangle, circle, circle, square, triangle, circle, circle, square, triangle, circle, circle
     ANSWER: ABCC
   - Drawings of circles: small, large, medium, small, large, medium, small, large, medium
     ANSWER: ABC

LEARN What Comes Next?

Students will extend various types of patterns.
Gather the blocks, yarn, and dyed pasta that you prepared.

1. String pasta on the yarn to show the following pattern: red, blue, yellow, red, blue, yellow, red, blue, yellow.

2. **Say:** Use words to say the pattern.
   ANSWER: red, blue, yellow, red, blue, yellow, red, blue, yellow

   Say: Use words to say the pattern core, or repeating part of the pattern.
   ANSWER: red, blue, yellow

3. Explain that students can use the pattern core to extend the pattern.

   Say: You can use the pattern core to tell the next object in the pattern. In this pattern, the pattern core repeats three full times, so the next object will start the core pattern over again at the first color, red.

   Have students string a red piece of pasta to the end of the pattern.

4. **Ask:** Now the pattern has started over. In the pattern core, what color comes after red?
   ANSWER: blue

   Have students string a blue piece of pasta to the end of the pattern.

5. **Ask:** What two colors come next?
   ANSWER: yellow, red

   Say: Yes. After yellow, the pattern starts over again with red. The pattern core keeps repeating.

   Have students string the next 2 pieces of pasta.

6. For each of the following patterns, have students extend with the next 3 items:

   - Cube trains: 1-train, 2-train, 3-train, 1-train, 2-train, 3-train, 1-train, 2-train, 3-train, 1-train
     ANSWER: 2-train, 3-train, 1-train

   - Blocks: circle, square, triangle, triangle, circle, square, triangle, triangle, circle, square, triangle, triangle, circle, square, triangle
     ANSWER: triangle, circle, square

   - Drawings of circles: small, small, large, small, small, large, small, small, large, small
     ANSWER: small, large, small

   - Rhythm (act it out): stomp, clap, snap, stomp, clap, snap, stomp, clap, snap, stomp
     ANSWER: clap, snap, stomp

7. As a further challenge, have students make their own patterns using any of the objects or using rhythm. Ask them to describe the pattern core. Then have students check your answer as you show the next three items in the pattern. Be sure to purposely give the wrong answer so that students will have to correct you. Ask them to explain why your answer is incorrect.

LEARN Continue the Patterns

ONLINE 15 min

Students will identify the pattern core of ABC and ABCC shape and number patterns. They will use the pattern core to extend the patterns.

DIRECTIONS FOR USING THE PATTERN BLOCKS LEARNING TOOL

1. Click Continue Pattern.
2. Select ABCC and ABC, and click Begin.
3. Read the instructions, and click Start.
4. Have students say the pattern core aloud. Then have them extend the pattern.
5. Continue as time permits.

Go to the next screen and continue with the Learn activity.

Objectives

- Identify the next element in simple repeating patterns and explain how the element was found (for example, rhythmic, numeric, color, and shape patterns).

TRY IT Identify and Extend Patterns

OFFLINE 10 min

Students will practice extending patterns. Give students the Identify and Extend Patterns activity page from their Activity Book and read the directions with them.

Students should say the pattern aloud. The words' rhythm may help them continue the pattern. It might also be helpful for students to circle the pattern core.

Objectives

- Identify the next element in simple repeating patterns and explain how the element was found (for example, rhythmic, numeric, color, and shape patterns).

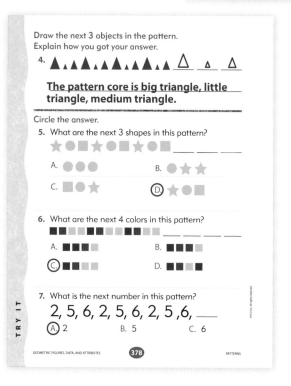

Patterns
Identify and Extend Patterns

Name:

Draw the next 3 objects in the pattern.

1. | 2 | 3 | 2 | 2 | 3 | 2 | 2 | 3 | 2 | 2 |

| 3 | 2 | 2 |

2.

3.

Draw the next 3 objects in the pattern.
Explain how you got your answer.

4.

The pattern core is big triangle, little triangle, medium triangle.

Circle the answer.

5. What are the next 3 shapes in this pattern?

A. ●●●
B. ●★★
C. ■●★
D. ★●■

6. What are the next 4 colors in this pattern?

A. ■■■■
B. ■■■■
C. ■■■■
D. ■■■■

7. What is the next number in this pattern?

2, 5, 6, 2, 5, 6, 2, 5, 6, ___

A. 2   B. 5   C. 6

GEOMETRIC FIGURES, DATA, AND ATTRIBUTES   377   PATTERNS

GEOMETRIC FIGURES, DATA, AND ATTRIBUTES   378   PATTERNS

CHECKPOINT

Objectives

- Identify the next element in simple repeating patterns and explain how the element was found (for example, rhythmic, numeric, color, and shape patterns).

Print the Checkpoint and have students complete it on their own. Read the directions, problems, and answer choices to students, if necessary. Use the answer key to score the Checkpoint, and then enter the results online.

Checkpoint   Math | Geometric Figures, Data, and Attributes | Patterns

Name _____ Date _____

Checkpoint Answer Key

Read the problem and follow the directions.

(2 points)
1. What 4 solids come next in this pattern?

How do you know? Write the answer.

The pattern core is cube, cylinder, cone, cone or ABCC.

(2 points)
2. What 2 shapes come next in this pattern?

How do you know? Write the answer.

The shapes follow an ABC pattern of small triangle, large triangle, medium triangle.

Circle the answer.

(1 point)
3. What are the next 3 numbers in this pattern?

1, 3, 6, 1, 3, 6, 1, 3, 6, ____, ____, ____

A. 1, 6, 3   **B.** 1, 3, 6   C. 3, 6, 1   D. 6, 3, 1

(1 point)
4. Jemma has planted flowers in a repeating pattern.
Choose the flower that will come next.

A. ❀   B. 🌷   C. ❋

1 of 1

Tally Charts and Bar Graphs

Lesson Overview

Skills Update	5 minutes	ONLINE
LEARN Data in Tally Charts	10 minutes	ONLINE
LEARN Create Tally Charts	20 minutes	OFFLINE
LEARN Read Bar Graphs	10 minutes	ONLINE
TRY IT Data in Charts and Graphs	15 minutes	OFFLINE

▶ Lesson Objectives

- Use tally charts to represent data.
- Use tally charts and bar graphs to compare data (for example, find largest, smallest, most often, least often).

▶ Advance Preparation

Place the blocks in a paper bag.
  Print the Tally Chart.

▶ Content Background

Students will learn about tally charts and bar graphs. They will learn how to create and interpret tally charts. Students will learn only how to interpret bar graphs—they will not learn how to create bar graphs in this lesson.

Materials to Gather

SUPPLIED

blocks – B (3 red, 2 green), E (2 red, 2 yellow), F (3 yellow, 3 blue)

Tally Chart (printout)

Data in Charts and Graphs activity page

ALSO NEEDED

paper bag

Keywords

bar graph – graph that uses nonadjacent bars to show quantities for comparison purposes
data – pieces of information; the singular is *datum*
tally chart – a chart used to record the frequency of data, displaying hand-drawn marks in groups of five, called tally marks

---

ONLINE
10min

LEARN Data in Tally Charts

Students will learn how to make a tally chart by watching the step-by-step process of how a tally chart is created. This sample tally chart will show how many birds, cats, and dogs are in a group of animals. Have students count aloud as each tally mark is drawn.

  Then students will answer questions about tally marks. As students count tally marks, remind them to count each group of five as 5—they do not need to count each individual tally mark in the group.

Objectives

- Use tally charts to represent data.
- Use tally charts and bar graphs to compare data (for example, find largest, smallest, most often, least often).

Tips

Remind students that the fifth tally mark is shown with a diagonal.

LEARN Create Tally Charts

Students will represent data in tally charts. Then they will use their charts to talk about the data.

Give students the bag of blocks and the Tally Chart.

TALLY CHART 1

1. Have students write "Shapes" as the title of the first chart. In the left column, have them list these words: "circles," "squares," and "triangles."

2. **Say:** Pull a block from the bag. Make a tally mark in your chart to show what shape you pulled. Then set the block aside.

3. Repeat Step 2 until the bag is empty. Make sure students pull only 1 block at a time.

4. When students have completed the Shapes tally chart, have them use their chart to talk about the shapes that were in the bag. They can fill in shape names in statements such as the following:

   - There were more _____ than any other shape.
   - There were fewer _____ than any other shape.
   - There were more _____ than circles.
   - There were fewer _____ than circles.

TALLY CHART 2

5. Have students put the blocks back in the bag.

6. Have students write "Colors" as the title of the second chart. In the left column, have them list these words: "red," "yellow," "blue," and "green."

7. Have students pull blocks from the bag, one at a time, and record their colors in the tally chart. Have them continue until the bag is empty.

8. When students have completed the Colors tally chart, have them use their chart to talk about the colors of blocks that were in the bag. They can fill in color names in statements such as the following:

   - There were the same number of _____ blocks as _____ blocks.
   - There were fewer _____ blocks than any other color.
   - There were more _____ blocks than blue blocks.
   - There were fewer _____ blocks than blue blocks.

Objectives

- Use tally charts to represent data.
- Use tally charts and bar graphs to compare data (for example, find largest, smallest, most often, least often).

Tips

Remind students how to show the fifth tally mark with a diagonal.

LEARN Read Bar Graphs

Students will learn how to read horizontal and vertical bar graphs. First they will learn the meaning of each part of the graph (title, labels, numbers, bars). Then they will learn how to compare data by looking at the height or length of the bars. Emphasize that in vertical bar graphs, the taller the bar, the greater the value it represents. In horizontal bar graphs, the longer the bar, the greater the value it represents.

Objectives

- Use tally charts and bar graphs to compare data (for example, find largest, smallest, most often, least often).

TRY IT Data in Charts and Graphs

Objectives

Students will practice creating and interpreting tally charts. They will also practice interpreting bar graphs. Give students the Data in Charts and Graphs activity page from their Activity Book and read the directions with them.

- Use tally charts to represent data.
- Use tally charts and bar graphs to compare data (for example, find largest, smallest, most often, least often).

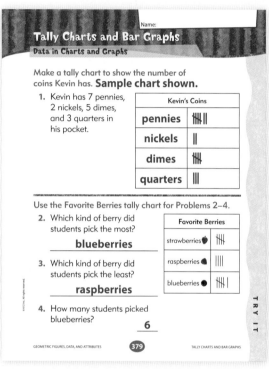

Tally Charts and Bar Graphs
Data in Charts and Graphs

Name: _____

Make a tally chart to show the number of coins Kevin has. **Sample chart shown.**

1. Kevin has 7 pennies, 2 nickels, 5 dimes, and 3 quarters in his pocket.

Kevin's Coins	
pennies	卌 II
nickels	II
dimes	卌
quarters	III

Use the Favorite Berries tally chart for Problems 2–4.

2. Which kind of berry did students pick the most?

   blueberries

3. Which kind of berry did students pick the least?

   raspberries

Favorite Berries	
strawberries	卌
raspberries	IIII
blueberries	卌 I

4. How many students picked blueberries?

   6

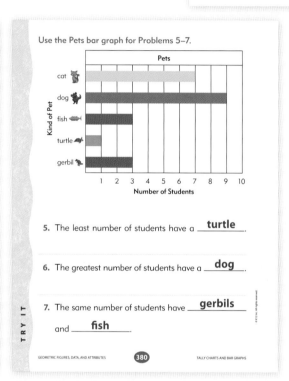

Use the Pets bar graph for Problems 5–7.

5. The least number of students have a ___**turtle**___.

6. The greatest number of students have a ___**dog**___.

7. The same number of students have ___**gerbils**___ and ___**fish**___.

Read the problem and follow the directions.

8. Make a tally chart to show how many of each bear.

Bears	
(gray bear)	III
(dark bear)	II
(small bear)	IIII

9. Robert looked at his list of chores. He has to do 3 chores on Tuesdays, 7 chores on Wednesdays, and 2 chores on Thursdays.

   Make a tally chart to show how many chores Robert has to do on these days.

Robert's Chores	
Tuesday	III
Wednesday	卌 II
Thursday	II

10. This tally chart shows the types of books Claire has. Which type of book does Claire have the fewest of? Circle the answer.

    A. animals
    B. plants
    C. people
    D. cartoons

Claire's Books	
animals	卌 IIII
plants	II
people	卌
cartoons	卌 I

---

11. Look at the bar graph. Keisha likes to count the birds in the park. On which day did she count the most birds?

    Thursday

Data in Pictures and Graphs

Skills Update	5 minutes	**ONLINE**
LEARN Data in Pictures	10 minutes	**ONLINE**
LEARN Data in Picture Graphs	10 minutes	**ONLINE**
LEARN Make Picture Graphs	15 minutes	**OFFLINE**
TRY IT Show and Compare Data	10 minutes	**OFFLINE**
CHECKPOINT	10 minutes	**OFFLINE**

▶ Lesson Objectives
- Use pictures and picture graphs to represent data.
- Use pictures and picture graphs to compare data (for example, find largest, smallest, most often, least often).

▶ Prerequisite Skills
- Use objects, pictures, and picture graphs to record the results of data collection from a sample size up through 10.
- Use tally charts and bar graphs to compare data (for example, find largest, smallest, most often, least often).

▶ Advance Preparation
Print one copy each of the Horizontal Picture Graph and Vertical Picture Graph.
   Place the cubes in one container. Place the circles, rectangles, and triangles in the other container.

▶ Content Background
Students will learn how to use pictures and picture graphs to show information. Then they will compare the data shown in the pictures and on the graphs.
   A picture graph is a graph that uses pictures to represent data. A key is provided to describe how many each picture represents.

Keywords	**picture graph** – a graph that uses pictures to represent data

Materials to Gather

SUPPLIED

blocks – O (1 red, 3 blue, 4 yellow, 7 green)

blocks – B (2 any colors), D (5 any colors), E (1 any color), K (6 green)

Horizontal Picture Graph (printout)

Vertical Picture Graph (printout)

Show and Compare Data activity page

Checkpoint (printout)

ALSO NEEDED

containers – 2

LEARN Data in Pictures

ONLINE 10min

Students will use pictures to represent data and then compare data shown in pictures.

As students progress through the screens, have them ask themselves questions such as the following:

- How many pictures are in each group?
- Which group has the most objects?
- Which group has the fewest objects?
- Do any of the groups have the same number of objects?

Objectives

- Use pictures and picture graphs to represent data.
- Use pictures and picture graphs to compare data (for example, find largest, smallest, most often, least often).

LEARN Data in Picture Graphs

ONLINE 10min

Students will learn about the parts of a picture graph, including the title, labels, pictures, and key. Then they will create a picture graph. They will use their graph to answer questions about the data. Students may count the pictures in the rows or look at the lengths of the rows to answer the questions.

Objectives

- Use pictures and picture graphs to represent data.
- Use pictures and picture graphs to compare data (for example, find largest, smallest, most often, least often).

LEARN Make Picture Graphs

OFFLINE 15min

Students will collect data about blocks and record the results in a picture graph. They will first place the blocks themselves on the graph, and then they will make drawings to represent the blocks.

Gather the printouts and the containers filled with blocks.

Objectives

- Use pictures and picture graphs to represent data.

HORIZONTAL PICTURE GRAPH

1. Give students the Horizontal Picture Graph printout and the container of cubes. Have students name the different colors of the cubes.

2. Have students label each row of cubes with the appropriate color name or at least the first letter of the color name. Then have them write a title for the graph, such as "Cubes" or "Cube Colors."

3. Have students sort the cubes by color in rows on the graph. Make sure students put each cube in its own square and in the correct row on the graph.

4. Have students check that they put each cube in its own box and that, moving from left to right, they haven't left any boxes empty between the first cube and last cube in each row.

5. Have students move aside 1 cube at a time and color the box the color of the cube they removed.

6. **Say:** You've made a picture graph to show the different colors of cubes. Each picture in the graph represents 1 cube.

Tips

If you wish, help students position the cubes and blocks in the graphs, or help them trace.

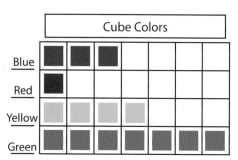

Each picture in the boxes equals 1.

VERTICAL PICTURE GRAPH

7. Give students the Vertical Picture Graph printout and the container of circles (B), rectangles (D), squares (E), and triangles (K).

8. **Say:** You just made a picture graph that shows data in rows. You can also make a picture graph that shows data in columns. Columns go up and down on the page.

9. Have students name the different shapes of the blocks. They should label each column with the appropriate shape name or at least the first letter of the shape name.

10. Have students write a title for the graph, such as "Shapes."

11. Have students sort the blocks by shape in the columns on the graph. Make sure they put each shape in its own square of the graph and in the correct column on the graph.

12. **Say:** We read this graph from bottom to top. Check that, moving from the bottom, you haven't left any boxes empty between the first block and the last block in each column.

13. Have students trace around each shape. Have them move aside each shape after they trace it.

14. **Say:** You've made a picture graph to show the different shapes of the blocks. Each picture in the graph represents one block.

15. Show students that a horizontal picture graph can be turned to look like a vertical picture graph and vice versa.

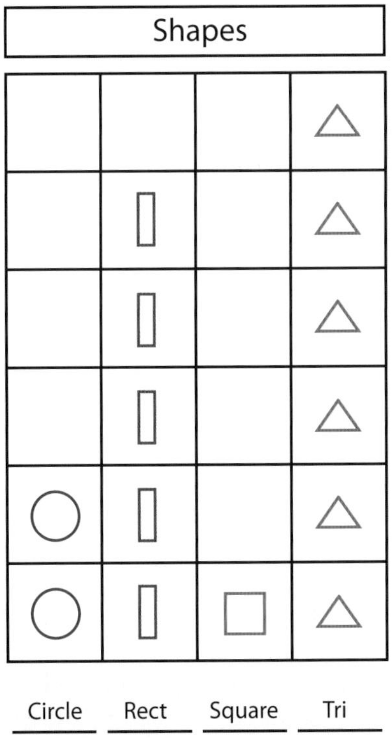

Shapes			
			△
	▯		△
	▯		△
	▯		△
○	▯		△
○	▯	□	△
Circle	Rect	Square	Tri

Each picture in the boxes equals 1.

TRY IT Show and Compare Data

Objectives

- Use pictures and picture graphs to represent data.
- Use pictures and picture graphs to compare data (for example, find largest, smallest, most often, least often).

Students will practice answering questions about data. They will also practice creating and analyzing picture graphs. Give students the Show and Compare Data activity page from their Activity Book and read the directions with them.

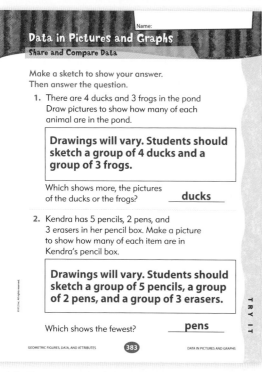

Name:

Data in Pictures and Graphs

Share and Compare Data

Make a sketch to show your answer.
Then answer the question.

1. There are 4 ducks and 3 frogs in the pond Draw pictures to show how many of each animal are in the pond.

   Drawings will vary. Students should sketch a group of 4 ducks and a group of 3 frogs.

   Which shows more, the pictures of the ducks or the frogs? _____ducks_____

2. Kendra has 5 pencils, 2 pens, and 3 erasers in her pencil box. Make a picture to show how many of each item are in Kendra's pencil box.

   Drawings will vary. Students should sketch a group of 5 pencils, a group of 2 pens, and a group of 3 erasers.

   Which shows the fewest? _____pens_____

GEOMETRIC FIGURES, DATA, AND ATTRIBUTES **383** DATA IN PICTURES AND GRAPHS

TRY IT

Violet took a picture to show how many of each type of sand toy she has. Use the picture to complete the sentence.

3. Violet has the fewest _____buckets_____ .

4. Violet has the most **sand molds**

Make the graph. Then complete the sentence.

5. Jose made 4 chocolate cupcakes, 2 strawberry cupcakes, and 3 vanilla cupcakes. Make a picture graph to show how many of each type of cupcake Jose made.

Jose's Cupcakes							
Chocolate	🪣	🪣	🪣	🪣			
Strawberry	🪣	🪣					
Vanilla	🪣	🪣	🪣				

Each picture in the boxes equals 1.

6. Jose made the most **chocolate** cupcakes.

GEOMETRIC FIGURES, DATA, AND ATTRIBUTES **384** DATA IN PICTURES AND GRAPHS

TRY IT

Make the graph. Then complete the sentence.

7. A gym has 5 basketballs, 2 footballs, 8 jump ropes, and 5 flying disks. Make a picture graph to show how many of each toy is in the gym.

Gym Toys			
		〜	
		〜	
		〜	
◯		〜	⬯
◯		〜	⬯
◯		〜	⬯
◯	🏈	〜	⬯
◯	🏈	〜	⬯

basketballs footballs jump ropes flying disks

Each picture in the boxes equals 1.

8. The gym has the same number of **basketballs** and **flying disks** .

9. The gym has more **jump ropes** than any other toy.

GEOMETRIC FIGURES, DATA, AND ATTRIBUTES **385** DATA IN PICTURES AND GRAPHS

TRY IT

OFFLINE
10 min

Print the Checkpoint and have students complete it on their own. Read the directions, problems, and answer choices to students, if necessary. Use the answer key to score the Checkpoint, and then enter the results online.

- Use tally charts to represent data.
- Use tally charts and bar graphs to compare data (for example, find largest, smallest, most often, least often).
- Use pictures and picture graphs to represent data.
- Use pictures and picture graphs to compare data (for example, find largest, smallest, most often, least often).

Checkpoint

Math | Geometric Figures, Data, and Attributes | Data in Pictures and Graphs

Name   Date

Checkpoint Answer Key

Read each problem and follow the directions
(1 point)
1. Daniel asked his friends where they wanted to go for their vacation. 7 friends wanted to go to the beach, 3 friends wanted to go to the mountains, and 8 friends wanted to go to a city.

   Make a tally chart to show where Daniel's friends wanted to go for their vacation.

Favorite Places	
Beach	卌 II
Mountains	III
City	卌 III

(1 point)
2. This tally chart shows the colors of marbles Marvin has.

Marvin's Marbles	
Green	卌 I
Blue	IIII
Red	III
Yellow	II

   Marvin has the most of which color marble? Circle the answer.

   (A.) green   B. blue   C. red   D. yellow

Checkpoint

Math | Geometric Figures, Data, and Attributes | Data in Pictures and Graphs

Name   Date

(1 point)
3. Stacy has 3 yellow fish, 6 red fish, and 2 blue fish in a fish bowl. Draw a picture graph that shows the fish that Stacy has.

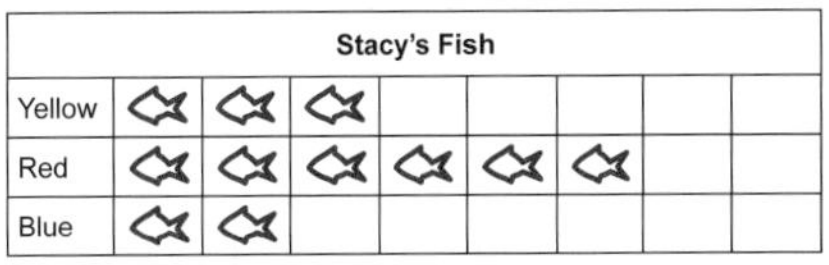

Stacy's Fish							
Yellow	🐟	🐟	🐟				
Red	🐟	🐟	🐟	🐟	🐟	🐟	
Blue	🐟	🐟					

   Each picture in the boxes equals 1

(1 point)
4. The graph shows how often Franco went swimming over 3 months. In which month did Franco go swimming the least often?

   March

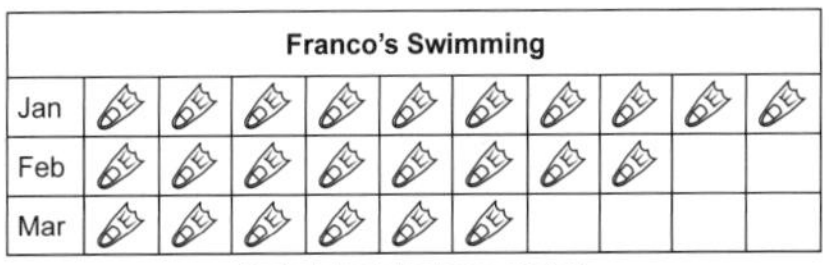

Franco's Swimming									
Jan	🥽	🥽	🥽	🥽	🥽	🥽	🥽	🥽	🥽
Feb	🥽	🥽	🥽	🥽	🥽	🥽	🥽		
Mar	🥽	🥽	🥽	🥽	🥽				

   Each picture in the boxes equals 1

Unit Review

UNIT REVIEW Look Back	20 minutes	**ONLINE**
UNIT REVIEW Checkpoint Practice	20 minutes	**OFFLINE**
⬆ **UNIT REVIEW** Prepare for the Checkpoint		

▶ Unit Objectives

This lesson reviews the following objectives:

- Identify, describe, and compare plane figures, such as rectangle, square, triangle, circle, oval, including those on the faces of solid figures.
- Use concrete objects to show how two or more shapes can be put together or taken apart to create a different shape.
- Explain which attributes, such as color, position, shape, size, roundness, or number of corners, are being used for classification of familiar plane and solid figures.
- Sort objects and data by common attributes, such as geometric figures, tall or short, numbers less than 50 or numbers 50 and above, striped or solid or polka-dotted.
- Describe the categories that were used to sort objects and data by common attributes.
- Identify the next element in simple repeating patterns and explain how the element was found (for example, rhythmic, numeric, color, and shape patterns).
- Use tally charts to represent data.
- Use tally charts and bar graphs to compare data (for example, find largest, smallest, most often, least often).
- Use pictures and picture graphs to represent data.
- Use pictures and picture graphs to compare data (for example, find largest, smallest, most often, least often).

▶ Advance Preparation

In this lesson, students will have an opportunity to review previous activities in the Geometric Figures, Data, and Attributes unit. Look at the suggested activities in Unit Review: Prepare for the Checkpoint online and gather any needed materials.

Materials to Gather

SUPPLIED

blocks – F (2)

Checkpoint Practice activity page

ALSO NEEDED

crayons

Keywords

attribute	oval
bar graph	pattern
circle	pattern core
cone	picture graph
corner	rectangle
cube	rectangular prism
curved figure	side
cylinder	square
data	tally chart
face of a solid figure	triangle

UNIT REVIEW Look Back

Objectives

- Review unit objectives.

In this unit, students have learned how to identify, describe, and compare plane figures. They discovered that they could make shapes by taking apart and putting together plane figures. Students have sorted objects and shapes by common attributes and described how the objects were sorted. They have identified and continued repeating patterns. Students also have explored different ways to display data, including tally charts, bar graphs, and picture graphs and answered questions about data displayed in each way. Students will review these concepts to prepare for the Unit Checkpoint.

UNIT REVIEW Checkpoint Practice

Objectives

- Review unit objectives.

Students will complete a Checkpoint Practice activity page to prepare for the Unit Checkpoint. If necessary, read the directions, questions, and answer choices to students. Have students answer the problems on their own. Review any missed problems with students.

Gather the blocks and crayons.

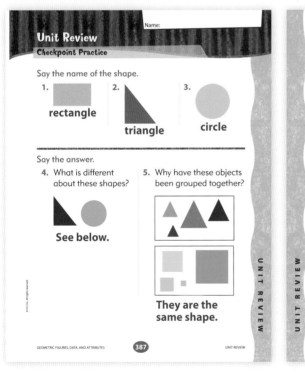

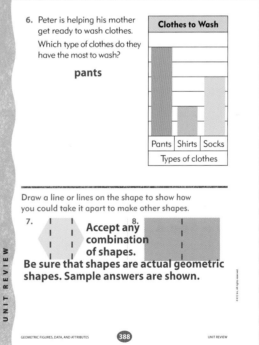

Additional Answers

4. Students should correctly describe one difference. A sample answer may include that one shape has a curved side and the other shape has straight sides.

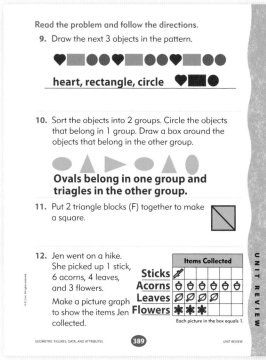

Read the problem and follow the directions.

9. Draw the next 3 objects in the pattern.

❤️⬜⚫⚫❤️⬜⚫⚫❤️⬜⚫⚫

heart, rectangle, circle ❤️⬛⚫

10. Sort the objects into 2 groups. Circle the objects that belong in 1 group. Draw a box around the objects that belong in the other group.

Ovals belong in one group and triagles in the other group.

11. Put 2 triangle blocks (F) together to make a square.

12. Jen went on a hike. She picked up 1 stick, 6 acorns, 4 leaves, and 3 flowers.

Make a picture graph to show the items Jen collected.

Items Collected						
Sticks	✏️					
Acorns	🌰	🌰	🌰	🌰	🌰	🌰
Leaves	🍃	🍃	🍃	🍃		
Flowers	✳️	✳️	✳️			

Each picture in the box equals 1.

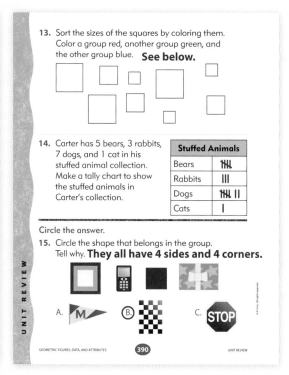

13. Sort the sizes of the squares by coloring them. Color a group red, another group green, and the other group blue. **See below.**

14. Carter has 5 bears, 3 rabbits, 7 dogs, and 1 cat in his stuffed animal collection. Make a tally chart to show the stuffed animals in Carter's collection.

Stuffed Animals	
Bears	卌
Rabbits	III
Dogs	卌 II
Cats	I

Circle the answer.

15. Circle the shape that belongs in the group. Tell why. **They all have 4 sides and 4 corners.**

A. [flag] B. [checkerboard] C. STOP

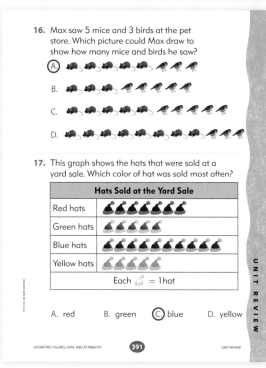

16. Max saw 5 mice and 3 birds at the pet store. Which picture could Max draw to show how many mice and birds he saw?

Ⓐ [5 mice, 3 birds]

B. [mice and birds]

C. [mice and birds]

D. [mice and birds]

17. This graph shows the hats that were sold at a yard sale. Which color of hat was sold most often?

Hats Sold at the Yard Sale	
Red hats	🎩🎩🎩🎩🎩🎩
Green hats	🎩🎩🎩🎩🎩
Blue hats	🎩🎩🎩🎩🎩🎩🎩🎩🎩🎩🎩
Yellow hats	🎩🎩🎩🎩🎩
Each 🎩 = 1 hat	

A. red   B. green   Ⓒ blue   D. yellow

Additional Answers

13. Students should color the small squares one color, the medium squares another color, and the large squares the third color.

➡️ **UNIT REVIEW** Prepare for the Checkpoint

What you do next depends on how students performed in the previous activity, Unit Review: Checkpoint Practice. If students had difficulty with any of the problems, complete the appropriate review activity listed in the table online.

Unit Checkpoint

UNIT CHECKPOINT Online	20 minutes	ONLINE
UNIT CHECKPOINT Offline	40 minutes	OFFLINE

▶ Unit Objectives

This lesson assesses the following objectives:

- Identify, describe, and compare plane figures, such as rectangle, square, triangle, circle, oval, including those on the faces of solid figures.

- Use concrete objects to show how two or more shapes can be put together or taken apart to create a different shape.

- Explain which attributes, such as color, position, shape, size, roundness, or number of corners, are being used for classification of familiar plane and solid figures.

- Sort objects and data by common attributes, such as geometric figures, tall or short, numbers less than 50 or numbers 50 and above, striped or solid or polka-dotted.

- Describe the categories that were used to sort objects and data by common attributes.

- Identify the next element in simple repeating patterns and explain how the element was found (for example, rhythmic, numeric, color, and shape patterns).

- Use tally charts to represent data.

- Use tally charts and bar graphs to compare data (for example, find largest, smallest, most often, least often).

- Use pictures and picture graphs to represent data.

- Use pictures and picture graphs to compare data (for example, find largest, smallest, most often, least often).

Materials to Gather

SUPPLIED

blocks – B (10 red, 10 blue)

blocks – C, D, E, F, G, H, I, J, K, L, M

blocks – S

Unit Checkpoint (printout)

ONLINE
20min

UNIT CHECKPOINT Online

Students will complete this part of the Unit Checkpoint online. Read the directions, problems, and answer choices to students. If necessary, help students with keyboard or mouse operations.

Objectives

- Assess unit objectives.

UNIT CHECKPOINT Offline

Objectives

• Assess unit objectives.

Students will complete this part of the Unit Checkpoint offline. In Part 1, students will take a performance-based assessments. In Part 2, students will complete the problems on their own. Print the Checkpoint. Read the directions, problems, and answer choices to students, if necessary. Use the answer key to score the Checkpoint, and then enter the results online.

Gather the blocks.

○ Checkpoint   Math | Geometric Figures, Data, and Attributes | Unit Checkpoint

Name _____   Date _____

Unit Checkpoint Answer Key

Part 1

Follow the instructions for each item. Choose the response that best describes how the student performed on the task.
(1 point)
1. Show the student the triangular pyramid (S) and triangle (K).

   Say, "What is the same about these shapes?"

   Did the student name one thing the same about the shape and the figure, such as the shape is a triangle and the figure has faces that are shaped like triangles?

   A. Yes   B. No

(1 point)
2. Show the student the circle blocks (B).

   Say, "Why have these blocks been grouped together?"

   Did the student say that they are all the same shape?

   A. Yes   B. No

(1 point)
3. Give the student the assorted blocks (C, D, E, F, G, H, I, J, K, L, and M).

   Say, "Sort these shapes into 2 groups by the number of sides."

   Did the student sort into 2 groups by the number of sides?

   A. Yes   B. No

Give students Part 2 of the assessment.

○ Checkpoint   Math | Geometric Figures, Data, and Attributes | Unit Checkpoint

Name _____   Date _____

Part 2
(1 point)
Read the problem and follow the directions.

4. Draw a line on the shape below to show how to make 2 rectangles.

Semester Review

SEMESTER REVIEW Look Back	20 minutes	ONLINE
SEMESTER REVIEW Checkpoint Practice	20 minutes	OFFLINE
▶ **SEMESTER REVIEW** Prepare for the Checkpoint		

▶ Semester Objectives

This lesson reviews the following objectives:

- Write and solve addition or subtraction number sentences for problem-solving situations with sums and minuends up through 100.
- Describe the length of objects by using nonstandard units (for example, length of a page = 10 paper clips; width of a desk = 3 pencils).
- Use a nonstandard unit to describe how the lengths of two or more objects compare.
- Identify, describe, and compare plane figures, such as rectangle, square, triangle, circle, oval, including those on the faces of solid figures.
- Explain which attributes, such as color, position, shape, size, roundness, or number of corners, are being used for classification of familiar plane and solid figures.
- Use tally charts and bar graphs to compare data (for example, find largest, smallest, most often, least often).
- Justify the procedures selected for addition or subtraction problem-solving situations with sums or minuends up through 100.
- Recognize and solve word problems involving numbers up to 100 in which two quantities are compared by the use of addition or subtraction.
- Recognize and solve word problems involving numbers up to 100 in which one quantity must be changed to equal another quantity.
- Recognize and solve word problems involving sums or minuends up through 100 in which one quantity changes by addition or subtraction.
- Recognize and solve word problems involving sums up through 100 in which two quantities are combined.
- Represent equivalent forms of the same number through the use of diagrams through 20.
- Represent equivalent forms of the same number through 20 through the use of number expressions, such as $7 = 4 + 3$, or $5 + 2$, or $1 + 2 + 4$.
- Demonstrate understanding of place value by grouping given numbers into sets of tens and ones, such as $64 = 6$ tens and 4 ones.
- Use concrete objects or sketches to model and solve addition or subtraction computation problems involving sums and minuends up through 100.
- Use pictures and picture graphs to compare data (for example, find largest, smallest, most often, least often).
- Solve addition problems with a one- and a two-digit number with sums through 100 by using regrouping.

Materials to Gather

SUPPLIED
base-10 blocks
Checkpoint Practice activity page

ALSO NEEDED
crayon
pencil that is longer than a crayon
paper clips – 20

- Solve subtraction problems with a two-digit minuend and a one-digit subtrahend by using regrouping.
- Use a nonstandard unit to describe the weight of an object and compare the weights of two or more objects (for example, the pencil is as heavy as 12 paper clips, and the marker is as heavy as 19 paper clips).

▶ Advance Preparation

In this lesson, students will have an opportunity to review previous activities from the semester. Look at the suggested activities in Semester Review: Prepare for the Checkpoint online and be prepared to gather any needed materials.

SEMESTER REVIEW Look Back ONLINE 20min

Objectives

- Review semester objectives.

This semester, students learned how to use standard and nonstandard units to measure the length and weight of objects. They explored the attributes of plane geometric figures. Students used charts, graphs, and tables to display data. Then they explored the place value of numbers through 100 and learned how to represent numbers in different ways. They used their knowledge of place value to complete addition and subtraction problems in which they needed to regroup. Students applied their knowledge to solve story problems and to justify and explain their answers. Students will review key concepts from the semester to prepare for the Semester Checkpoint.

You may notice that some of the objectives in the Semester Review are not necessarily included in the Semester Checkpoint. Some of these concepts are particularly important to review in order to be successful with the upcoming topics students will encounter, and others contribute to a greater understanding of the concepts that are being assessed. Therefore, a complete review of the objectives in this lesson is recommended.

To review, students will play a Super Genius game. If students answer a problem incorrectly, the correct answer will display. Be sure to help students understand why the answer is correct before they move on to the next problem. If they miss several problems, have students play the game again.

SEMESTER REVIEW Checkpoint Practice OFFLINE 20min

Objectives

- Review semester objectives.

Students will complete a Checkpoint Practice activity page to prepare for the Semester Checkpoint. If necessary, read the directions, questions, and answer choices to students. Have students answer the problems on their own. Review any missed problems with students.

Gather the crayon, base-10 blocks, paper clips, and pencil. Have students use the materials as directed by the problems.

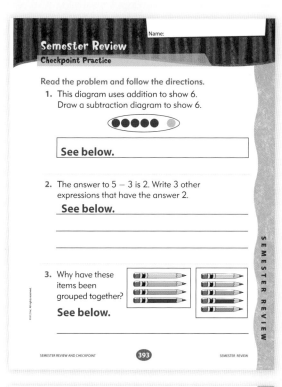

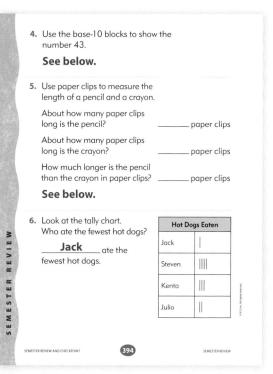

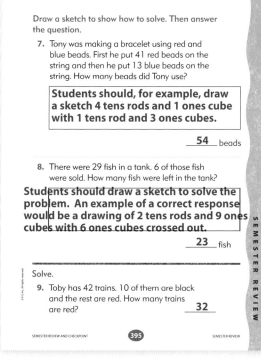

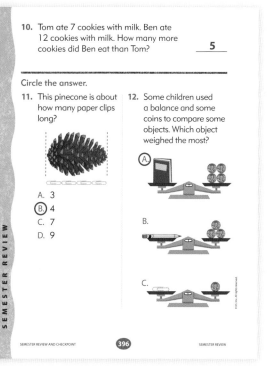

Additional Answers

1. Students should draw a subtraction diagram that shows 6. Answers will vary. Accept any reasonable answer. **Examples:** ⊘⊘⊘⊘⊘⊘⊘⊘⊘⊘⊘ ⊘⊘⊘⊘⊘⊘⊘

3. The pencils in each box are the same size.

5. Students should correctly measure the pencil and crayon with the paper clips. They should correctly compare the length of the pencil to the crayon in paper clips.

2. Answers will vary. Accept any reasonable answer.
   Sample responses: $2 + 0, 1 + 1, 9 - 7, 2 - 0$, $12 - 10$

4. Students should show the number 43 with the base-10 blocks. **Examples:** 4 tens and 3 ones, 3 tens and 13 ones, 2 tens and 23 ones, 1 ten and 33 ones, 43 ones

13. What is the shape of the faces on this figure?

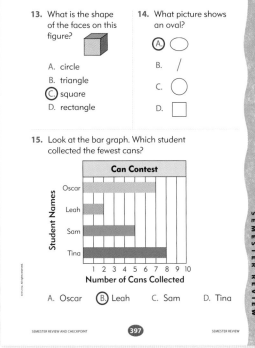

A. circle
B. triangle
C. square
D. rectangle

14. What picture shows an oval?

Ⓐ ⬭
B. /
C. ◯
D. ▢

15. Look at the bar graph. Which student collected the fewest cans?

Can Contest

Student Names: Oscar, Leah, Sam, Tina

Number of Cans Collected: 1 2 3 4 5 6 7 8 9 10

A. Oscar   Ⓑ Leah   C. Sam   D. Tina

16. Tom made a picture graph showing the number of bike rides he took each week
Which week did he take the most rides?

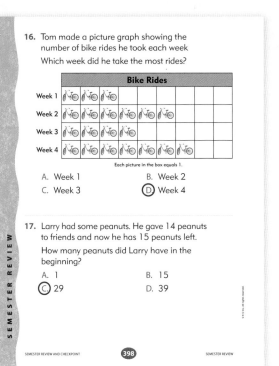

Bike Rides

Week 1
Week 2
Week 3
Week 4

Each picture in the box equals 1.

A. Week 1   B. Week 2
C. Week 3   Ⓓ Week 4

17. Larry had some peanuts. He gave 14 peanuts to friends and now he has 15 peanuts left.

How many peanuts did Larry have in the beginning?

A. 1   B. 15
Ⓒ 29   D. 39

18. Which number sentence correctly solves this story problem?

Walter had some money. He gave away $21 to his sister and now Walter has $34 left.

How much money did Walter have in the beginning?

A. $34 - 21 = ?$
B. $21 - 34 = ?$
Ⓒ $34 + 21 = ?$

19. Keisha's paper chain has 45 links. If she takes 12 links off, Keisha's chain will have the same number of links as Mia's chain.

How many links are on Mia's paper chain?

A. 12
Ⓑ 33
C. 45
D. 57

20. Which best explains how to correctly solve this problem?

Peter picked 27 apples and Anna picked 12 apples. How many more apples did Peter pick than Anna?

A. $12 - 27$ because Anna picked more apples than Peter.
Ⓑ $27 - 12$ because Peter picked more apples than Anna.
C. $27 + 12$ because Peter picked more apples than Anna.

21. Which best explains how to correctly solve this problem?

Jonas has a coin collection. He had 24 quarters in his collection. He just added 6 new quarters.

How many quarters does Jonas have in his collection now?

A. $24 - 6$ because Jonas now has 6 fewer quarters than when he started.
B. $24 - 6$ because Jonas now has 6 more quarters than when he started.
Ⓒ $24 + 6$ because Jonas now has 6 more quarters than when he started.

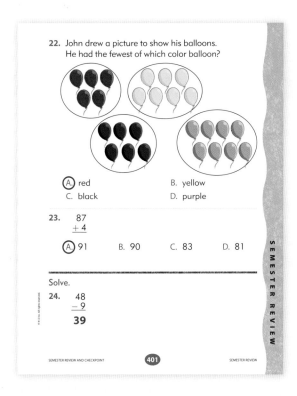

22. John drew a picture to show his balloons. He had the fewest of which color balloon?

Ⓐ red
C. black
B. yellow
D. purple

23. 87
    + 4

Ⓐ 91   B. 90   C. 83   D. 81

Solve.

24. 48
    − 9
    39

⇥ **SEMESTER REVIEW** Prepare for the Checkpoint

What you do next depends on how students performed in the previous activity, Semester Review: Checkpoint Practice. If students had difficulty with any of the problems, complete the appropriate review activity listed in the Unit Review tables online.

Because there are many concepts to review, consider using the Your Choice day to continue preparing for the Semester Checkpoint.

Semester Checkpoint

SEMESTER CHECKPOINT Offline   60 minutes · **OFFLINE**

▶ Semester Objectives

This lesson assesses the following objectives:

- Write and solve addition or subtraction number sentences for problem-solving situations with sums and minuends up through 100.

- Describe the length of objects by using nonstandard units (for example, length of a page = 10 paper clips; width of a desk = 3 pencils).

- Use a nonstandard unit to describe how the lengths of two or more objects compare.

- Identify, describe, and compare plane figures, such as rectangle, square, triangle, circle, oval, including those on the faces of solid figures.

- Explain which attributes, such as color, position, shape, size, roundness, or number of corners, are being used for classification of familiar plane and solid figures.

- Use tally charts and bar graphs to compare data (for example, find largest, smallest, most often, least often).

- Justify the procedures selected for addition or subtraction problem-solving situations with sums or minuends up through 100.

- Recognize and solve word problems involving numbers up to 100 in which two quantities are compared by the use of addition or subtraction.

- Recognize and solve word problems involving numbers up to 100 in which one quantity must be changed to equal another quantity.

- Recognize and solve word problems involving sums or minuends up through 100 in which one quantity changes by addition or subtraction.

- Recognize and solve word problems involving sums up through 100 in which two quantities are combined.

- Represent equivalent forms of the same number through the use of diagrams through 20.

- Represent equivalent forms of the same number through 20 through the use of number expressions, such as $7 = 4 + 3$, or $5 + 2$, or $1 + 2 + 4$.

- Demonstrate understanding of place value by grouping given numbers into sets of tens and ones, such as $64 = 6$ tens and 4 ones.

- Use concrete objects or sketches to model and solve addition or subtraction computation problems involving sums and minuends up through 100.

- Use pictures and picture graphs to compare data (for example, find largest, smallest, most often, least often).

- Solve addition problems with a one- and a two-digit number with sums through 100 by using regrouping.

- Solve subtraction problems with a two-digit minuend and a one-digit subtrahend by using regrouping.

- Use a nonstandard unit to describe the weight of an object and compare the weights of two or more objects (for example, the pencil is as heavy as 12 paper clips, and the marker is as heavy as 19 paper clips).

Materials to Gather

SUPPLIED

base-10 blocks

Semester Checkpoint (printout)

Objectives

- Review semester objectives

Students will complete the Semester Checkpoint offline. In Part 1, students will take a performance-based assessment. In Part 2, students will complete the problems on their own. Print the Semester Checkpoint. Read the directions, problems, and answer choices to students, if necessary. Use the answer key to score the Checkpoint, and then enter the results online.

Gather the base-10 blocks.

⚙ Checkpoint   Math | Semester Review and Checkpoint | Semester Checkpoint

Name _____ Date _____

Semester Checkpoint Answer Key

Part 1

Follow the instructions for each problem. Choose the response that best describes how the student performs on each task.

(1 point)

1. Say, "Use base-10 blocks to show the number 25."

   Did the student show 25 with base-10 blocks? **See below.**

   A. Yes   B. No

(1 point)

2. Say, "The pet shop had 20 fish. One week 9 baby fish were born. How many fish does the pet shop have now?

   How would you solve this problem to get the correct answer?

   How did you decide whether to add or to subtract?

   Did the student explain how he or she would solve the problem?

   A. Yes   B. No

   Did the student explain how he or she decided to add or subtract?

   A. Yes   B. No

   Example: I would add 20 and 9 because I need to find out how many fish there are after 9 are added to the original 20.

   Give students Past 2 of the assessment.

⚙ Checkpoint   Math | Semester Review and Checkpoint | Semester Checkpoint

Name _____ Date _____

Part 2
Circle the answer.
(1 point)

3. What is the same about these two shapes?

   [ ]   [ ]

   A. They both have round sides.

   B. They both are squares.

   C.) They both have 4 corners.

   D. They both have 3 sides.

(1 point)

4. Which has the same answer as 15 − 4?

   A. 15 + 4   B. 4 + 5   C.) 10 + 1

(1 point)

5. Jay has 24 toy cars.

   Michael has 13 toy cars.

   How many toy cars does Jay need to give away to have as many toy cars as Michael?

   Which best explains how to correctly solve this problem?

   A. 24 + 13 because Michael has 13 more toy cars than Jay.

   B. 13 + 24 because Jay has 24 more toy cars than Michael.

   C.) 24 − 13 because I want to figure out the difference between 24 and 13.

Additional Answers

1. Students should show 2 tens and 5 ones, or 1 ten and 15 ones, or 25 ones.

Name _____   Date _____

Read the problem and follow the directions.
(1 point)
6. Paul made a house of cards with 27 cards.
Beth made a house of cards with 19 cards.

How many cards should Paul remove from his house to
have the same number of cards as Beth? Write the answer. __**8**__

(1 points)
7. Tony collected 32 rocks.

If he throws 11 rocks back
into the creek, he will have
the same number of rocks
as Marie.

How many rocks does Marie
have? Write the answer.

__**21**__

(1 points)
8. Complete the number
sentence to solve this story
problem.

Holly ate 18 carrots. She then
ate 6 more carrots.

How many carrots did Holly
eat in all?

18 ⊕ __**6**__ = __**24**__

(1 point)
9. Which number sentence correctly solves this story problem?

Helen collected 27 leaves.
Six of the leaves are red and the rest are green.

How many leaves are green?

Circle the answer.

A. $27 + 6 = 33$
Ⓑ $27 - 6 = 21$
C. $6 - 27 = 21$

Name _____   Date _____

(1 point)
10. Roger has 34 medals.

Wayne has 9 more medals than Roger.

How many medals does Wayne have? Write the answer. __**43**__

(1 point)
11. Tony has 12 cards in his baseball card collection.

He has 2 fewer cards than Saul.

How many baseball cards does Saul have? Circle the answer.

A. 2   B. 10   C. 12   Ⓓ 14

(1 point)
12. Nina had 25 blocks.

Sarah gave her some more.

Now Nina has 69 blocks.

How many blocks did Sarah give Nina? Circle the answer.

A. 25   Ⓑ 44   C. 84   D. 94

(1 points)
13. Claire had some pencils.

She gave 15 pencils to Jennifer.

Claire now has 41 pencils.

How many pencils did Claire
have at the beginning? Write
the answer.

__**56**__

(1 points)
14. Alan bought 25 craft sticks for
an art project.

He painted 3 of them white
and the rest green.

How many craft sticks did Alan
paint green? Write the answer.

__**22**__

Name _____   Date _____

(1 point)
15. How many tens are in 87? Write the answer. __**8**__

Circle the answer.
(1 point)
16. Look at the bar graph.

Which student did the fewest sit-ups?

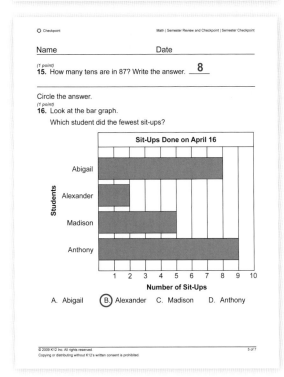

A. Abigail   Ⓑ Alexander   C. Madison   D. Anthony

Name _____   Date _____

(1 point)
17. This tally chart shows the colors of marbles Marvin has.

Marvin's Marbles	
Green	𝍦𝍦 I
Blue	IIII
Red	III
Yellow	II

Marvin has the fewest of which color marble?

A. green   B. blue   C. red   Ⓓ yellow

(1 point)
18. How many corners does this shape have?

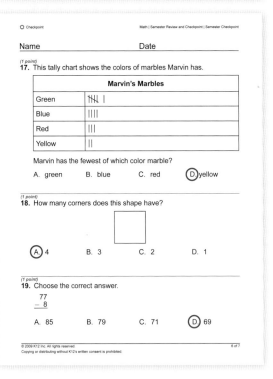

Ⓐ 4   B. 3   C. 2   D. 1

(1 point)
19. Choose the correct answer.

$$\begin{array}{r} 77 \\ -\ 8 \\ \hline \end{array}$$

A. 85   B. 79   C. 71   Ⓓ 69

Name _____ Date _____

Read the problem and follow the directions.

(1 point)
20. Choose the correct answer.

91 − 6

(A) 85   B. 95   C. 96   D. 97

(1 point)
21. Solve. Write the answer.

$$\begin{array}{r} 65 \\ +\ 8 \\ \hline \textbf{73} \end{array}$$

(1 point)
22. Solve. Write the answer.

55 + 5 = **60**

(1 point)
23. Which will give the same answer as 3 + 4? Circle the answer.

A. 3 + 5
(B) 9 − 2
C. 4 + 6
D. 8 − 7